IR Part-66

Aircraft Maintenance Licence

Distance Learning Modules

Module 2 - Physics

Chris Strike

Barry College

ICAT
International Centre
for Aerospace Training

Published by:
Barry College
International Centre for Aerospace Training
Cardiff Airport Business Park
Port Road
Rhoose
Vale of Glamorgan
CF62 3DP
Wales
United Kingdom

+44 (0) 1446 719821

info@part66.co.uk

www.part66.co.uk

Liability

Whilst the advice and information in this book are believed to be true and accurate at the date of going to press, neither the author nor the publisher can accept any legal responsibility or liability for any errors or omissions that may be made.

Author: Chris Strike

IR Part-66   MODULE 2

PHYSICS

Knowledge Levels

The basic knowledge requirements for categories A, B1 and B2 certifying staff are indicated in the contents list of the module notes by knowledge level indicators 1, 2 or 3 against each chapter.

Level 1
A familiarisation with the principal elements of the subject

Objectives

The student should be familiar with the basic elements of the subject.

The student should be able to give a simple description of the whole subject using common words and examples.

The student should be able to use typical terms.

Level 2
A general knowledge of the theoretical and practical aspects of the subject. An ability to apply that knowledge.

Objectives

The student should be able to understand the theoretical fundamentals of the subject.

The student should be able to give a general description of the subject using, as appropriate, typical examples.

The student should be able to use mathematical formulae in conjunction with physical laws describing the subject.

The student should be able to read and understand sketches, drawings and schematics describing the subject.

The student should be able to apply knowledge in a practical manner using detailed procedures.

CONTENTS

Chapter Zero – Foundation Knowledge Requirement

Chapter One – Matter

Knowledge Levels: A – 1   B1 – 1   B2 – 1

Chapter Two – Mechanics

Barry College

ICAT

International Centre
for Aerospace Training

Barry College

ICAT
International Centre
for Aerospace Training

Knowledge Levels: A – 1   B1 – 2   B2 – 2

Knowledge Levels: A – 2   B1 – 2   B2 – 2

viii

Knowledge Levels: A – 1   B1 – 2   B2 – 1

Chapter Three – Thermodynamics

Knowledge Levels: A – 2   B1 – 2   B2 – 2

Knowledge Levels: B1 – 2   B2 – 2

Chapter Four – Optics

Knowledge Levels: B1 – 2   B2 – 2

Chapter Five – Wave Motion and Sound

Knowledge Levels: B1 – 2   B2 – 2

Foundation Knowledge Requirement

Fundamental Science

SI Units

The *Systeme Internationale (SI)* is an international body that tries to bring all the different measurement systems used by the various nations throughout the World into one, internationally accepted, set of standards. The seven (7) base units of this system are listed in table 1:

Name	Unit	Abbreviation
Length	Metre	m
Mass	Kilogram	kg
Time	Second	s
Electric Current	Ampere	A
Temperature	Kelvin	K
Luminous Intensity	Candela	cd
Amount of substance	Mole	Mol

Table 0.1 – List of SI Base Units

The ampere, candela and the mole are not used in these notes and are included for interest only. The unit of liquid measurement is the litre (l), which is equivalent to 1000 cubic centimetres.

The Systeme Internationale (SI) is known as a coherent system such that when one unit is multiplied or divided by another unit it will give a third unit which is derived from the other two. Some examples are listed on the next page.

www.part66.co.uk

- Unit area (m²) results when unit length (m) is multiplied by unit length (m)

- Unit velocity (m/s) results when unit length (m) is divided by unit time (s)

- Unit force (Newton) results when unit mass (kg) is multiplied by unit acceleration (m/s²)

Each SI unit may also be expressed as a multiple or as a sub-multiple of that unit. This is normally done in powers of ten.

Value	Abbreviation	Multiple
Kilo	k	10^3
Mega	M	10^6
Giga	G	10^9

Table 0.2 – Commonly used Multiples

The most commonly used multiples are tabulated in table 2. When raising 10 to a power, it equates to 1 multiplied by 10×10 etc;

For example,

kilo is 10^3, which is $1 \times 10 \times 10 \times 10$ or one thousand.

Value	Abbreviation	Multiple
Centi	c	10^{-2}
Milli	m	10^{-3}
Micro	μ	10^{-6}

Table 0.3 – Commonly used Sub-multiples

For numbers less than one (for example decimals - sub-multiples are used which are shown in table 0.3).

When raising 10 to a negative power, it equates to 1 divided by 10×10 etc.

For example,

milli is 10^{-3}, which is $\dfrac{1}{10 \times 10 \times 10}$ or one thousandth.

www.part66.co.uk

Typical examples of these multiples and sub-multiples in everyday use are:

$$1 \text{ kilometre} = 10^3 \text{ metres} \quad 1 \text{ kN} = 10^3 \text{ Newtons}$$

$$1 \text{ kg} = 10^3 \text{ grams} \quad 1 \text{ MN} = 10^6 \text{ Newtons}$$

$$1 \text{ millimetre} = 10^{-3} \text{ metre} \quad 1 \text{ mg} = 10^3 \text{ kg}$$

$$1 \text{ litre} = 10^3 \text{ cm}^3 \quad 1 \text{ Gpa} = 10^9 \text{ Pascals}$$

$$1 \text{ Metric tonne} = 10^3 \text{ kg}$$

Derived Units

Derived units are obtained when you multiply or divide base units. The following paragraphs give some common examples.

Area

To find the area of a rectangle we multiply its length by its width. If a rectangle is 3m long and 2m wide then its area is:

$$3\text{m} \times 2\text{m} = 6\text{m}^2$$

Note that if the rectangle was 1m wide and 1m long, the rectangle's area is alternatively $1,000,000\text{mm}^2$ or $1 \times 10^6 \text{mm}^2$

$$1\text{m} \times 1\text{m} = 1\text{m}^2$$

Volume

To find the volume of a box, we multiply its length by its width by its height. If a box is 6m long, 4m wide and 5m high then its volume will be:

$$6\text{m} \times 4\text{m} \times 5\text{m} = 120\text{m}^3$$

Gas and liquid volumes are often measured in litres and 1 litre = 1000 cubic centimetres (cm^3)

3

www.part66.co.uk

Density

The density of a body is defined as *the mass per unit volume* and is represented by the Greek letter ρ, pronounced 'rho'. Therefore, if a mass measured in kilograms (kg) is divided by its volume in cubic metres (m³), then its density is measured in kilograms/cubic metre or kg/m³.

Relative density

It is often easier to express the concentration of high-density materials as a relative density against a known standard. The density of water is 1000 kg/m³ and this convenient figure is used as a base standard for measurement of relative densities. For example, the density of lead is 11,300kg/m³. Its relative density can therefore be derived by dividing this figure by the density of water as follows:

$$\frac{11300\text{kg/m}^3}{1000\text{kg/m}^3} = 11.3$$

Notice there are no units for relative density as it is a comparison figure.

Force

The SI unit of *Force* is the *Newton* (**N**) and is defined as:

'The force, which when applied to a mass of one kilogram gives it an acceleration of 1 metre per second per second (m/s²).'

Force may be calculated by multiplying an object's mass* (kg) by its acceleration (m/s²).

*Mass and Weight

The *Mass*, measured in kilograms (kg), of an object is defined as *the amount of matter in the body*. However, an object's mass must not be confused with its weight, as the latter is a force and would be expressed in Newtons. To convert mass to weight we need to know the acceleration applied to the object.

Objects placed on the Earth's surface are subjected to acceleration due to gravity, which is accepted as 9.81m/s²; but 10 m/s² can be used for close approximations. For example, if a box has a mass of 100kg, its weight would be 100 kg × 9.81m/s² = 981N.

Pressure

The effect of a force applied to a surface depends very much on the area over which the force is applied. If a person stands on your foot whilst wearing flat heeled shoes the effect would not be as severe as the same person standing on your foot wearing stiletto heeled shoes. The effect is the result of *Pressure* (*P*) and is derived by dividing the applied force by the area. The unit of pressure is the *Newton per square metre* (N/m²), which is also called the *Pascal* (Pa); both mean the same so be prepared to encounter either.

Work

When a force is exerted against some form of resistance through a distance. For example, a box is pushed along a floor, it is said that '*work* ' is done. Equally, work is also done if the box were to be lifted vertically upwards against gravitational force. The SI unit of work is the *Joule* (J) and is defined as:

'*The work done when a force of one* (1) *Newton is exerted over a distance of one* (1) *metre in the direction of the applied force.*'

For example, if a force of 10N is applied to move a box 20m, the work done would be:

$$10N \times 20m = 200J$$

In addition, if a box with a mass of 10kg is lifted vertically through a distance of 20m, the work done is:

$$10kg \times 9.81m/s^2 \times 20m = 1962J \text{ or } 1.962kJ$$

Power

Power is defined as *the rate of doing work*, measured as work done per second. The SI unit of power is the *Watt (W)* and 1 Watt = 1J/second. For example, if a force of 10N is applied to move a box 20m in 5 seconds, the power expended is:

$$\frac{10N \times 20m}{5s} = 40W$$

Energy

When a body is capable of doing work, it is said to possess *Energy*. This energy can take many forms but its relationship to work means that the SI unit for energy is also the *Joule* (J).

Summary

You should now have sufficient knowledge to identify the SI base units and express them as multiples and sub-multiples of those units. You should also be able to identify the units that are derived from them to express, area, volume, force, pressure, density, relative density, work, power and energy.

Temperature Scales and Conversions

Temperature is the degree of hotness or coldness of a body measured by means of a thermometer. It is not related in any way to the size or nature of the body or the heat energy it contains. Our sense of touch is not a reliable guide so we use a thermometer to give us an accurate indication of hotness on a given scale.

Thermodynamic Scale

The SI unit of *Temperature* is the *Kelvin* (K) and the zero degree (0°) point on the Kelvin scale is where a body would possess no thermal energy at all. In practice, it is impossible to reach this point. For our purposes, we need to know that ice melts at exactly 273.15K under standard atmospheric conditions.

www.part66.co.uk

As one degree Kelvin is equal to one degree Celsius (°C), we can say that 0°C is equal to 273.15K. Therefore, using this knowledge we can also say that if the boiling point of water is 100°C then expressed in Kelvin, the boiling point of water is 373.15K. From this you should be able to easily convert degrees Celsius to Kelvin and vice versa.

Celsius Scale

This scale is based on the division of the temperature difference between two fixed points by one hundred. These two fixed points are the freezing point and boiling point of fresh water. Therefore, the freezing point of water under, standard atmospheric conditions is considered to be 0°C and the boiling point 100°C.

The Fahrenheit Scale

This scale identifies the freezing point of water as 32°F and the boiling point as 212°F, so there are 180° in the scale. This means 1.8°F equates to 1°C.

Though not used in physics, the Fahrenheit scale is often used in American specifications so it is important that you learn how to convert Fahrenheit to Celsius and vice versa, illustrated below:

Temperature Scale Conversions:

$$°C = K - 273$$
$$K = °C + 273$$
$$°F = \frac{°C \times 9}{5} + 32$$
$$°C = (°F - 32) \times \frac{5}{9}$$

Imperial Units

The *Imperial*, or *FPS* (foot/pound/second) system, is a British measurement system and its base units are the foot, pound, second and the gallon, listed in table 4:

Name	Unit	Abbreviation
Length	Foot	ft
Mass	Pound	lb
Time	Second	sec
Volume	Gallon	gall

Table 0.4 – List of Imperial Base Units

Typical examples of the multiples and sub-multiples of this system in everyday use are:

Length

12 inches (in)	= 1 foot (ft)
3 feet (ft)	= 1 yard (yd)
1760 yards (yd)	= 1 statute mile (SM)
5280 feet (ft)	= 1 statute mile (SM)
6080 feet (ft)	= 1 nautical mile (NM)

Weight

16 ounces (oz)	= 1 pound (lb)
14 pounds (lb)	= 1 stone (st)
2 stones (st)	= 1 quarter (qtr)
112 pounds (lb)	= 1 hundredweight (cwt)
20 hundredweight(cwt)	= 1 ton
2240 pounds (lb)	= 1 ton

Liquid Measure

20 fluid ounces (fl.oz)	= 1 pint (pt)
2 pint (pt)	= 1 quart (qt)
4 quarts (qt)	= 1 gallon (gal)

Time

60 seconds (sec)	= 1 minute (min)
60 minutes (min)	= 1 hour (hr)
3600 seconds (sec)	= 1 hour (hr)

8

Derived units

As with SI units, there are units that are derived from the multiplication and division of the base units. The following paragraphs illustrate the more common examples.

Area

Square inches (in^2), Square feet (ft^2), Square yards (yd^2),

Square statute miles (SM^2) or square nautical miles (NM^2)

Volume

Cubic inches (in^3), Cubic feet (ft^3), Cubic yards (yd^3)

Velocity

Feet per second (ft/s), Miles per hour (mph), Revolutions per minute (rpm)

Acceleration

Feet per second per second (ft/s^2)

Force

Pound force (lbf)

Work

Foot pound (ft-lb)

Power

Foot pound per second (ft-lb/s)

Energy

Foot pound (ft-lb)

Pressure

Pounds per square inch (lb/in^2 or psi), Pounds per square foot (lb/ft^2)

Angular Motion Units

If something is moving in a circular path there are two ways of measuring the distance travelled. The distance travelled by a point on the circumference of the circle or, the degrees swept by the radius of the circle that are expressed in *radians*.

Angular Displacement

If you mark a spot on the surface of a shaft it will move in a complete circle during one revolution of the shaft. A line drawn from the spot to the centre of the shaft will be the *radius* of the shaft. The radius will sweep through 360° in one revolution. This is known as *Angular Displacement*. The unit used is the *Radian*. One radian is defined as the angle at the centre of a circle that is subtended by an arc on the circumference equal in length of the radius. This angle or *radian* is approximately 57.3°.

In light of the above definition of the radian, and the fact that the circumference of a circle is $2\pi r$, then it can be seen that the point on the circumference of the shaft travels through 2π arcs and thus radians in one revolution of the shaft.

The radian can also be used to show the angular distance theta represented by the symbol θ, travelled by the point; for example:

In 10 revolutions of the shaft the point would travel $2\pi \times 10$ REVS = 62.8 radians

The radian can also be used to show *Angular Velocity*, represented by the symbol Omega (ω), for example:

If the shaft rotates 10 revolutions in one second then the angular velocity is 62.8 radians/sec.

The radian can also be used to show *Angular Acceleration*, represented by the symbol Alpha (α), for example:

If the shaft accelerates from rest to 10 revs per second in 5 seconds then its angular acceleration can be calculated using the formula:

$$\text{Angular Acceleration } (\alpha) = \frac{\text{Final speed } (\omega_2) - \text{Initial speed} (\omega_1)}{\text{time } (t)}$$

$$\alpha = \frac{62.8 - 0 \text{ rad/s}}{5 \text{ s}}$$

$$\alpha = 12.56 \text{ rad/s}^2$$

The generally accepted symbols for use in angular motion formulae are therefore:

θ (Theta), for distance in radians

ω (Omega) for angular velocity in radians per second

α (Alpha) for angular acceleration in radians per second^2

Get to know them!

A note of caution however, you should be careful to look at how revolutions are described. If the rotational speeds are given in revolutions per minute, you will need to convert them to revolutions per second before conducting calculations in radians.

This is easily done by dividing RPM by 60 to derive RPS.

A useful aspect of using the radian for measuring angular displacement is its relationship the radius. To find the linear values of a point on the circumference of a shaft, simply multiply its value in radians by the radius of the circle.

USA Units

The United States of America (USA) have not accepted the metric system and do not use SI units. This means that you will encounter imperial units when dealing with American aircraft and equipment. However, you must be aware that the Americans have adjusted some of these units for their own use. The system is known as *US customary units* and you must check which units are being used, British or USA.

www.part66.co.uk

To avoid confusion, it is common practice to annotate the unit being used; eg US gallon or US short ton. Only those units, which differ from British Imperial units, are shown below and the UK/US comparisons are shown for convenience.

Fluid Capacity

US Fluid ounce	= 0.0296 litre	= 0.0625 of a US pint
UK Fluid ounce	= 0.0284 litre	= 0.05 of a UK pint
US pint	= 0.473 litres	= 0.83 UK pint
UK pint	= 0.568 litres	= 1.2 US pints
US gallon	= 3.785 litres	= 0.83 UK gallons
UK gallon	= 4.546 litres	= 1.2 US gallons

Weight

US short hundredweight	= 100lb	= 45.3kg
20 US cwt	= 1 US short ton	
US long hundredweight	= 112lb	= 50.8kg
20 UK cwt in 1 US long ton		
US short ton	= 2000lb	= 8896N
US long ton	= 2240lb	= 9963.52N
Kip (kilo pound)	= 1000lb	= 4448N

Fundamental Mathematics

Transposition of Formulae

It is important that you can transpose formulae to make any part of a formula the subject. In order to transpose formulae, there are a few simple rules that you need to follow.

Anything you do to a formula must be done equally to both sides. For example, you can move a term from one side of the equals sign (=) to the other by subtracting the term from both sides. But do note that the sign changes as you do this, as illustrated in the following example:

In the formula v= u + at, we want to make 'a' the subject. The first step is to subtract u from both sides:

$v - u = u + at - u$; this will result in:

$v - u = at$ (Note how u was subtracted out on the right hand side).

The next step is to divide both sides by the term 't' to get rid of it on one side:

$$\frac{v - u}{t} = \frac{at}{t}$$

and now the t cancels out on right side, leaving a as the subject of the formula:

$$\frac{v - u}{t} = a \quad \text{Which is the same as:} \quad a = \frac{v - u}{t}$$

Let us look at another example to show you a different rule. Using the previous formula let us make 't' the subject.

$$\frac{v - u}{t} = a$$

To get rid of the 't' on the left hand side, we multiply both sides by 't' to get:

$$t \times \frac{v - u}{t} = a \times t$$

13

This changes nothing!

Cancelling gives:

$$v - u = at$$

(No change)

Now divide both sides by a to get:

$$\frac{v - u}{a} = \frac{at}{a}$$

Cancelling gives

$$\frac{v - u}{a} = t$$

Work a few examples to get used to these rules. Substitute terms for simple numbers and you will be able to check you have it right. To help you let us bring the above formula back to v as subject.

Cross multiply: $\qquad\qquad v - u = at$

Add u to both sides $\qquad\quad v - u + u = u + at$

This results in: $\qquad\qquad v = u + at$

(*Check you understand this*)*!*

Another rule will help you to deal with squared terms and square roots, for example:

$v^2 = 2gs$ $\qquad\qquad$ make v the subject of the formula

If we take the square root of both sides, the formula becomes:

$$v = \sqrt{2gs}$$

To return the formula to its original status we simply square both sides.

Now try another formula:

$$s = {}^1\!/_2 gt^2$$

Make t the formula's subject:

Multiply both sides by 2 we get:

$$2s = gt^2$$

Dividing both sides by g we get:

$$\frac{2s}{g} = \frac{gt^2}{g}$$

and as g cancels on the right side, the formula becomes:

$$\frac{2s}{g} = t^2$$

Finally, by taking the square root both sides we get:

$$\sqrt{\frac{2s}{g}} = t$$

You now have all the tools required to deal with the transposition of formulae but you need to practice until you become confident as this physics module will require you to do this many times with different formulae.

Use of Indices

The standard form of writing very large and very small numbers is by using indices. It is important that students undertaking this module should be familiar with the use of indices and with the multiplication and division of numbers expressed in this form as *calculators are not permitted in the JAA examination*.

You have already encountered the use of indices in the SI unit section of this chapter and to refresh your mind, here are some examples:

25,000,000 can be expressed as 25×10^6 or 2.5×10^7

692,000 can be expressed as 6.92×10^5 or 692×10^3

0.0000054 can be expressed as 5.4×10^{-6} or 54×10^{-7}

As indices are based on the power of ten, they tell you how many places to move the decimal point to display the original number.

For Example

5000 is 5×10^3, ie moving the decimal point to the right three places gives 5000.

0.005 is 5×10^{-3}, ie moving the decimal point to the left three places gives 0.005.

If you wish to multiply numbers expressed in indices, you simply multiply the numbers together then add the indices and show the product as the new indices. For example:

$$(5 \times 10^3) \times (4 \times 10^3) = 20 \times 10^6$$

You must be careful of negative indices when doing this. For example:

$$(5 \times 10^{-6}) \times (4 \times 10^3) = 20 \times 10^{-3}$$
$$(5 \times 10^{-3}) \times (4 \times 10^{-3}) = 20 \times 10^{-6}$$
$$(5 \times 10^6) \times (4 \times 10^{-3}) = 20 \times 10^3$$

If you wish to divide numbers expressed in indices then you simply divide the numbers and then subtract their indices to derive the result. For example:

$$(6 \times 10^6) \div (3 \times 10^3) = 2 \times 10^3$$

Again, be careful when using negative indices. For example:

$$(6 \times 10^{-6}) \div (3 \times 10^3) = 2 \times 10^{-9}$$
$$(6 \times 10^6) \div (3 \times 10^{-3}) = 2 \times 10^9$$

Simple Trigonometry

In the course of this Physics Module, you will encounter many situations where you will need to identify an angle or side of a right-angled triangle. You can of course calculate sides by using the *Pythagoras rule*, which states that:

'In a right-angled triangle, the square of the hypotenuse is equal to the sum of the squares of the other two sides.'

This rule is useful but does not help you find angles. To do this, all that is required is for you to learn the simple trigonometric relationship of an angle to the sides of a right-angled triangle.

Draw a right-angled triangle, as in figure 1, and ignore the 90° angle and choose one of the remaining angles; in this case angle 'a'.

www.part66.co.uk

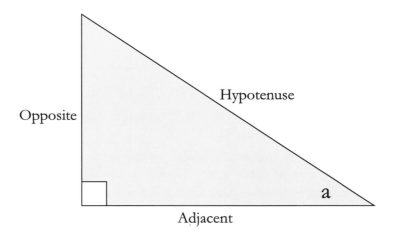

Figure 0.1 – Simple Right-Angled Triangle

The side that is directly opposite angle 'a' is known, rather obviously, as the *Opposite* side, while the side next to it, which is not the *Hypotenuse*, is known as the *Adjacent* side.

The following relationship now applies:

The sine of angle 'a' is equal to the *Opposite* side divided by the *Hypotenuse*

The cosine of angle 'a' is equal to the *Adjacent* side divided by the *Hypotenuse*

The tangent of angle 'a' is equal to the *Opposite* side divided by the *Adjacent* side

Schoolchildren find a useful method of remembering this relationship as follows:

SOHCAHTOA (*pronounced sock a toe-ar*) **or Sine is (O/H) Cosine is (A/H) Tangent is (O/A)**

Why bother with trigonometry when your exam does not allow calculators? Well you do not need a calculator if you remember the major angles that are convenient and commonly used by question setters.

For example,

Sine of 30°	= 0.5
Cosine of 60°	= 0.5
Tangent of 45°	= 1

Now try the following SAQ to see if you understand the concept of trigonometry:

A person drags a wooden crate along a floor using a rope. The rope is at an angle of 60° to the floor and the tension in the rope is 100N. What proportion of this force is acting horizontally and usefully used in dragging the crate?

Taking into account what we already know, we can say that the rope forms the hypotenuse of a right angle triangle and has a magnitude of 100N. The angle is 60° and so its cosine is 0.5 Now the cosine of this angle equals the adjacent divided by the hypotenuse and therefore:

$$\text{If cos of } 60° = \frac{\text{Adjacent}}{100} \text{ by transposition of formula:}$$

$$\text{Adjacent} = 100 \times \cos 60° = 100 \times 0.5 = 50\text{N}$$

Area and Volume

With a subject like physics, it is always useful to remember the formulae for the areas and volumes of common shapes and objects and some of these are shown below:

Area of a rectangle	= length × width (breadth)
Area of a triangle	= ½ its base × its vertical height
Area of a circle	= πr^2 or $\frac{\pi d^2}{4}$
Area of a semi-circle	= $\frac{1}{2}\pi r^2$
Circumference of a circle	= $2\pi r$ or πd
Area of a parallelogram	= Its base × its vertical height
Area of an open cylinder	= $2\pi rh$, where r is its radius and h its height
Area of a cone	= πrl, where r is its radius and l its slant height

Area of a sphere	$= 4\pi r^2$
Volume of a cylinder	$= \pi r^2 h$
Volume of a cube	$= \text{Length} \times \text{breadth} \times \text{height}$
Volume of a cone	$= \frac{1}{3} \text{ area of the base} \times \text{its height}$
Volume of a pyramid	$= \frac{1}{3} \text{ area of base} \times \text{its height}$
Volume of a sphere	$= \frac{4}{3} \pi r^3$

Whilst dealing with the subject of mathematics and its formulae, it is worth mentioning the *3:4:5 triangle*; for example, if a right-angled triangle has sides that equate to a ratio of 3:4:5, then if the magnitude of two sides are known, the third is easy to derive.

For example:

If a right-angled triangle has two sides of 9 cm & 12 cm, the third side must then be 15cm:

> 9cm = 3 x 3, 12cm = 3 x 4, 15cm = 3 x 5;
>
> a 3:4:5 triangle!

A right-angled triangle has two sides of 20cm & 25cm, what is the length of its third side?

Again, it is very convenient for questioners to use this type of triangle when setting mental arithmetic problems where the use of calculators is not allowed.

The tables on the following pages gather into one place all the conversion factors you will come across in this Module.

SI Conversion Factors

The following tables give some useful conversions for common use units. The list of units is not exhaustive and further units and their equivalents will appear in the relevant texts of this module

Unit name	Symbol	Quantity	SI equivalent	Unit
Bar	bar	pressure	101	KPa
Barrels(US) = 42 gal	bbl	volume	0.159	m^3
British Thermal Unit	Btu	energy	1.055	kJ
Calorie	cal	energy	4.186	J
Cubic foot	ft^3	volume	0.028	m^3
Cubic inch	in^3	volume	16.387	cm^3
Cubic yard	yd^3	volume	0.765	m^3
Foot	ft	length	30.48	cm
Foot per second	ft/s	velocity	0.305	m/s
Gallon(UK)	gal	volume	4.546	ltr
Gallon(US) = 231 in^3	gal	volume	3.785	ltr
Horsepower	hp	energy	0.746	kW
Inch	in	length	2.54	cm
Kilogram-force	kgf	force	9.81	N
Knot		velocity	1.852	km/h
Litre	l	volume	1×10^{-3}	m^3
Micron	μ	length	1	μm
Mile(nautical)		length	1.852	km
Mile(statute)		length	1.609	km
Mile per hour	mph	velocity	1.609	km/h
Ounce (avoirdipois)	oz	mass	28.349	g
Ounce (troy) = 480 gr		mass	31.103	g
Pint (UK)	pt	volume	0.568	ltr
Pound	lb	mass	0.454	kg
Pound-force	lbf	force	4.448	N
Pound-force/in^{-2}		pressure	6.895	kPa
Poundal	pdl	force	0.138	N
Pounds per square inch	psi	pressure	6.895×10^3	kPa
Slug		mass	14.594	kg
Square foot	ft^2	area	0.093	m^2
Square inch	in^2	area	6.452	cm^2
Square mile (statute)		area	2.590	km^2
Square yard	yd^2	area	0.836	m^2
Standard Atmosphere	atm	pressure	101	kPa
Stokes	St	viscosity	1	cm^2/s
Therm = 10^5btu		energy	0.105	GJ
Ton = 2240 lb		mass	1.016	Mg
Ton-force	tonf	force	9.964	kN
Ton-force/in^{-2}		pressure	15.444	MPa
Tonne	t	mass	1	Mg
Yard	yd	length	0.915	m

Conversion Factors

Conversion Factors – Imperial to Metric

	Conversion form	Convert to	Multiply by
Length	inches	millimetres	25.4
	inches	centimetres	2.54
	feet	metres	0.3048
	yards	metres	0.9144
	statute miles	kilometres	1.6093
	nautical miles	kilometres	1.852
Area	square inches	square centimetres	6.4516
	square feet	square metres	0.0929
	square yards	square metres	0.8361
	acres	hectares	0.4047
	square miles	square kilometres	2.5899
Volume	cubic inches	cubic centimetres	16.3871
	cubic feet	cubic metres	0.0283
	cubic yards	cubic metres	0.7646
Capacity	UK fluid ounces	litres	0.0284
	US fluid ounces	litres	0.0296
	UK pints	litres	0.5682
	US pints	litres	0.4732
	UK gallons	litres	4.546
	US gallons	litres	3.7854
Weight	ounces(avoirdupois)	grams	28.3495
	ounces(troy)	grams	31.1035
	pounds	kilograms	0.4536
	tons(long)	tonnes	1.016

Conversion Factors

Conversion Factors - Metric to Imperial

	Conversion form	Convert to	Multiply by
Length	millimetres	inches	0.0394
	centimetres	inches	0.3937
	metres	feet	3.2808
	metres	yards	1.0936
	kilometres	statute miles	0.6214
	kilometres	nautical miles	0.54
Area	square centimetres	square inches	0.155
	square metres	square feet	10.764
	square metres	square yards	1.196
	hectares	acres	2.471
	square kilometres	square miles	0.386
Volume	cubic centimetres	cubic inches	0.061
	cubic metres	cubic feet	35.315
	cubic metres	cubic yards	1.308
Capacity	litres	UK fluid ounces	35.1961
	litres	US fluid ounces	33.8150
	litres	UK pints	1.7598
	litres	US pints	2.1134
	litres	UK gallons	0.2199
	litres	US gallons	0.2642
Weight	grams	ounces(avoirdupois)	0.353
	grams	ounces(troy)	0.0322
	kilograms	pounds	2.2046
	tonnes	tons(long)	0.9842

Conversion Factors

Further Metric Measurements and their Imperial Equivalent

		Metric Units	Imperial
Length		1 millimetre	0.03937
	10mm	1 centimetre	0.39 in
	10cm	1 decimetre	3.94 in
	100cm	1 metre	39.37 in
	1000m	1 kilometre	0.62 mile
Area		1 square millimetre	0.0016 sq in
		1 square centimetre	0.155 sq in
	100 sq cm	1 square decimetre	15.5 sq in
	10,000 sq cm	1 square metre	10.76 sq ft
	10,000 sq m	1 hectare	2.47 acres
Volume		1 cubic millimetre	0.016 cu in
	1000 cu cm	1 cubic centimetre	61.024 cu in
	1000 cu dm	1 cubic metre	35.31 cu ft
			1.308 cu yds
Liquid Volume		1 litre	1.76 pints
	100 litres	1 hectolitre	22 gallons
Weight		1 gram	0.035 oz
	1000 g	1 kilogram	2.2046 lb
	1000 kg	1 tonne	0.0842 ton

www.part66.co.uk

Conversion Factors

Further Imperial Measurements and their Metric Equivalent

		Imperial Units	Metric
Length		1 inch	2.54 cm
	12 in	1 foot	30.48 cm
	3 ft	1 yard	0.9144 m
	1760 yd	1 mile	1.6093 km
Area		1 square inch	6.45 sq cm
	144 sq in	1 square foot	0.0929 sq m
	9 sq ft	1 square yard	0.836 sq m
	4840 sq yd	1 acre	0.405 ha
	640 acres	1 square mile	259 ha
Volume		1 cubic inch	16.3871 cu cm
	1728 cu in	1 cubic foot	0.028 cu m
	27 cu ft	1 cubic yard	0.765 cu m
Liquid Volume		1 pint	0.57 litres
	2 pints	1 quart	1.14 litres
	4 quarts	1 gallon	4.55 litres
Weight		1 ounce	28.3495 g
	16 oz	1 pound	0.4536 kg
	14 lb	1 stone	6.35 kg
	8 stones	1 hundredweight	50.8 kg
	20 cwt	1 ton	1.016 tonnes

www.part66.co.uk

Matter

Nature of Elements

An element is defined as a pure substance that cannot be split up into simpler substances by chemical reaction. There are over 100 chemical elements known to man, of which 75% are metals. Most occur naturally, but a few are man-made. All elements are made up of small particles called *Atoms*, which are defined as the smallest portions of an element that can take place in a chemical change.

Structure of Atoms & Molecules

Atom

An atom is typically only 10^{-10}m across and 100 million, million atoms would only cover a single square millimetre. Deep inside the atom is a tiny dense nucleus typically 10^{-14}m across, which is surrounded by a cloud of electrons.

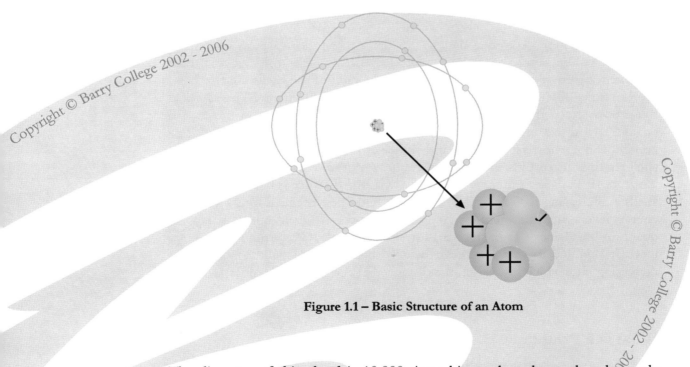

Figure 1.1 – Basic Structure of an Atom

The diameter of this cloud is 10,000 times bigger than the nucleus but only carries approximately one four thousandth of the atoms mass. As you can see, an atom has a lot of empty space!

The atom's nucleus contains smaller particles, the chief ones being the *Proton*, which carries a *positive* electrical charge, and the *Neutron*, which carries *no* charge.

The atom nuclei of different chemical elements have different numbers of protons and neutrons. However, within atoms of the same element, the number of protons and neutrons are fixed for every atom of that element. Protons have approximately the same mass as neutrons.

The electron cloud surrounding the nucleus contains a number of fast orbiting electrons, the number of which matches the exact number of protons contained in the nucleus.

An *Electron* is the smallest particle in an atom and possesses a *negative* electrical charge. It has a wave-like motion and so only a given number of electrons can occupy a particular orbit. Depending on the number of protons in the atom's nucleus, its electrons take up positions in definite orbits at increasing radii from the nucleus. If there are sufficient electrons, the orbits are filled in a standard order, the inner containing two (2) electrons, the next eight (8), then 18, 32 and so on. The number of electrons in each shell can be calculated using the formula $2N^2$, where N is the number of shells, starting with the innermost shell. For example, the electron count for N = 3 (Third Shell) is $2 \times (3 \times 3) = 18$. Each electron consistently changes its orbital path, which is commonly called a *shell* rather than an orbit, as this is what it appears to be when several fast orbiting electrons create this illusion.

Each electron shell has a different energy level. The inner shell contains electrons at the lowest energy level. The energy increases in very precise steps from the inner shell to the outermost shell. The increase in energy required by an electron to jump from one shell to the next one out decreases in steps from the inner to the outer shell. The outer shell *valence* electrons are the most highly energised. At ordinary temperatures, the radii of the shells are fixed and the electrons in each shell have very precise amounts of energy. This is called the *ground* state. If an electron is given the exact amount of energy increase to enable it to move out to the next shell the atom is said to be *excited*. The condition does not last for long and the electron will fall back to its original shell emitting its surplus energy as an *electro-magnetic* packet of light called a *Photon*. IR Part-66 examiners like to ask what the distance is between electron shells at increasing radii from the nucleus. I think they intended to ask what the energy levels are but there you are. The answer to their question lays in quantum mechanics not in standard Physics textbooks! The amount of energy increase required to step out through each shell and sub-shell decreases with increasing radii which infers that the distance between them also decreases.

What is a Proton?

A proton is a positively charged particle present in the nucleus of an atom. Each element has a different number of protons that identify its atomic number, which is unique to that element.

www.part66.co.uk

What is a Neutron?

The neutron is a particle present in the nucleus of all atoms except hydrogen. It has no electrical charge and being only marginally heavier than a proton is considered as having the same mass.

What is an Electron?

The electron is a negatively charged particle having almost negligible mass. The electrons orbit the nucleus in ever changing orbital paths giving the impression of shells. The electrons occupying the outermost shell are known as *valency electrons* as they are the only ones to be involved in chemical bonding.

Each shell is situated at increasing radii from the nucleus and the energy level of the electrons in them increases with radii, the inner shell containing the lowest energy level. The total number of negatively charged electrons in an atom matches the number of positively charged protons in the nucleus, leaving the atom with no residual charge; in other words, it is electrically neutral.

Atomic Number

As already discussed above, atoms of different elements have different numbers of protons in their nuclei. The number of protons in the atom's nucleus is its *Atomic Number*. For example, the Hydrogen atom, which is the smallest atom of all, has only one (1) proton in its nucleus and so the atomic number of Hydrogen is 1. Carbon has six (6) protons and its atomic number is 6.

Mass Number

An atom's *Mass Number* is the total number of protons and neutrons in its nucleus. For example, Lithium has three (3) protons and four (4) neutrons in its nucleus so its mass number is seven (7).

Relative Atomic Mass

When the mass number of atoms was decided, the element chosen on which to relate the mass of all atoms was *Carbon*. Carbon 12, as it is known has six (6) protons and six (6) neutrons and so has an atomic number 6 and a mass number 12.

Therefore, Hydrogen, which has one proton and no neutrons, has a mass number 1 which is one twelfth that of Carbon.

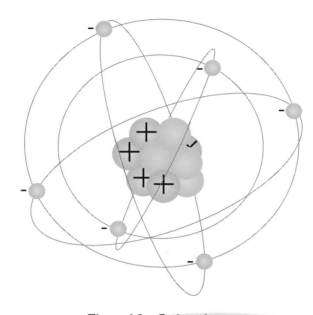

Figure 1.2 – Carbon Atom

Ions

Due to the standard distribution of electrons in the shells, the atom's outer shell may be incomplete, for example, have a shortfall of electrons, due to the number of protons not matching the standard distribution. Atoms will always take the opportunity to adjust their outer shell electron content to eight (8) electrons to balance their wave motion.

As the protons in the atom's nucleus attract the negatively charged electrons, they also spread their attraction to any neighbouring atom's outer shell electrons.

The degree to which an atom attracts electrons to itself is defined as its *Electronegativity* and its tendency to lose electrons its *Electropositivity*. Due to the different degrees of electro-negativity and electropositivity found throughout the elements, atoms may *steal* one or more electrons from the outer shells of neighbouring atoms, or lose one or more electrons from their own outer shells.

If an atom gains an extra electron, then the sum of its negatively charged electrons will be greater than the sum of its positively charged protons and so there will be a residual negative charge. When this occurs, it is called a *Negative Ion* or *Anion*.

Conversely, if the atom loses an electron the sum of its positively charged protons exceeds the sum of its remaining negatively charged electrons and so the atom will have a residual positive charge and will have become a *Positive Ion* or *Cation*.

Isotope

Isotopes are atoms that have the same atomic number but different mass numbers. If an atom gains or loses one or more neutrons from its nucleus, it will become an isotope of the element. This means that, as its proton number will not have altered, it retains its atomic number but its mass number will have changed.

The hydrogen atom, for example can have three variants:

1. *Proton Hydrogen* which is the normal Hydrogen atom having one proton and no neutron

2. *Deuterium*, which has one proton and one neutron

3. *Tritium* which has one proton and two neutrons

All have the atomic number of 1, but proton Hydrogen has a mass number 1, Deuterium 2 and Tritium 3; the latter two are isotopes of the Hydrogen atom.

Isotopes are present in most elements and may also be man made in a neutron bombardment process. Some elements become radioactive because of being transformed into radioisotopes. For example, Cobalt and Caesium.

The Periodic Table of Elements

The *Periodic Table*, shown in figure 1.3 is formed by positioning the elements in horizontal rows called periods and in vertical columns called groups.

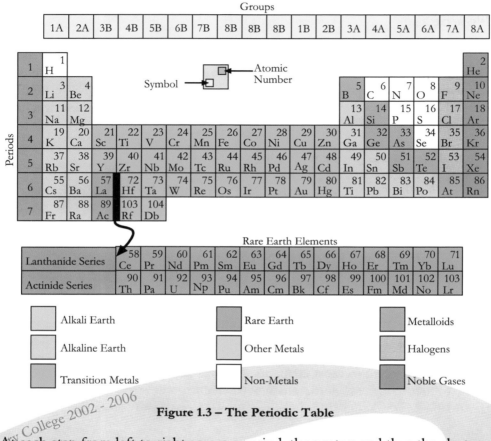

Figure 1.3 – The Periodic Table

At each step from left to right across a period, the proton and thus the electron count increases by one. This means that the atomic number of the elements in a row increases from left to right and the outer shell electron count reaches eight for each element on the extreme right of each row.

When the elements in one period are compared with those occupying neighbouring periods it can be seen that each element can be matched to another, both in chemical properties and outer shell electron count. These similar elements are arranged in vertical columns or *Groups*. Each vertical group contains elements that have the same number of outer shell or *valency* electrons.

Although the elements in a group have similar chemical properties, there is a gradual change as we look down a group. Going down group one, the melting point decreases and reactivity increases.

Examining the periodic table shows that 75% of the elements are metals and the rest non-metal, which are to be found in the top right hand corner of the table. The non-metals on the extreme right of the table have complete outer electron shells and consist of the *Noble Gases*

Element	Symbol	At. No.	At. Wt.	Element	Symbol	At. No.	At. Wt.
Actinium	Ac	89	227	Mendelevium	Md	101	256
Aluminium	Al	13	26.982	Mercury	Hg	80	200.59
Americium	Am	95	243	Molybdenum	Mo	42	95.94
Antimony	Sb	51	121.75	Neodymium	Nd	60	144.24
Argon	Ar	18	39.948	Neon	Ne	10	20.183
Arsenic	As	33	74.922	Neptunium	Np	93	237
Astatine	At	85	210	Nickel	Ni	28	58.71
Barium	Ba	56	137.34	Niobium	Nb	41	92.906
Berkelium	Bk	97	247	Nitrogen	N	7	14.007
Beryllium	Be	4	9.012	Nobelium	No	102	257
Bismuth	Bi	83	208.98	Osmium	Os	76	190.2
Bohrium	Bh	107	264	Oxygen	O	8	15.999
Boron	B	5	10.811	Palladium	Pd	46	106.4
Bromine	Br	35	79.909	Phosphorous	P	15	30.974
Cadmium	Cd	48	112.4	Platinum	Pt	78	195.09
Calcium	Ca	20	40.08	Plutonium	Pu	94	242
Californium	Cf	98	249	Polonium	Po	84	210
Carbon	C	6	12.011	Potassium	K	19	39.102
Cerium	Ce	58	140.12	Praseodymium	Pr	59	140.907
Caesium	Cs	55	132.905	Promethium	Pm	61	147
Chlorine	Cl	17	35.453	Protractinium	Pa	91	231
Chromium	Cr	24	51.996	Radium	Ra	88	226
Cobalt	Co	27	58.993	Radon	Rn	86	222
Copper	Cu	29	63.54	Rhenium	Re	75	186.2
Curium	Cm	96	247	Rhodium	Rh	45	102.905
Dubinium	Db	105	262	Rubidium	Rb	37	85.47
Dysprosium	Dy	66	162.5	Ruthenium	Ru	44	101.07
Einsteinium	Es	99	254	Rutherfordium	Rf	104	261
Erbium	Er	68	167.26	Samarium	Sm	62	150.35
Europium	Eu	63	151.96	Scandium	Sc	21	44.956
Fermium	Fm	100	253	Seaborgium	Sg	106	266
Fluorine	F	9	18.998	Selenium	Se	34	78.96
Francium	Fr	87	223	Silicon	Si	14	28.086
Gadolinium	Gd	64	157.25	Silver	Ag	47	107.87
Gallium	Ga	31	69.72	Sodium	Na	11	22.991
Germanium	Ge	32	72.59	Strontium	Sr	38	87.62
Gold	Au	79	196.967	Sulphur	S	16	32.064
Hafnium	Hf	72	178.49	Tantalum	Ta	73	180.948
Hassium	Hs	108	269	Technetium	Tc	43	98
Helium	He	2	4.003	Tellurium	Te	52	127.6
Holmium	Ho	67	164.93	Terbium	Tb	65	158.924
Hydrogen	H	1	1.008	Thallium	Tl	81	204.37
Indium	In	49	114.82	Thorium	Th	90	232.038
Iodine	I	53	126.904	Thulium	Tm	69	168.934
Iridium	Ir	77	192.2	Tin	Sn	50	118.69
Iron	Fe	26	55.847	Titanium	Ti	22	47.9
Krypton	Kr	36	83.8	Tungsten	W	74	183.85
Lanthranum	La	57	138.91	Uranium	U	92	238.03
Lawrencium	Lr	103	257	Vanadium	V	23	50.942
Lead	Pb	82	207.19	Xenon	Xe	54	131.3
Lithium	Li	3	6.939	Ytterbium	Yb	70	173.04
Lutetium	Lu	71	174.97	Ytterium	Y	39	88.905
Magnesium	Mg	12	24.312	Zinc	Zn	30	65.37
Manganese	Mn	25	54.938	Zirconium	Zr	40	91.22
Meitnerium	Mt	109	268				

Elements in the middle of the table are called *Transition Metals* and those on the left *Pure Metals*. However, hydrogen is a special case as having the atomic number '1', it naturally appears on the top left of the table but it is not a metal.

Metals

Metals have a number of common properties that are listed below:

- Apart from Mercury, they are solid at room temperature

- Most have high melting and boiling points

- They display a shiny surface when cut

- They are good conductors of electricity and heat

Non-Metals

In contrast, many non-metals are gases and most have low melting and boiling points. The solids show dull surfaces when cut and are all poor conductors of electricity and heat.

The Molecule

A molecule is a group of two or more similar or dissimilar atoms which have bonded together in a particular way. In the latter case, the molecule formed would be a chemical compound. Atoms will attempt to form enough bonds with each other to achieve eight (8) electrons in their outer shells.

Metals form *Metallic Bonds* that do not produce molecules and are the weakest of all bonds. Metals and non-metals form *Ionic Bonds*. Non-metals form *Covalent Bonds* which do produce molecules and are the strongest of the three types of bond.

Inter-molecular Forces

Inter-molecular forces hold molecules together and are chiefly responsible for many of the materials we see around us. In fact, we are held together by them. The atoms making up the large protein molecules that we consist of, are the same as those found in common substances, for example, carbon, hydrogen, oxygen and an array of metallic trace elements. In reality, you could say that we are made up of old star debris.

In this chapter, we are going to discuss three (3) of the inter-molecular forces.

1.   *Dipole-dipole Interaction*

2.   *Van der Waal's Forces*

3.   *Hydrogen Bonding*

Dipole-Dipole Interaction

These occur when non-metallic elements covalently bond. The protons and electrons in the contributing atoms are not always evenly distributed in the bonds of the molecule. This often results in the molecule having positive and negative poles. The molecules will align their poles with the opposite poles of their neighbours. The force of attraction is quite strong.

Van der Waal's Forces

An uneven distribution of electrons can give rise to regions of positive and negative charges in a molecule. This gives rise to a number of dipoles. Long chain molecules like those found in plastic materials would form many of these. The molecules align their positive and negative regions and the sum resultant force of attraction can range from very weak to fairly strong.

Hydrogen Bonding

If hydrogen covalently bonds to any of the three most electro-negative elements, for example, fluorine, oxygen or nitrogen the bond is very *polar*. (The electrons are shared so unevenly that the exposed proton at the hydrogen end is attracted to the non-bonding electrons on other molecules.) This is the strongest of all intermolecular forces of attraction.

Valency

The *valency* of an atom is usually defined as the number of bonds it can make with a monovalent atom such as hydrogen. Elements in the transition metal series, however, may have variable valencies. A general guide to valency is given in table 1.2

Group	1A	2A	3A	4A	5A	6A	7A	8A
Valency	1	2	3	4	3	2	1	0

Table 1.2 – Valency Grouping

If you look along the valency row on page 33, the valencies are described as:

1. Monovalent

2. Bivalent

3. Trivalent

4. Tetravalent

Note that in order to form a single covalent bond an atom's outer shell must provide one electron and one empty space. An atom with four outer shell electrons can provide four potential bonds and will thus be *tetravalent*. Groups 5, 6 and 7 can actually have two valencies. For example, Group 5 can be *trivalent* or *pentavalent* in some chemical reactions. In covalent bonding the three spaces necessary to make three bonds in Group 5 elements are available, making them trivalent. In some Group 5 elements and using subshells, five spaces necessary to make five covalent bonds are available making them pentavalent. But, if you consider ionic bonding they can gain three electrons making them trivalent. The usual definition is as shown in table 1.2.

In ionic substances, the valency of each ion is equal to its charge. To work out a formula for two (2) elements joined together, write down the symbols of each element with their valencies from the chart shown (table 1.2), and then swap the numbers around. An example of this procedure is illustrated here.

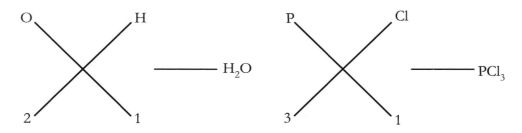

Figure 1.4 – How Valency Formulae are calculated

Notice that oxygen and hydrogen used as an example in figure 1.4 above, results in a molecule of water and phosphorous and chlorine results in a molecule of phosphorous chloride.

You will need to use the periodic table and the valency chart as to complete this process for other substances. However, if the chart is unavailable, you can still work out the formula, but it requires a more cautious approach. For example, phosphorous is a group 5 element and is trivalent, which means it can make three bonds with monovalent atoms.

Therefore, phosphorous could make three bonds with chlorine for example, which is group 7 and is monovalent. The resulting molecule would then have the formula PCl_3, as shown in figure 1.4.

You may have noticed that Group 8 elements have a valency of zero (0). However, if you look at the elements in this group you will see that they are all noble gases, which are described as being *inert*, in other words they cannot form bonds with any other atom. This is because their outer electron shells are already complete with eight (8) electrons and so they have no ability to bond.

The outermost electron shell of any atom never has more than eight electrons. As soon as the shell contains this number of electrons, it becomes stable, even though the sum of its sub-shell capacities may be more than eight. Any further electrons added to an atom will start to fill other sub-shells and then in turn any incomplete inner main shells. This process leads to the transition elements shown in the centre of the periodic table.

With any atom, it is only the electrons in the outer shell, which can take part in chemical bonding. Consequently, these are called '*Valence Electrons* '. Because an atom's outermost shell can never hold more than eight (8) electrons, the number of 'valence electrons' must always be always less than eight (8) if the atom is to bond.

If eight electrons are present in the atom's outer shell, then as already mentioned, it becomes stable like the inert gases and cannot form bonds.

Now that you understand a little about the mechanisms that allow chemical bonding, we need to examine the types of chemical bonds that can occur.

Inter-atomic Bonds

The bonds between atoms make it possible for them to combine in large amounts to form other substances. Inter-atomic bonds are of three main types:

1.   *Covalent*

2.   *Ionic*

3.   *Metallic*

The attractive forces in all three are directly associated with the valence electrons. The atom's outer electron shell that contains the valence electrons is in the highest *Energy State* and is relatively unstable. It may steal or lose electrons in an attempt to bring its number to eight (8), or it may share electrons with another atom. This is how atomic bonds are formed.

IONIC OR ELECTROVALENCY

Covalent Bond

The covalent bond results from the *sharing* of pairs of valence electrons by two or more atoms to form molecules. The bond only occurs between atoms of non-metals and is the strongest of the three bonds.

As an example of a *covalent bond*, let us examine the water molecule, H_2O. Oxygen is in Group 6 and is bivalent. This means that with its atomic number of '8', it has two (2) inner shell electrons and six (6) in its outer shell. This shell could be made complete, (increased to eight (8)), by sharing the single electron in the shell of each of two (2) monovalent hydrogen atoms.

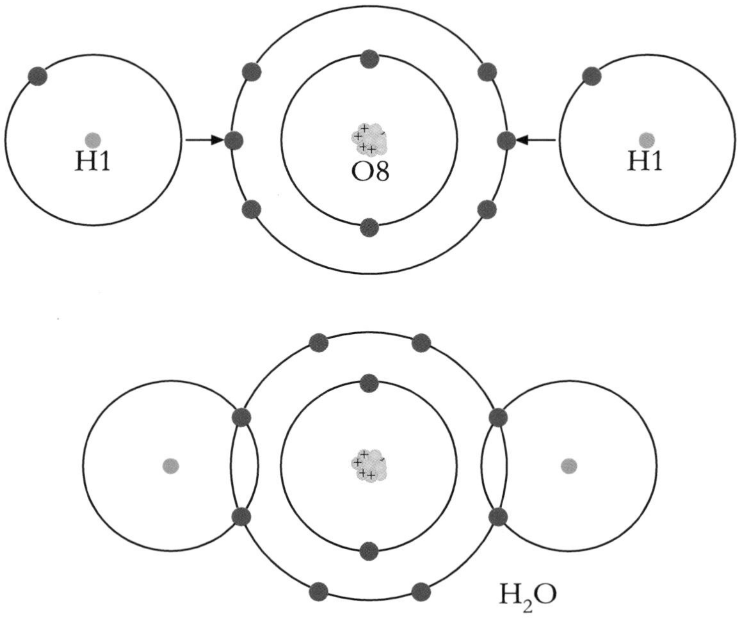

Figure 1.5 - Water Molecule produced by Two Covalent Bonds

SHARING OF ELECTRONS

In return, the hydrogen atoms can each share an electron in the oxygen atom's outer shell to make two (2) in their outer shells. See figure 1.5.

In the absence of hydrogen, two oxygen atoms can share electrons to bond and the oxygen molecule 0_2 is formed.

When one pair of electrons is shared between two atoms, it is called a *single* covalent bond; when two pairs are shared, it is called a *double* covalent bond, and as you might perhaps expect, with three pairs shared it is called a *triple*. These bonds are so strong that non-metals will not conduct electricity and are poor conductors of heat.

Ionic Bond

The ionic bond involves the *transfer* of electrons between two or more atoms. This bond occurs between the atoms of metals and those of non-metals. A metal atom is electropositive. It will easily lose outer shell electrons under the strong attraction of an electronegative, non-metal, atom that wishes to fill an incomplete outer shell.

When this occurs, a positive metal ion is formed and a negative non-metal ion is formed. Due to their residual charges, the two ions will be attracted to each other; hence the name ionic given to this type of bond.

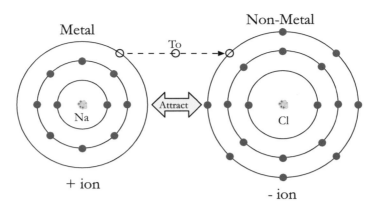

Figure 1.6 – Typical Ionic Bond

ELECTROVALENT

Metallic Bond

Metal atoms are electropositive in nature, losing outer shell electrons easily. When a large number of metal atoms are in close proximity, each has an equal attraction to its own outer shell electrons and those of close neighbouring atoms.

As a result, the atoms lose their outer shell electrons, which then drift loosely in an *electron cloud*.

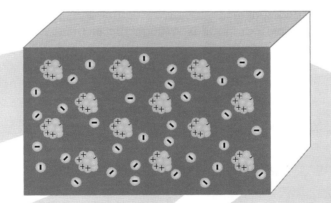

Figure 1.7 – Metallic Bonding

This cloud has a strong *negative* charge and the *positive* metal ions are all attracted to it. Naturally, positive ions would repel each other, so they take up geometric patterns or '*lattices*' where they can stay as far away from each other whilst remaining in close proximity to the cloud of electrons. In this way, crystalline structures form in solid-state metals.

The ease with which their electrons can move makes metals good conductors of electricity. Heat causes the electrons to vibrate and the vibration is easily transmitted through the cloud. This makes metals good conductors of heat.

37

www.part66.co.uk

When metals are first cut, the moving electron cloud reflects light, giving the cut surface a bright appearance. Oxygen in contact with the cut surface, can bond with the surface atoms forming an oxide of the metal.

Iron oxide forms on iron when it is exposed to the air.

The metallic bond is the weakest of the three bonds. Its strength depends on the number of electrons that each atom can give up to the cloud. Metallic bonds allow malleability and ductility.

Chemical Compounds

A chemical compound is defined as:

'A substance made up of different elements that are chemically bonded and are so united that the whole has properties of its own, which are unlike those of its constituents.'

This definition should tell you the clear difference between single elements and the compounds in which they are combined. Unlike elements, compounds can be split up by chemical reaction in a process called *Analysis*.

Two early classifications of chemical compounds were *Organic* and *Inorganic*. All organic compounds contain the element carbon, while those that do not are inorganic. Organic compounds were once only associated with living organisms, but a large number of organic compounds have now been synthesised, (put together artificially, which does not occur in nature), so this distinction is no longer valid.

There are now two main sorts of compounds:

- Ionic compounds   Dissimilar

- Covalent compounds   Similar

An ionic compound forms a giant regular structure called a continuous lattice, while covalent compounds contain individual units we have already identified as molecules. When different metallic elements are mixed, they result in an alloy, which has a continuous metallic lattice structure.

When a compound is formed, it has a resultant chemical formula. We have already discovered how to use the periodic table and the valency of elements to write simple formulae. Of course, there will be many occasions when compounded elements will form bonds with other elements or compounds in order to produce new ones. Whenever a compound is formed, the resulting chemical equation must balance. This means that the number of each type of atom must be the same on both sides of the equation.

www.part66.co.uk

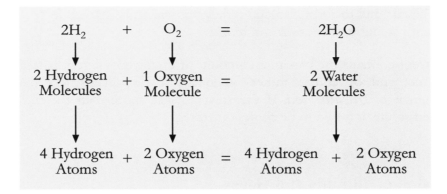

At this point, it would be appropriate to return to the groups of elements in the periodic table and learn a little more about them. The main elements are in Groups 1A - 8A and the Group B elements are transition metals.

- Group 1A Alkali metals (except for hydrogen)

- Group 2A Alkaline earth metals

- Group 6A Chalcogens (chalk formers)

- Group 7A Halogens (salt formers)

- Group 8A Noble gases (inert gases)

The transition metals in Group 3B to 2B are hard and dense, have high melting and boiling points and are much less reactive than Group 1A metals. Many transition metal compounds are coloured, copper sulphate is blue and iron oxide is red. The Group 1A metals on the other hand, are soft and low density, have low melting and boiling points and are very reactive.

It is worth remembering that all elements in the same group have similar chemical properties, for example, Group 1A are all metals (except hydrogen) and form positive ions and their oxides will form alkaline solutions when dissolved in water. All Group 7A are non-metals; form negative ions and their oxides will form acids when dissolved in water.

Solubility of Substances

When a substance dissolves in a solvent to an appreciable amount it is said to be *Soluble* in that solvent, (for example, water). If it will not dissolve in a solvent, it is *Insoluble*.

The *Solvent* is defined as the medium that disperses the *Solute*, which is the substance that dissolves.

If two liquids mix to form a solution, they are said to be *Miscible*. If they do not go into solution, they are *Immiscible*.

If a solvent contains the maximum amount of dissolved solute it is said to be *Saturated*, and of course rather obviously, if it contains less than the maximum it is *Unsaturated*. If the solvent takes more than the maximum dissolved solute, it is said to be *Supersaturated*.

Diffusion of Liquids and Gases

Diffusion is the way in which freely moving particles in liquids and gases spread out to fill all the space available to them. For example, even a gas that is denser than air will spread out evenly. The smaller the gas particle, the higher its average speed will be, so the faster it can diffuse. Substances that dissolve in liquids spread through those liquids by diffusion.

States of Matter

Matter can exist in one of three (3) states:

- Solid

- Liquid

- Gaseous

The Kinetic Theory of Matter

In 1827, the botanist Robert Brown was examining pollen grains floating on the surface of water. He recorded that the pollen was in a continuous state of rapid and erratic movement. Many years later, it was proved that this movement was the result of fast moving water molecules colliding with the pollen grains. The motion is now called *Brownian Movement.*. This movement can also be observed in smoke particles as air molecules collide with them.

It is now known that the molecules in liquids and gases are in a state of continuous motion. Even molecules in solids are vibrating in their fixed positions.

If heat energy is added to matter, the molecules gain kinetic energy and the movement becomes more vigorous. The kinetic theory predicts that all particles contain similar average energy levels at a given temperature.

This means that small particles will move very quickly whilst large particles will move slowly.

It has been further discovered that molecules are very particular about the distances they keep between themselves. If they get too close, they begin to repel each other. If they get too far apart, they begin to attract each other. These forces alter depending on whether the matter is in a solid, liquid or gas state.

Solids

The molecules in a solid have kinetic energy and vibrate about their fixed positions. This means they are alternately attracting and repelling each other. The molecules in a non-metal or the atoms in a metal arrange themselves into a geometric pattern that builds up into a lattice like structure. Such structures are called *Crystalline Structures*. Particles in a solid are close-packed and the strong forces between them prevent free movement. This is why they can only vibrate in their fixed positions and cannot move about.

Solids are dense and have a fixed volume and shape. Pressure cannot be transmitted through a solid material.

Some substances may appear to be solid but in fact are not. Pitch appears solid but if it is left for a long period of time it will gradually flow into the shape of any container it is in.

Liquids

The kinetic energy of the molecules in a liquid cause them to move around. They are attracted to other molecules but never remain with any particular one. This freedom of movement permits a liquid to take up the shape of any container it is placed in. Liquids have a fixed volume but do not have a fixed shape. Like solids, liquids are not compressible but unlike solids, pressure can be transmitted through liquids.

Gases

The molecules in a gas move at high velocity creating collisions between molecules and the walls of any container they may be in. Gas molecules are spaced further apart than those in liquids which reduces the attraction between them. Gases have no fixed volume or shape. They will expand to fill any container. Gases can be compressed and pressure can be transmitted through them.

Changes between States

As you probably already know and would expect, matter does not have to remain in a single state and given the right conditions, substances can usually change from solid to liquid to gas and vice versa.

Solid to Liquid - Fusion

If a solid is heated, the heat energy causes the particles in the solid to vibrate with increased energy with the result that they move further apart. If heat energy continues to be added to the solid, the particles eventually move far - enough apart to weaken their attractive forces enough to allow them to move through the substance. The crystalline structure of the solid breaks down and becomes non-crystalline or *Amorphous*. The solid has at this point become a liquid. This process is called *Fusion* and the heat energy required to complete the process of converting a unit mass of a substance from solid to liquid state without change of temperature is called the *Latent Heat of Fusion*.

Liquid to Gas - Vaporisation

If heat energy is added to a liquid, the molecules of that liquid become more energised and then move around with increased velocity. If heat energy is continuously added, a point will be reached where molecules will have gained enough energy to jump right out of the liquid and vaporisation commences.

As highly energised molecules leave the liquid, the sum total of molecular energy remaining in the liquid will reduce and so heat will have to be continually applied to replace this loss as more molecules jump clear. The result is that although heat energy is being added, it merely replaces the energy lost as the numbers of remaining molecules reduce, so the temperature of the liquid does not rise. The heat energy required to vaporise a unit mass of liquid without temperature rise is called the *Latent Heat of Vaporisation*.

Gas to Liquid - Condensation

Condensation is the process where a gas returns to a liquid state. If a gas is cooled, heat energy will be lost and the molecular energy level will fall. The result of this is that the molecules will not have sufficient energy to expand against atmospheric pressure and remain out of the liquid state and will therefore fall into a pool of condensed liquid. The molecules can only return to a liquid state if they lose energy and this is given out as heat energy. This expelled heat energy is the *Latent Heat of Condensation*.

www.part66.co.uk

During the condensation process, there will be a pause in the temperature fall as latent heat is expelled. An example of this can be experienced if steam condenses back into water on the skin. The latent heat expelled in the process causes a scalding burn, which is far worse than the effect of hot water alone.

Liquid to Solid - Solidification

When a liquid is cooled, it loses heat energy. The molecular energy falls and the particles move closer together where they come under the influence of the attractive force between them.

These forces of attraction and repulsion cause the particles to arrange themselves into the lattice structure of a solid. The loss of molecular energy is the *Latent heat of Solidification* and is expelled during the process so that on cooling to a solid, there will be period where solidification takes place without further reduction in temperature.

Sublimation

Some solid substances when heated do not melt but form a *Vapour*. A solid that changes to a vapour state without passing through a liquid state is called a *Sublimate*. A solid air freshener tablet is a good example of this in everyday use. Dry ice vaporising directly into carbon dioxide gas is another example.

Evaporation

Some liquids have a low boiling point, and so easily change from a liquid to a vapour at room temperature. These are called *volatile* liquids. Methylated spirits and ether are good examples of this type of liquid.

If one of these liquids is placed on the skin, it will feel cold. The reason for this is that the liquid requires latent heat to make the change to a vapour. It will take this from your skin, which loses heat and feels cool. Water will also evaporate more slowly than highly volatile liquids, producing a cooling effect.

In the evaporation process, the heat gained by the liquid from its surrounding increases the molecular energy of its molecules to the point where some will jump clear of the liquid. Many molecules will immediately lose energy gained and fall back into the liquid. However, if the liquid is placed in a draught, the escaping molecules will be blown away and be unable to return. This is the way body sweat produces a cooling effect.

The Effect of Pressure on Melting Points

Most substances contract during solidification, while some expand. For example, paraffin wax will contract during solidification, leaving a deep cleft in its surface, while water expands, which is why it bursts pipes in freezing conditions. Pressure also affects the melting point of substances. If the substance expands on solidification, additional pressure will lower its melting point. For example, if you stand on ice, it melts under your foot creating a thin film of water. This makes the surface very slippery, a factor ice skaters and skiers rely on. Conversely, if a substance contracts on solidification, its melting point will be raised by the application of pressure.

Regelation

Regelation literally means '*refreezing*'. This phenomenon can be examined if a block of ice is rested on two supports and a thin copper wire with heavy weights attached at both ends is positioned across it. After some time has elapsed, the wire will have passed completely through the block and dropped to the floor, but the ice will remain as a solid block.

What is happening is that the application of pressure on the ice causes it to lower its melting point and liquefy, allowing the wire to pass. Once the pressure above the wire is removed, the water refreezes.

During refreezing, latent heat is expelled, which is conducted down through the copper wire providing it with additional heat, accelerating the rate of melting, as shown in figure 1.8.

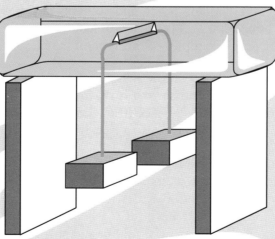

Figure 1.8 – Ice Melting Experiment

The Effect of Pressure on Boiling Points

If a liquid is put into a sealed container and held at a given temperature, some of the liquid will evaporate filling the air space above it with vapour. The vapour molecules will be moving at high speed colliding with the container walls and causing a pressure. Some molecules will return to the liquid whilst others leave. A point will be reached where the air space is saturated with vapour. The vapour pressure at this point is called the *Saturated Vapour Pressure (SVP)* for the liquid at the given temperature.

If the liquid at this temperature should ever be exposed to a pressure equal to or below it's SVP it will immediately vaporise or in other words boil. This applies whether there is an air space over the liquid or not.

If the liquid in the sealed container is heated, the value of the SVP will rise. Atmospheric pressure varies from day to day and with altitude. If the atmospheric pressure is high then a higher SVP is required, so the temperature at which the liquid boils will be higher. Conversely, a low atmospheric pressure will lower the boiling point of the liquid. This can be witnessed if you pump the air out of a sealed jar of water. The pressure will drop to the point where the water will boil at room temperature. Imagine trying to make a cup of tea at the summit of Everest where water would boil at around 60°C – lukewarm.

If the air pressure above the water is raised its boiling point will also rise. This is why the radiator of a car does not boil even though the water temperature is around 130°C – until you remove the cap of course!

The atmospheric pressure above the fuel in aircraft tanks is important. Aviation gasoline has a SVP of 7 psi at about 30°C. If gasoline at this temperature is ever exposed to the atmospheric pressure at 18,000 ft it will boil. Jet fuels have a SVP of around 0.2 psi, this is the atmospheric pressure around 62,000 ft. Any increase in fuel temperature will also raise the SVP so it is normal practice to maintain fuel tank airspaces at a pressure well above atmospheric pressure to avoid risk.

The Anomalous Expansion of Water

You may have wondered why ice forms on the surface of a pond. As the water temperature reduces, the water becomes denser and sinks to the bottom. This continues until all the water in the pond is at its maximum density, which is +4°C. If the temperature falls further, any water cooling below +4°C will become less dense and rise to the surface. The surface water will freeze at 0°C leaving the lower depths of the pond at +4°C. This is why fish move into deeper water in freezing conditions.

Do remember that water is at its maximum density at +4°C!

Diffusion

When two gases or two liquids are put together and are left undisturbed, they will gradually mix by a process called Diffusion. This process would also apply to a solid such as a soluble crystal dissolving in a fluid. The speed with which molecules move around at a given temperature depends on their mass. The molecules of a heavy gas for example move slower than those of a lighter gas, such as hydrogen. *Graham's Law of Diffusion* states

'At constant temperature a gas diffuses at a rate which is inversely proportional to the square root of its density'.

Diffusion rates can vary from minutes to weeks and more depending on the mass of the molecules.

Radioactivity

Atoms of the same element with differing numbers of neutrons are called *Isotopes*. Their proton count will not have changed so they retain their original atomic number, but their mass number will have changed. Some isotopes are unstable and will emit radiation in one or more forms.

Alpha Radiation (α), can be stopped by a sheet of paper, a thin sheet of aluminium foil or a few centimetres of air. It consists of one or more Helium nuclei and is positively charged.

Beta Radiation (β), can be stopped by several millimetres thickness of aluminium. It consists of high-speed electrons and is negatively charged.

Gamma Radiation (γ) is the most penetrating of all radiation and can be partially absorbed by several centimetres of lead or several metres of concrete. It consists of electromagnetic waves and has a neutral charge.

Revision

Matter

Questions

1. **The mass number of an element is based on:**

   a) The number of neutrons in its nucleus

   b) The number of protons in its nucleus

   c) The total number of protons and neutrons in its nucleus

2. **The atomic number of the atom of an element is based on:**

   a) The number of protons in its nucleus

   b) The total number of protons and neutrons in its nucleus

   c) The number of neutrons in its nucleus

3. **An atom that gains one or more additional electrons is called:**

   a) A positive ion

   b) A negative ion

   c) An isotope

4. **Two or more elements that are chemically bonded together and have an even mass distribution form a:**

   a) Chemical compound

   b) Substance

   c) Mixture

5. The chemical bonding of two or more elements is called:

   a) Chemical analysis

   b) Chemical synthesis

   c) Chemical fusion

6. A substance that passes from the solid to the vapour state without passing through the liquid state is called:

   a) A solvent

   b) A sublimate

   c) A distillate

7. If $2H_2$ is bonded to 0_2 the result is:

   a) $2H_20$

   b) $2H0$

   c) $2H_20_2$

8. Non-metals form:

   a) Ionic bonds

   b) Metallic bonds

   c) Covalent bonds

9. Ionic bonding involves:

   a) Electron sharing

   b) Electron transfer

   c) Attraction to a free electron cloud

10. Brownian Movement describes:

a) The motion of molecules

b) The movement in convection currents

c) The attraction of electrons

11. Pure water is at its greatest density at:

a) 0° Centigrade

b) –4° Centigrade

c) +4° Centigrade

12. When water freezes, heat energy is:

a) Absorbed

b) Released

c) Retained

13. Valency electrons are:

a) Outer shell electrons

b) All electrons

c) Free electrons

14. Neutrons carry:

a) A positive electrical charge

b) A negative electrical charge

c) No electrical charge

15. The number of electrons in a stable atom equals:

a) The number of neutrons in the nucleus

b) The number of protons and neutrons in the nucleus

c) The number of protons in the nucleus

16. Electrons carry a:

a) Positive electrical charge

b) Negative electrical charge

c) No electrical charge

17. An isotope of an element has:

a) The same atomic number but a different mass number

b) The same mass number but a different atomic number

c) A different mass and atomic number

18. Elements on the extreme right of the periodic table are:

a) Metals

b) Transition metals

c) Non-metals

19. Oxygen, atomic No. 8, is:

a) Trivalent

b) Bivalent

c) Univalent

20. The atomic weight of all atoms is related to:

a) Hydrogen

b) Helium

c) Carbon

21. **A 'Group' in the periodic table of elements contains elements that:**

    a) Have the same number of outer shell electrons

    b) Have the same number of electrons

    c) Increase in atomic number sequence from top to bottom

22. **A 'Period' in the periodic table of elements contains atoms that:**

    a) Have the same number of outer shell electrons

    b) Have the same number of electrons

    c) Increase an atomic number sequence from left to right

23. **A group 5A element is:**

    a) Univalent

    b) Bivalent

    c) Trivalent

24. **Two gases mix by a process known as:**

    a) Infusion

    b) Diffusion

    c) Fusion

25. **The maximum number of electrons that can be held in the outer electron shell of an atom is:**

    a) Six

    b) Four

    c) Eight

Revision

Matter

Answers:

1.   **C**
2.   **A**
3.   **B**
4.   **A**
5.   **B**
6.   **B**
7.   **A**
8.   **C**
9.   **B**
10. **A**
11. **C**
12. **B**
13. **A**
14. **C**
15. **C**
16. **B**
17. **A**
18. **C**
19. **B**
20. **C**
21. **A**
22. **C**
23. **C**
24. **B**
25. **C**

Mechanics - Statics

Forces

Scalar and Vector Quantities

Scalar quantities can be fully defined by just a number, as there is no direction associated with the quantity. For example, time is a scalar quantity as are mass and volume. We can describe the mass of a car by saying that it is 1200kg or the volume of its fuel tank by saying it is one (1) cubic metre. In this case, the numbers fully describe the mass and volume respectively and do not require any other information such as direction or start and finish points.

If we want to add two scalar quantities together then we simply add the two numbers together, which would give the sum total.

For example, 10kg + 5kg = 15kg.

Vector quantities require both a number and a direction to be fully defined. Force, velocity, acceleration, momentum and the moment of a force are typical examples of vector quantities. These can be represented by an arrowhead line drawn to scale, indicating the magnitude and direction of the quantity. (For example: a force of 20N acting vertically downwards). The number 20N on its own would not say anything with regard to the direction it was acting.

Vector quantities cannot be added by just considering their sizes; their directions also have to be taken into account. For example, if two forces of 200N and 400N act on an object, it is not possible to specify the resultant force without knowing the directions of the applied forces in the first place. For example, if two forces were acting in opposite directions then their resultant force would be different to that produced if they were acting in the same direction.

Force

Force is a vector quantity and to specify it completely its size, direction and point of application must be stated; the point of application being the point where a force is applied to a body. Forces cannot be directly observed; only their effects can be seen. These could be the acceleration of an object due to unbalanced forces acting on it, or the distortion of an object's shape due to compression or extension.

53

www.part66.co.uk

The term *Dynamics* is used to describe the study of the motion of a body under the action of unbalanced forces. The term *Statics* is used to describe the study of bodies at rest when forces are balanced. The remainder of this section is concerned with the subject of Statics.

Compression, Tension and Shear Forces

When a pair of forces applied to an object squeeze it, (they try to reduce its length), the forces are said to be *Compressive*. When a pair of forces try to extend an object, (they try to increase its length), the forces are said to be *Tensile*.

When a pair of forces tries to cause one face of a material to slide relative to an adjacent face, then the forces are said to be *Shear*. All these are illustrated in figure 2.1.

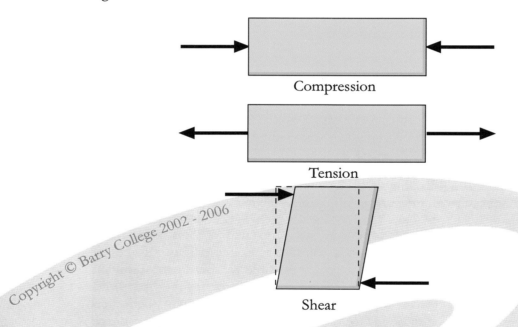

Compression

Tension

Shear

Figure 2.1 – Compressive, Tensile and Shear Forces

It is common to see structural components that combine two or even more of the above-mentioned forces. These forces can be described as being *bending forces* or *torsion forces*.

1. The main spar of an aircraft wing in flight is subjected to an upward bending force. The top of the spar will be in compression whilst the bottom will be in tension.

2. When an aileron is deflected in flight, it will try to twist the wing, which puts the wing skin into both tension and compression.

3. A rudder deflection will try to twist the fuselage putting its structural components into tension or compression.

4. Rivets in the joints holding the metal skins will react in shear force.

It is vitally important, especially in the aviation industry, to consider all the forces that will occur in structures when they are used in their different configurations.

From the above, you should now understand that bending and torsion forces are a combination of compressive, tensile and shear forces, figure 2.2.

Each force can of course act on it's own. For example, a rotating helicopter blade will be experiencing centrifugal force, which puts the blade into tension.

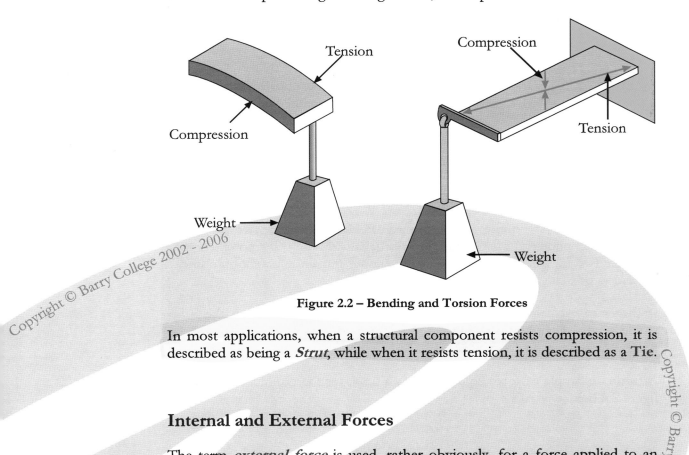

Figure 2.2 – Bending and Torsion Forces

In most applications, when a structural component resists compression, it is described as being a *Strut*, while when it resists tension, it is described as a **Tie**.

Internal and External Forces

The term *external force* is used, rather obviously, for a force applied to an object from outside its boundaries. The term *internal force* is used, again rather obviously, for a force induced in the object to react against the externally applied force.

For example, when you stand on the floor, you are applying a force through your feet onto the floor due to the product of your mass and the acceleration due to gravity. However, you do not fall through the floor because the floor pushes up against your feet with an equal force called the *Reaction*.

Forces and Reactions

In the last section, we looked at the example of a person standing on a floor and understood that there is a good reason why he/she does not fall through it. It is important to recognise that to every force acting on a body there will be an equal and opposite force or reaction. If you examine the drawing in figure 2.3 of a lamp hanging from a ceiling, you should see that the weight of the lamp exerts a downward pull on the cable and the cable exerts an upward pull on the lamp.

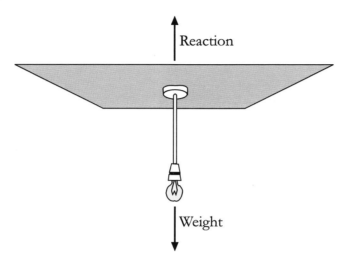

Reaction

Weight

Figure 2.3 – Reaction

Since the lamp is stationary, it is in a state of equilibrium; (the two forces are equal in magnitude and opposite in direction). You should really note here that there are two (2) forces present, as a body cannot remain in equilibrium under the action of a single force.

If the lamp cable in figure 2.3 were cut, the only force acting on the lamp would be its weight and it would fall to the ground. The forces shown are the forces of gravity acting downward and the reaction force acting upwards.

A further example of force equilibrium, is a book resting on a table, shown in figure 2.4 below.

www.part66.co.uk

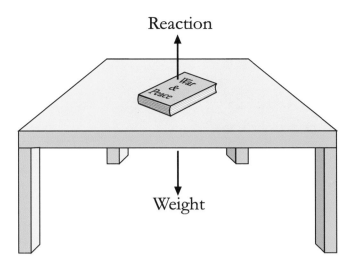

Figure 2.4 – Book Resting on a Table

You should observe that although the book is resting on the table, the same rule applies.

In other words, this time the table is reacting with the same force upwards as the weight of the book acts down, both forces being equal and opposite.

Mass and Weight

Mass describes the amount of material in a body and it is usually expressed in kilograms (kg) or pounds (lb). This does not express the weight of the body. To prove this suspend a one kilogram object on a spring balance and adjust the scale to read one kilogram exactly while you are in Cardiff. If you take the balance to the Arctic it will read over one kilogram. If you take it to Central Africa it will read less than one kilogram. Finally, take it to the Moon and it will register hardly anything at all. The amount of material in the body has clearly not altered but something has.

All Earthbound matter is attracted by the gravitational pull of the Earth and this force originates at the Earth's centre. The Earth is not a perfect sphere it bulges at the Equator so if you move around the Earth you are at varying distances from its centre. The Moon has a very small gravitational pull.

Different gravitational forces are influencing the object, so the spring balance is reading this force not the mass. We call this force the *Weight* of the object. A spring balance can only measure weight. Weight is a force expressed in Newtons or lbf. Mass is not a force.

Force is the product of mass and acceleration. To find a body's weight we multiply its mass by the acceleration due to gravity.

$$\text{Force} = \text{Mass} \times \text{Acceleration}$$

In most textbooks and for the purposes of this Module, we use a figure for the acceleration due to gravity based on that found in NW Europe, which is 9.81 m/s². Therefore, our 1kg mass would have a weight of:

$$1\text{kg} \times 9.81\text{m/s}^2 = 9.81 \text{ Newtons}$$

It is vital to remember that weight is a force, mass is not. To convert mass to weight you must multiply the mass by 9.81m/s². To convert weight back to mass you must divide by 9.81m/s².

Representation of a Force by a Vector

A force has magnitude, direction and a point of application. A quantity that just has magnitude and direction is a *Vector Quantity* and can be represented by a straight line whose length on a known scale represents the *magnitude* of the quantity, and whose *direction* is the same as the line of action of that quantity. Such a line is known as a *Vector* and an arrowhead indicates its direction.

Quadrature of a Vector

The quadrature of a vector is drawn at 90° to the original vector.

This question frequently appears in IR Part-66 examinations so do remember it!

Equilibrium

When two or more forces act on a body in such a way that the body remains at rest or moves at constant speed in a straight line, the forces are said to be in Equilibrium.

For two forces to be in equilibrium:

1.   They must be equal in magnitude

2.   They must be concurrent, (having lines of action that pass through the same point)

3.   They must act in exactly opposite directions.

Look at figure 2.5 below showing two tractors pulling a rope.

www.part66.co.uk

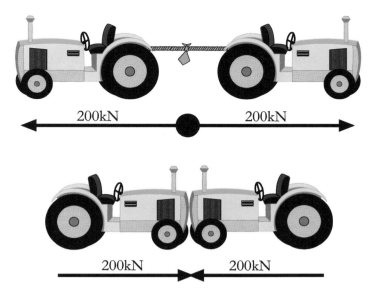

Figure 2.5 – Two Forces in Equilibrium

For three forces to be in equilibrium:

1. They must be coplanar, (they act in the same plane).

2. They must be concurrent, (have lines of action passing through one point).

3. They must be capable of being represented in magnitude and direction by arrowhead vectors, which when taken in order of the forces, form a closed triangle known as the *Triangle of Forces*

Drawing a Triangle of Forces

A triangle of forces can be constructed as follows:

Space Diagram

1. Draw a *space diagram* depicting the three (3) forces as straight lines set down in the correct angular relationship to each other and showing their direction by using arrowheads

2. Decide whether to take the forces, in the sequence in which they occur, in either a clockwise or anti-clockwise order – either way will do.

3. Use *Bow's Notation* to identify the spaces between the lines A, B and C in cyclic order and in the direction decided above

www.part66.co.uk

Vector Diagram

1. Select a suitable scale to represent the forces

2. Draw an arrowhead line to scale representing the first force, which lies between the notations A and B; this will be vector *ab* and will point in the direction A to B shown in the space diagram

3. The next line drawn is vector *bc*, which will start at B and point in the direction B to C as shown in the space diagram

4. Draw the line for force *ca*

5. If the forces were in equilibrium, the end point A of the third force will join up with the start point A of the first force completing a closed triangle in which the three (3) forces will form a continuous path in the same direction around it.

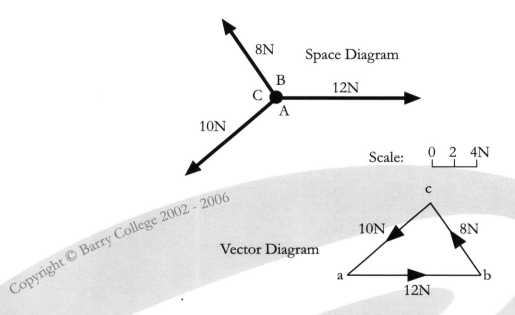

Figure 2.6 - Three (3) Forces in Equilibrium

For more than three forces to be in equilibrium:

They must be coplanar, (all lie in the same plane).

They must be concurrent, (all lines of action pass through one point)

If these forces are represented in magnitude and direction by arrowhead straight lines, then these lines when taken in order of the forces must form a closed polygon known as the *Polygon of Forces*

Drawing a Polygon of Forces

A polygon of forces may be drawn as follows:

Space Diagram

1. Draw a space diagram representing the forces as straight lines set down in their correct angular relationship to each other and showing their direction by use of arrowheads

2. Decide whether to take the forces in the sequence they occur in either a clockwise or anticlockwise direction, either direction will do.

3. Use Bow's Notation to identify the spaces between the lines in cyclic order in the direction decided above.

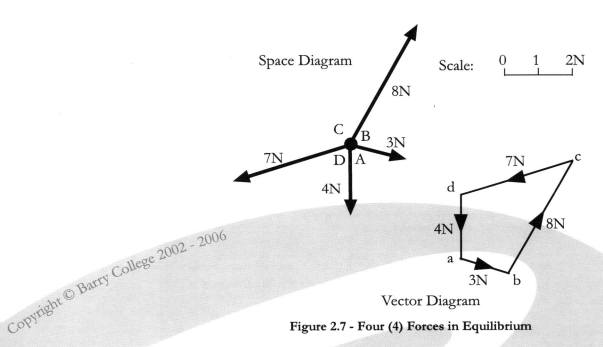

Figure 2.7 - Four (4) Forces in Equilibrium

Vector Diagram

1. Select a suitable scale to represent the forces

2. Draw lines to scale representing each of the forces taken in order to complete the polygon of forces

3. If the forces are in equilibrium, the endpoint of the last force will join up with the start point of the first force and the forces will form a continuous path in the same direction around the polygon.

In order to check your understanding of these concepts, let us look at a couple of real life problems.

Example 1

Consider a load W suspended by two cables from a beam, figure 2.8.

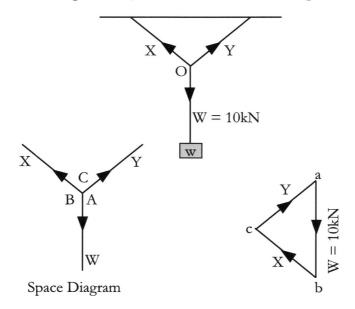

Space Diagram

Figure 2.8 – Load suspended from a beam

If gravity exerts a pull of 10kN on the load the tension in the cable attached to it will also be 10kN. The arrow shows this force as acting vertically downwards from point 0. The tensional forces in cables X and Y have to balance this downward force of 10kN by acting together to produce an upward pull of 10kN acting on point 0.

Therefore, we can say that the resultant of the forces X and Y acts vertically upwards and is equal and opposite to the 10kN weight of the load, which is the equilibrant force in this case.

If we were given enough information to draw a space diagram showing the angular relationship of the cables, we could draw a triangle of forces. Then, using a chosen scale we could obtain figures for the actual values of the forces X and Y, see figure 2.9.

Note in these diagrams, the direction of the forces, and the identification of the resultant R and the equilibrant E.

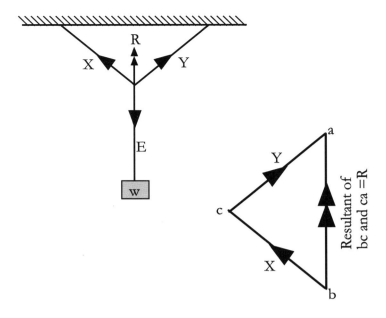

Figure 2.9 – Triangle of Forces for the load in figure 2.8

Example 2

A construction site crane has a jib 11m long and a tie cable 8½ m long. Both are attached to a pillar 3m high. What would the forces be in the jib and tie cable if the crane held a load of 4 ½ metric tonne?

The first step is to determine the weight of the object, which is:

$$4,500 \text{kg} \times 9.81 \text{m/s}^2 = 44.145 \text{kN}$$

Using the dimensions given in the problem you can draw a diagram of the crane that will then show the angular relationships of the jib, tie rod, post and rope, figure 2.10 overleaf.

The space diagram, also shown in figure 2.10, is formed out of the jib, tie rod and cable and is notated A, B and C. Once the triangle of forces has been drawn to scale, 1 cm = 10kN (1mm=1kN) in this case, the forces in the jib and tie rod can be obtained by measurement, using the scale.

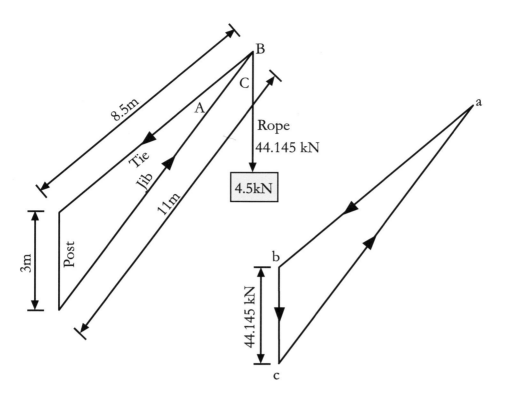

Figure 2.10 – Crane

Note: that by looking at the direction of the arrows, you can see that the jib is in compression and the tie rod is in tension.

A useful tip, you can use a set square and ruler to transfer the jib and tie force lines from the space diagram to your vector diagram. By taking scale measurements you can determine that the force in the jib is 162kN and the force in the tie is 125kN.

You could have done this mathematically of course and avoided the need to draw anything. IR Part-66 questions would not involve difficult numbers as you do not use calculators or use drawing implements in the exam. The examples are given here to allow you to understand the principles involved. *Get to know them and be prepared to use the mathematical solution shown below:*

$$\text{Force in Jib} = 44.145 \times \frac{11}{3} = 161.8\text{kN}$$

$$\text{Force in Tie Rod} = 44.145 \times \frac{8.5}{3} = 125\text{kN}$$

Parallelogram of Forces

If we need to find the resultant of two inclined forces, this is the same as adding two vectors together. However, as we have previously discussed, you cannot simply add two vector quantities together by adding their magnitudes.

Therefore, if we draw the two forces to scale as vectors in their correct angular relationship, we can then draw a parallelogram by drawing lines parallel to both vectors. Once this is drawn, we can then draw in the diagonal starting at the intersection point of the two vectors as shown in figure 2.11.

Using the drawings scale, we can then determine the resultant force, which is the sum of the combined effect of the two forces.

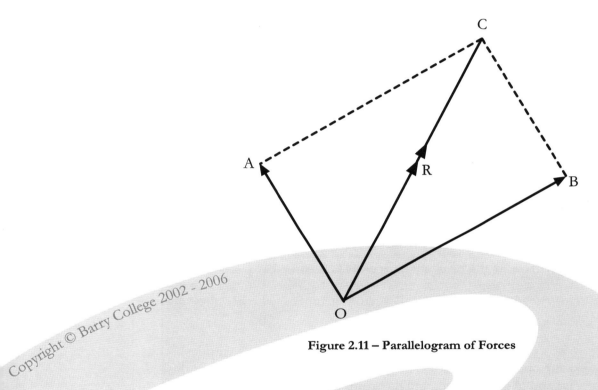

Figure 2.11 – Parallelogram of Forces

Addition and Subtraction of Vectors

When two or more physical quantities of the same type exert an influence on a body, it is often necessary to know the total or resultant effect. As we have seen, simple numerical addition or subtraction can resolve scalar quantities but with vector quantities, this is only possible if they all act in the same direction.

An example of vector addition would be a series of displacements where a body moves given distances in specific directions. The result would be that the body would end up displaced from the start point by a distance that was not the sum of all the distances, which on their own would be scalar. What does all that mean?

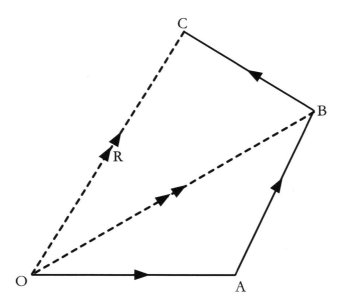

Figure 2.12 – Resultant of Several Forces Acting on a Body

The line OC represents the resultant of the vectors.

For example:

$$\text{Vector Sum} = \text{OA} + \text{AB} + \text{BC} = \text{OC}$$

Or, the line OB represents the resultant of vectors OA and AB.

The same rules of addition apply to all vector quantities whether they are displacements, velocities, accelerations or forces.

Suppose now we need to find the difference between two vector quantities. If they act in exactly opposite directions, the problem is simple to solve, but this is rarely the case and in general, they will have different directions.

If an aircraft flying in a straight line increased its speed from 30 m/s to 40 m/s the difference in speed is 10m/s. That seemed easy but we were dealing with scalar quantities in that example.

What if the aircraft was flying due East at 30 m/s and then turned due South changing velocity to 40 m/s. We now have to consider the magnitudes and directions of vector quantities. Our answer will not be a simple subtraction of speeds. The change in velocity is 50 m/s shown in the direction of the arrow.

www.part66.co.uk

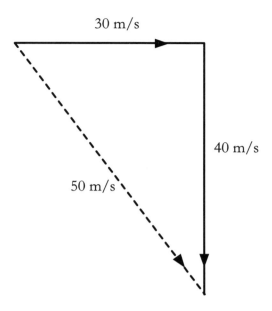

Figure 2.13 – Vector Subtraction

Resolution of Vectors

We have examined how a number of vectors can be combined to give their resultant effect. Conversely, it is possible to resolve a single vector into component parts. A single vector quantity can always be resolved into any number of components in a variety of ways. A simple illustration of this would be the case of a person pulling a box along a floor using a rope over one shoulder.

The rope would be at an angle to the floor so if you wanted to know what useful force was being applied to the box in a horizontal direction or, what force was actually trying to lift the box vertically off the floor, you would need to resolve the tension force in the rope into its horizontal and vertical components. These would form the vector sum of the force in the rope.

This could of course, be done by constructing a *scaled* drawing of the vector representing the magnitude of the tension force in the rope, its direction and its angle from the floor. You could then drop a vertical line to the floor and this would give the lifting force by measuring off against the scale. The horizontal line would then represent the useful horizontal pulling force being applied to the crate.

However, this method is OK for simple problems but is sometimes difficult to apply due to inaccuracies of measurement and the scale itself.

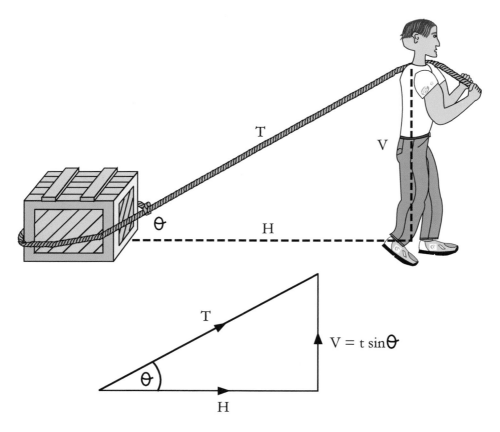

Figure 2.14 – Splitting a Vector into its Horizontal and Vertical Components

Therefore, the vertical component of applied force T is given by the formula:

$$v = t \times Sin\theta$$

And the horizontal component is given by the formula:

$$h = t \times Cos\theta$$

$$Sin\theta = \frac{v}{t} \quad \& \quad Cos\theta = \frac{h}{t}$$

In the simple case illustrated in figure 2.14, when resolving forces into their horizontal and vertical components we are using a right-angled triangle. Therefore, this method is called the **_Rectangular Resolution_** of a force.

The forces you need to resolve may not always be simple horizontals and verticals. In the case shown in figure 2.15 you can use a parallelogram of forces to resolve the inclined components of tension T.

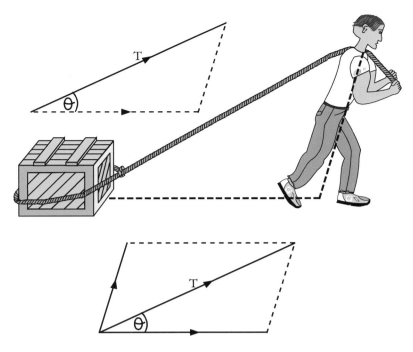

Figure 2.15 – Using a Parallelogram to Split Vectors

You may also note that, referring to the earlier example of the use of the parallelogram of forces; the diagonal T is also the resultant of the two component forces.

Worked Example

Triangle of forces: Two co-planar forces X and Y act at a point 0. Force X is 4kN and acts vertically downwards from point 0. Force Y is 3kN and acts horizontally to the right of point 0. Find the value and direction of a third force, which would be required to create equilibrium.

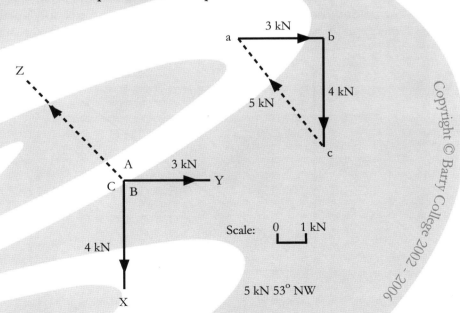

Figure 2.16 – Triangle of Forces

Polygon of Forces

Three co-planar forces X, Y and Z act at a point 0. Force X is 5N and acts horizontally due East of point 0. Force Y is 4N and acts at 45° North East of 0. Force Z is 3N and acts horizontally due West of 0. Determine the value and direction of a fourth force required to create equilibrium.

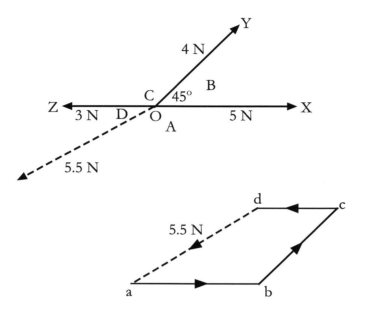

Figure 2.17 - Example of Polygon of Forces

Parallelogram of Forces

Two co-planar forces act at a point 0. Force A is 8N and acts horizontally due East of point 0. Force B is 6N and acts vertically upwards due North of point 0. Determine the value of a single force that would replace forces A and B.

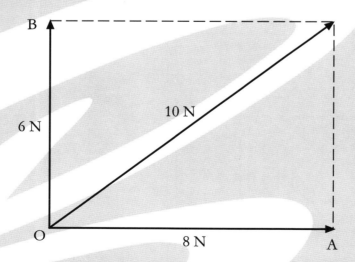

Figure 2.18 – Example of Parallelogram of Forces

Resolution of Forces

A light aircraft pulled by a tow cable attached to its nose wheel. The tension force in the cable is 100N.

Determine the vertical component of this force if the tow cable makes an angle of 30° with the ground.

Vertical force = 100N x Sin30°

Since: Sin30° is 0.5

Vertical force = 50N

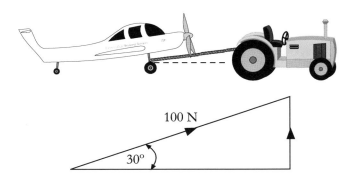

Figure 2.19 – Example of Resolution of Two Forces

Vector Addition

A forklift vehicle raises a crate vertically at a velocity one metre per second whilst travelling horizontally forwards at two metres per second. Determine the resultant velocity of the crate.

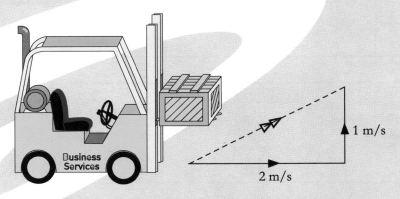

Figure 2.20 – Example of Vector Addition

You could draw this to scale but you can use Pythagoras' Rule.

For example: The square of the hypotenuse equals the sum of the squares of the other two sides.

$$2^2 + 1^2 = 5$$
$$\sqrt{5} = 2.236 \text{ m/s}$$

Note: These could easily be included as multi-choice questions!

Moments and Couples

When a force is applied to a body, it may either cause it to move in a straight line or cause it to rotate or even do both. It may also cause it to change shape. The turning effect or *Moment* of a force about a point or fulcrum, figure 2.21, is dependent on two quantities.

1.   The magnitude (size) of the force.

2.   The perpendicular distance of the point from the line of action of the force, referred to as the *moment arm*.

If either the magnitude of the force or the moment arm is altered then the turning moment will alter. For example, if the force or distance is increased, the turning moment will also increase.

Also, if the direction of the applied force changes (figure 2.21), then either a clockwise (CW) or anticlockwise (ACW) rotation is produced at the moment arm pivot point.

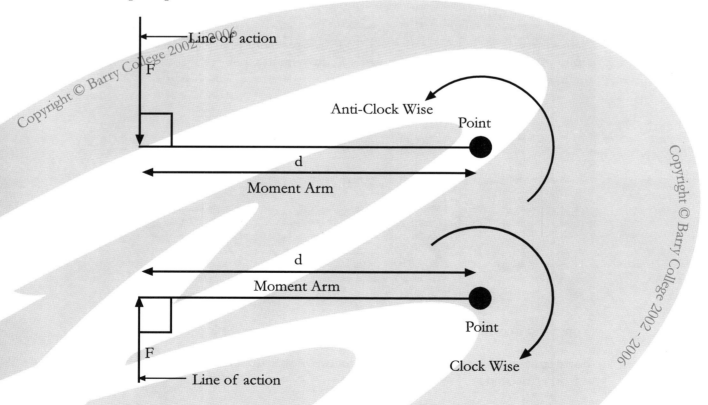

Figure 2.21 – Turning effect or Moment

www.part66.co.uk

The units used to express moments may result from the product of a force in Newtons and a distance in metres Newton metres (Nm). Moments can also be expressed in pounds-feet (lb ft) or pounds inches (lb in).

Where more than one force acts on a body, the total turning moment will be the algebraic sum of the moments of the forces. Let us look at a practical example, figure 2.22.

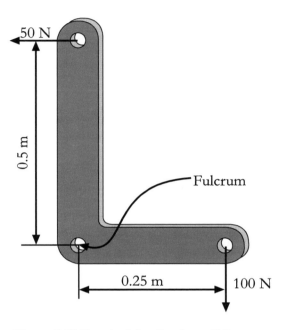

Figure 2.22 Practical Application of Moments

If you examine the bell-crank lever shown you will notice that there are two forces and two moment arms. Look closer and you will see that the 100N force is exerting a clockwise turning moment whilst the 50N force is exerting an anticlockwise turning moment.

If the sum of the clockwise moments equals the sum of the anticlockwise moments the bell-crank lever will be at rest. The anticlockwise moment can be considered as being a negative moment, so when you add it to the clockwise moment the result is zero, in other words, no resultant turning moment.

The Principle of Moments

If any numbers of coplanar forces acting on a body are in equilibrium, the algebraic sum of the moments of these forces about any point in the plane must be zero. This may be stated simply as:

If a body is at rest under the action of several forces, the sum of the clockwise moments about any axis is equal to the sum of the anticlockwise moments about the same axis.

www.part66.co.uk

For example:

$$Y \times b = X \times a$$

For the beam shown in figure 2.23 to be in equilibrium, the clockwise moment must equal the anticlockwise moment.

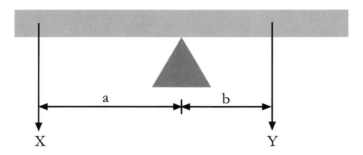

Figure 2.23 – Beam in Equilibrium Levers

A simple lever can be a bar or beam turning on a pivot or fulcrum. Levers can be designed to be straight or cranked. The forces applied to a lever may be perpendicular to it or angled.

A uniform straight lever is one that has its mass distributed evenly along its length and its weight will therefore act through its centre of gravity in the very centre of the lever.

You can use the principle of moments to resolve unknown forces and moment arms if you are given sufficient information.

Example

A uniform lever is supported on a knife-edge fulcrum positioned at its centre, figure 2.24.

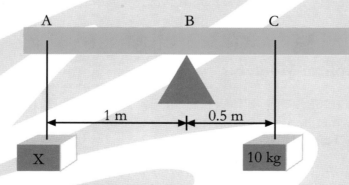

Figure 2.24 – Lever Supported on a Knife-Edge

If a mass of 10kg is suspended at a point C, 0.5m to the right of the fulcrum B, let us calculate the mass, which would have to be suspended at a point A, 1m to the left of the fulcrum B to keep things in equilibrium.

$$\text{Weight of 10 kg mass} = 10 \times 9.81 = 98.1N$$
Therefore the clockwise moment of this force is:
$$98.1N \times 0.5m = 49.05Nm$$

To calculate the mass (X) in figure 2.24 we first need to calculate its overall anticlockwise moment, which is:

$$(X \times 9.81) \times 1m = 9.81XNm$$

Using the principles of moments, we can calculate the value of 'X' by:

$$9.81X = 49.05$$
$$\therefore X = \frac{49.05}{9.81} = 5kg$$

Note: We changed the 10kg mass into a weight in Newtons, which is the correct way to calculate a turning moment in Nm. You could have short cut this by using kilogram metres.

For example,

Clockwise moment Xkg × 1m = Anticlockwise moment 10kg × 0.5m

Therefore X = 5kgm/1m = 5kg

Other types of straight lever are illustrated in figure 2.25.

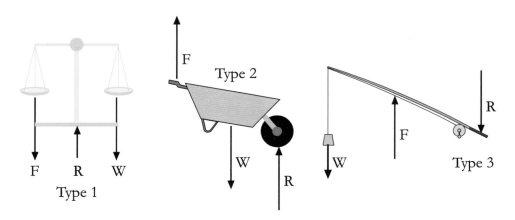

Figure 2.25 – Other Types of Straight Lever

Type 1 is a lever we have just looked at in our worked example. Examples of this type of lever in common use are:

- Beam balances where the arms are of equal length

- Weighing machines - where the arms are of unequal length and a mass can be moved along one graduated arm to balance a mass on the other arm

Type 2 is a lever arrangement that can best be seen in the design of a wheelbarrow.

Type 3 is an arrangement where a large effort moves through a small distance to overcome a small load, which moves through a large distance. If you have used a fishing rod, you will have used this type of lever.

Equilibrant of Parallel Forces

A study of the levers used in the examples shows that the lever's fulcrum is opposing, or balancing, the downward forces by exerting a single upward force, which is the equilibrant of the other forces. To understand this better, let us look at another, more complex, working example, in figure 2.26.

www.part66.co.uk

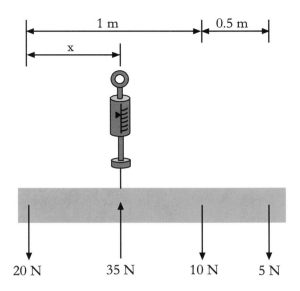

Figure 2.26 - Beam with several Forces acting on it

The single upward force must be equal and opposite to the downward forces and so its value is 35N. For example, 20N+10N+5N

Note: In this example we consider the beam to be weightless.

We now need to establish the position of the fulcrum as a distance from the left hand end of the beam. We will choose to use the left hand end of the beam as an imaginary fulcrum or datum. We start by finding the sum of the clockwise moments acting on the beam around our imaginary datum.

$$(20N \times 0m) + (10N \times 1m) + (5N \times 1.5m) = 17.5Nm$$

Now the anti-clockwise moment opposing this must be:

$$35N \times Xm = 35X \, Nm$$

As the clockwise and anti-clockwise moments must be equal for equilibrium to exist we can say that:

$$35XNm = 17.5Nm$$
$$X = \frac{17.5}{35} = 0.5m$$

From this we can therefore say that an upward force of 35N positioned 0.5m from the left-hand end of the beam will balance the three downward forces.

Reactions on a Simply Supported Beam

A simply supported beam is one that is supported at two points. An aircraft can be looked at theoretically like a beam that is supported at its nose wheel and main wheels. Indeed, it is treated as such when calculations are made for the reactions at these points and these are used for locating its *Centre of Gravity (C of G or CG)* position. Again, to understand this better, let us look at another working example, figure 2.27.

A simply supported uniform beam 6m long rests on two supports A and B that are 4m apart, A being at the left-hand end of the beam. The mass of the beam itself is 10kg and in addition, a mass of 5kg is hung from the beam 2m from A.

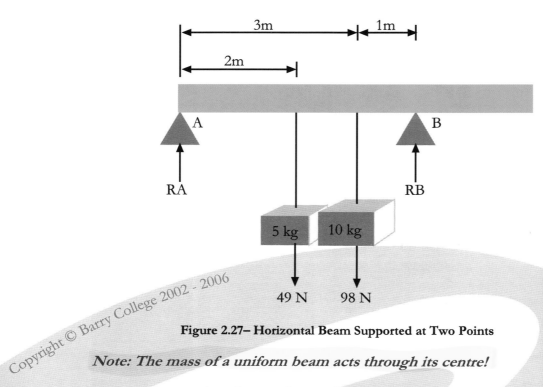

Figure 2.27– Horizontal Beam Supported at Two Points

Note: The mass of a uniform beam acts through its centre!

To find the reaction force a B we need to take the moments about A as follows:

Clockwise Moment = (49N x 2m) + (98N x 3m)
= 392Nm

Now when looking at the anti-clockwise moment:

Anti-clockwise Moment = Reaction Force B x 4

392Nm = 4RB

$RB = \dfrac{392}{4} = 98N$

www.part66.co.uk

As the total downward weight is shared between the two supports, the reaction force at A will be:

$$(98N + 49N) - 98N = 49N$$

The reaction force at A is therefore 49N and at B is 98N

Locating the Centre of Gravity of a Simply Supported Loaded Beam

A body's *Centre of Gravity (C of G)* is the point that its total weight is said to act through in a vertically downward direction. To find a body's C of G is a relatively simple operation, but in order to achieve this we need to remember a couple of simple rules:

1. All moment arms forward of, or in the case illustrated in figure 2.27 to the left of, the reference datum are considered negative. All moment arms behind or in this case to the right of, the reference datum is considered positive. We chose the LH end of the beam to be the datum.

2. It makes sense, to choose a reference datum at the most forward position or in this case the extreme left hand end of the body as there will not be any negative moments if we do this.

The centre of gravity can be calculated by dividing the total moment around the reference datum by the total weight of the beam and anything hung from it. For instance, looking at the example in figure 2.27, we can create a table to show the moments.

Item	Weight (Newtons)	Moment Arm (Metres)	Moment (Newton Metres)
Reaction Force at A	49	0	0
Reaction Force at B	98	4	+392
Total Weight	147	Total Moment	+392

Table 2.1 - Locating the Centre of Gravity of a Simply Supported Loaded Beam

$$\text{Centre of Gravity Position} = \frac{\text{Total Moment}}{\text{Total Weight}}$$

$$= \frac{392}{147} = +2.6m$$

In straightforward English, this means that the Centre of Gravity position in figure 2.27 is 2.6m from end A.

Locating the Centre of Gravity of an Aircraft

The example illustrated in figure 2.27, is very similar to the calculation required to locate the centre of gravity of an aircraft. An aircraft is weighed by placing weighing scales under its nose and main wheels. To illustrate this, let us look at a practical example shown in figure 2.28.

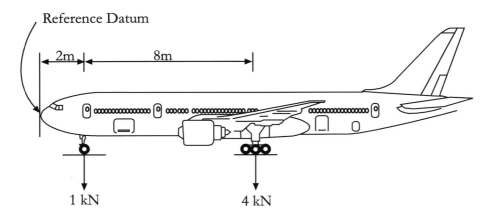

Figure 2.28 – Determining an Aircraft's Centre of Gravity

In this example, the nose wheel reaction is recorded as 1kN and the port and starboard main wheel reactions are recorded as 2kN each. Assuming the reference datum for this aircraft is at the nose, the nose wheel centre is 2m from the reference datum and the main wheel centre line is 10m from the reference datum. You will see, we can now tabulate this data and calculate the aircraft's C of G.

Item	Weight (Newtons)	Moment Arm (Metres)	Moment (Newton Metres)
Reaction Force at Nose Wheel	1000	2	2000
Reaction Force at Port Main Wheel	2000	10	20,000
Reaction Force at StarboardMain Wheel	2000	10	20,000
Total Weight	5000	Total Moment	42,000

Table 2.2 - Locating the Centre of Gravity of an Aircraft

www.part66.co.uk

$$\text{Centre of Gravity Position} = \frac{\text{Total Moment}}{\text{Total Weight}}$$

$$= \frac{42 \times 10^3}{5 \times 10^3}$$

$$= +8.4\text{m behind the datum}$$

The Couple

When two equal and opposite forces act on a body, not in the same straight-line, their moment about any point in the plane is always the same, figure 2.29.

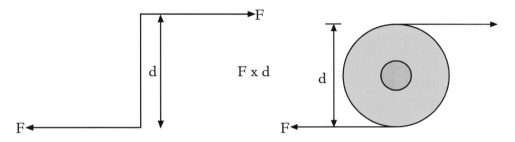

Figure 2.29 – Two Forces Not Acting on the Same Line

Two such forces are said to be a *Couple* and their turning moment is frequently called *Torque*. To calculate the moment exerted by the couple, the force F is multiplied by the distance between the two forces (d).

A single force cannot balance a couple. It can only be balanced by an opposing couple of equal magnitude. Do note that in order to be called a couple; there must be two (2) forces. In figure 2.30, a car steering wheel is shown.

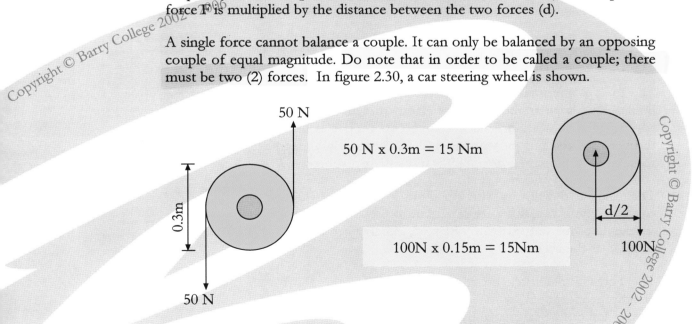

Figure 2.30 – A Couple versus a Turning Moment

In the left part of figure 2.30, the wheel is being turned using two hands. This is a *Couple*.

The drawing on the right shows only one hand being used. This is a *lever* using the *wheel centre* as a *fulcrum*.

Centre of Gravity (C of G or CG)

We have already discussed the concept of a centre of mass where we consider all the gravitational forces acting on a body pass through it. This point is called the object's *Centre of Gravity (C of G or CG)*. This concept was used in calculations for determining the centre of gravity position of a simple system of distributed forces acting on a beam and on an aircraft. Before we move on to discuss CG in more detail, we need to define some of the terms we use.

Gravity

Gravity is the name given to the force of attraction that exists between any two masses. Newton's Law of Gravitation states that:

'The force of gravity is proportional to the product of the two masses, M1 and M2, and a gravitational constant (G) all divided by the square of the distance between them.'

As a formula, this becomes:

$$F = \frac{G(M1 \times M2)}{d^2}$$

The force is almost negligible between two small bodies but when one of the bodies is as large as the Earth, its effect on a smaller body like the moon is appreciable. The distance between the two masses is always measured from their centres and this presents a problem in establishing a global figure for the force of gravity on the Earth, as it is not a perfect sphere.

The distance 'd' will vary with longitude, lowest at the Poles and highest at the equator. These variations are small but to establish a figure for global use the acceleration due to gravity at 9.81m/s², experienced in NW Europe, has been adopted as the average.

The gravitational force on a body situated on the Earth's surface will be directly proportional to the mass of that body and the acceleration due to gravity and can be calculated by:

$$F = Mass \times Acceleration$$

www.part66.co.uk

Where the mass is in kilograms (kg) and acceleration is taken as 9.81 m/s^2.

Centre of Gravity of a Body

The mass of a body must, of necessity, occupy a volume that is distributed according to the body's shape. The force due to gravity must also be distributed among all the particles that make up the body, each having its own discrete value. However, it is easier to think of this distribution of forces as a resultant single force that acts vertically downwards through a point considered to be the body's centre of mass. In practical terms, if a body were supported on a knife-edge, positioned at its C of G, there would be no moments causing rotation and the body would be in equilibrium.

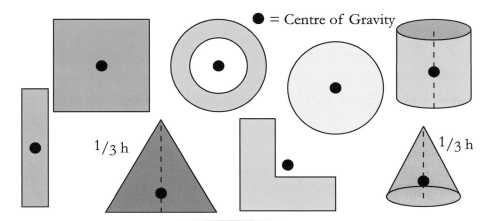

Figure 2.31 – Examples of C of G Position

Of course, if the supported body tilts, the C of G may move out of alignment with the support and a turning moment would then exist. A body's stability would depend on where the C of G was located in the body. If it were low then the turning moment created would be lower than if the C of G were placed at a higher position.

The C of G position may be located inside a body or outside it. An annular ring would have its C of G, for example, in space in the centre as would a hollow sphere or ball. *Whereas an L shaped plate would have its C of G outside the material.*

Stable, Unstable and Neutral Equilibrium

A body is said to be in *Stable Equilibrium* when, if slightly displaced from its position, the forces acting upon it tend to cause it to return to that position. A body is said to have *Unstable Equilibrium* when, if slightly displaced from its position the forces acting upon it cause it move further away from that position.

A body is said to possess *Neutral Equilibrium* when, if slightly displaced from its position, the body tends to remain in the displaced position with no tendency to return to its original position; or displace further away from its new position.

These conditions are illustrated in figure 2.32.

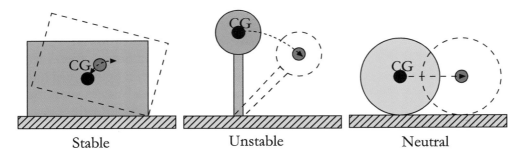

Stable   Unstable   Neutral

Figure 2.32 – Bodies in various forms of Equilibrium

Centre of Gravity of an Unevenly Loaded Beam

If a beam is described being uniform, it means that its cross section and density are even throughout its length and that its C of G position is exactly at its centre. If other forces act on the beam, however, the C of G position could move as a result of where the force is placed and what moment arm it generates.

Let us take an example of a uniform beam 4m long having a mass of 50kg that supports three masses, 20kg, 10kg and 5kg respectively. As shown in figure 2.33, the masses' are distributed at 1m, 1.5m and 3m respectively from the left end of the beam, designated as reference datum A. The beam is resting on a flat smooth surface and the task is to locate the position of its C of G so that it can be lifted safely.

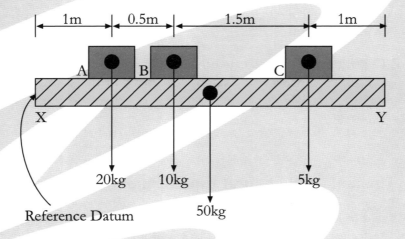

Figure 2.33 – Unevenly Loaded Beam

The beam is too heavy to lift by hand and so its balance point, (C of G), cannot be found by experimentation. Now using the reference datum at A, we need only deal with clockwise moments as tabulated

Item	Mass (kg)	Moment Arm (Metres)	Moment kg Metres (kgm)
Beam	50	2	100
Mass A	20	1	20
Mass B	10	1.5	15
Mass C	5	3	15
Total Mass	85	Total Moment	150

Table 2.3 - Centre of Gravity of an Unevenly Loaded Beam

$$\text{Centre of Gravity Position} = \frac{\text{Total Moment}}{\text{Total Weight}}$$

$$= \frac{150}{85}$$

$$= 1.76 \text{ from datum A}$$

Note: This calculation was completed with using Mass in kg; the same answer would be obtained if Newtons had been used. Try it for yourself and see!

Centre of Gravity of Symmetrically Shaped Uniform Flat Plates

When looking at symmetrically shaped objects, it is possible to determine the body's C of G diagrammatically. Figure 2.34 shows some typical shapes with their respective C of G positions shown.

www.part66.co.uk

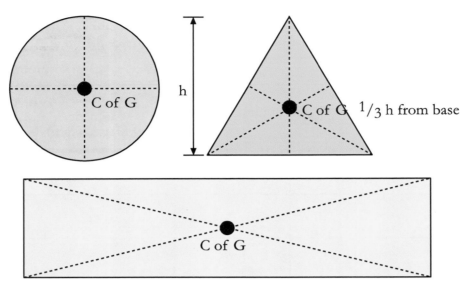

Figure 2.34– C of G of Various Symmetrically Shaped Objects

Centre of Gravity of Symmetrically Shaped Homogeneous Solids

Rectangular Plate: CG is at the intersection of the diagonals.

Triangular Plate: CG is at the intersection of the medians or lines joining an apex to the mid-point of the opposite side. It is one-third the distance from the mid-point towards the apex.

Circular Plate: CG is at the centre.

Sphere: CG is at the centre.

Cylinder: CG is at the mid-point of the axis.

Ring: CG is at the centre. Not in the body of the ring.

Circular Cone: CG is three quarters along the axis from the apex towards the base or, one quarter the axis form base towards the axis.

Rectangular Prism: CG is at the centre.

Uniform Beam: CG is at mid-point of length.

www.part66.co.uk

Centroid

The Centroid is the centre of area whereas the centre of gravity is the centre of mass. A homogeneous body is one that has uniform density throughout. No heavy spots. An object such as a flat plate may also have uniform thickness. In these cases the centre of the plate's area also corresponds with the position of its centre of gravity. Do note however that a flat plate having a varying thickness will retain its centroid position but the centre of gravity will have moved to a different position.

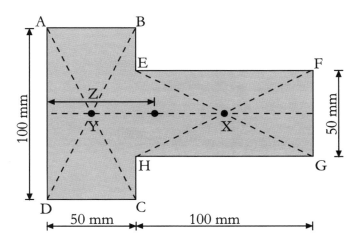

Figure 2.35 – Determining the Position of a T shaped Plate's C of G

Area of section ABCD $= 50 \times 100$ $= 5000\text{mm}^2$

Area of section EFGH $= 50 \times 100$ $= 5000\text{mm}^2$

Total Area of T shape $= 5000 + 5000 = 10{,}000\text{mm}^2$

C of G position Y of area ABCD is 25mm from edge AD

C of G position X of area EFGH is 100mm from edge AD

Taking the moments from side AD we can use the principle that:

Total moment of T shape = The sum of the moments of its parts

Therefore: $(10{,}000 \times Z) = (5000 \times 25) + (5000 \times 100)$

Distance Z represents the C of G of the T shape from side AD is:

$$\frac{125{,}000 + 500{,}000}{1000}$$

C of G is 62.5mm from the edge AD on the centre line

Note: This calculation was carried out using the moments of areas. If we assume that 1mm^2 equates to one (1) Newton in weight, it would have had no effect on the figures above.

An Aircraft's Centre of Gravity Position

An aircraft's C of G position is of critical importance to its flying characteristics and we have previously already seen how this is calculated using weighing scales placed under the aircraft's main and nose gear.

However, the total *lift* forces on an aircraft are usually represented by a single force acting through its *Centre of Pressure (CP)*.

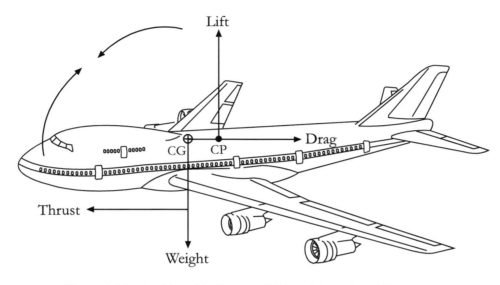

Figure 2.36 – An Aircraft's Centre of Lift and Associated Forces

If the CP is positioned behind the C of G position then the lift force will act through a moment arm to depress the nose of the aircraft, (it will pitch down). The thrust force line of action shown in figure 2.36 is below the C of G position and this acts through a moment arm to lift the nose of the aircraft, (pitch up, counteracting the effect of the lift moment). This results in a stable situation and if an engine were to fail, the nose of the aircraft would lower, (pitch down, to establish it on the correct glide angle for a controlled descent).

If we now consider the case of when the C of G is positioned behind the CP, you should be able to see from figure 2.36 that both lift and thrust forces would raise the aircraft's nose, (it would pitch up, which could cause it to stall).

Therefore, the effect of the C of G's position must always be considered during the loading of an aircraft. If, for example, the C of G were too far forward the lift force would act over a greater moment arm and cause the nose to pitch down.

To compensate for this, the pilot would have to trim the aircraft's nose up, which is not advisable as this trim facility is limited. In an extreme situation, a pilot would need to use the trim system's entire range making it difficult for the crew to maintain control and a situation could be reached where the pilot would have no pitch up control left when required, leading to an uncontrolled dive.

Looking at the opposite case where the C of G position is too far aft, the moment arm of the lift force would be reduced causing a pitch up tendency. In trying to compensate for this, the useful control range would again be lost, which could cause an uncontrolled pitch up leading to the aircraft stalling, particularly during low speed flight when larger control movements are required.

If the C of G position is coincident with the CP position, then the aircraft becomes very difficult to control due to its tendency to move off position following any slight disturbance. A good analogy of this is to try and imagine balancing an aircraft on a knife-edge; a very unstable proposition.

Aircraft Loading and Centre of Gravity Position

As mentioned above, an aircraft's C of G position is of critical importance to its flying characteristics and any pilot must ensure that their aircraft, be it a small trainer up to a large passenger aircraft like the Boeing 747, is properly loaded and its C of G known before attempting to take-off.

Let us consider a simple light aircraft equipped with a nose wheel, that has been weighed and the reactions measured as:

- 500kg at the nose wheel

- 1000kg at each main wheel

If the nose and main wheels are 1m and 5m respectively behind the reference datum, which is at the nose position, let us now calculate:

1. The position of the C of G from the reference datum

2. The new position of the C of G if a crate of mass 40kg is loaded 6m behind the datum

To calculate C of G position

Item	Mass (kg)	Moment Arm (Metres)	Moment kg Metres (kgm)
Nose Reaction	500	1	500
Port Main-wheel Reaction	1000	5	5000
Stbd main-wheel Reaction	1000	5	5000
Total Mass	2500	Total Moment	10500

Table 2.4 - C of G Position

$$\text{Centre of Gravity Position} = \frac{\text{Total Moment}}{\text{Total Mass}}$$

$$= \frac{10500}{2500}$$

$$= 4.2\text{m from datum}$$

This is the C of G position without the load; now let us calculate how it alters the aircraft's to C of G:

Item	Mass (kg)	Moment Arm (Metres)	Moment kg Metres (kgm)
Aircraft	2500	4.2	10500
Crate	40	6	240
Total Mass	2540	Total Moment	10740

Table 2.5 – Altered C of G Position

$$\text{The New C of G Position} = \frac{\text{Total Moment}}{\text{Total Mass}}$$

$$= \frac{10740}{2540}$$

$$= 4\cdot23\text{m from datum}$$

Therefore, the addition of the crate has moved the C of G 0·03m rearwards. Note that the C of G is still forward of the main wheel line, essential on nose wheeled aircraft. See figure 2.37.

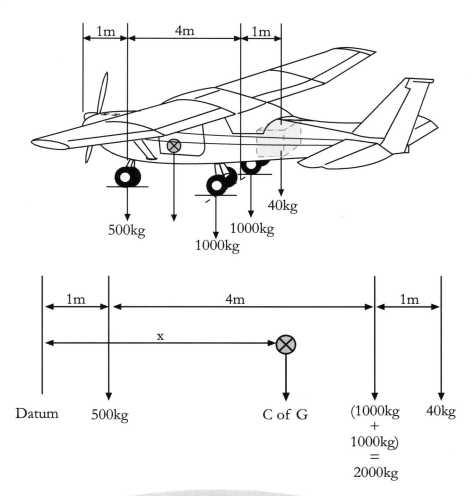

Figure 2.37 – Aircraft Loading & Centre of Gravity Position

Stress, Strain and Elasticity

Stress, strain and elasticity can be felt by all things that are subjected to a load, including the human body. We are now going to look at the affects of these forces individually.

Stress

When a material has a force exerted upon it, stress is created in the material, which can be considered as mechanical pressure. Its value can be calculated by dividing the applied force by the original cross-sectional area of the material, which is at a right angle to the force.

$$\text{Stress (N/m}^2 \text{ or Pa)} = \frac{\text{Force}}{\text{Cross-sectional area (CSA)}}$$

If a beam is subjected to pulling forces or tension, the force per unit area of the beam's cross-section is said to be *Tensile Stress*. If the beam is subjected to compressive forces, the force per unit area of the beam's cross-section is said to be *Compressive Stress*.

When forces are applied to a material, they cause distortion; e.g. tensile forces will cause an elongation and compressive forces will cause a reduction in the material's dimensions. In both cases, there is also a change to the material's cross-sectional area, but when calculating stress values, the original cross-sectional area is always used.

Most materials have an elastic property and providing the applied forces are not so great as to exceed the limit of this elasticity, they will return to their original proportions when these forces are removed. However, if the applied forces do exceed the material's elastic limit, then it will have exceeded its limit of proportionality and will remain permanently distorted.

By studying the formula above, you can see that either reducing the applied force or increasing the cross-sectional area can reduce stress values. Aircraft designers have to strike a balance when looking at these forces. Reducing the applied force limits operational loading. Increasing cross-sectional area will increase weight to a point where an aircraft is no longer commercially viable.

The SI unit of stress is the *Newton per square metre (N/m²)*, which is now commonly referred to as the *Pascal (Pa)*.

Strain

When a beam is pulled it stretches and if the increase is expressed as a fraction its original length then a ratio value is obtained which is called *Strain*.

If a beam is put under a compressive stress, then there is a reduction in length and again, the reduction can be expressed as a fraction of the original length to give a value for strain.

This value has no units, as strain is purely a ratio of two lengths and is frequently expressed as a percentage. Do note that it is important to ensure when calculating the strain exerted on an object, the same units are used for the original length and its extension or compression.

The Tensile Test

A tensile test involves stretching a test piece of material by gradually increasing the forces applied to it and monitoring the resulting extensions to see what forces the object can withstand. The results are displayed in a graphical form that will show the material's initial elastic range as a linear slope where the stress in the material is proportional to the strain.

The maximum point at which this proportionality holds, called the *Limit of Proportionality*, sometimes called the *Yield Point* (point B in figure 2.38), once reached shows how much stress the material can take before permanent distortion. If the applied forces are then continually increased, the material goes through a plastic, non-proportional, range up to its ultimate tensile stress limit (F) and then on to fracture of the test specimen.

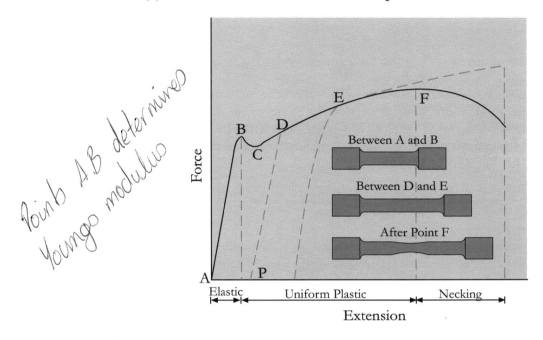

Point AB determined Youngs modulus

Figure 2.38 – A Tensile Test for low Carbon Steel

This is best described by looking at the results of such a test as illustrated here. A mild steel test piece is subjected to a constantly increasing force. As this force increases, it goes through various stages that are discussed in the following paragraphs.

Elastic stage

This is the initial stage of the test and if the mild steel test piece is unloaded during this phase it will return to its original unstretched length. Over this stage, the material obeys *Hooke's Law* in that the extension is proportional to the applied load and the strain is proportional to the stress represented by line AB.

Limit of Proportionality

Point B represents the *Limit of Proportionality* or *Yield Point* and if the applied force increases beyond this point, the material no longer obeys Hooke's law and becomes non-proportional.

Elastic Limit

The stress value at which a permanent extension occurs is called the *Elastic Limit*, which, as its name implies, is where the material is no longer elastic. In many materials, the limit of proportionality and the elastic limit are so close together they cannot be distinguished.

Yield Stress

At point C in figure 2.38, the metal stretches with little increase in load. This is called the *Yield Point* and the corresponding stress value, the *Yield Stress*. The graph shows a slight dip at the yield point, which for mild steel indicates an upper and lower yield stress. When a material reaches its yield point, it continues to yield at a slightly lower load.

Permanent Set

If the material is taken beyond B, representing the elastic limit, and is unloaded at any stage after this, it will have a permanent extension called the *Permanent Set*.

Plastic Stage

Beyond point C, the mild steel test piece is still partly elastic and if the test piece were unloaded from any point beyond C, the permanent extension would be AP, the line PD representing the unloading line approximately parallel to line AB.

Work Hardening

During the plastic phase, the steel will be *Work Hardening* and increasing in strength. Due to the reducing cross sectional area, however, the rate of extension increases.

Waisting

Point F represents the maximum load, which the test piece can withstand. At this point, extension is no longer uniform along the length of the test piece but becomes localised at one point. The test piece begins to *Neck* or *Waist* down at this point, the area at the waist portion decreasing rapidly. Local extension now continues with a decreasing load until fracture occurs.

94

Ultimate Tensile Stress

An object's ultimate tensile stress (UTS) is defined as:

$$UTS(N/m^2) = \frac{\text{Maximum Load(N)}}{\text{Original area (m}^2)}$$

Modulus of Elasticity

For a material loaded within its elastic range *Hooke's law* states that the extension is proportional to the force and that strain is proportional to stress. Therefore, if we looked at the test piece at any point in its elastic range and divided the stress value at that point by the strain value we would derive the same value, which is known as ***Young's Modulus of Elasticity (E)*** (in mathematical terms):

$$\frac{\text{Stress}}{\text{Strain}} = \text{Constant E (N/m}^2 \text{ or Pa)}$$

Young's modulus of Elasticity is a value that represents the degree of resistance a material will offer when attempts are made to stretch or compress it.

Percentage Elongation

This is a useful measure of the ductility of a material under test and is calculated by the formula:

$$\text{Percentage(\%) elongation} = \frac{\text{Final length - Original length}}{\text{Original length}} \times 100$$

Percentage Reduction in Area

This figure is a useful indication of how much an object will reduce before fracture and is derived from measurements of the original cross-sectional area and the cross-sectional area at fracture, calculated by the formula:

$$\text{Percentage reduction in area} = \frac{\text{Original area - Final area}}{\text{Original area}} \times 100$$

Proof Stress

Many materials under tensile test do not show a well-defined yield point, which would clearly indicate on a graph the value of the elastic limit. For engineering purposes, it is often desirable to know the stress to which a highly ductile material, such as aluminium, can be loaded safely before a permanent extension takes place. This stress is known as the *Proof Stress*. It is defined as the stress at which a specified permanent extension has taken place, which would equate to the material's yield point.

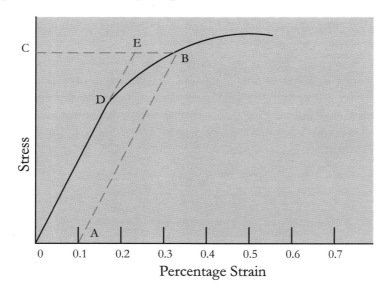

Figure 2.39 – Typical Tensile Test for a Light Alloy

In figure 2.39, point D represents the limit of proportionality for the specimen under test, while line OE represents the stress/strain relationship if the strain remained directly proportional to the stress. At the limit of proportionality, we can see that the curve departs from line OE at D, but for engineering purposes, we need to find a more accurate value. To do this, we take a line AB commencing at the 0.1% strain value and extend it parallel to line OE, to cut the curve at B. If we now draw a horizontal line BC to cut the stress axis at C, we will have a value called the *0.1% strain*. As a definition statement, this position, (the 0.1% proof stress), is that stress which will produce a permanent extension of 0.1% in the length of a given material specimen and can be calculated mathematically using the formula:

$$\text{Proof Stress} = \frac{\text{Proof force}}{\text{Original cross-sectional area}}$$

Material Properties from Stress/Strain Graphs

We can identify material properties from the shape of their stress/strain graphs. Figure 2.40 shows the stress/strain graphs for a typical aluminium alloy in three (3) different heat treatment states.

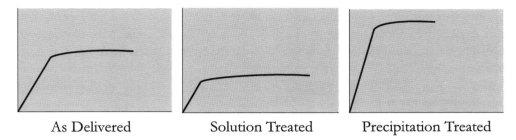

As Delivered   Solution Treated   Precipitation Treated

Figure 2.40 – Stress/Strain Graphs for Typical Aluminium Alloy

As delivered – in this state, the material is fairly soft and ductile. When solution treated, it becomes even more soft and ductile, note the length of the plastic range. When precipitation treated, the material becomes strong in that it resists extension and is less ductile.

Factor of Safety

When designers are deciding on the strength of structures, they base their calculations on the elastic limit rather than the ultimate tensile or compressive strengths, though these remain important. Once the everyday working load that the structure is expected to support is known, it does not make sense to design a structure that would deform immediately if this load were exceeded.

Therefore, designers use a *Factor of Safety* to increase the strength of structures by a multiple of the expected working load. During the life of the structure, fatigue, corrosion, wear and occasional overstress will reduce this margin but the structure would still remain safe.

In mechanical engineering, the ideal factors of safety are:

- Dead loads x 4

- Live loads x 6

- Alternating loads x 12

These are the ideal safety factors and will vary depending on the situation.

When applied to aircraft design, however, safety factors do present a problem as an aircraft is subjected to many different stresses and strains. Introducing a factor of safety implies that either the cross-section of components should be greater, adding weight, or operating loads should be reduced, limiting performance, which is not a practical proposition. Aircraft designers, therefore, calculate the expected maximum working loads an aircraft will be expected to endure throughout its life and work on these figure. For example, a Boeing 747 can expect to encounter up to +2½G and -½G loads during its operational life. Therefore, aircraft designers use two safety factors when looking at aircraft design.

1.   Proof Load Limit

2.   Ultimate Load Limit

Proof Load Limit

The word '*proof*' in this context is based on proof stress, which we have examined above, and is based on material deformation, not fracture. The proof load limit includes the factor of safety, which for aircraft is:

1.125 x the expected maximum working load.

If an aircraft exceeds this figure, its structure would be distorted. Now you know how fine the factor of safety is for aircraft, it should bring home to you the importance of preventing corrosion, incidental damage and fatigue. It can be calculated using the following formula:

$$\text{Proof factor of safety} = \frac{\text{Proof stress}}{\text{Safe working stress}}$$

Ultimate Load Limit

The ultimate load limit is based on the ultimate tensile strength of the materials used in constructing an object. For aircraft, this limit is set at $1\frac{1}{2} \times$ the maximum working load. For example, a Boeing 747 with an expected maximum working load of +2½G has an ultimate load limit of +3.75G. If the aircraft were to exceed this limit, its structure could break. It can be calculated using the following formula:

$$\text{Ultimate factor} = \frac{\text{Ultimate tensile strength}}{\text{Safe working stress}}$$

www.part66.co.uk

Example Calculations in Stress, Strain and Factor of Safety

You would not be expected to carry out complex calculations in the examination but they do illustrate to you the use of the formulae involved.

You will be expected to remember the formulae.

Example 1

A solid round steel bar, 5mm diameter and 1m long, stretches 1mm when subjected to a tensile load of 5kN. Determine Young's Modulus of Elasticity for the material.

$$\text{Modulus of Elasticity} = \frac{\text{Stress}(\text{N}/\text{m}^2)}{\text{Strain}}$$

$$\text{Stress} = \frac{\text{Load (N)}}{\text{Area (m}^2)} = \frac{5000}{(\pi \times 0.005^2)/4} = 255\text{MN}/\text{m}^2$$

$$\text{Strain} = \frac{\text{Extension}}{\text{Original length}} = \frac{1\text{mm}}{1000\text{mm}} = 0.001$$

$$\text{Modulus of Elasticity} = \frac{255\text{MN}/\text{m}^2}{0.001} = 255\text{GN}/\text{m}^2$$

Example 2

A structural tie rod has a proof stress of 100MN/m². Determine the permissible working stress in the tie rod if it has a proof factor of safety of two.

$$\text{Proof factor of safety} = \frac{\text{Proof Stress}}{\text{Permissable working stress}}$$

$$\text{Permissable working stress} = \frac{\text{Proof Stress}}{\text{Proof Factor of Safety}}$$

$$= \frac{100\text{MN}/\text{m}^2}{2} = 50\text{MN}/\text{m}^2$$

Factor of safety is sometimes determined by the formula:

$$\text{Factor of safety} = \frac{\text{Tensile strength}}{\text{Permissable tensile stress}}$$

99

The tensile strength of a material is the maximum tensile load the material can withstand before fracture divided by the original cross-sectional area of the material. In other words, the ultimate tensile stress! In our example above we used the proof stress, which is the maximum stress possible before deformation takes place. Note the use of the term 'tensile strength' for ultimate tensile stress. Also make sure you are dealing with 'proof stress' if you want the limit to be based on deformation. Ultimate tensile strength or stress is based on fracture.

Shearing

Shear stress occurs in a body when forces cause material to slip in opposite directions either side of a surface inside the body. Try pushing a pack of cards with your left hand against the topside of the pack and your right hand at the lower opposite side of the pack. The cards will slide over each other.

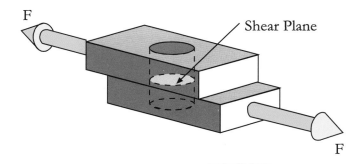

Figure 2.41– Example of Shear

Examples of shear include the stress in a rivet or the pin in a fork ended control rod. In the example illustrated above, the rivet is subject to shear stress across the plane. This is known as *single shear* and can be calculated using the formula:

$$\text{Shear stress} = \frac{\text{Shear force}}{\text{Shear plane area}}$$

Double Shear

Figure 2.42 shows an example of a fork-ended joint and the shear stress is being imposed across two faces.

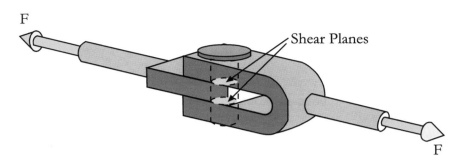

Figure 2.42 – Example of Double Shear

This is known as double shear and can be calculated using the formula:

$$\text{Shear stress} = \frac{\text{Load}}{2 \times \text{cross-sectional area}}$$

Shear strain (ϕ)

Shear strain represented by the Greek letter Phi (ϕ), is the angle of deformation caused by a shear force, expressed in radians.

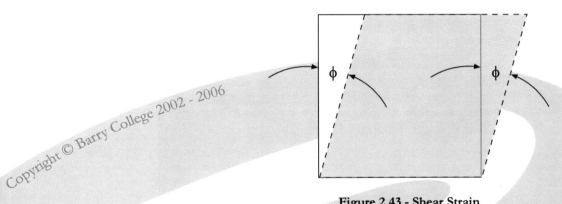

Figure 2.43 - Shear Strain

Shear Modulus - Modulus of Rigidity

Resistance to shearing forces is called *Rigidity* and can be calculated using the formula:

$$\text{Shear Modulus(G) N/m}^2 = \frac{\text{Shear stress}(\tau)}{\text{Shear strain}(\phi)}$$

A good example of a shear force is the twisting of a bar of material. If just one area on the surface of a bar is considered, then the twisting of the rod is displayed by the shear forces acting on that area. Twisting forces are also called *Torsional* forces.

Let's look at some example calculations for single and double shear stress.

You will be expected to remember the formulae!

Example 1 (Single Shear)

Two light alloy plates are lap jointed using two 5mm diameter rivets. Determine the maximum shear load that can be applied if the safe working shear stress of the joint is not to exceed 40MN/m².

$$\text{Shear stress} = \frac{\text{Load}}{2 \times \text{area}} \quad \text{Note that there are TWO rivets}$$

Therefore:
Load = shear stress x (2 x area)
Load = $(40 \times 10^6)\text{N/m}^2 \times \dfrac{(2 \times \pi \times 0.005^2)\text{m}^2}{4}$

Load = 1571N or 1.571kN

Example 2 (Double Shear)

A fork-ended joint on a control cable is secured by a pin 10mm diameter. Determine the maximum load that can be applied if the shear stress is not to exceed 10MNm².

$$\text{Shear stress} = \frac{\text{Load}}{2 \times \text{area}} \quad \begin{array}{l} \text{Note that there is one pin,} \\ \text{two shear forces} \end{array}$$

Therefore:
Load = shear stress x (2 x area)
Load = $(10 \times 10^6)\text{N/m}^2 \times \dfrac{(2 \times \pi \times 0.01^2)\text{m}^2}{4}$

Load = 1571N or 1.571kN

Example 3 (Shear Strain)

A thin metal rod 4mm diameter is subjected to single shear force of 500N causing it to deform in shear by 0.6°. Determine the Modulus of Rigidity for the material.

$$\text{Modulus of Rigidity} = \frac{\text{Shear stress(N/m}^2)}{\text{Shear strain(rad)}}$$

$$\text{Shear stress} = \frac{\text{Shear force}}{\text{area}}$$

$$= \frac{500\text{N}}{(0.5 \times \pi \times 0.004^2)\text{m}^2} = 39.6\text{MN/m}^2$$

$$\text{Shear strain} = 0.6^{\circ} = 0.0105 \text{ radian (1 radian is } 57.3^{\circ})$$

$$\text{Modulus of Rigidity} = \frac{(39.6 \times 10^6)\text{N/m}^2}{0.0105 \text{ rad}} = 3.78\text{GN/m}^2$$

Note: You will not be expected to carry out complex calculations in IR Part-66 exams. You must know formulae and be able to quote units used. You should also be able to transpose the formulae.

Nature and Properties of Solids, Fluids and Gases

You will have encountered the *Periodic Table of Elements* in Chapter one. The table is reproduced here to enable you to identify the general element group descriptions and their positions in the table.

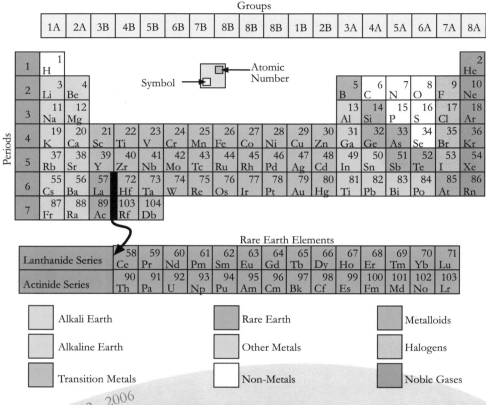

Figure 2.44 – The Periodic Table

There are over 100 elements out of which around 75% are metals. The elements are positioned in horizontal rows from left to right called *Periods*. These identify elements in order of ascending atomic number. The elements listed in the vertical columns of the table represent *families* or *groups of elements*. The elements listed from top to bottom in a group contain the same number of outer shell electrons and have similar chemical properties. For example Group 1A elements all have one outer shell electron and are highly reactive. All outer shell electrons are at the highest energy level and are known as the *valency* electrons.

You need to be able to recall the identity and positions of the following groups.

www.part66.co.uk

Metals

Everything that appears on the extreme left of the table with the exception of Hydrogen, for example groups 1A and 2A. Metals are Electropositive.

Transition Series Metals

These are in the centre portion of the table. They move from left to right bridging the gap between metals and non-metals ending with metalloids that are actually non-metals that resemble metals. For example, Astatine, Antimony, Arsenic, Boron, Germanium, Selenium and Tellurium.

Non-Metals

These are mainly found on the upper right hand side of the table. They are electronegative by nature. Group 8A on the extreme right lists the *Noble* gases. These are inert in the sense they have the full eight outer shell electron content making them completely un-reactive.

The Kinetic Theory of Matter

All matter may be grouped under three headings, *solids*, *liquids* and *gases*. These are called the three states of matter.

The Kinetic Theory of Matter proposes that all matter consists of particles that are in a state of continuous motion. The particles are in fact molecules or, in the case of a metal, they are its atoms. The motion of the particles is related to the heat energy contained by the matter.

In solids, the particles are held in fixed positions by strong molecular or inter-atomic bonds. They still have kinetic energy however and vibrate about their positions. As the heat energy content rises the particles gain more kinetic energy and break free of their fixed positions. They begin to move freely around as the solid becomes a liquid.

With the addition of further heat energy, the particles gain considerable kinetic energy and move rapidly enough to leap clear of the surface of the liquid and become a gas.

A subsequent reduction in heat energy will reverse the process. As the particles lose kinetic energy they fall back into the liquid state and can eventually enter the solid state.

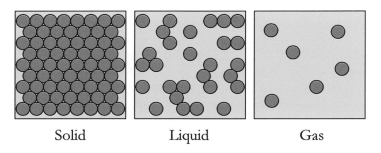

Solid   Liquid   Gas

Figure 2.45 – Solids, Liquids & Gases

The temperature at which all particle motion ceases is known as *Absolute Zero*. This temperature has never been reached as the normal laws of physics forbid it.

States of Matter

Solids

Solids are crystalline, dense and have a fixed volume and shape. They cannot be compressed. Pressure cannot be transmitted through them.

Liquids

Liquids have a fixed volume but no fixed shape. They can adopt the shape of any container they are in. They are non-crystalline or amorphous. Liquids cannot be compressed. Pressure can be transmitted through them.

Gases

Gases have no fixed volume or shape. They can expand to fill any container they are in. They are compressible and pressure can be transmitted through them.

Metals and Non-Metals

You should already be aware that 75% of the known elements are metals. The remainder are called non-metals. It is important to know that there are many differences in the properties of these two groups.

Metals

These can exist in all three states: solid, liquid or gaseous; with the exception of Mercury which remains a liquid. Metals will be in the solid state at room temperature. They can undergo chemical change into an oxide through corrosion.

Metals are lustrous when cut, are good conductors of electricity and heat, are malleable and ductile.

Pure metals do not form molecules and are bound together by *Metallic Bonding*. They are electropositive by nature in that they easily lose their outer shell electrons. Metallic gases are *monatomic* consisting of individual atoms. During solidification metals form one of three crystalline structures where the atoms arrange themselves into regular patterns. Some metals are *Polymorphic* in that they can exist in different crystalline structures dependent on temperature.

The mechanical properties of metals are:

Malleability: The degree to which a metal can be beaten or rolled into a new shape.

Ductility: The degree to which a metal can be drawn out.

Hardness: A metal's resistance to abrasion or penetration. Expressed as a *Brinell* or *Vickers* hardness number.

Toughness: A metal's resistance to bending or impact forces. Expressed as an *Izod* or *Charpy* impact test value.

Brittleness: A metal's tendency to fracture during impact or bending. Established during the *Izod* or *Charpy* impact test.

Strength: A metal's resistance to tensile or compressive forces. Established during tensile or compression tests. Strength is expressed as *tensile strength*.

Elasticity: A metal's ability to return to its original shape after deformation. Expressed either as a Modulus of Elasticity or a Modulus of Rigidity.

The Crystalline Structure of Metals

You have already studied the Metallic Bond in relation to the chemical bonds between metal atoms. The atoms are strongly attracted to the negatively charged electron cloud but are repelled by their positively charged neighbours.

The only way the atoms can remain in contact with the cloud and stay as far away from their neighbours as possible is to form geometric or crystalline patterns.

There are three well-known patterns, the *body centred cubic*, the *face centred cubic* and the *hexagonal structure*. These are illustrated opposite.

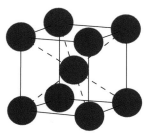 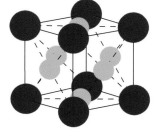 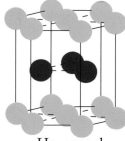

Body Centred Cubic   Face Centred Cubic   Hexagonal
                                                       Close Packed

Figure 2.46 – Metal Crystalline Structures

Iron can exist in either body centred cubic or face centred cubic form. Other examples of the body centred cubic form include chromium and tungsten. Face centred cubic forms appear in metals like aluminium and copper. Magnesium and zinc appear in hexagonal form.

Deformation of Metals

The attraction of forces between positively charged metallic atoms and the negatively charged electron cloud in the *Metallic Bond* are weaker than the ionic or covalent bonds found in other substances.

If a small force is applied to a metal it will put a strain on its atomic structure. This will attempt to make rows or planes of atoms slide over each other. The force of attraction will resist this and will re-align the rows as soon as the force is removed. This is the elastic property of the metal.

If the applied force is increased until it can overcome the attractive force the atoms will slide over each other and take up a new position in the structure. Permanent deformation will have occurred. This is the plastic stage of the metal. If the applied force is big enough, a point will be reached where the movement of the planes of atoms over each other will continue until separation or failure occurs.

Alloys

Many pure metals are too soft and ductile to be of practical use. The mechanical properties of a metal can be improved upon by *alloying* it with another metal or in some cases carbon.

Alloying is a process of molten mixing of given proportions of each metal. Alloys may result in stronger and tougher material, harder materials or corrosion resistant materials. Heat resisting steels are produced in this way.

www.part66.co.uk

Deterioration of Metals

Many of the metals we use in industry are extracted from ores. The conversion of an ore to a metal raises the energy levels of its atoms. This makes the metal reactive and it will readily chemically react by ionically bonding with non-metals to form the compounds we know as corrosion products. These form alkaline solutions if mixed with moisture.

All group 1 metals are highly reactive. Transition metals are less reactive and corrosion rates are therefore slower. Silver, gold and platinum are hardly reactive at all and these are referred to as *Noble Metals*.

Most metals are also prone to *electro-chemical corrosion*. Due to the free roaming nature of their electrons, metals can lose them and become positive. The element that steals these electrons becomes negative and all that is needed is an *electrolyte* for the metallic ions to move into. Rates of this type of corrosion depend on the electrical potential set up between the two elements.

Fatigue

Metals experience this phenomenon when subjected to cyclic and repetitive stresses. It results in failure of the material at values well below its normal tensile strength. Fatigue commences with the appearance of a small crack which then propagates through the material reducing its cross sectional area. This increases the stress in the material and it eventually fails.

Creep

Creep is another phenomena affecting solid materials. When these materials are subjected to a sustained tensile force they experience a slow and permanent extension. This occurs at load values well below the elastic limit. The rates of extension are directly related to both the applied load and the temperature of the material.

Creep has three stages: *primary creep* which is an initial and barely measurable extension occurring when the load is first applied. *Secondary creep* which is a steady extension over time, and *tertiary creep* which is a rapid and unpredictable extension leading to failure.

Non-Metals

The elements on the upper right hand side of the periodic table are non-metals. Many of these are gases particularly the Group 0 Noble Gases found on the extreme right. Group 7 contains the Halogens of which some are gaseous and other liquid or solids.

Non-metals, with the exception of Graphite and Iodine, are not lustrous when cut. They tend to be brittle when in solid form, they are not ductile or malleable and, with the exception of Graphite, they are extremely poor conductors of electricity and heat.

Non-metals form *Covalent Bonds* with each other and *Ionic Bonds* with metals. The covalent bond is the strongest of the three chemical bonds. Non-metals form molecular structures that are held together by inter-molecular forces of attraction. Most non-metal materials found in common use are compounds of various elements. These include the range of plastic materials.

Plastic materials are produced in a process known as *Polymerisation* where long chain molecules are created. These are bound together by attractive forces called *Van Der Waal's Forces*. These are similar to dipole forces. These forces can be increased by introducing cross-linking atoms which form covalent bonds with atoms in the long chain molecules. This method is used when curing plastic resins or vulcanising rubber.

Plastic materials fall into three distinct groups.

1.   *Thermoplastic materials* that will soften with heat and can be re-shaped.

2.   *Thermosetting materials* that will not soften with heat and are fixed in permanent shape.

3.   *Elastomers* that are thermosetting by nature but have an elastic property.

Most non-metallic solids have a form of crystalline structure where their molecules arrange themselves in patterns. The long chain molecules in plastic materials find this difficult to achieve however and are thus non-crystalline.

Non-metals do not corrode as metals do because they have a powerful hold over their valency electrons. They will cause corrosion in metals, however, if they come into contact with them as they are strongly electronegative and will readily steal the loose electrons from metals.

The powerful attraction that non-metals have for their valency electrons make them very poor conductors both of heat and electricity.

Deterioration of Non-Metal Solids

Non-metals do not suffer from corrosion. Like metals, they are prone to fatigue and creep. Plastic materials are susceptible to deterioration as a result of exposure to electromagnetic radiation or Ozone. You may recognise the effect as 'perishing'. Radiation causes vibration in long chain molecules with an attendant risk of fracture. Ultra-violet, X-ray and Gamma radiations are all capable of doing this. The highly reactive oxygen molecule Ozone (0_3) causes indiscriminate cross-linking between long chain molecules leading to brittleness in plastics materials. Sources of Ozone are found in emissions from electrical motors and switching gear.

Compounds and Mixtures

Compounds consist of two or more elements that are chemically bound together in fixed proportions. They may be found in solid, liquid or gaseous form. A compound is homogeneous which means the constituents are evenly distributed throughout. Compounds have the same chemical composition and mass distribution throughout. Compounds require a chemical reaction to join or separate their constituent elements. The properties of a compound are different to the properties of the elements making it up.

Mixtures contain constituents that are not chemically reacted and can be separated by purely physical means like filtering. The constituents are present in any proportion and a mixture is not homogeneous. The properties of a mixture rely on those of the substances in it.

Solutions

When two or more constituents are mixed together and form a homogeneous substance it is called a solution. Solutions may be found in solids, liquids and gases. The constituents or solutes in a solution are normally fully dissolved in a solvent.

Suspensions

A suspension is formed when a substance fails to dissolve in a solvent and remains as suspended particles. The suspended particles will eventually settle as sediment in the solvent. Suspensions are heterogeneous mixtures, which mean that they do not have an even distribution throughout.

Colloidal Solutions

These solutions consist of very fine solid particles that do not dissolve in the solvent but do not settle out as sediment. Smoke is a good example of this.

Emulsions

When a colloidal solution consists of two liquids instead of a liquid and solid it is called an emulsion. An example would be fat suspended in milk or oil in water.

Liquids

Metals and non-metals can exist in liquid form. Liquids are amorphous in that they do not have a crystalline structure.

The freezing, or solidification point and the boiling, or vaporisation point are dependent on the type of liquid. Boiling and freezing points can vary with atmospheric pressure. The boiling point of liquids will rises as pressure rises. Freezing points depend on whether the substance expands or contracts on freezing. If the substance expands, its freezing point lowers with pressure. If the substance contracts then the freezing point rises with pressure.

The addition of substances in solution with liquids alters their freezing and boiling points. For example, salt will lower the freezing point of water and raise its boiling point.

Liquids change their *viscosity* in relation to temperature. Viscosity is defined as resistance to flow. Liquids experience a lowering in viscosity as temperature rises. The degree to which the liquid changes in viscosity over a given temperature range is known as the liquid's *viscosity index*. A liquid that exhibits little change in viscosity over a given temperature range is said to have a high viscosity index.

The pressure exerted by a liquid is the same in all directions and acts at right angles to any surface the liquid contacts. The pressure at any height in a liquid will be the same at that horizontal level. Pressure can be transmitted through a liquid.

Gases

Gases are amorphous and obey the Gas laws:

The volume of a fixed mass of gas at constant temperature is inversely proportional to its pressure. (*Boyle's Law*).

The volume of a fixed mass of gas at constant pressure is proportional to its absolute temperature. (*Charles' Law*)

The pressure of a fixed mass of gas at constant volume is proportional to its absolute temperature. (*Pressure Law*).

All three Gas laws can be combined to give:

$$\frac{Pressure \times Volume}{Temperature} = A\ Constant$$

Similar to liquids the pressure exerted by a gas is the same in all directions and acts at right angles to any surface the gas contacts. Pressure can be transmitted through a gas.

Pressure and Buoyancy in Liquids

Pressure

Pressure, when applied to fluids is defined as force per unit area. Fluids may be liquids or gases and the term *Fluid Pressure* is commonly used to describe this term. Due to the free flowing nature of fluids, the force exerted by a fluid is always at right angles to the containing surface, or to any surface in contact with the fluid. The force exerted on a unit area of any such surface is defined as the fluid's pressure.

Measurement of Pressure

The pressure gauges you encounter in everyday use only measure pressure above atmospheric pressure. A tyre pressure gauge for example may read zero but the room it is in will be at an atmospheric pressure of around 15psi. This pressure does not register on your gauge. This type of gauge reads *Gauge Pressure*.

Gauge pressure is the difference between 'absolute pressure' and atmospheric pressure.

$$Absolute\ pressure = Gauge\ pressure + Atmospheric\ pressure$$

The SI unit of pressure can be either, the Newton per square metre (N/m^2) or the Pascal (Pa). Both are the same value and the choice of which to use is yours. The imperial unit of pressure is the pound per square inch (psi).

Variation of Pressure with Depth

In the figure 2.47, a tank filled with liquid contains an imaginary column. The density of the liquid in kg/m³ is represented by the symbol ρ (Rho). Let the height of the column be h and the cross-sectional area be a. The top surface of the column is exposed to atmospheric pressure but we will ignore that for now. We are going to concentrate on determining the gauge pressure at the bottom of the column.

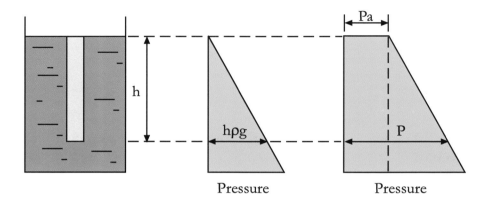

Figure 2.47 – Cylindrical Column in a Tank of Fluid

Volume of liquid in column	$=$ area x height $(ah)m^3$
Mass of liquid in column	$=$ density $(ah\rho)$ kg

If 'g' is the gravitational force in Newtons acting on a mass of 1 kg of liquid then:

Weight of liquid in column $= ah\rho g$ Newtons

Pressure on bottom face $= \dfrac{\text{Force}}{\text{Area}} = \dfrac{ah\rho g}{a}$ N/m^2

Note that the area (a) cancels out from the top and bottom lines

Pressure on lower surface $= h\rho g$ N/m^2

Note: Remember you can use N/m^2 or Pascals (Pa)

The downward-pressure exerted at the bottom of the column is balanced by an equal upward-pressure. We can say that if atmospheric pressure is ignored, the pressure in a liquid is directly proportional to its depth. The pressure calculated above is the *Gauge Pressure*; to obtain the *Absolute Pressure* we must add on the value of the atmospheric pressure 'pa' acting on the surface of the liquid.

Total pressure at depth h $= Pa + h\rho g$

Density and Relative Density

The density of a substance is defined as its mass per unit volume and is expressed in SI units as kg/m³, for example, the density of fresh water is 1000 kg/m³. However, high densities are usually expressed as the density relative to water. This is achieved by dividing the density of the material by the density of water. The result is a ratio. Relative density has no units. Therefore, a relative density of 1.2 would equate to a density of 1200kg/m³ and a relative density of 0.8 would equate to 800kg/m³.

Take care and make sure you convert relative density figures to real densities before using them in any calculations.

Example 1

A tank 1m high is filled with fresh water. Determine the absolute pressure at the bottom of the tank if atmospheric pressure is 100kPa. Assume that the acceleration due to gravity is 10m/s^2

Gauge pressure	$= h\rho g$
	$= 1\text{m} \times 1000\text{kg/m}^3 \times 10\text{m/s}^2$
	$= 10 \text{ kPa}$
Absolute pressure	$= 10 \text{ kPa} + 100\text{kPa}$
	$= 110\text{kPa}$

Note: The density of fresh water is 1000kg/m³ you are expected to remember this. Also, in IR Part-66 exams it is often convenient to round up the value for the acceleration due to gravity.

Example 2

A column of Mercury 1m high has a relative density of 13.6. Determine the absolute pressure at the base of the column if atmospheric pressure is 100kN/m². Assume the acceleration due to gravity to be 10m/s².

Gauge pressure	$= h\rho g$
	$= 1\text{m} \times 13600\text{kg/m}^3 \times 10\text{m/s}^2$
	$= 136 \text{ kN/m}^2$
Absolute pressure	$= 136 \text{ kN/m}^2 + 100\text{kN/m}^2$
	$= 236\text{kN/m}^2$

Properties of Liquid Pressure

There are certain properties than can be applied to all liquid pressure and these are:

1. The pressure at any point in a stationary liquid is the same in all directions.

2. The pressure exerted in a stationary liquid is the same at all points in the same horizontal plane.

3. The pressure exerted by a stationary liquid on a solid surface is perpendicular to that surface.

This can be shown diagrammatically as in figure 2.48. If you examine view 1 of figure 2.48 you should see that if the pressure were not acting equally in all directions the liquid at the point shown would be constantly on the move.

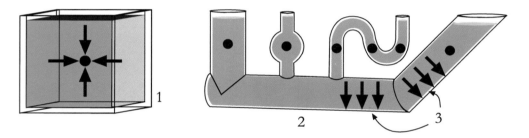

Figure 2.48– Properties of Liquid Pressure

From figure 2.48 examine view 2 and see that the pressure at each of the dots shown must be the same, and that the level of the liquid in each of the tubes must be the same. The pressure is related to the vertical distance beneath the surface not the volume of liquid.

The water reservoir feeding the taps in houses must be above the level of the taps and no part of the supply pipe must ever exceed the level of water in the reservoir.

Look at view 3 and note that the pressure must act at a right angle to the tube wall. If it did not, the liquid would move.

Pressure and Thrust

The liquid in a container will exert a force on the sidewalls and base. This force or thrust is the product of the pressure and the area of the surface.

Try an example:

A square tank has sides 1m long and 1m high. It is full of heating oil at relative density 0.8. Determine:

1. The force acting on the base of the tank.

2. The force acting on one sidewall.

At 1m depth the:
Gauge pressure
$= h\rho g$
$= 1m \times 800kg/m^3 \times 10m/s^2$
$= 8kPa$

Thrust on tank bottom $=$ Pressure x Area
$= 8kPa \times 1m \times 1m$
$= 8kN$

Thrust on side wall $= 4kPa$ (Average pressure) x 1m x 1m
$= 4kPa$

Note: When calculating the pressure on a vertical sidewall of a tank full of the same liquid, the average pressure is used. This is the pressure at half depth. Also, the gauge pressure is used as atmospheric pressure acts on both sides of the tank wall and cancels itself out.

The tank shown is 4m high, 6m long at the top and 2m wide. The base is 3m long and 2m wide. Determine the thrust on the sloping wall of the tank if it is completely filled with fresh water.

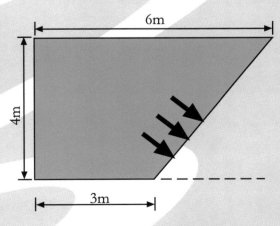

Figure 2.49 – Tank Filled with Water

Assume the acceleration due to gravity to be 10m/s²

Average gauge pressure will occur at a depth of 2m

Gauge pressure = hρg
= 2m x 1000kg/m³ x 10m/s²
= 20kPa

The pressure will act at right angles to the sloping wall.

Using the 3:4:5 ratio the sloping wall is 5m long.

Thrust on sloping wall = pressure x area
= 20kPa x 5m x 2m
= 200kN

Now try this:

If we wish to find the 'total' thrust on the wall using absolute pressure.

Absolute pressure = 20kPa + 100kPa
= 120kPa

Total Thrust on sloping wall = 120kPa x 5m x 2m
= 1200kN

Note: Do remember that atmospheric pressure also acts on the outside of the tank and exerts a force on it.

So: Thrust on outside sloping wall = 100kPa x 5m x 2m
= 1000kN

Difference in thrust between inside and outside wall is 200kN.

Be sure you know what the question is asking for!

www.part66.co.uk

The Manometer

The simplest way of measuring the gauge pressure of a gas in a container is to attach to the container one limb of a U-tube containing a liquid while the other limb is left open to the atmosphere, figure 2.50.

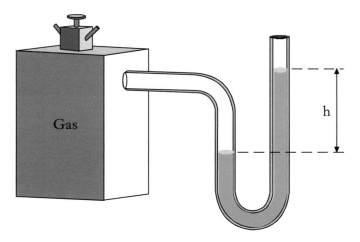

Figure 2.50 – Simple Manometer

If the pressure of the gas in the container changes, it will cause the level of the liquid in the connected column to go up or down and the level in the open column to rise or fall.

If the pressure increases, the excess pressure, in Pascals, above that of atmospheric will be given by the height of the displaced liquid 'h'. This type of pressure gauge is known as a *Manometer*.

When the gas pressure in the container is greater than atmospheric pressure, the level of the liquid is forced down the attached limb and up the open limb.

If the difference in the liquid levels in the two limbs is 'h' and the density of the liquid is 'ρ', the difference between the gas pressure in the container and atmospheric pressure can be found by calculating the pressure exerted by the height of h of the column of liquid 'hρg'.

Gauge Pressure = Absolute Pressure(P_{abs}) - Ambient Pressure(P_{amb})

Remember that a manometer will only measure gauge pressure.

Example

If the absolute pressure of the gas in a container is 202 kPa and the liquid in a manometer is fresh water, what would the difference in column heights be? Assume atmospheric pressure to be 101 kPa.

$$Gauge\ Pressure = Absolute\ Pressure - Ambient\ Pressure$$
$$h\rho g = 202000 - 101000$$
$$h = \frac{101000}{1000 \times 9.81} = 10.3m$$

This would obviously be ridiculous in a practical situation as the manometer would be gigantic. The solution would be to use a higher density liquid in the U tube. For this reason, Mercury is normally chosen as it has a high density of $13600\ kg/m^3$.

Using mercury in the U tube in the worked example above, the difference in column heights would be: 0.76m or 76cm.

You should note that atmospheric pressure at 101 kPa is equivalent to 76 cm of mercury.

In conclusion, a manometer indicates the pressure of a gas supply that *exceeds* atmospheric pressure, (gauge pressure), and can be calculated by applying 'hρg' to the difference in column height, or by just reading the height of the difference in cm of mercury.

The Barometer

A simple barometer can be made by taking a glass tube (sealed at one end) and filling it with mercury. The tube is then inverted and its open end is submerged in a dish of mercury. You should notice that the column of mercury in the tube would drop until its height above the level of mercury in the dish is 760mm. The column of mercury is being supported by the atmospheric pressure acting on the surface of the mercury in the dish. As atmospheric pressure changes from day to day, these changes will be registered as changes in the column height. The space above the mercury in the scaled tube is a *Torricellian* vacuum, which, apart from a little mercury vapour, does not differ from a true vacuum. Therefore, the barometer only measures absolute pressure. Some typical barometers are shown in figure 2.51.

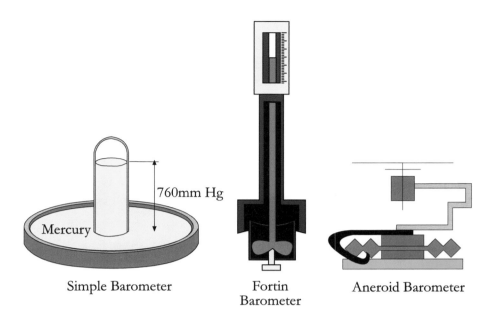

Figure 2.51 – Typical Barometers

Remember that a barometer measures absolute pressure!

The Fortin Barometer

The Fortin Barometer is used for the accurate measurement of atmospheric pressure. As the instrument measures absolute pressure only this makes it capable of doing this. The glass tube filled with mercury is inserted in an outer brass tube so that only the upper part is visible. This protects the glass and allows a millimetre (mm) scale to be read. The level of mercury in the glass tube can be adjusted for calibration purposes by use of a thumbscrew, which alters the volume of a leather bag that contains the reservoir of mercury. The outside of the leather bag is exposed to atmospheric pressure. This arrangement makes the level of mercury in the tube alter as the external pressure on the leather bag alters.

The Fortin barometer measures atmospheric pressure in mm of mercury. The SI unit used is mmHg, Hg being the chemical symbol for mercury.

The Aneroid Barometer

Aneroid Barometers do not use liquid. The essential part of the aneroid barometer is a flat cylindrical box or capsule that is hermetically sealed after being exhausted of air. Increases in atmospheric pressure cause the evacuated capsule to collapse slightly, while a decrease allows it to expand. The movements of the box are magnified by a lever system and transmitted to a chain wrapped around the spindle of a pointer. The chain is kept taut by a hairspring while the pointer moves over a calibrated scale. The construction of the aneroid barometer is similar to the altimeter used in aircraft.

Buoyancy

When anything is placed in a liquid, it experiences an *up-thrust*. Early experiments to measure the up-thrust resulted in *Archimedes's Principle*, which states:

When a body is wholly or partially immersed in a fluid, it experiences an up-thrust equal to the weight of the fluid displaced.

The term fluid applies to liquids and gases. When a body is immersed in a liquid, it experiences an apparent loss of weight and this will equal the weight of water displaced.

Floating bodies

When a piece of wood with a density that is less than that of water is placed in water it starts to sink until the weight of water displaced equals the wood's weight; it then floats. This is the *Law of Flotation*, which states:

A floating body will displace its own weight of the fluid in which it floats.

Worked Example

A ship of mass 1200 tonne floats in seawater. What volume of seawater does it displace? The relative density of seawater is 1.03.

$$\text{Volume of sea water displaced} = \frac{\text{Mass}}{\text{Density}}$$

$$= \frac{1200 \times 10^3 \text{kg}}{1000 \times 1.03}$$

$$= 1165 \text{m}^3$$

Convert tonnes to kg.
relative to fresh water

Hydrometers

The modern form, of hydrometer consists of a scaled glass tube weighted at one end with lead shot. The upper end of the tube is marked with a graduated scale displaying relative density. The total mass of liquid displaced will equal the mass of the floating hydrometer, which is always a constant. The hydrometer is calibrated in fresh water.

Depending on the density of the liquid the hydrometer floats in, it will sink to a greater or lesser degree. In low-density liquids, it will sink further to displace a greater volume of the fluid until that weight of fluid displaced matches the weight of the hydrometer. In this way, the hydrometer compares liquid densities to that of water. Mass of liquid displaced equals volume × density.

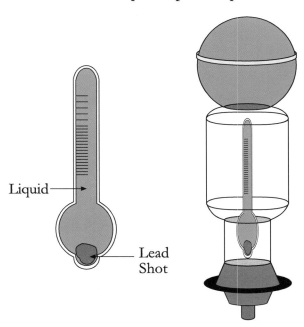

Liquid

Lead
Shot

Figure 2.52 - Typical Hydrometer

Revision

Statics

Questions

1. **Which of the following are NOT vector quantities:**

    A. Force, Velocity and Acceleration

    B. Mass, Volume and Time

    C. Displacement, Weight and Momentum

2. **A physical quantity that is completely described by a real number is a:**

    A. Vector quantity

    B. Scalar quantity

    C. Component

3. **The sum of two vectors is called:**

    A. Vector sum

    B. Equilibrant

    C. Resultant

4. **A man drags a box across a floor with a rope that is at an angle of 60° to the floor. If the tension in the rope is 500N, the horizontal component of the tension is:**

    A. 430N

    B. 250N

    C. 100N

www.part66.co.uk

5.   A mass of one metric tonne has a weight of:

   A. 981N

   B. 9.81kN

   C. 98.1kN

6.   A 6ft uniform beam AB is pivoted at its centre. If a mass of 20lb is hung from end A, a mass of 30lb used to balance the beam must be positioned:

   A. 1 foot from end B

   B. 2 foot from end B

   C. 18 inches from end B

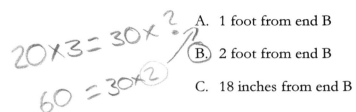
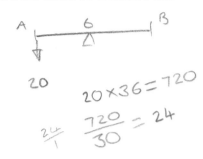

7.   A uniform beam AB is 6m long and has a mass of 10kg. A mass of 6kg is placed 1m from end A. The centre of gravity of the beam and its suspended mass will be:

   A. 1.6m from end A

   B. 2m from end A

   C. 2.25m from end A

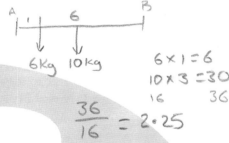

8.   A driver applies a force of 60N with each hand to turn a steering wheel 0.5m diameter. If his hands are placed diametrically opposite each other, the turning moment will be:

   A. 60Nm

   B. 30Nm

   C. 15Nm

www.part66.co.uk

9. A sailor pulls on a rope 17m long attached to the top of a vertical mast. If the tension in the rope is 500N and it makes an angle of 45°to the mast, the turning moment exerted on the mast will be:

    A. 4.25kN

    B. 8.5kN

    C. 3.25kN

10. Two co-planar forces act on the same point. One force acts horizontally to the West of the point and is 30N. The second force acts due North of the point and is 40N. A third force used to create equilibrium will be:

    A. 40N acting North of West

    B. 50N acting South of East

    C. 70N acting South of East

11. An aircraft undergoing weighing has a nose-wheel 2m from the nose and two main-wheels 10m from the nose. The nose reaction is 2kN and the main wheel reactions are 4kN each. If the reference datum is at the nose, the aircraft's centre of gravity will be:

    $8 \times 10 = 80$
    $2 \times 2 = 4$

    A. 8.4m in front of the main-wheels

    B. 4.4m behind the nose

    C. 8.4m behind the nose

12. The quadrature component of a vector will be:

    A. At 180° to the vector

    B. At 90° to the vector

    C. At 45° to the vector

13.   **Mechanical stress is:**

  A. Force/Area

  B. Area/Force

  C. Area × Force

14.   **Strain is:**

  A. Original Length/Extension

  B. Extension/Original Length

  C. Original Length + Extension

15.   **The modulus of Elasticity is:**

  A. Strain/Stress

  B. Stress/Strain

  C. Stress × Strain

16.   **A steel bar 2m long has a cross-sectional area of 0.01m² and stretches 2mm for a pull of 10kN. The Modulus of Elasticity for the steel is:**

  A. 1GPa

  B. 1MPa

  C. 1kPa

17.   **A fork-ended tie rod exerts a pull of 1kN on its connecting pin. The cross sectional area of the pin is 500mm². The shear stress will be:**

  A. 1MNm²

  B. 0.5MNm²

  C. 2MNm²

18. **Shear strain is:**

   A. Extension/Original Length

   B. The angle of deformation in radians

   C. The Modulus of Rigidity

19. **Pressure can be transmitted through:**

   A. Solids, Liquids and Gases

   B. Liquids only

   C. Liquids and gases only.

20. **Metallic gases are:**

   A. Molecular

   B. Crystalline

   C. Monatomic

21. **Gauge pressure is:**

   A. Absolute Pressure – Atmospheric Pressure

   B. Absolute Pressure + Atmospheric Pressure

   C. Equivalent to Absolute Pressure

22. **A diver swims at a depth of 6m in fresh water. The gauge pressure at this depth is:**

   hⲣg

   6 × 1000 × 10

   A. 160kPa

   B. 110kPa

   C. 60kPa

www.part66.co.uk

23.   A tank measuring 5m × 5m × 5m is completely filled with fresh water. The force exerted on one side-wall will be:

hρg

A. 625kN

2.5 × 1000 × 10

B. 1.25MN

C. 726kN

5 × 5 × 25K

25 × 25 = 625KN

24.   The instrument that measures absolute pressure is:

A. A manometer

B. A hydrometer

C. A barometer.

25.   A ship displaces 100m^3 of seawater, relative density 1.03. The mass of the ship is:

A. 1030 tonne

B. 103 tonne

C. 10.3 tonne

1000 × 1.03 × 100

$$\frac{103000}{1000} = 103 \text{ Tonne}$$

Revision

Statics

Answers:

1.	**B**	
2.	**B**	
3.	**C**	
4.	**B**	Horizontal component = $500N \times \cos 60^\circ = 250N$
5.	**B**	$1000kg \times 9.81m/s^2 = 9810N – 9.81kN$
6.	**A**	$20lb \times 3\,ft = 30lb \times 2ft$. Mass will be 1ft from end B
7.	**C**	$(10kg \times 3m) + (6kg \times 1m) = 2.25m$
8.	**B**	This is a couple. Force $\times$ distance $= 60N \times 0.5m = 30Nm$
9.	**A**	T x Perpendicular distance to pivot. $500N \times 8.5m = 4.25kN$
10.	**B**	
11.	**C**	$(2kN \times 2m) + (8kN \times 10m) / 10kN = 8.4m$ from nose.
12.	**B**	
13.	**A**	
14.	**B**	
15.	**B**	
16.	**A**	Strain $= 0.002m/2m = 0.001$. Stress $= 10,000N/0.01m^2 = 1MPa$ $E = 1MPa/0.001 = 1GPa$
17.	**A**	Load/2 $\times$ CSA. $1000N/0.001m^2 = 1MNm^2$
18.	**B**	
19.	**C**	
20.	**C**	
21.	**A**	
22.	**C**	$6m \times 1000kg\,m^3 \times 10m/s^2 = 60kPa$
23.	**A**	Average P$\times$ Area. $\frac{1}{2} \times 5m \times 1000kg\,m^3 \times 10m/s^2$ $= 25kPa$. $25kPa \times 5m \times 5m = 625kN$
24.	**C**	
25.	**B**	$100m^3 \times 1030kg\,m^3 = 103,000kg = 103$ tonne

www.part66.co.uk

Mechanics - Kinetics

Introduction

The dictionary definition of *Kinetics* is: 'The science of the action of force in producing or changing motion.'

Linear Movement

Linear Movement is uniform motion in a straight line and motion is the change of position of a body with reference to another body. A body is considered to be in motion or at rest, depending on some other body used as a reference point. A building is considered to be at rest with reference to the Earth but it has motion with the Earth in reference to the Sun. A person sitting in a car that is not moving is at rest with reference to the car and the Earth. When the car is moving the person is in a state of motion in relation to the Earth but is still in a state of rest in relation to the car they are sitting in. However, if a rear seat passenger in a moving car changes seats, they are in a state of motion in relation to both car and Earth. In moving across the car, their motion with reference to the car is across, but in relation to the Earth, they are moving forward in a diagonal line from one side of the carriageway to the other.

Displacement

If a person walked 7 km, it is not assumed that that person will end up 7 km from the start point. The person may have walked 3 km east and then 4 km north in which case they will end up 5 km from the start point.

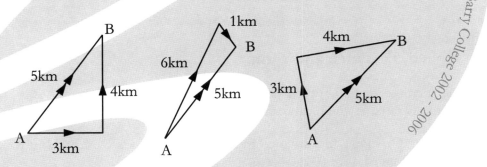

Figure 2.53 – Displacement

A change of position is called *Displacement* and is independent of the physical path followed and of the time taken.

For example, the person that has walked 7 km could have reached the same displacement by walking North-North-East and then southeast.

Since the displacement has both magnitude and direction, it is a vector quantity. See figure 2.53 on the previous page.

Speed

Speed tells us how quickly an object is moving at any given point in time. If you know how far the object has travelled in a given time then you can only determine its average speed. The object may have actually started from rest and changed speed several times during the passage of time. Speed does not take direction into account so it is a scalar quantity. 200m/s is a value but you are not told in what direction the object is travelling. *Average speed is derived by dividing the distance travelled by the time taken.*

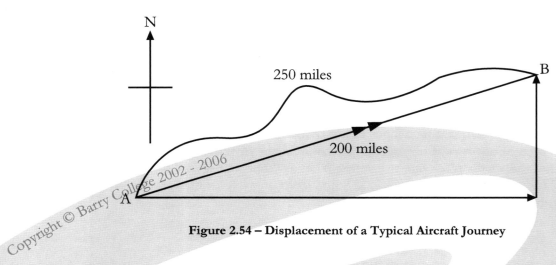

Figure 2.54 – Displacement of a Typical Aircraft Journey

In figure 2.54, an aircraft takes one hour to fly from A to B. It does not fly in a straight line, however, and covers 250 miles. Although the direct distance from A to B is only 200 miles the average speed of the aircraft is actual distance covered divided by the time taken which is 250 miles per hour.

Speed, Distance and Time

The connections between distance and time and speed and time can be demonstrated in graphical form.

This graph shows the distance travelled in 5 seconds by a body moving at a constant speed of 5m/s.

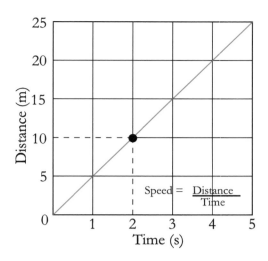

Figure 2.55 – Distance and Time

Examine it and see that the speed is derived by dividing the distance by the time at any point on the slope of the graph.

This graph shows a body travelling at constant speed for 5 seconds.

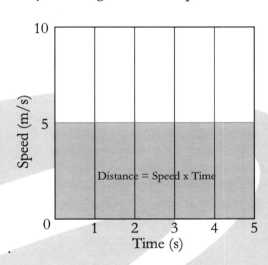

Figure 2.56 – Speed and Time

The area enclosed by the graph displays the distance travelled. Distance is derived by multiplying speed by the time, which in the case shown is 25m.

$$\text{Speed} = \frac{\text{Distance}}{\text{Time}}$$

$$\text{Distance} = \text{Speed} \times \text{Time}$$

$$\text{Time} = \frac{\text{Distance}}{\text{Speed}}$$

Worked Example

A person runs a distance of 0.72 km in 3 min, their average speed is:

$$\text{Speed} = \frac{\text{Distance}}{\text{Time}}$$

$$= \frac{720m}{180s}$$

$$= 4m/s$$

Speed Variation

If we now consider a car starting from rest and accelerating up to a constant cruising speed and then decelerating down to rest again, the slope of the distance/time graph will look different. As the initial and final speeds are both zero, the slope of the graph at the beginning and end will also be zero.

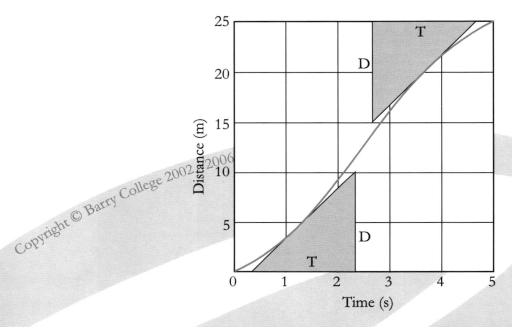

Figure 2.57 – Distance Time for Variation in Speed

You can find the speed at any point on the acceleration or deceleration curves. Draw a tangent to the curve and divide the vertical component of the gradient D by the horizontal component T.

$$\text{Speed} = \frac{\text{Distance}}{\text{Time}}$$

$$= \frac{10m}{2s}$$

$$= 5m/s$$

This graph shows a body accelerating and decelerating over time. The area under the graph still represents the distance travelled. Finding this area is a bit more complicated.

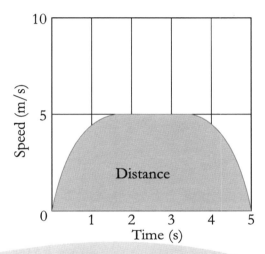

Figure 2.58 – Speed Variation and Time

You will not be expected to do this in an IR Part-66 exam. It can be done by multiplying the average height by the time or by dividing the area up into sections or coordinates.

Velocity

There is an important difference in the terms *velocity* and *speed*. Speed has no direction and is a *Scalar* quantity. Velocity on the other hand includes direction, distance in a straight line and time and is a *Vector* quantity. The aircraft in figure 2.54 moved 200 miles East North East from A to B in one hour. Therefore its velocity was 200mph East-North-East.

Acceleration

If the velocity of an object increases over time it is described as *Accelerating*. If the velocity decreases the object is described as *Decelerating* or *Retarding*.

Consider that a car increases its speed by 2m/s every second from rest until it reaches a speed of 20m/s. After one second it is travelling at 2m/s. After two seconds it is travelling at 4m/s. If you carry this through you should see that after 10 seconds it would be travelling at 20m/s.

Acceleration is *The Rate of Change of Velocity over Time*. If the rate of change is constant then the acceleration is described as being uniform.

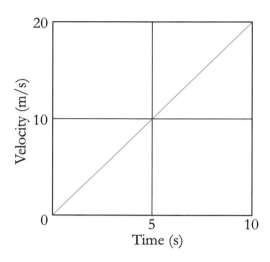

Figure 2.59 – The Rate of Change of Velocity

If the car was already travelling at an initial constant velocity 'u', and then accelerated with a uniform acceleration 'a' to a final velocity 'v' then the change of velocity would be 'v-u'. Therefore, as acceleration 'a' is the rate of change of velocity, then:

$$a = \frac{v - u}{t}$$
$$v = u + at$$

If 'u' and 'v' are expressed in metres per second (m/s) and 't' is in seconds (s), then acceleration is expressed in metres per second per second (m/s^2), see figure 2.60.

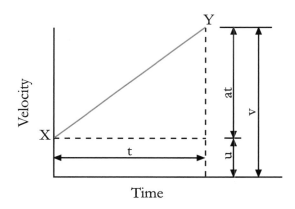

Figure 2.60 - Acceleration

Since the velocity is varying at a uniform rate between u and v, it is represented by a straight line XY.

The average velocity is the average of u and v, which is:

$$\frac{1}{2}(u+v)$$

If a body is travelling at a constant velocity or accelerating it must cover a distance, represented here by the letter 's' and so:

$$s = \frac{1}{2}(u+v)t$$

and

$$s = ut + \frac{1}{2}at^2$$

Equations of Motion

You are not expected to know how to prove the velocity and acceleration formulae. All the formulae you need are listed in this section. They are like a box of spanners. There will be one to suit any problem! They are easy to learn but make sure you know what the lettered symbols mean and the units that go with them.

- Initial velocity   'u'
- Final velocity   'v'
- Acceleration   'a'
- Distance   's'
- Elapsed time   't'

Look at the next four formulae. They suit all occasions. Even if you are not given the value for time the last equation in the list does not need it. It is useful to learn how to transpose each of the formula in case you need to extract a value.

$$v = u + at$$
$$s = \frac{1}{2}(u + v)t$$
$$s = ut + \frac{1}{2}at^2$$
$$v^2 = u^2 + 2as$$

Free Falling Objects

When a stationary object is released and free falls under the attraction of the force of gravity, it will accelerate at 9.81 m/s². Therefore, for free-falling objects, the acceleration 'a' will be 9.81 m/s²; this value is given the symbol 'g'. When an object is thrown upwards, its deceleration will be -9.81 m/s².

As the initial velocity u of objects freefalling from rest is always zero, the equations of motion can be rewritten as shown here.

$$v = gt$$
$$s = \frac{1}{2}gt^2$$
$$v = \sqrt{2gs}$$

Remember, in a multi-choice exam you will possibly be directed to use 10m/s² as a value for the acceleration due to gravity. It is an approximation that will lead you to identify the correct answer.

Example 1 (Displacement)

An aircraft flies due North for 20km and then changes direction to fly due East. Determine the distance travelled in an Easterly direction when the aircraft's displacement is 25km NNE.

Think about this one. The mental diagram you should see is of a 3:4:5 right-angled triangle with the resultant displacement of 25km being its hypotenuse. The Easterly distance must be 15km.

Example 2 (Speed, distance and time)

An aircraft flies at 80km/hr for 15 minutes and at 120km/hr for a further 5 minutes. How far has it travelled and what is its average speed?

In first 15 minutes it flies a quarter of 80km = 20km

In next 5 minutes it flies a twelfth of 120km = 10km

Total distance travelled = 30km

$$\text{Average speed} = \frac{\text{Distance}}{\text{Time}}$$
$$= \frac{30\text{km}}{20\text{min}}$$
$$= 1.5\text{km/min}$$
$$= 90\text{km/hr}$$

Example 3 (Velocity and acceleration)

An aircraft touches down at 100m/s and decelerates uniformly at -5m/s² to a full stop. How long did it take for the aircraft to stop and what was the braking distance?

For time taken:

$$v = u + at$$
Transposed to:
$$\frac{v - u}{a} = t$$

$$t = \frac{0 - 100\text{m/s}}{-5\text{m/s}^2} = 20 \text{ seconds}$$

For braking distance:

$$s = \frac{1}{2}(u + v)t$$

$$= \frac{1}{2}(100 + 0)20$$

$$= 1000 \text{ m}$$

You may have noticed that deceleration is given as a minus figure. This is normal. You could have used another formula for part 2 of the question but it would be less simple for mental arithmetic.

$$s = ut + \frac{1}{2}at^2$$
$$= (100\text{m/s} \times 20\text{s}) + (\frac{1}{2} \times -5\text{m/s}^2 \times 20\text{s} \times 20\text{s})$$
$$= 2000 + -1000$$
$$= 1000\text{m}$$

Example 4 (Free-falling objects)

Watch this one it often appears in the exam! A ball is dropped from a height of 10m how long does it take to reach the ground?

Assume the acceleration due to gravity to be 10 m/s²

You are going to have to use:

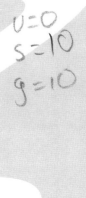

$$s = \frac{1}{2}gt^2$$

Transpose to:

$$\sqrt{\frac{s}{\frac{1}{2}g}} = t$$

$$\sqrt{\frac{10}{\frac{1}{2} \times 10}} = t$$

$$\text{Time} = \sqrt{2} = 1.414\text{secs}$$

Relative Velocity

At the beginning of this section, we looked at how the motion of a body is relative to that of another. For example, if two trains are travelling East on parallel tracks and train A is travelling at 100 km/hr while train B is travelling at 50 km/hr, train A will be travelling at 50 km/hr East relative to train B. Therefore, to a passenger on train A, train B is travelling at 50 km/hr West.

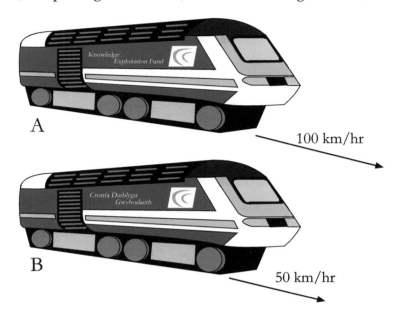

100 km/hr

50 km/hr

Figure 2.61 – Two Trains Travelling in the Same Direction

However, if we now look at a situation where train B is travelling West at 50 km/hr; to an observer on this train, train A would be travelling at 150 km/hr Eastwards and to an observer on train A, train B would be travelling westwards at 150 km/hr.

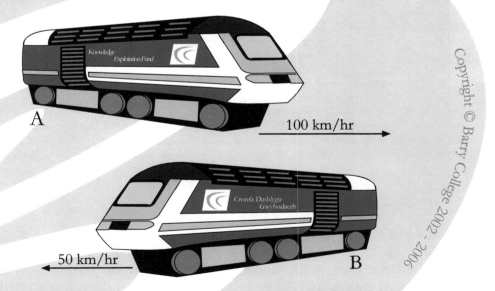

100 km/hr

50 km/hr

Figure 2.62 – Two Trains Travelling in Opposite Directions

If both trains were on a collision course, to an observer on either train A or B, the other train would be closing at 150 km/hr.

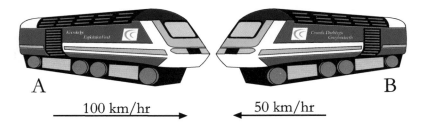

Figure 2.63 – Two Trains on a Collision Course

Resultant of Two Velocities

An aircraft is flying eastwards at 300km/hr ground speed in a constant side-wind of 50km/hr blowing from the North. Vector CA in figure 2.64 represents the side-wind velocity of 50km/hr South. Vector AB represents the aircraft velocity of 300km/hr East.

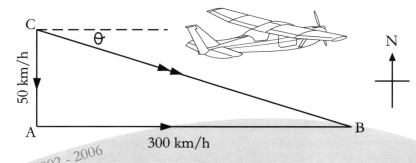

Figure 2.64 – An Aircraft Affected by a Side Wind

The vector sum of CA and AB is represented by CB, which is the resultant velocity of the aircraft relative to the ground.

Using Pythagoras'

$$CB = \sqrt{CA^2 + AB^2} = 304\text{km/hr South East}$$

Example 1

A flat bed lorry is travelling along a flat, straight road at 10 m/s. An oil drum rolls across the bed of the lorry at 3 m/s at right angles to the direction of travel of the lorry. What is the resultant velocity of the oil drum and its direction relative to the lorry?

www.part66.co.uk

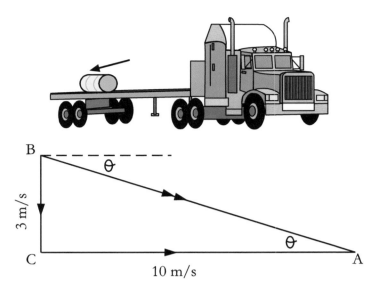

Figure 2.65 – Example 1 – Flat Bed Lorry

Using simple trigonometry this time for a change.

$$\text{Tangent of } \theta = \frac{\text{Opposite}}{\text{Adjacent}} = \frac{3}{10} = 0.3$$

$$\text{Invert Tangent} = 16.7°$$

You could find the vector BA by Pythagoras' of course:

$$\text{Vector BA} = \sqrt{3^2 + 10^2} = 10.4 \text{m/s}$$

You do not have the luxury of a calculator in a IR Part-66 exam so any figures presented in a question will have to be numbers that are easily resolvable. The question may not even ask for an arithmetic solution. For example, what is the sum of two vectors? Answer: A resultant.

In the example above, simple numbers with the use of Pythagoras' can make a useful multi-choice question.

Rotational Movement

As its name implies, rotational movement is concerned with motion that is not in a straight line. When a disc rotates, a point on the rim of the disc moves in a circular path, figure 2.66.

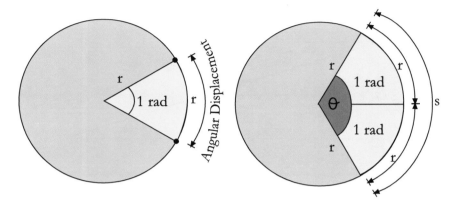

Figure 2.66 - Angular Displacement

Angular Distance θ

If a line is drawn from the point to the axis of rotation, this line, which would be the radius, sweeps through an angle, which is called the *Angular Displacement* of that point.

The unit representing this angular displacement is the *Radian*, usually shortened to *rad*, where one radian is *the angle subtended by the arc of a circle equal in length to the radius*. The number of arcs, equal in length to the radius that can fit into the circumference of a circle is 2π, equivalent to 6.284 as π is 3.142. From this, you should be able to see that the radius of a circle must sweep through 2π radians in one revolution and as the radius will also have swept through 360°, then each radian is equivalent to 57.3°. However, once you get used to it, it is generally easier to remember that 2π radians equals 360°.

When looking at angular displacement, the number of radians swept by the radius is usually denoted by the Greek letter Theta (θ), which is the angular distance travelled, while the linear distance travelled by a point on the rim is denoted by the letter 's'. It is easy to convert a value in radians to a linear value for a point moving on a circumference.

For example, what is the distance moved by a point on the rim of a wheel with a radius 400mm, if it rotates through 20 radians?

Angular distance θ is 20 rads, which means the point must have travelled around the rim a distance equal to 20 times the radius. Therefore, we can say:

$$s = r\theta = 400 \times 20 = 8000mm = 8m$$

From this you can see that if we are only given the linear distance (s) and the radius (r) then it is a simple matter to convert this into angular distance θ.

$$\theta = \frac{s}{r} = \frac{8000mm}{400mm} = 20 \text{ rads}$$

Angular Velocity ω

Calculating the angular distance on its own may be useful but it would be nice if we could relate the distance covered to a given time, in other words the angular speed. To call this angular velocity we would of course need to know the direction as well. Angular velocity is represented by the Greek letter ω(omega). The value is expressed in radians per second (rad/s). The average velocity is derived by dividing the distance travelled θ in radians by the time taken 't' in seconds.

There are 2π rads in one revolution, so a shaft rotating at for example, ten revolutions per second would have an angular velocity of 2π × 10 rad/s.

$$\omega = \frac{\theta}{t}$$

Worked Example

If a shaft is rotating at 2000 rpm, what is its angular velocity?

$$\omega = \frac{2\pi n}{60} = \frac{2\pi \times 2000}{60} = 209.5 \text{ rad/s}$$

Note: To obtain rad/s you must change rpm into revolutions/second in the formula, which is why 2πn, where 'n' represents the rpm, is divided by 60 in the formula.

Angular Acceleration α

Acceleration, as discussed previously, is the change of velocity with respect to time. In constant acceleration, the velocity will be changing by equal amounts in equal intervals of time. Angular acceleration is denoted by the Greek letter Alpha (α).

Angular acceleration can be calculated mathematically and is best demonstrated by looking at the worked example below.

Worked Example

A shaft starts rotating from rest and reaches an angular velocity of 300 rad/s in 60 s. The average angular acceleration is:

$$\alpha = \frac{\omega_2 - \omega_1}{t} = \frac{300 \text{ rad/s} - 0 \text{ rad/s}}{60s} = 5 \text{ rad/s}^2$$

Note: We have identified the initial velocity ω_1 and the final velocity ω_2.

Relationship between Angular and Linear Motion

Providing we know the value of the rotating body's radius (r), we can use the relationship between the radius and the radian to convert angular values to linear values and vice versa. Therefore, it is possible to calculate the linear distance, velocity and acceleration of a point on the rim of a rotating body using the following formulae:

Linear distance (s) $= r\theta$

Linear velocity (v) $= r\omega$

Linear acceleration (a) $= r\alpha$

Worked Example

The angular velocity of a flywheel with a radius of 400 mm, increases from 5 rad/s to 50 rad/s in 30 s. The values of its average angular and linear accelerations for a point on the rim are:

Angular acceleration $\alpha = \frac{50 - 5}{30} = 1.5 \text{ rad/s}$

Linear acceleration $a = 0.4 \times 1.5 = 0.6 \text{m/s}$

Equations of Angular Motion

The equations of angular motion are similar to those for linear motion and table 2.6 shows these angular motion equations with their linear equivalents.

Angular Equations	Linear Equations
$\omega_2 = \dfrac{\theta}{t}$	$v = \dfrac{s}{t}$
$\omega_2 = \omega_1 + \alpha t$	$v = u + at$
$\theta = \omega_1 t + \dfrac{1}{2}\alpha t^2$	$s = ut + \dfrac{1}{2}at^2$
$\omega_2{}^2 = \omega_1{}^2 + 2\alpha\theta$	$v^2 = u^2 + 2as$

Table 2.6 – Linear and Angular Equations of Motion

Remember, the symbols used for angular motion

Angular distance	Theta (θ)
Initial angular velcocity	Omega one (ω_1)
Final angular velocity	Omega two (ω_2)
Angular acceleration	Alpha (α)

The symbols used for linear motion are:

Linear distance	(s)
Initial linear velocity	(u)
Final linear velocity	(v)
Linear acceleration	(a)

147

Calculations for Angular Motion

Example 1 (Angular and linear velocity)

A wheel diameter 0.7m rotates 20 revolutions in 5 seconds. Determine the average angular velocity and the average linear velocity of a point on its rim.

The radius of the wheel is 0.35m.

$$\omega = \frac{2\pi n}{5} = \frac{2\pi \times 20}{5} = 25 \text{ rad/s}$$

$$v = r\omega = 0.35\text{m} \times 25 \text{ rad/s} = 8.75\text{m/sec}$$

Example 2 (Angular and Linear Acceleration)

A flywheel spins through 50 revolutions starting from rest and attains 150rpm. Determine the average angular acceleration and the linear acceleration of a point on its rim if the radius of the fly-wheel is 500mm.

$$\text{Angular Velocity attained} = \frac{2\pi n}{60} = \frac{2\pi \times 150}{60} = 15.7 \text{ rad/s}$$

You have not been given the time, which limits your formula choice:

$$\omega_2^2 = \omega_1^2 + 2\alpha\,\theta \text{ maybe? Transpose for } \alpha$$

$$\alpha = \frac{\omega_2^2 - \omega_1^2}{2\theta} = \frac{(15.7 \text{ rad/s})^2 - 0^2}{2 \times 2\pi \times 50} = \frac{246.5 \text{ rad/s}}{628.3} = 0.4 \text{ rad/s}^2$$

$$\text{Linear acceleration} = r\alpha = 0.5\text{m} \times 0.4 \text{ rad/s}^2 = 0.2 \text{ m/s}^2$$

Note: You will not be expected to carry out such a complex calculation in the IR Part-66 exam. This example is used to show you the use of the formulae. A likely question for multi-choice is to give you a linear value for a point on the rim of a wheel of given radius and ask you to convert it to an angular value, or vice versa.

Out of passing interest you could now establish the time taken for the fly - wheel to spin up. You now know the acceleration.

www.part66.co.uk

So:

$$\omega_2 = \omega_1 + \alpha t$$

$$\text{therefore: } t = \frac{\omega_2 - \omega_1}{\alpha} = \frac{15.7 - 0}{0.4} = 39.25s$$

If you have worked your way through this you deserve a cup of tea or maybe something stronger! See you in the next section.

Centrifugal and Centripetal Forces

If you have ever swung an object around on the end of a cord, you will know that the cord appears to be trying to pull itself out of your hand. If you consider what is happening, you could equally say that while the object was in motion in a circular path, you have to exert a constant pull on the cord to keep it in your hand.

From Newton's first law of motion, a body in uniform motion tends to continue in a straight line unless it is acted upon by an external force. Therefore, when we cause a body to move in a circular path, a continuous force must be applied to it to keep it in that circular path, preventing it from travelling in a straight line, which would be tangential to the circle it is rotating in; this is *Centripetal Force*.

According to Newton's third law, to every action there is an equal and opposite reaction and so in this case, the reaction to the centripetal force is called the *Centrifugal Force*, which acts in an outwards direction.

Centripetal force is directly proportional to the mass of the object in circular motion. For example, if the mass of the object is doubled and its speed remains constant, the pull or centripetal force will be doubled to keep the object in its circular path.

Centripetal force is inversely proportional to the radius of the circle in which the object travels. For example, if the cord is shortened and the speed remains constant, the pull on the cord must be increased to force the object more rapidly from its linear path into the smaller radius circular path. Its directional change is greater, so the applied force must also be greater.

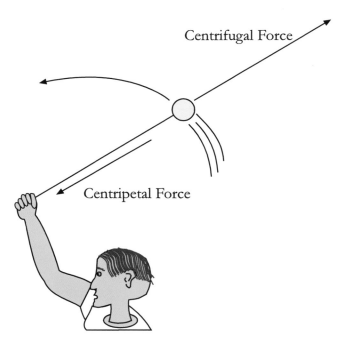

Figure 2.67 – Centripetal and Centrifugal Forces

Force is the product of mass times acceleration, so we can say that the object has an inwards acceleration, called *Centripetal Acceleration*, which when multiplied by the object's mass gives the centripetal force. There is also an outward acceleration, which together with the object's mass, gives the reaction force or centrifugal force.

Consider a mass '*m*' rotating clockwise with constant speed '*v*' in a circular path of radius '*r*', figure 2.68.

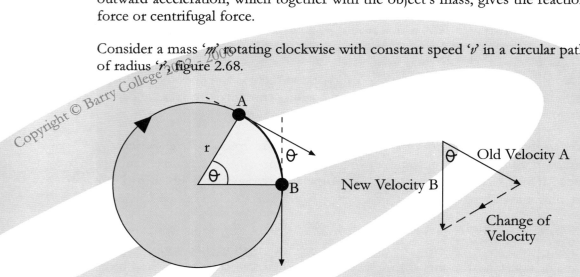

Figure 2.68 – Rotating Object with Mass '*m*'

At point A in figure 2.68, the linear velocity will be *v* in the tangential direction indicated. At point B, which will be reached in time *t*, the velocity will be the same but in a different linear direction.

If the direction has changed by θ radians, then the amount by which the velocity will have changed from direction A to the new direction B can be established by a vector as shown in figure 2.68. You will not be required to explain the proof for the formulae for centripetal acceleration and force.

The equations required for centripetal acceleration and force can be expressed both in linear and angular form. Both are given here.

$$\text{Angular:} \quad \text{Centripetal acceleration} = \alpha = \omega^2 r$$
$$\text{Centripetal force} \quad = F = m\omega^2 r$$
$$\text{Linear:} \quad \text{Centripetal acceleration} = a = \frac{v^2}{r}$$
$$\text{Centrepetal force } F = \frac{mv^2}{r} \text{ or sometimes } \frac{Wv^2}{gr}$$

The symbols used are:

a   linear acceleration

F   Force

g   acceleration due to gravity

m   mass

r   radius of circular path

v   linear velocity

W   weight

α centripetal acceleration

ω angular velocity

Aircraft Turning and Banking

As with objects whirling on a cord, aircraft that are turning on a circular flight path will require a centripetal force to hold them in that circular path. In this case, the centripetal force is created as a component of the aircraft lift and weight. To achieve this, the aircraft has to adopt an angle of bank. However, if this angle is too great, the aircraft will be pushed towards the centre of the turn; if the angle is not big enough the aircraft will slide out of the turn; but at the correct angle, the aircraft will turn on a constant radius, figure 2.69

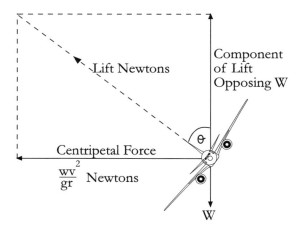

Figure 2.69 – Aircraft Turning

To determine the correct angle of bank for a given turn radius and aircraft velocity we can use standard trigonometry:

$$Tan\theta = \frac{Opposite}{Adjacent} = \frac{\frac{wv^2}{gr}}{w} = \frac{v^2}{gr}$$

Where 'w' = the weight of the aircraft, (its mass x acceleration), 'g' is gravity and 'r' is the radius of the turn.

Note: That the weight 'W' cancels out in the equation. Therefore the weight of an aircraft has no bearing on establishing the correct angle of bank, turn radius or airspeed.

Worked Example

An aircraft is flying on a circular path of radius 1000m at a velocity of 100m/s. Determine the correct angle of bank. Assume the value for g to be 10m/s².

www.part66.co.uk

$$\text{Tan } \theta = \frac{v^2}{gr} = \frac{100 \times 100}{10 \times 1000} = \frac{10000}{10000} = 1$$

$$\theta = \text{Tan}^{-1}(1) = 45°$$

Therefore the angle is 45°

Calculations for Centripetal Acceleration and Force

Example 1 (Centripetal force)

Determine the centripetal force required to keep a 10kg mass turning in a circular path 4m radius when it is travelling at 20m/s.

$$F = \frac{mv^2}{r} = \frac{10kg \times 20 \text{ m/s} \times 20 \text{ m/s}}{4m} = \frac{4000}{4m} = 1kN$$

An interesting point can be observed here. If you doubled the velocity of the 10kg mass at the same radius you would find that the centripetal force would rise by 4. This tells you that the centripetal force is proportional to the square of the velocity of a body. For example if you trebled the velocity the centripetal force would rise 9 times.

[handwritten: $\frac{10 \times 40 \times 40}{4}$ $\frac{16000}{4} = 4000 = 4kN$ $\frac{10 \times 60 \times 60}{4}$ $\frac{36000}{4} = 9000 = 9kN$]

Example 2 (Centripetal and Centrifugal Force)

Determine the maximum speed at which a car can pass over a humped back bridge radius 10m. Here is an interesting case. If the centrifugal force were to equal the weight of the car, the car would become weightless and leave the road.

So:

Centrepital force $\frac{mv^2}{r}$ = weight of car mg

therefore: $mv^2 = mgr$ and $v^2 = \frac{mgr}{m}$

m cancels out leaving $v^2 = gr$ or $v = \sqrt{gr}$

Now we can do it. $v = \sqrt{10 \times 10} = 10m/s$

Note: That the weight of the car plays no part in finding the maximum speed at which the vehicle leaves the road. *Only radius and speed matter.*

www.part66.co.uk

Example 3 (Centripetal acceleration)

An object of 5kg mass is turning in a circular path radius 10m. Determine the centripetal acceleration and force if the object is travelling at 20m/s.

$$\text{Centripetal acceleration} = \frac{v^2}{r} = \frac{20 \text{ m/s} \times 20 \text{ m/s}}{10m} = 40 \text{ m/s}^2$$

$$\text{Centripetal force} = \frac{mv^2}{r} = \frac{5kg \times 20 \text{ m/s} \times 20 \text{ m/s}}{10m} = 200N$$

Periodic Motion

If you consider a simple to and fro or oscillating movement that repeats itself in equal time intervals then you can describe that motion as being *Periodic*. *The Periodic Time* (t) is the time taken for one complete to and fro movement, which we call a *Cycle*. The number of cycles occurring in one second is called the *Frequency* and this is measured in *Hertz* **(HZ)**, one HZ being equivalent to one cycle per second. The maximum displacement of a body from its middle or rest position is called the *Amplitude*.

If the body always accelerates towards one fixed point in its path, like the bob-weight of a pendulum does towards its rest position, and the acceleration is proportional to the amplitude, the *Periodic Motion* is described as being *Simple Harmonic Motion*.

The Simple Pendulum

A simple pendulum may be constructed by suspending a mass (m) by a light string, which is attached at its other end to a fixed point.

When the mass is then displaced from its rest position with the string taut it will accelerate back in an arc towards its rest position.

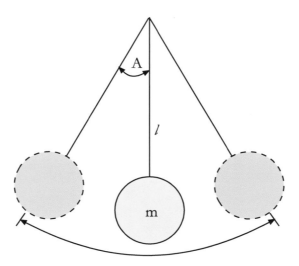

Figure 2.70 – A Simple Pendulum

When displaced the mass has potential energy, which changes to kinetic energy as it accelerates back towards its original rest position. The mass then decelerates to a stop as it reaches an opposite displacement and then accelerates back reaching maximum velocity again through the rest position. The mass always accelerates towards the original rest position.

One complete to and fro movement of the mass is called an *Oscillation* or *Cycle*. The time taken to complete one oscillation is the *Periodic Time (t)*. The distance or angle between the rest and the maximum displacement point is called the *Amplitude. The Length (L)* of the pendulum is measured from the fixed suspension point to the centre of gravity position in the mass.

Providing the amplitude is not excessive, the periodic time will depend solely on the length of the pendulum and the acceleration due to gravity. The mass of the pendulum's bob-weight and its amplitude, have absolutely no effect at all on the periodic time.

The periodic time is proportional to the square root of the length of the pendulum. Let me clarify this. If you were to double the length of a pendulum, the periodic time would increase by $\sqrt{2}$ which is 1.414 times the original periodic time.

For a pendulum of fixed length the time taken for one complete to and fro movement will remain the same no matter what amplitude is given to the bob-weight.

The equations for frequency and periodic time can be expressed in a simple form or a more complex form. Both are shown here. Remember that it is a multi-choice examination so the figures will be kept simple. You can also be questioned on the relationships between length, time and frequency rather than calculations.

155

Frequency

Remember that the frequency is measured in cycles or oscillations per second and is expressed in Hertz.

$$\text{Frequency (f)} = \frac{1}{t} \text{ and } t = \frac{1}{f}$$

Example 1

A pendulum has a periodic time of a quarter of a second.

The frequency will be:

$$\text{Frequency} = \frac{1}{0.25} = 4\text{Hz}$$

Another formula is:

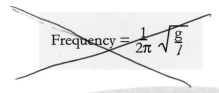

$$\text{Frequency} = \frac{1}{2\pi} \sqrt{\frac{g}{l}}$$

Example 2

A pendulum swings on a cord 2½ m long. The frequency will be:

(Assume g = 10 m/s² and π = 3.)

$$\text{Frequency} = \frac{1}{6} \sqrt{\frac{10}{2.5}} = 0.33\text{Hz}$$

Periodic Time

Remember that the periodic time is the time taken to complete one complete swing to and fro. The periodic time is proportional to the square root of the pendulum's length. It is dependent only on the length of the pendulum and the acceleration due to gravity. For a fixed length pendulum the periodic time remains constant regardless of the amplitude of the swing and the mass of the pendulum.

$$\frac{t^2}{l} = \text{a constant k} \qquad \text{By transposition: } t = \sqrt{l\,k}$$

Example

Assuming the value of k to be 4 calculate the periodic times for pendulum lengths of 2m, 4m and 8m and show that periodic time increases by $t\sqrt{2}$ if you double the length of a pendulum.

For length	2m	$t = \sqrt{2 \times 4} = 2.83$		
For length	4m	$t = \sqrt{4 \times 4} = 4$	same as	$2.83 \times \sqrt{2}$
For length	8m	$t = \sqrt{8 \times 4} = 5.656$	same as	$4 \times \sqrt{2}$

Another formula is:

$$\text{Periodic time} = 2\pi \sqrt{\frac{l}{g}}$$

Note: Periodic time is often given the symbol p rather than t. Be prepared to see it like this or even as t_p.

Example

Calculate the length of a simple pendulum that has a periodic time t of 3 sec. Assume g = 10 m/s² and π = 3

$$t = 2\pi \sqrt{\frac{l}{g}} \text{ transposes to: } l = \frac{gt^2}{4\pi^2} \text{ or } \left(\frac{t^2}{4\pi^2}\right) \times g = \left(\frac{9}{36}\right) \times 10 = 2.5\text{m}$$

You could do it easier! For example:

$$\frac{t^2}{l} = \text{a constant}$$

If you had used the correct value for π and g = 9.81 m/s² in the calculation above the length would have been 2.24m. Using the exact value for the constant k of 4.0243.

$$\frac{t^2}{l} = k \quad \text{transposes to:} \quad l = \frac{9}{k} = 2.24m$$

Note: You would not be expected to juggle these formulae or carry out complex calculations in the IR Part-66 exam. They are illustrated here just to get you used to the relationships. Be prepared to use the simpler formulae though.

Springs

Springs obey Hooke's Law, which is concerned with the elasticity in materials. If a spring is fixed at one end and you subject the free end to a pull force then the extension of the spring will be proportional to the applied force.

This is subject to you not distorting the spring permanently by overloading it of course.

If you were to suspend a mass to the free end of a vertical spring and then pull it down and release it the mass would oscillate up and down. The force causing the mass to accelerate back through its rest position, results from the elastic energy that is stored in the spring as it extends and compresses.

Springs have different values of stiffness. Each spring has a stiffness value that is expressed as its 'spring constant' k. The spring constant will affect the amplitude, frequency and periodic time of the oscillation of the spring. It will also affect the value of the restoring force should you extend or compress it.

If you were to hang a beam from two springs, each having the same spring constant, it would be the same as hanging the beam from one spring that has a spring constant, and a restoring force, twice that of one of the original springs. If you used three similar springs then they can be replaced by one spring having three times the constant and so on.

We can look at some formulae used to demonstrate these relationships:

$$\text{Frequency (f)} = \frac{1}{2\pi} \sqrt{\frac{k}{m}}$$

Where k is the spring constant m is the suspended mass

Example 1

A 2kg mass is suspended from a spring with a constant of 2kN/m. If the spring is set into oscillation the frequency will be:

$$f = \frac{1}{2\pi} \sqrt{\frac{2000}{2}} = 5Hz$$

If the mass were supported by more than one spring, let us say four springs for example, then we have to look at this formula:

$$f = \frac{1}{2\pi} \sqrt{\frac{4k}{m}}$$

Note: The value k is multiplied by 4.

Example 2

A beam mass 2kg is supported by 4 springs each having a spring constant of 500N/m. If the beam were set in oscillation its frequency would be:

$$f = \frac{1}{2\pi} \sqrt{\frac{4 \times 500}{2}} = 5Hz$$

It was pretty obvious it would be the same as the first example but we did this to illustrate the point. If one spring can exactly replace a number of springs then its spring constant will be the sum of all the springs it replaces. You may wonder how these relationships could be framed into a multi-choice question. They can!

Example 3

The diagram shows an arrangement of three vertically mounted springs supporting a 1kN load. If one of the springs would extend 60mm under this load, how far does the 1kN load drop when suspended as shown assuming that all three springs have a similar spring constant?

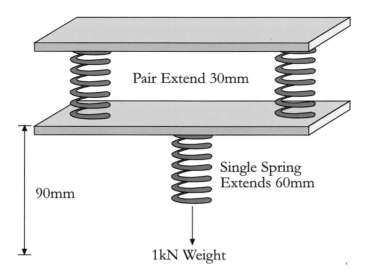

Figure 2.71 – Load Suspended by Springs

The restoring force of the top two springs is twice that of the single lower spring. So, the top pair extends 30mm and the bottom spring extends 60mm. The beam drops 90mm. This is typical of a multiple-choice question involving spring constants.

If the beam had been suspended by the three springs all attached to the ceiling, and a 1kN force had pulled down the beam; the beam would have descended by only 20mm. You need to puzzle out a few different arrangements for practice.

Spring Force

The force (F), which is extending a spring, can be calculated by multiplying the value (m) of the suspended mass by the acceleration due to gravity (g). This is exactly the same as multiplying the extension (E) by the spring constant (k).

$$\text{Force (F)} = mg = kE$$

$$\text{If } mg = kE \text{ then the spring constant } k = \frac{mg}{E}$$

$$\text{Also: Extension E} = \frac{mg}{k}$$

You can determine any value if you know two of the values from either mass, extension or spring constant.

You have done enough at this point to solve simple problems associated with springs. We will now go on to look at how simple harmonic motion can affect rotating machinery.

www.part66.co.uk

Simple Theory of Vibration, Harmonics and Resonance

We have already introduced periodic motion and know that it is any sort of motion that repeats itself in equal intervals of time. In addition, we know the time taken for one complete back and forth movement of a pendulum is the periodic time 'T' and the number of complete movements per second is the frequency 'f', expressed in Hertz (Hz).

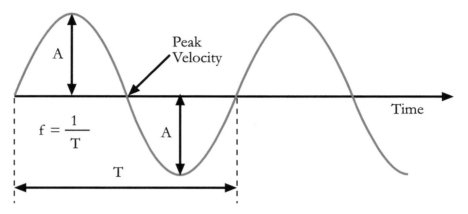

Figure 2.72 – Simple Harmonic Motion

The amplitude 'A' is the maximum displacement a body takes from its rest position; the range of displacement being ±A, figure 2.72.

Periodic motion is said to be *Simple Harmonic Motion* when the acceleration is always directed towards a fixed point in its path and is proportional to its displacement from that point. Since force is equal to the product of mass and acceleration, the internal restoring force of the system in motion is always directed towards a fixed point and is proportional to the displacement from that point.

A useful illustration that represents harmonic motion is the movement of a point on a circular path that has constant angular velocity.

Imagine the point as crossing the horizontal diameter of the circle from left to right to left again. The point accelerates to the left, stops and then accelerates back to the centre. It reaches maximum velocity at the centre and then decelerates to the right and stops again. As the point rotates around the circumference, the imaginary point takes the reverse route back to the left of the diameter.

www.part66.co.uk

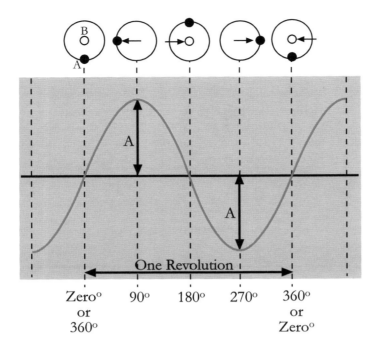

Figure 2.73 – Motion of a Point on a Circular Path

If this were an unbalanced point on a rotating shaft, can you see how this simple harmonic motion would cause vibration.

As point 'A' on the circumference of the circle rotates through 360°, point 'B' on the diameter aligned with point 'A' will travel a distance of one radius on each 90° travel of point 'A'.

Phase Relationship

The illustrations below show the relationships between the displacement, velocity and acceleration phases during one cycle. Figure 2.74 shows the displacement moving from rest to maximum between 1 and 2 and then returning to rest at 3.

Between 3 and 4 it moves to a maximum again returning to rest at 5.

The amplitude of the cycle is the vertical distance between the rest position and a peak.

www.part66.co.uk

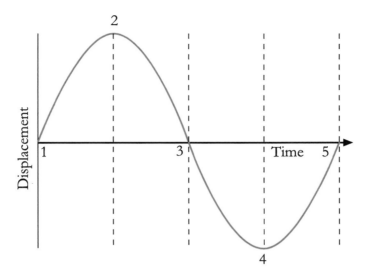

Figure 2.74 – Displacement Phase

Figure 2.75 illustrates that where the displacement curve crossed the rest position, velocity is at its maximum value as shown by positions 1, 3 and 5.

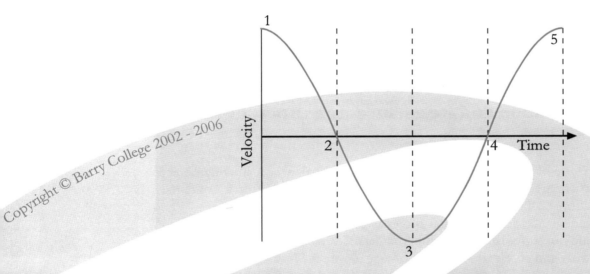

Figure 2.75 – Velocity Phase

Where the displacement reached a maximum the velocity is zero as shown in positions 2 and 4.

Figure 2.76 illustrates that deceleration occurs as displacement increases and that acceleration occurs as displacement decreases.

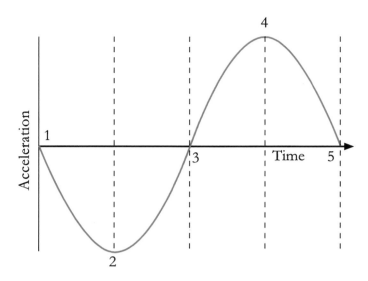

Figure 2.76 – Acceleration Phase

Deceleration occurs between 1 and 2, 3 and 4.

Acceleration occurs between 2 and 3, 4 and 5.

Put simply, acceleration occurs as the displacement reduces towards zero.

Forced Vibration and Resonance from Rotating Assemblies

The chief cause of vibration from rotating parts is unbalance. A moving object has kinetic energy and oscillation of an unbalanced part causes a continual transformation of kinetic energy to potential energy to kinetic energy. The effects of unbalance are centrifugal forces, which impose forced vibration on bearings and in supporting structure that can lead to early failure through increased wear and accelerated fatigue damage, figure 2.77.

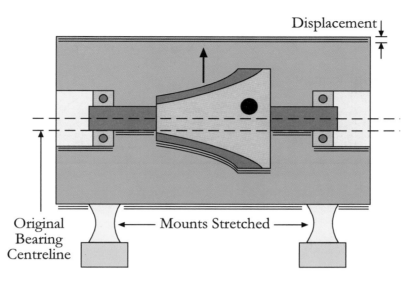

Figure 2.77 – Examples of Unbalanced Objects

When a mass is rotating on a circular path its velocity is tangential. There is also a centripetal acceleration towards the centre of rotation. A balanced rotor will rotate around an axis of rotation. This is the centre line of the bearings. An unbalanced rotor, however, will try to rotate about a different axis called the inertial axis. The forces created by an unbalanced rotor are centrifugal and these increase to the square of the rotor speed.

This means that at low rotational speeds the rotor turns around its bearing axis but as speed increases it tries to rotate around its inertial axis. This sets up harmonic motion where the forces now oscillate forcing the shaft against its bearings in a cyclic repetitive motion.

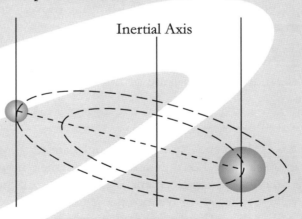

Figure 2.78 – Inertial Axis of Rotation

Unbalanced rotors will exert rotating forces on bearings and supports that transmit to other components. An unbalanced rotating mass moving upwards will apply an upwards-bending force on its shaft, which will change with time as the mass rotates over the top of its circular path.

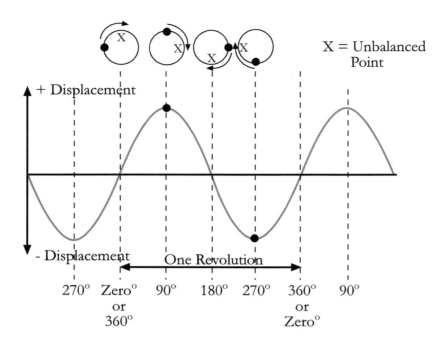

Figure 2.79 – Displacement of Unbalanced Shaft

As the mass then moves downward the force will reverse, exerting a downwards-bending force on the shaft again changing with time. One complete revolution will produce one complete oscillation or vibration and the speed of the shaft will determine the frequency. The velocity, displacement and acceleration of the unbalanced mass are changing during a 360° rotation.

In this context:

- Displacement - is the amount of housing movement resulting from the mass rotating about its axis

- Velocity - is the rate of change of the displacement

- Acceleration - is a measure of how fast velocity is changing with time

You should now be able to see that a rotating unbalanced rotor will alternately displace its bearing support housing upwards and then downwards in one revolution. The amount of displacement or amplitude of the vibration will depend on the value of the out of balance mass, the speed of rotation and the spring constant of the shaft. Displacement downwards is generally the same as the upward displacement.

Using the fact that a single point unbalanced shaft vibrates at one cycle per revolution it is possible to detect the frequency of vibration and its amplitude and then identify the shaft causing it. Vibration sensors use the inertia of a seismic mass to transfer the vibration into a crystal. The *Piezo-Electric Principle* shows that when a crystal is deformed it will give an electrical output.

www.part66.co.uk

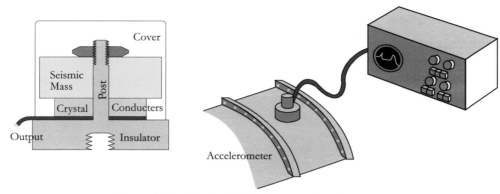

Figure 2.80 – Typical Vibration sensing Accelerometer

When these sensors are placed on the casing of a gas turbine engine, for example, they immediately detect any vibration present, emitting an alternating milliamp current whose frequency matches that of the vibration. The value of the milliamperage gives an indication of the amplitude of the vibration.

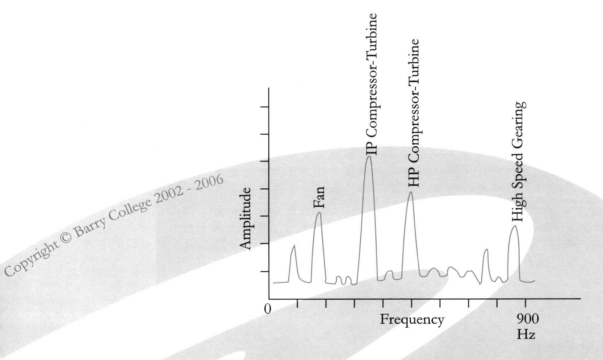

Figure 2.81 – Surveying Vibration Sources

Vibration

Vibration is described as the physical and alternating displacement of a body about its rest position. It is caused by disturbing forces. The parameters of vibration are its displacement, velocity, acceleration and frequency.

Displacement

This is the total distance travelled by the vibrating body from one peak to rest. It is the amplitude of the periodic movement.

Velocity

The velocity of a vibrating body reaches zero at each displacement peak. It reaches a maximum value as it passes through its natural rest position.

Acceleration

The vibrating body changes its velocity from zero at a displacement peak position to maximum velocity through the rest position. The change of velocity over time or, the rate of change of velocity, is the acceleration.

Frequency

The number of complete cycles in one second is the frequency and is measured in Hertz (Hz).

Natural Vibration

When a body oscillates under the action of its own gravitational or elastic forces with no external forces being present it is described as having a free or natural vibration. The pendulum and spring may be set into oscillation by external forces; but the subsequent oscillations are caused by their internal forces only.

Resonant Frequency

Many objects, because of their shape and material, have a natural vibration frequency, which occurs if the object is struck. This natural frequency is the resonant frequency of the object.

Forced Vibration

If an external disturbing force is continuously applied to a body it will continue to vibrate until the forces are removed. This is forced vibration. If a tuning fork is struck it will vibrate at its resonant frequency. If its stem is then pressed onto a tabletop, for example, the tabletop will be forced to vibrate at the same frequency.

Resonance

When a body is subjected to forced vibration it will vibrate with the frequency of the disturbing forces. The amplitude set up will be proportional to the disturbing forces. If, however, the forced vibration frequency matches the resonant frequency of the body the amplitude will increase dramatically.

This is due to the fact that the natural frequency of the body would try to damp out the amplitude of other frequencies but cannot damp out its own natural frequency. The two amplitudes combine to produce resonance. When a forced vibration matches the resonant frequency of a body and the amplitude rises sharply, resonance is said to be occurring.

Transient Vibration

When an object is struck and vibrates at its resonant frequency the vibration will slowly die away. This is known as transient vibration.

Effects of Forced Vibration and Resonance

The cyclic or periodic nature of the forces produced by vibration stemming from unbalanced rotors, transmit through the bearing housings into the supporting structure. These forces also cause elastic deformation of rotating shafts. If resonance occurs the effects are sharply amplified. The effects are found in the increased rates of wear and accelerated fatigue damage.

Velocity Ratio, Mechanical Advantage and Efficiency

Machines utilise some form of motion to convert an applied force into a useful work output. There are a number of devices in everyday use that fall under the description of a machine. Levers, inclined planes, block and tackle, screw jacks, winches, gearwheels to name but a few. Each of these converts an input force into a useful output force. The input force is often amplified many times by the machine so that we can overcome a heavy load with little effort.

www.part66.co.uk

The term Velocity Ratio describes the ratio of the distance the effort is required to move in comparison with the distance the load moves in the same time.

The term Mechanical Advantage describes the ratio of load moved with the effort required to move it.

Some machines are better than others at converting effort into moving loads. Friction and slippage can detract from the efficiency of a machine. A rusty car jack will have a low mechanical advantage because much of the effort would be used to overcome the friction of a corroded screw thread.

If the rope on a winch was slipping the effort would have to move a lot further than necessary and the velocity ratio would be too high.

We use the term Efficiency to describe the ratio of the useful work done by a machine to the total work put into it. This will never reach 100%. Even the best of machines will have some friction requiring extra effort to overcome it.

Velocity Ratio

The ratio of the distance moved by the effort to the distance moved by the load in the same time.

$$\text{Velocity Ratio} = \frac{\text{Distance moved by effort}}{\text{Distance moved by load}}$$

Mechanical Advantage

The ratio of the load to the effort

$$\text{Mechanical Advantage} = \frac{\text{Load}}{\text{Effort}}$$

Efficiency

The ratio of the useful work done by the machine to the total work put into the machine.

$$\text{Efficiency} = \frac{\text{Work output}}{\text{Work input}} \times 100\% \quad \text{or:} \quad \frac{\text{Mechanical advantage}}{\text{Velocity Ratio}} \times 100\%$$

With the three ratios in mind it will be useful to now look at some common examples of machines.

Lever

The description lever can be applied to any device that pivots on a fulcrum and uses the principle of moments. A force is applied at one end of the lever and produces a force at the other end. Levers include devices such as pliers and wheelbarrows. The crowbar is a very simple example of a lever.

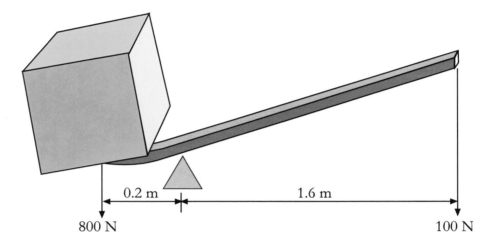

Figure 2.82 – Mechanical Advantage of a Lever

Using the Principle of Moments:

800N x 0.2m = 100N x 1.6m

If you transpose this you can get: $\dfrac{800N}{100N} = \dfrac{1.6m}{0.2m}$

Mechanical Advantage $= \dfrac{Load}{Effort} = \dfrac{800N}{100N} = 8$

When dealing with a lever you could also have used the moment arm of the load from the fulcrum divided by the moment arm of the effort from the fulcrum. Do be careful how you measure the moment arms. See note below.

Important Note:

Examine how the moment arms have been measured in the illustration. When a force is applied at any angle other than a right angle to a lever, the moment arm cannot be taken as the actual length of the lever from the fulcrum. The moment arm has to be measured from the fulcrum to a point, which is at right angles to the line of action of the force.

Put simply, *the moment arm is the shortest distance between the line of action of the force and the fulcrum.*

Pulleys

A pulley wheel has a circumferential groove to accept a rope. Pulley wheels can be set up in a number of different arrangements ranging from a single pulley wheel to a number of wheels mounted in a block.

The effort is applied by pulling on a rope. The tension created in the rope and the movement are transmitted through the arrangement to the load. The single fixed pulley is a convenient means of lifting a light load. The tension force in the rope is the same on both sides of the pulley.

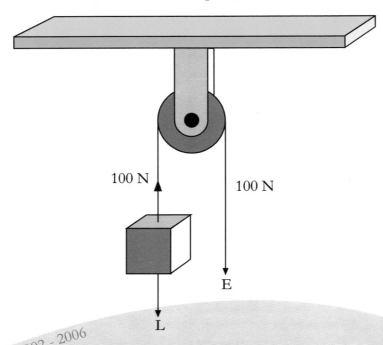

Figure 2.83 – Single Fixed Pulley

The problem is the forces act in opposite directions on each side. If you assume that there are no frictional forces to overcome, the effort you apply will exactly equal the load you can lift. In addition, the distance moved by the effort will be the same as the distance moved by the load.

$$\text{Mechanical advantage} = \frac{\text{Load}}{\text{Effort}} = \frac{100\text{N}}{100\text{N}} = 1$$

As the distance moved by the effort is the same as the distance moved by the load, the Velocity Ratio would also be 1.

A different arrangement can be made using a single moving pulley. In this arrangement the tension in the rope will again be the same on both sides of the pulley. This time, however, both the tension forces act upwards giving you a total upward pull of twice the effort you apply.

If a load of 40N is suspended from the pulley then the effort to hold it will be only 20N. Look at the two upward arrows each side of the pulley. They combine to give you a 40N pull.

$$\text{Mechanical Advantage} = \frac{40}{20} = 2$$

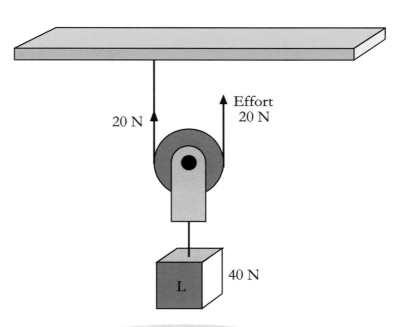

Figure 2.84 – Single Moving Pulley

The distance moved by the effort will be the same as the distance moved by the load so the Velocity Ratio will only be 1.

In all diagrams of pulley arrangements, consideration must be given to the direction in which the force arrows are drawn on the ropes. If you examine a diagram of a person holding a mass suspended on a string the arrow pointing upwards represents a force that the string exerts on the mass while an arrow pointing downwards represents a load exerted by the string on the hand.

Block and Tackle

In this arrangement you will see that there are four ropes pulling up on the lower pulley block and the load. The tension in each rope is the same as the effort so the total upward force will be four times the effort.

Do note that the total upward pull has to support the load and the weight of the lower pulley block and ropes. The ropes would need to act vertically to these loads to achieve the full upward pull. Frictional forces in the pulley bearings also have to be overcome as well.

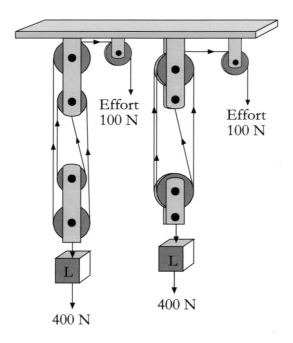

Figure 2.85 – Simple Block and Tackle

Note that the number of ropes supporting the lower block equals the total number of pulleys in the whole arrangement. If you were to apply a 100N effort the four ropes would each have a 100N tension force acting upwards. This would produce a 400N total upward pull. Also, if you pulled the effort through say one metre this would pull a metre of rope out of the arrangement. This would shorten each of the four ropes by one quarter of a metre and lift the load one quarter of a metre. The Velocity Ratio is thus 4 and the Mechanical Advantage is also 4.

$$\text{Mechanical advantage} = \frac{\text{Load}}{\text{Effort}} = \frac{400\text{N}}{100\text{N}} = 4$$

Note: Load value includes weight of lower pulley block.

$$\text{Velocity Ratio} = \frac{\text{Distance moved by effort}}{\text{Distance moved by load}} = \frac{1\text{m}}{0.25\text{m}} = 4$$

Velocity Ratio

The Velocity Ratio (VR) is the speed ratio of a machine. In machines where the mechanical advantage is greater than one, we would be able to lift a much greater load than the effort required to put in. The price we would have to pay for this advantage is that our effort will have to move over a much greater distance than that moved by the load. A car jack is a perfect example of this where many turns on the jack result in a small movement of the car.

Conversely, if you examine a bicycle, which has a mechanical advantage of less than one, one revolution of the pedal crank, *the effort*, results in several turns of the rear wheel, *the load*.

In the illustration shown in figure 2.85, you should notice that to raise the load by ¼ metre each supporting rope has to be shortened by ¼ metre. This means that the effort has to move through 1 metre to achieve this.

$$\text{Velocity Ratio} = \frac{\text{Distance moved by Effort}}{\text{Distance moved by the Load in the same time}}$$

Efficiency

If we consider that work is force × distance and apply that to the examples above, we will see that theoretically the work put in, effort × distance, will equal the work done, load x distance. In practice, the two never balance as work from the effort is also used to overcome friction and slip in the machine, which amounts to wasted work. A rusty car jack requires a great deal more effort to move the same load as a well-oiled car jack. In this case, a lot of effort is expended in overcoming the friction of the seized parts creating heat as lost energy, which is not transferred to the load. In practice, the work done by a machine is always less than the work done by the effort put into it.

The efficiency of a machine is the ratio of the useful work done by the machine to the total work put into the machine.

$$\text{Efficiency} = \frac{\text{Work Output}}{\text{Work Input}} \times 100$$

Relationship between Mechanical Advantage, Velocity Ratio and Efficiency

Since work = force × distance then the following statement is also true:

$$\text{Efficiency} = \frac{\text{Load}}{\text{Effort}} \times \frac{\text{Distance Load moves}}{\text{Distance Effort moves}}$$

$$\therefore \text{Efficiency} = \text{Mechanical Advantage} \times \frac{1}{\text{Velocity Ratio}}$$

$$= \frac{\text{Mechanical Advantage}}{\text{Velocity Ratio}} \times 100\%$$

This equation is useful in solving problems but should not be used as a definition of efficiency.

The Inclined Plane

The Egyptians discovered that heavy blocks of stone could be raised more easily if they were pulled up over a sloping surface than if they were just lifted vertically.

The addition of rollers under the load reduced the frictional losses and improved the efficiency of this simple device. If you examine this illustration you will see that the effort has to be exerted over a much longer distance, equal to the length of the inclined plane, than the vertical distance moved by the load.

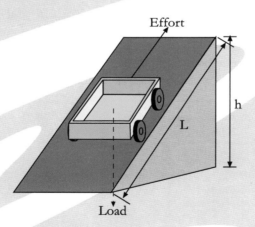

Figure 2.86 – An Inclined Plane

Note that the load acts vertically downwards all the time. In this case, the velocity ratio is:

www.part66.co.uk

$$\text{Velocity Ratio} = \frac{\text{Distance moved by effort}}{\text{Distance moved by load}} = \frac{L}{h}$$

The mechanical advantage of the inclined plane can be obtained by using the principle of work. Neglecting the work done against friction, for a perfect plane:

$$\text{Load} \times \text{Distance} = \text{Effort} \times \text{Distance}$$

$$\therefore \text{Mechanical Advantage} = \frac{\text{Load}}{\text{Effort}} = \frac{\text{Distance Effort moves}}{\text{Distance Load moves}} = \frac{L}{h}$$

The Screw

The distance between the crests of the threads of a screw is called the *Pitch* and one revolution of the screw will move it a distance equal to the pitch. If a nut mounted on the screw is turned through one revolution, it will advance a distance equal to the pitch.

The car jack is again a good example of a machine based on the screw. As the screw is turned with the aid of a handle, an extension mounted on the nut raises the car vertically.

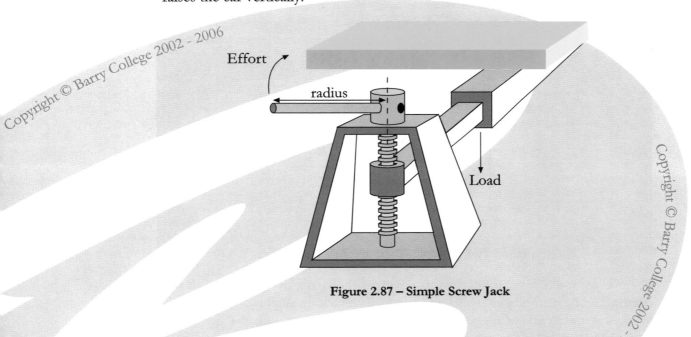

Figure 2.87 – Simple Screw Jack

In this illustration, figure 2.87, ignoring friction, the effort required to raise the car is:

Work Done by Effort = Work done by Load

Effort **X** circumference of circle created by turning handle = Load x Screw Pitch

$$\therefore \text{Effort} = \frac{\text{Load x Screw Pitch}}{2\pi \times \text{Radius of Turning handle}}$$

Example

A screw jack lifts a load of 5kN. The screw pitch is 4mm and the length of the turning bar 0.3m.

$$\text{Effort} = \frac{\text{Load x Pitch}}{2\pi \times \text{radius}} = \frac{5000\text{N} \times 0.004\text{m}}{2\pi \times 0.3\text{m}} = \frac{20}{1.88} = 10.6\text{N}$$

Wheel and Axle

Taken together, a wheel and axle assembly is another machine that consists of a large diameter wheel with a grooved rim, which allows a rope to be passed over the wheel; applying a pull on this rope rotates the wheel.

The axle of the wheel has a small diameter and a rope wound around this is attached to the load, figure 2.88.

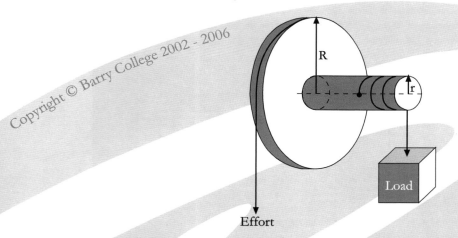

Figure 2.88 – Simple Wheel and Axle Assembly

For one complete revolution, the effort moves through a distance equal to the circumference of the large wheel and the load moves through a distance equal to the circumference of the axle; therefore, the velocity ratio can be calculated by:

$$\text{Velocity Ratio} = \frac{\text{Distance moved by effort}}{\text{Distance moved by load}} = \frac{2\pi \times \text{Radius of wheel (R)}}{2\pi \text{ Radius of axle (r)}} = \frac{\text{R}}{\text{r}}$$

www.part66.co.uk

To find the mechanical advantage of this arrangement:

Load x Radius of axle = Effort x Radius of wheel

$$\text{Mechanical Advantage} = \frac{\text{Load}}{\text{Effort}} = \frac{\text{Radius of wheel (R)}}{\text{Radius of axle (r)}} = \frac{R}{r}$$

So you can find the MA or VR of this arrangement simply by dividing the larger radius of the wheel by the smaller radius of the axle. Make sure you do use the radii and use the same units. The value of the MA in this instance would be hypothetical in that it ignores the effects of friction and wind resistance.

Windlass

This machine is similar to the wheel and axle. It consists of a drum around which a rope is wrapped with one end supporting the load. The drum is turned with a cranked turning handle, figure 2.89.

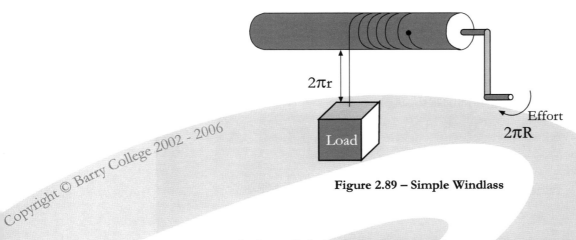

Figure 2.89 – Simple Windlass

In one revolution of the turning handle this type of winch lifts the load a distance equal to the circumference of the drum. The effort moves a distance equal to the circumference of the path of the turning handle. Once again you can establish the MA and VR by dividing the large radius of the turning handle by the smaller radius of the drum. The value of the MA in this instance would be hypothetical in that it ignores the effects of friction and wind resistance. There are a number of different examples of the wheel and axle arrangement. This is one of them. A steering wheel on a car is essentially the same.

www.part66.co.uk

Gears

We will examine a simple gear train containing two gears. One gear is the *Driver* and other is the *Driven*.

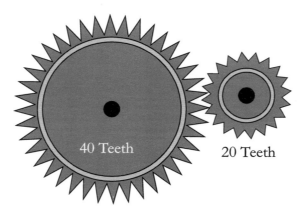

Figure 2.90– Typical Gear Arrangement

Which one is the driver depends on what you want from the system. If the small gear is the driver then you will get a large Mechanical Advantage and a large Velocity Ratio. The small gear will have to turn a number of times to turn the larger gear once.

On the other hand, if the large gear is the driver it will spin the smaller driven wheel a number of revolutions whilst it turns once. This will give a low Mechanical Advantage and Velocity Ratio.

A simple method is:

$$\text{Velocity Ratio} = \frac{\text{Number of teeth on Driven gear}}{\text{Number of teeth on Driver gear}}$$

The diameter of gear wheels is irrelevant. It is the number of teeth that are important. The reason for this is that the effort acts on the input shaft and the load is applied to the output shaft.

The Hydraulic Press

The simple *Hydraulic Press* consists of a load cylinder and piston of a large diameter, which is connected by pipeline to a smaller cylinder that is a force pump.

www.part66.co.uk

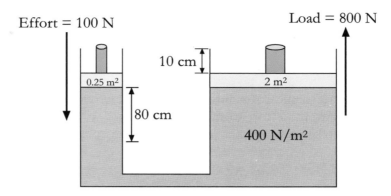

Figure 2.91 – Simple Hydraulic Press

Effort applied to the small piston in the force pump creates fluid pressure in the system, which is calculated by dividing the effort by the piston's cross-sectional area. This pressure is transmitted equally throughout the whole system, including the large piston area in the lift cylinder, which exerts a lifting force that is the product of the pressure and the piston's cross-sectional area. In this way, a small amount of effort can be used to lift a large load.

Worked Example

If the force pump has a piston area of 0.25m² and an effort of 100N is applied to it, a pressure of 400N/m² is created. If this pressure is applied to a lift piston having an area of 2m² then the lift force produced will be 800N.

The distance moved by the force pump piston is 0.8m. If we multiply this by the area of 0.25m² we will have established the volume of fluid transferred to the load cylinder. This volume will be sufficient to raise the load piston 0.1m.

$$\text{Mechanical Advantage} = \frac{\text{Load}}{\text{Effort}} = \frac{800N}{100N} = 8$$

$$\text{Velocity Ratio} = \frac{\text{Distance moved by effort}}{\text{Distance moved by load}} = \frac{0.8m}{0.1m} = 8$$

The same result could be obtained if we just divided the two piston areas:

$$\text{Velocity Ratio} = \frac{\text{Area of Load Piston}}{\text{Area of Effort Piston}} = \frac{2m^2}{0.25m^2} = 8$$

For simplicity we used a large area force piston. If the area were reduced to say 0.1m² the pressure would have been 1kN/m². This pressure acting on a 2m² area lift piston would have given a lift force of 2kN. For a 100N effort we would have got a 2000N output.

This would be a Mechanical Advantage of 200. These hydraulic machines are powerful but require the effort to move a long way. To lift an aircraft just a few inches would take many strokes of the jack handle.

Efficiency

We have discussed ways in which the work output from a machine can be far less than the work input. Friction will reduce the Mechanical Advantage whilst slip in the machine will increase the Velocity Ratio.

Now look at the following example.

Example

Let's examine the case of the screw jack in figure 2.87. If it only lifted a load of 4.5kN instead of 5kN for the same effort of 10.6N the Mechanical Advantage would be:

$$\text{Mechanical Advantage} = \frac{\text{Load}}{\text{Effort}} = \frac{4500N}{10.6N} = 424.5$$

If the velocity ratio is 470, the Efficiency will be:

$$\text{Efficiency} = \frac{MA}{VR} \times 100\% = \frac{424.5}{470} \times 100\% = 90\%$$

We could have arrived at this figure by:

$$\text{Efficiency} = \frac{\text{Load} \times \text{Distance moved}}{\text{Effort} \times \text{Distance moved}} \times 100\%$$

$$= \frac{4500N \times 0.004m}{10.6N \times 1.88m} \times 100\% = 90\%$$

Equally, the screw jack could have lifted the 5kN load at the expense of a greater effort. The result would be the same. Efficiency would be less than 100%.

182

www.part66.co.uk

Revision

Kinetics

Questions

1.   A vehicle travels 6km in 10 min. Its average speed is:

   A. 1 m/s

   B. 10 m/s

   C. 100 m/s

$$\frac{6000}{600} = 10 \, m/s$$

2.   A vehicle accelerates from rest to 84 m/s in 3 s. Its acceleration is:

   A. 28m/s^2

   B. 12 m/s^2

   C. 24 m/s^2

$$\frac{84}{3} = a$$

3.   An aircraft starts from rest at the end of a 3000m runway. It accelerates at a rate of 20 m/s^2. If the lift off speed is 200 m/sec, it will:

   A. Run off the end of the runway

   B. Lift off at the 1000m marker

   C. Lift off at the 2000m marker

$$v^2 - u^2 = 2as \qquad s = \frac{v^2 - u^2}{2a}$$

$$\frac{40000}{40}$$

4.   An object is dropped from an aircraft. It takes 12 sec to reach the ground. Assuming g = 10m/sec^2, the aircraft will be at an altitude of:

   A. 720 m

   B. 60 m

   C. 72 m

$$t = 12$$
$$g = 10$$
$$s = \frac{1}{2}gt^2$$

$$\frac{1440}{2} = 720$$

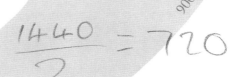

5. A man falls from a balloon 20m high into water. Assuming $g = 10m/s^2$, he will hit the water at:

   A. 200 m/s

   B. 160 m/s

   C. 20 m/s

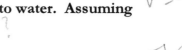

6. A velocity of 36km/hr is equivalent to:

   A. 600 m/s

   B. 0.16 m/s

   C. 10 m/s

7. An object moves in a radius of 5m at an angular velocity of 5 rad/s. Its linear velocity will be:

   A. 25 m/s

   B. 50 m/s

   C. 5 m/s

8. The centrifugal force acting on a fan blade depends on:

   A. The engine RPM only

   B. The engine RPM and the mass of the blade

   C. The engine RPM, the mass of the blade and its radius

9. Centripetal acceleration may be calculated using:

   A. mvr

   B. v^2 / r

   C. mr^2 / v

www.part66.co.uk

10. A ball is dropped from a height of 10m. The time taken to reach the ground is:

S10 *s = ½gt²*

A. 1.414 s

g10 *10*

B. 1 s

t ?

C. 2 s

11. A flywheel is rotating at 60 RPM, the angular velocity is:

A. 3 rad/s

$$\frac{2\pi \times 60}{60}$$

B. 1 rad/s

C. 6 rad/s

12. The centripetal force required to keep a 5Kg mass turning in a circular path 2m radius while moving at 10 m/s is:

A. 50N

B. 250N

C. 25N

13. A pendulum mass 2kg and 2m long swings with a period P. If its length is extended to 4m, the new period will be:

A. 2P

B. $P\sqrt{2}$

C. 4P

14. A pendulum in simple harmonic motion has a frequency of 4HZ. Its period will be:

A. ¼ s

B. 1/8 s

C. 1 s

15.   A weight on a spring is pulled down, stretching the spring, until it is 10cm from the floor. When released the weight rises to 24cm above the floor. The amplitude is:

A. 14 cm

B. 28 cm

C. 7 cm

16.   An aircraft of mass 1 tonne is accelerating at 10 m/s^2. The engines are giving a total thrust of 70kN. The drag force is:

A. 60 kN

B. 80 kN

C. 40 kN

17.   In periodic motion the periodic time T of a swinging pendulum is the time taken to :

A. Travel from the rest position to maximum displacement

B. Travel between the maximum displacement positions

C. Travel one complete to and fro movement

18.   In periodic motion, the amplitude of the swing of a pendulum is the distance:

A. Between the maximum displacement positions

B. Between the maximum displacement and rest positions

C. Of one complete to and fro movement

19.   Resonance is said to occur.

A. When a body oscillates at its own natural frequency

B. When a body is forced to vibrate by contact with another

C. When a body vibrates under elastic or restoring forces

www.part66.co.uk

20. **In simple harmonic motion:**

   A. Velocity reaches maximum value at maximum displacement

   B. Velocity remains constant

   C. Velocity reaches maximum value through the rest position

21. **Mechanical Advantage is:**

   A. Effort/Load

   B. Load/Effort

   C. Effort − Load/100

22. **Velocity Ratio is:**

   A. Distance moved by load/distance moved by effort

   B. Distance moved by effort/distance moved by load

   C. Distance moved by effort −distance moved by load/100

23. **Efficiency is:**

   A. MA / VR × 100

   B. VR / MA × 100

   C. MA − VR/100

24. **A winding drum has a crank handle of radius 33cm and a drum of diameter 22cm. The velocity ratio is:**

   A. 0.3

   B. 1.5

   C. 3

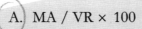

$$Vr = \frac{Effort}{Load}$$

$$\frac{33}{11} = 3$$

25. **A winding drum is used to lift a 48kgf load by application of a 20kgf effort. The crank handle is 33cm radius and the drum is 11cm radius. The efficiency of the windlass is:**

   A. 125%

   B. 80%

   C. 60%

$$E = \frac{MA}{Vr}$$

$$Ma = \frac{L}{E} = \frac{48}{20} = 2.4$$

$$\frac{2.4}{3} \times 100$$

$$Vr = \frac{33}{11}$$

187

Revision

Kinetics

Answers

1. **B** Speed = Dis/Time. 6000m/10min ×60 s = 10m/s

2   **A** a = (v-u)/t = (84m/s – 0)/3s = 28m^2

3. **B** t = (v-u)/a = (200m/s – 0)/20m^2 = 10 s

    s = ½ (v-u)t = ½ (200m/s + 0) × 10 s = 1000m

4. **A** s = ½ gt^2 = ½ × 10m/s^2 × 12 s × 12 s = 720m

5. **C** V = √2gs = √2 × 10 × 20 = √400 = 20m/s

6. **C** 36,000m/ 3,600s = 10m/s

7. **A** V = rω = 5m × 5rad/s = 25m/s

8. **C** F = Mv^2/r

9. **B** v^2/r

10. **A** S = ½ gt^2 t = √S/½g = √2 = 1.414 s

11. **C** 2π n = 2π × 60RPM/60 = 6rad/s

12. **B** F = mv^2/r = (5kg × 10^{2}m/s)/2m = 250

13. **B**

14. **A** Freq = 1/P   4Hz = 1/0.25 P = ¼ s

15. **C** 24cm – 10cm = 14cm. Therefore amplitude = 7cm

16. **A** F=Ma 1000N × 10m/s^2= 10,000N thrust required

    Drag = 70,000N – 10,000 N = 60,000N = 60kN

17. **C**

18. **B**

19. **A**

20. **C**

21. **B**

22. **B**

23. **A**

24. **C** VR = R/r = 33cm/11cm = 3

25. **B** MA = L/E = 48kgf/20kgf = 2.4   VR = R/r = 33cm/11cm =3

    Efficiency = MA/VR = 2.4/3 × 100 = 80%

Mechanics – Dynamics

Introduction

Dynamics is a branch of physical science and subdivision of mechanics that is concerned with the motion of material objects in relation to the physical factors that affect them. Such as, mass, force, inertia, work, power, energy, heat and efficiency.

Mass

The mass of a body is the quantity of matter that it contains, and its basic SI unit is the *kilogram (kg)*. The weight of a body is the force the body exerts on anything that supports it. As force is mass times acceleration (m × a), then the force exerted by the mass depends on acceleration due to gravity. On the Moon, where gravity is much less than on Earth, an object's mass would remain the same but the force that it would exert would be far less than on Earth.

Gravity is a weak force of attraction that occurs between two masses. It can be calculated by multiplying the two masses (m_1 and m_2) together, multiplying the result by the *Gravitational Constant (G)* and then dividing the product by the square of the distance (d) between the centres of the two masses;

$$\text{Gravitational Force} = \frac{m_1 m_2 G}{d^2}$$

Note: The gravitational constant is not the same as the acceleration due to gravity and has a value of 6.67×10^{-11} Nm^2/kg^2. You are not expected to remember this!

Putting this into words, the universal law of gravitation states:

The attraction between two particles of matter is directly proportional to the product of their masses and inversely proportional to the square of the distance between their centres.

The earth is not a perfect sphere, so the distance of any object on its surface from the centre will depend on where it is placed geographically. The globally accepted figure for the acceleration due to the Earth's gravity is 9.81m/s^2. Therefore, the weight of a body can be calculated by multiplying its mass in kilograms (kg) by the acceleration due to gravity, for example, 9.81m/s^2, to arrive at a value for its weight in Newtons (N).

If you intend a reader to know you are dealing with the weight of a body, the use of the unit kilograms-force (kgf) is acceptable but you must convert this to Newtons if you wish to define it as a force. To do this multiply it by 9.81 m/s^2

Example 1

A mass of 10kg resting on a table will exert a force of:

$$\text{Force} = \text{Mass} \times \text{Acceleration} = 10\text{kg} \times 9.81 \text{ m/s}^2 = 98.1\text{N}$$

Example 2

An object having a weight of 98.1N would have a mass of:

$$\text{Mass} = \frac{\text{Force}}{\text{Acceleration}} = \frac{98.1\text{N}}{9.81\text{m/s}^2} = 10\text{kg}$$

Note: In IR Part-66 examinations you can arrive at mental estimates by assuming the acceleration due to gravity to be 10m/s^2.

Force

We cannot describe a force as we can a material object as we can only say what a force can do, (push or pull). A force is a vector quantity that has magnitude, direction and a point of application. The correct definition is:

A force is that which changes a body's state of rest or of uniform motion in a straight line. When a force is applied to a body, it will also cause it to distort in the direction of the applied force.

We have already encountered many types of forces in this module. For example, centripetal, centrifugal, compressive, tensile and shear, and we have seen that they can all be represented by vector lines drawn to scale.

Newton's Laws of Motion

Newton's First Law

A body continues in its state of rest or of uniform motion in a straight line unless compelled by some external force to change that state.

A force may be described as any push or pull action that affects the state of a body as described above.

Newton's Second Law

The rate of change of momentum of a body is proportional to the applied force and takes place in the direction in which the force acts.

This describes the effect that a force will have on a body.

Newton's Third Law

To every action there is an equal and opposite reaction.

You will be familiar with this one. If you leant on a brick wall you would not expect to fall through it or, be thrown away from it. The wall reacts the force you are applying to it by pushing back on you with an equal and opposite force. As a force is the product of mass and acceleration, then there will always be a reaction to any force that causes a mass to accelerate. Imagine the recoil action of a gun as the mass of the bullet accelerates forward.

Inertia

Inertia is the tendency of a body to remain at rest or if moving, to continue its motion in a straight line. The more mass a body has, the greater its inertia and the greater the force needed to overcome it to either accelerate it and give it momentum, or to decelerate it and destroy its momentum. Therefore, Newton's Second Law applies and gives us:

$$\text{Force (N)} = \text{Mass (kg)} \times \text{Acceleration (m/s}^2\text{)}$$

Momentum

Momentum is a combined effect of inertia and velocity, or mass and velocity; the greater the mass, the greater the momentum and the greater the inertia. Momentum is a function of a body's mass and its velocity in a given direction. Momentum applies to objects moving at constant velocity and is a vector quantity and therefore:

$$\text{Momentum (kg m/s)} = \text{Mass (kg)} \times \text{Velocity (m/s)}$$

Acceleration Forces

If a force acts on a body of mass m for a time t and causes its velocity to increase in the direction of the force from initial velocity u to a final velocity v then we have a change of velocity with time which is the acceleration a in the force formula:

$$\text{Force (N)} = \text{Mass (kg)} \times \text{Acceleration (m/s}^2)$$

The SI unit of force is the Newton, which is the force required to give a mass of 1 kg an acceleration of 1m/s².

The most effective method of understanding the effect of Newton's laws is to study examples of the laws as they influence different situations.

Example 1

A mass of 10kg is subjected to a uniform accelerating force of 100N.

$$\text{Force} = \text{Mass} \times \text{Acceleration therefore: Acceleration} = \frac{\text{Force}}{\text{Mass}}$$

$$\text{Acceleration} = \frac{100\text{N}}{10\text{kg}} = 10\text{m/s}^2$$

Example 2

A mass of 100kg is subjected to a force that accelerates it to 0.5 m/s². Neglecting friction and air resistance the force would have been:

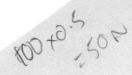

$$\text{Force} = \text{Mass} \times \text{Acceleration} = 100\text{kg} \times 0.5\text{m/s}^2 = 50\text{N}$$

Example 3

A body is subjected to a force of 100N that causes it to accelerate at 2m/s^2. Ignoring friction and air resistance the mass of the body would be:

$$\text{Mass} = \frac{\text{Force}}{\text{Acceleration}} = \frac{100\text{N}}{2\text{m/s}^2} = 50\text{kg}$$

Example 4

An aircraft mass 10 tonne starts its take-off run from rest. The engines give a constant thrust of 10kN. If the take-off velocity is 40 m/s, how much runway is needed?

We need to find the acceleration and the time.

$$\text{Acceleration} = \frac{\text{Force}}{\text{Mass}} = \frac{10000\text{N}}{10000\text{kg}} = 1\text{m/s}^2$$

$$\text{Time} = \left(\frac{v - u}{a}\right) = \frac{40\text{m/s} - 0\text{ m/s}}{1\text{ m/s}^2} = 40\text{s}$$

$$\text{Distance } S = \tfrac{1}{2}(u + v)\,t = \tfrac{1}{2} \times 40\text{ m/s} \times 40\text{s} = 800\text{m}$$

Note: You can now see how Newton's laws can be combined with velocity and acceleration in different situations.

Example 5

A 2 tonne light aircraft touches down at a velocity of 36km/hr on a level runway. It is slowed to a stop in 10s. Assuming the only retardation force to be the brakes, what was the braking force?

$$36 \text{ km/hr} = \frac{36 \text{km} \times 1000}{3600\text{s}} = 10 \text{ m/s}$$

$$\text{Deceleration} = \frac{v - u}{t} = \frac{0 \text{ m/s} - 10 \text{ m/s}}{10\text{s}} = -1 \text{ m/s}^2$$

$$\text{Retarding force} = 2000\text{kg} \times -1\text{m/s}^2 = -2\text{kN}$$

(This alone could be a JAR-66 question)

Example 6

A body of mass 10kg is moving in a straight line at a constant velocity of 10 m/s. Its momentum is:

$$\text{Momentum} = \text{Mass} \times \text{velocity} = 10\text{kg} \times 10 \text{ m/s} = 100\text{kg m/s}$$

These are questions easy to set in an IR Part-66 exam. It could have read:

A body travelling in a straight line at 10 m/s has a momentum of 100kg m/s. The mass of the body is:

$$\text{Mass} = \frac{\text{Momentum}}{\text{Velocity}} = \frac{100\text{kgm/s}}{10\text{m/s}} = 10 \text{ kg}$$

Motion in a Vertical Plane

We have only considered bodies accelerating horizontally up to now. If they accelerate or decelerate in a vertical plane, like in an elevator, we have to consider the reaction force exerted on the body by its support, like the floor of the elevator.

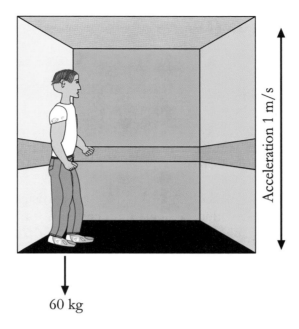

Figure 2.92 – Motion in Vertical Plane

The best way to learn this is to try a simple example:

You are standing in a lift. Your mass is 60kg. The lift accelerates upwards at 1m/s stops and then accelerates downwards at 1m/s. How much do you weigh on the upward trip and how much do you weigh on the downward trip?

Your normal weight $= 60\text{kg} \times 9.81\text{m/s}^2 = 588.6\text{N}$

Newton's Third Law says that you will exert 588.6N on the lift floor. The force accelerating you upwards at 1m/s^2 is: $60\text{kg} \times 1\text{m/s}^2 = 60\text{N}$

So, the floor had to exert an extra 60N on you to accelerate you up, so: your apparent weight when the lift is going up is: $588.6\text{N} + 60\text{N} = 648.6\text{N}$

The force accelerating you downwards is: $60\text{kg} \times 1\text{m/s}^2 = 60\text{N}$ (the same)

The downward acceleration force is taken off your weight, so:

Your apparent weight when the lift is going down is $588.6\text{N} - 60\text{N} = 528.6\text{N}$

Note: These apparent weight changes only occur during accelerations up or down. When the lift is travelling at a constant velocity your weight will be normal.

Now consider a situation where the lift accelerates uniformly downwards at 9.81m/s^2, which is the acceleration due to gravity. Can you see that there would be no reaction between the floor of the lift and your feet? You would be weightless! If the acceleration then increased you would be off the floor. Conversely, if the lift were to accelerate upwards at a uniform 9.81m/s, you would have doubled your weight.

Moment of Inertia (I)

When a mass like a flywheel is forced to rotate, its inertia has to be overcome. There will be a force resisting the flywheel's acceleration. To understand where this force originates, think of the flywheel as being made up of millions of particles, which it is of course. Now think that each particle has mass and is at a different radius from the centre of rotation. Each particle then exerts a moment of force, which is the product of its weight and its distance from the centre of the wheel. Not easy to work all those moments out!

What we do is consider that the total mass of all the particles is positioned at a given radius that would produce a single moment equal to the sum of all the particle moments. The radius used is called the *Radius of Gyration (k).*

Using this we can calculate the *Moment of Inertia (I)*, which is the product of the mass of the wheel and the square of the radius of gyration. The SI unit used to identify the moment of inertia is kgm^2.

$$Moment\ of\ Inertia\ (I) = Mass\ (kg) \times k^2\ (m)$$
$$or$$
$$I = mk^2$$

Example

A flywheel has a mass of 100 kg and a radius of gyration of 0.5m. Its moment of inertia is therefore:

$$I = mk^2 = 100 \times 0.5^2 = 25kgm^2$$

Torque

When you try to accelerate a flywheel you have to apply a force to overcome its inertia. The resisting force you are trying to overcome is called *torque*. This may be calculated by multiplying the moment of inertia by the angular acceleration of the wheel. The SI unit for torque is the Newton metre (Nm).

$$Torque\ (Nm) = Moment\ of\ Inertia\ (I) \times Angular\ Acceleration\ (\alpha)$$
$$or$$
$$T = I\alpha$$

www.part66.co.uk

Example

A flywheel has a mass of 100kg and a radius of gyration of 1m. What is the torque when the wheel is accelerated from rest to 20 rad/s in 10s?

$$I = mk^2 = 100kg \times 1m \times 1m = 100kgm^2$$

$$\alpha = \frac{\omega_2 - \omega_1}{time} = \frac{20 \ rad/s - 0 \ rad/s}{10s} = 2 \ rad/s^2$$

$$Torque = I\alpha = 100kgm^2 \times 2rad/s^2 = 200Nm$$

Work

Work is said to be "done" when a force is applied to a body and causes it to move any distance. If you were to push on a box lying on a concrete floor you would first have to overcome the resistance due to friction before it moved. You might just move the box a couple of feet or, you may push it all the way to the nearest railway station! The applied force will remain the same in both cases so we need a way to express the difference in distance moved. Well, you would have worked much harder in the second case. Work is the product of force and distance and the SI unit of work is the *Joule*.

$$Work \ (J) = Force \ (N) \times Distance \ (m)$$

One joule is the work done when a force of one (1) Newton is exerted through a distance of one (1) metre in the direction of the force.

Example 1

A wooden box is pushed for 10m across a level concrete floor with a horizontally applied force of 100N. The work done is:

$$Work = Force \times Distance = 100N \times 10m = 1 \ kilojoule \ (kJ)$$

Example 2

A crate is lifted vertically to a height of 10m off the floor. The tension force in the sling during the lift was 1kN. The work done during the lift was:

$$Work = Force \times Distance = 1000N \times 10m = 10kJ$$

Work done by an Inclined Force

We have already encountered the problem of resolving an inclined force into horizontal and vertical components, called the *Rectangular Resolution of a Force*. Using this, we can calculate the work done in a given direction.

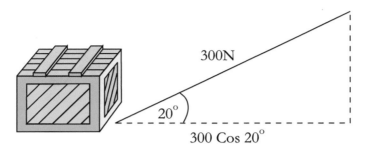

Figure 2.93 - Work done by an Inclined Force

A rope used to haul a crate 80m across a floor is inclined at 20° to the ground. The tension in the rope is 300N and therefore the work done in hauling the crate 80m is:

Horizontal component of 300N force = 300Cos20° = 282N

∴ Work = 282 x 80 = 22500J = 22.5kJ

Work done in Rotation

If you turn the handle of a car jack you will be doing work. The force you apply at right angles to the end of the turning handle; will be exerted by you over the circular path, traced by the handle as you turn it. The handle would in fact be the radius of the turning circle. The work will be the product of the force you apply and the circular distance your hand travels.

Example

You are turning the handle of a car jack by applying a force of 100N at right angles to the end of the handle. The length of the handle is 250mm. The work done by you in 10 revolutions of the jack will be:

Distance travelled = 2π x 0.25m x 10 revolutions = 15.7m

Work = 100N x 15.7m = 1.57kJ

Torque and Work

You can also determine the Torque (T) created by the jack's resistance to turning. One way to do this is to multiply the applied force of 100N by the length of the turning handle 0.25m. This will give you the turning moment, which in this case is the torque.

Torque (T) = Force (F) x Radius (r) = 100N x 0.25m = 25Nm

You can also calculate the Work done using the value of the Torque (T) multiplied by the Angular Distance (θ) travelled by the handle.

Example 1

Angular Distance θ travelled in 10 revolutions = 2π x 10
= 62.83 rad

Work = Torque(T) x Angular distance (θ)
Tθ = 25Nm x 62.83rad = 1.57kJ

Example 2

A pulley of 0.2m radius is being driven at 500RPM by a flexible belt that exerts a driving force of 1kN. Determine the work done in one minute.

Torque = 1000N x 0.2m = 200Nm
Angular distance travelled in one minute = 2π x 500 = 3141.6rad
Work = Tθ = 200Nm x 3141.6rad = 628.3kJ

Now we can use the other method:

Work = Force x Distance = 1000N x 2π x 0.2m x 500 = 628.3kJ

Do go and have a cup of tea!

Power

One drawback to just knowing the work done is that we do not know if it took all day or whether it was done in 5 minutes. We could dig over a garden in 6 months and still have done the same amount of work as if we did it all in one day. We therefore need to know the rate of doing work and that means relating work done to elapsed time. The unit of power is the *Watt (W)*, which is the equivalent of one (1) joule/second. Power may be calculated by:

$$Power = \frac{Force \times Distance}{Time}$$

The multiples of the Watt in the SI system are the same as for any other unit but it is sometimes useful, when dealing with particularly large numbers, to express power in *kilowatt-hours*. For your information 3.6 Mega Joules (MJ) is equivalent to one (1) kilowatt-hour (kWh).

Example

You push a box a distance of 5m across a level floor in 10s. The constant force applied is 100N. The power you use is:

$$Power = \frac{Force\ N \times Distance\ m}{Time\ s} = \frac{100N \times 5m}{10s} = 50W$$

Power in Rotation

If torque T is the turning moment in Nm and 'n' is the speed of rotation in revolutions/second then:

Work done/second (Power) = Torque (T) x Angular Speed (ω)

Power = T x $2\pi n$ Joules/second or Watts

$\therefore$ Power = ω T Watts

Example

A shoe brake is applied to the rim of a wheel 1metre diameter with a force of 100N. The wheel is spinning at 240RPM. What is the torque on the wheel and what power is absorbed by the brake?

$$\text{Torque} = Fr = 100N \times 0.5m = 50Nm$$

$$\text{Power} = \omega T = \left(\frac{2\pi \times 240rpm}{60 \text{ sec}}\right) rad/sec \times 50Nm = 1.26kW$$

Efficiency

In the real world, friction, air resistance, slip, leaks etc. all conspire to steal the hard work that you put into a machine. Consequently, the useful work the machine produces will be less than the work you put into it. Equally, the output power of the machine will be less than the input power. Electric motors will consume more power in Watts than the power they produce in Watts at their output shafts.

$$\text{Efficiency} = \frac{\text{Output Power}}{\text{Input Power}} \times 100\%$$

Example

An electric motor consumes 4kW of power and its output shaft produces 3kW of useful power. The efficiency of the motor

$$\text{Efficiency} = \frac{\text{Output Power}}{\text{Input Power}} \times 100\% = \frac{3kW}{4kW} \times 100\% = 75\%$$

Energy

Energy is the capacity to do work and is measured in Joules. Energy can appear in several guises. Mechanical, chemical, heat, electrical, and radiation are common forms of energy. In this section we are going to deal with Mechanical Energy. This form of energy appears in two form, *potential* and *kinetic energy*.

One important fact you must appreciate is that energy cannot be created from nothing and it cannot be made to disappear. It can only change from one form into other forms. Another important fact to remember is that energy cannot be converted into 100% work. A percentage of it will always appear in a less useful form such as wasted heat. But, work can be converted into 100% energy. There is no guarantee it will be in a useful form though.

201

Potential Energy

A body's *Potential Energy* is the energy it possesses by virtue of its position or state. For example, a mass raised to a height above the ground has potential energy since its weight is capable of doing work as it descends to the ground under the influence of gravity.

Another example of potential energy is found in a spring that is either compressed or extended. For example, energy is stored and has potential. A gas under pressure will also have stored potential energy, remove the cap of the container and we will soon have evidence of this.

Reservoirs contain potential energy due to their elevated position, the fluid they contain will move to a lower level, if allowed. Work can be done during this transfer. A body's potential energy can be calculated using the formula:

$$\text{Work (J)} = \text{Force (N)} \times \text{Distance (m)}$$

$$\text{Potential Energy} = \text{Mass (kg)} \times \text{g (9.81 m/s)} \times \text{Height above ground (h)}$$

Example

A crate having a mass of 100kg is suspended 10m above the ground. Its potential energy will be:

$$\text{Potential Energy} = \text{mgh} = 100\text{kg} \times 9.81 \text{ m/s}^2 \times 10\text{m} = 9.81\text{kJ}$$

Kinetic Energy

A body's *Kinetic Energy* is the energy it possesses by virtue of its motion. When a body is set in motion by a force doing work it acquires kinetic energy, which will do work against any forces that try to resist it. If a slate falls from a roof, it gains kinetic energy, which would be all too evident if someone were to get in its way. A body's kinetic energy can be calculated using the formula:

$$\text{Kinetic Energy} = \tfrac{1}{2}\,\text{mv}^2$$

Example

An aircraft with a mass of 10 tonne is flying at a constant velocity of 100m/s. Its kinetic energy will be:

$$\text{Kinetic Energy} = \tfrac{1}{2}\,\text{mv}^2 = 0.5 \times 10{,}000\text{kg} \times 100 \text{ m/s} \times 100 \text{ m/s} = 50\text{MJ}$$

Conservation of Energy

The principle of the *Conservation of Energy* states that:

Whenever energy is converted from one form to another, none of it is lost.

The sum of the energy can always be accounted for in other forms of energy that it may have converted into, such as heat, potential or kinetic energies.

A good example of this principle is the loose tile on the roof of a house. While in position it has potential energy due to its height above the ground. If it slips and falls, it will accelerate towards the ground under the force of gravity so gaining an increasing level of kinetic energy. As this happens, its height decreases so its potential energy is reducing.

If we examine this case carefully, we will see that the potential energy is converting fully into kinetic energy and that the kinetic energy possessed at the instant it strikes the ground will equal the potential energy it had on the roof.

Now you will ask, what happened to the energy after it hits the ground? The temperature of the tile will have increased. All the energy has converted into heat energy and this will dissipate into the air.

Example

A tile mass 1kg slips from a roof 10m high and falls to the ground. Determine the potential energy of the tile on the roof and the kinetic energy of the tile at the point of impact with the ground.

$$\text{Potential Energy} = mgh = 1kg \times 9.81m/s^2 \times 10m = 98J$$
$$\text{Velocity at impact: } v = \sqrt{2gs} = 14m/s$$
$$\text{Kinetic Energy at impact} = \tfrac{1}{2}mv^2 = 0.5 \times 1kg \times 14m/s \times 14m/s = 98J$$

Of course, 98J of heat will then dissipate into the air.

Energy and the Pendulum

The simple pendulum we are now familiar with is an example of potential energy converting to kinetic which then converts back to potential energy and so on. A reasonable question to ask from this is '*Why then do we not have perpetual motion?*'

The answer is that we do not live in a perfect world and the pendulum will be doing work against air resistance and friction if supported by a bearing. So where did this difference in energy go if energy is always conserved? Simply, it changes into heat, which is just another form of energy.

Heat Energy

Heat energy is energy that flows from a hot place to a cooler place. It cannot flow naturally the other way. Heat energy can transfer by any of three ways, conduction, convection and radiation. Heat energy can only be produced by conversion from another energy form.

The chemical energy in fuel is the predominant method employed to release heat energy. It can also be produced by work. Work put into a gas to compress it will raise its temperature as well as its potential energy. Do not confuse temperature with heat energy. Temperature is merely a measurement of the relative hotness or coldness of a body on a chosen scale.

Consider a machine where you put work (W) and heat energy (Q) into it. You could then say that you had raised the internal energy of the machine by a value (U). If the machine then does work, the internal energy level will fall as it converts into the work.

You can calculate the changes in a machine's internal energy level at any instant quite easily by adding or subtracting the energy being put in or the work and, maybe, waste heat leaving.

Example

During the compression stroke of a four-stroke piston engine the work done on the gas is 70 kJ/kg and the heat leaving the system is 40 kJ/kg. The change in internal energy would therefore be:

$$U = -Q + W = -40 + 70 = 30 kJ/kg$$

Note: Watch the positive and negative signs. This is a typical IR Part-66 question.

Calorific Value

Fuels used in aviation contain a considerable amount of heat energy. The calorific value of a fuel is the amount of heat energy that is contained in a unit mass of the fuel when it is completely burned. You will normally find the value quoted in *British Thermal Units (BTU)*. The *Calorie* is used to denote smaller quantities and the *Therm* is used to represent 100,000 BTU.

204

Mechanical Equivalent of Heat

The heat energy released by fuels has a mechanical work, or energy, equivalent. These are stated in both SI and Imperial units so we need to look at both.

One British Thermal Unit is equivalent to 778 ft lb of mechanical work. It is derived from the fact that it takes 778 ft lb of work to raise the temperature of one pound of water by one degree Fahrenheit. The British Thermal Unit is also equivalent to 1055.4J or, 1.0554kJ of work.

Another heat unit encountered is the *Centigrade (Celsius) Heat Unit (CHU)*. This unit is equivalent to 1400 ft lb of work required to raise the temperature of one pound of water by one degree Centigrade. In the SI system, one CHU is equivalent to 1.8BTU, which is approximately 1900J.

The Calorie is equivalent to 4.186J which is the heat required to raise the temperature of one gram of water by one degree Centigrade. The Therm is equivalent to 105.5MJ of work. One pound of aviation gas turbine fuel has a calorific value of approximately 18,500 BTU. As each BTU is equivalent to 1.0554kJ a pound of fuel is equivalent to 19.5MJ of work. One kilogram of fuel would equate 40,785 BTU, which is 43MJ of work.

Thermal Efficiency

Thermal Efficiency is the ratio of the useful work done by a machine to the heat energy put in to the machine. Using the mechanical equivalent of the heat units in the fuel we can calculate this efficiency. When considering a gas turbine engine the heat energy in the fuel that it consumes is used to drive the turbines and to produce useful thrust. We can only be concerned with the useful thrust in determining the thermal efficiency.

$$\text{Thermal Efficiency} = \frac{\text{Useful energy in a gas stream (J)}}{\text{Energy in fuel consumed (J)}} \times 100\%$$

The most efficient gas turbines in use today have thermal efficiencies of about 45%.

Momentum

A body's momentum is defined as the product of its mass and velocity and it has the SI unit *kg m/s*. When two bodies, one of low mass and the other of high mass, are acted upon by the same force for the same time, the low body mass will build up a higher velocity than the heavy mass.

Law of the Conservation of Momentum

When two or more bodies' act upon one another, their total momentum remains constant, provided no external forces are acting upon them. This can be explained by watching two bodies collide, for example, moving snooker balls; each ball has its own momentum before the collision. After the collision, the sum of the two balls' momentum will be the same as the sum prior to the collision even though their velocities may have changed.

Example 1

A ball mass 10kg travelling at 2m/s runs into another ball mass 5kg moving in the same direction at 1m/s. The two balls separate after impact with the first ball moving at 1m/s. The velocity, y, of the second ball after impact will be:

Sum of momentums of balls prior to impact = Sum of momentums after impact.

$$(10kg \times 2m/s) + (5kg \times 1m/s) = (10kg \times 1m/s) + (5kg \times ym/s)$$
$$25kg \, m/s = 10kg \, m/s + 5ykg \, m/s$$
$$y = \frac{25kg \, m/s - 10kg \, m/s}{5}$$
$$= 3m/s$$

Example 2

A car mass 2 tonne moving at a velocity of 4m/s has a head on collision with another car mass 3 tonne and moving at a velocity of 2m/s in the opposite direction. If the two cars lock together after impact they will move at a combined velocity of:

Momentum of 1st car – Momentum of 2nd car = Combined Momentum after impact.

$$(2t \times 4m/s) - (3t \times 2m/s) = 5t \times ym/s$$
$$y = \frac{2t \, m/s}{5t} = 0.4m/s$$

(The solution is positive therefore there is motion in the direction of the first car)

$$(2t \times 4m/s) - (3t \times 2m/s) = 5t \times y$$
$$2t \, m/s = 5ty$$
$$\frac{2}{5} = y = 0.4 \, m/s$$

www.part66.co.uk

Example 3

A field gun mass 100 tonne fires a shell mass 1 tonne with a velocity of 500m/s.

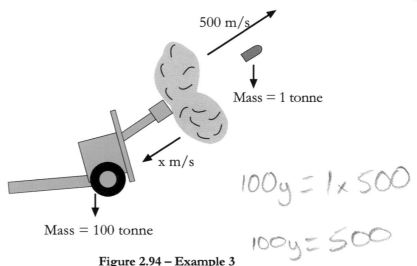

$100y = 1 \times 500$

$100y = 500$

$5_{m/s} = y$

Figure 2.94 – Example 3

The recoil velocity of the field gun will be:

Momentum of field gun = Momentum of shell

$$(100\text{tonne} \times y\text{m/s}) = (1\text{tonne} \times 500\text{m/s})$$
$$y = \frac{500}{100}$$
$$= 5\text{m/s}$$

You have to think about each situation. One thing to keep in mind is that the momentum of a bullet mass 0.2kg and travelling at a 1000m/s has the same momentum as a 200kg motorbike travelling at 1m/s.

Impulse

The term *Impulse* is used to describe the product of force and time. Impulse can also mean a change in momentum. For example, if we rest a hammer on top of the head of a nail, neither the hammer nor the nail has any momentum. However, if we bring the hammer down from a height to strike the nail sharply on its head, both the hammer and nail will move after impact. In a short time they will come to rest with the nail having penetrated whatever is under it, for example, a block of wood, figure 2.95.

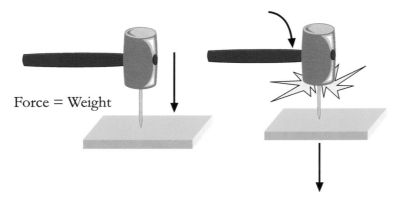

Figure 2.95 – Impulse

Impulse can be calculated using the formula:

Impulse (kg m/s) = Force (N) x Time (Seconds)

it can also be expressed as:

Impulse = Change in Momentum = Mass x Change in Velocity

Example 1

A hammer mass 5kg drops at a velocity of 10m/s and hits a nail. The hammer and nail come to rest in 0.2 of a second. The impulse and force on the nail were:

Impulse = Change in Momentum

Impulse = 5kg × (10m/s − 0m/s) = 50kgm/s

Impulse = Force × Time

$$\text{Force} = \frac{\text{Impulse}}{\text{Time}} = \frac{50\text{kgm/s}}{0.2\text{s}} = 250\text{N}$$

Also:

F = ma

where: $a = \dfrac{v - u}{t} = \dfrac{0 - 10}{0.2} = 50$

F = m × a

F = 5kg × 50 = 250N

www.part66.co.uk

Gyroscopic Principles

A gyroscope consists of a heavy metal rotor and shaft that rotate at high speed around a spin axis. The rotor assembly is mounted in a ring, which pivots inside another ring that pivots within a heavy fixed frame. This arrangement allows the rotor freedom to move about three axes each of which pass through the centre of gravity of the rotor and are perpendicular to each other. The three axes are: the spin axis AA, a horizontal axis BB and a vertical axis CC. The two rings that permit this freedom are called *Gimbals*.

Examine the illustration opposite. The spinning rotor has freedom to move independently around all three axes. It may *spin* about axis AA. It may *tilt* about axis BB. It may *veer* about axis CC.

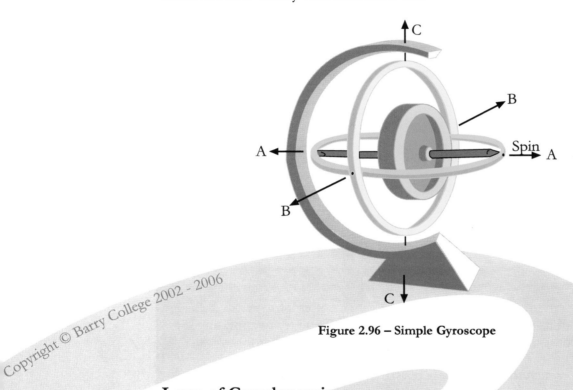

Figure 2.96 – Simple Gyroscope

Laws of Gyrodynamics

First Law

If a rotating body is mounted in such a way as to permit it to have complete freedom of movement about any axis passing through its centre of mass, then its spin axis will remain fixed in inertial space however much the frame may move.

To explain, if the gyro is a free gyro, that is, not constrained in any axis, then the spin axis will always point at a precise position in space. If you point the spin axis at any distant star it will remain pointing at that star and be oblivious to the fact that the earth may be rotating or that you may move the gyro to another geographic location. The gyro may as well be in space as it completely ignores the earth. For this reason, a *free gyro* is often referred to as a *space gyro*. If you deliberately constrained the gyro by not permitting it to veer or tilt at all, it would become a *tied gyro* or *earth gyro* in which case, the spin axis would move with the frame.

Second Law

If a rotating body is mounted in such a way as to permit it to have freedom of movement about any axis passing through its centre of mass, then any force applied to the body which is at right angles to the plane of its rotation will transfer 90° around the body in the direction of rotation and cause the body to move in the direction of that force.

To explain, look at the illustration of the gyroscope, figure 2.97. If you were to apply a force to the rim of the rotor at right angles to its plane of rotation, the force would transfer to a position 90° around the rim in the direction of spin. The rotor would then try to tilt or veer in that direction. Instead of tilting or veering in the direction of the force you were applying it would move in a different direction. This movement is called *precession.*

Gyroscopic Properties

A spinning rotor has two important properties. *Rigidity* and *Precession*. You need to examine each of these in detail.

Rigidity

This is a property of a gyro that makes it resist any attempt to make it change the direction of its plane of rotation. For example, if you try to apply any force to make the rotor tilt or veer the rotor will attempt to resist that force.

The degree to which the rotor offers resistance depends on three things.

1.   The mass of the rotor.

2.   The angular speed of the rotor.

3.   The radius of gyration (k) of the rotor.

We will deal with each of these in turn.

Mass

Rigidity is proportional to the mass of the rotor at any given rotational speed. The greater the mass, the greater the resistance the rotor offers to a change in the direction of its plane of rotation. Rotors are usually constructed out of heavy metals such as brass to increase their rigidity.

www.part66.co.uk

Speed

Rigidity is proportional to the speed of the rotor. The higher the speed the greater the resistance offered for a given mass. Gyroscopes rotate at controlled speeds up to 20,000RPM to ensure their rigidity.

Radius of Gyration

Do you remember this? It is the radius, or moment arm, that the mass of the rotor is said to act over and produce torque. The bigger the radius of gyration is, the greater the rigidity of the rotor will be for a given rotational speed. If the rotor is dish shaped, so that the bulk of its mass is out near the rim, the radius of gyration will be large and the rigidity will be high.

Precession

Precession is angular change in direction of the plane of rotation of a gyro rotor whilst being influenced by an applied force.

Sperry's Rule

This rule predicts the direction of precession if you know the direction of rotation and direction of the disturbing force.

1. Follow the plane of the applied force onto the rim of the rotor.

2. Move the point of application of the force on the rotor rim 90° around the rim in the direction of rotation of the rotor.

3. Precession will occur in the direction of the force at this new point of application.

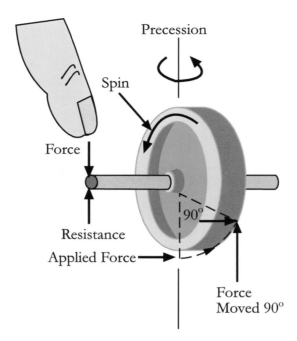

Figure 2.97 – Gyroscopic Precession

If you examine the illustration above, you will see that when a force is applied perpendicular to the spin axis in an attempt to tilt the plane of rotation. It is the same as if the force had been applied to the rim of the rotor. The force then transfers itself 90° around the rim of the rotor in the direction of its rotation causing the rotor to veer. Conversely, if you had applied a force in an attempt to veer the rotor it would tilt either up or down depending on which direction you had tried to veer it.

Precession will stop the instant the applied force is removed. If you continued to apply the force, however, precession would continue until the plane of rotation aligned itself with the force.

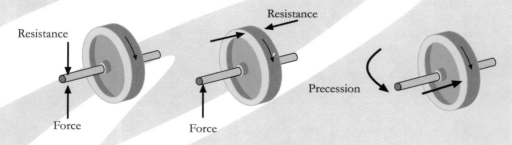

Figure 2.98– Second Law of Gyroscopic Dynamics

www.part66.co.uk

The rate, or speed, at which a gyro rotor precesses is dependent on three things:

1.   The value and direction of the applied force.

2.   The angular velocity of the rotor.

3.   The moment of inertia (I).

We will deal with each of these in turn:

Value and Direction of the Force

The rate of precession is proportional to the value of the applied force. Increase the force and the rate of precession increases and vice-versa. The rotor will precess in a direction in accordance with Sperry's Rule.

Angular Velocity

The rate of precession is inversely proportional to the angular speed of the rotor. The slower the rotor spins, the greater the rate of precession and vice-versa. This may surprise you but remember that as speed reduces, rigidity reduces also.

Moment of Inertia (I)

The rate of precession is inversely proportional to the moment of inertia.

Note: In IR Part-66 examinations, questions on the factors that influence rigidity and precession are frequently asked.

Apparent Drift

We are now going to observe the behaviour of free gyroscopes that are placed on the surface of the Earth. The gyros are free to move in the three axes of, spin, tilt and veer and are mounted in frictionless bearings.

To help you, this illustration shows examples of three gyroscopes numbered 1, 2 and 3, sat on the Earth and a fourth gyroscope that is moved from the South Pole to the North Pole.

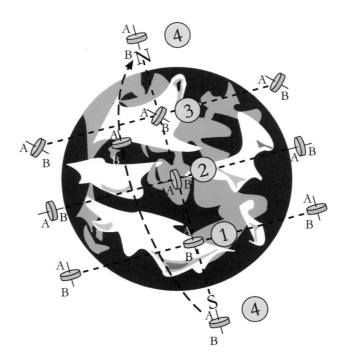

Figure 2.99 - Free Gyros as Observed from Earth

Gyroscope 1

If you locate this gyroscope on the illustration you will see that its spin axis AB is aligned exactly with the Earth's spin axis NS. As the Earth rotates at 15° every hour it will have rotated 90° in 6 hours and 180° in 12 hours. This will take the gyro from West to East. To an observer sat watching the gyro throughout this time it will not display any apparent movement in relation to the Earth's surface. The spin axis will always point to the same region in space and, as it is aligned with the Earth's axis, it will always appear to be in the same position.

Gyroscope 2

This gyroscope has its spin axis AB aligned at 90° to the Earth's spin axis NS. At the extreme West position, you would notice that the spin axis would be vertical with end A pointing upwards. 6 hours later, you would observe that the spin axis AB was horizontal to the Earth's surface.

The gyro spin axis would appear to have rotated 90°. It has not of course because it always points at the same region in space.

It is the Earth that has rotated, not the gyro spin axis. 6 more hours later, a total of 12 hours from start, the gyro will be at the extreme Eastern position. If you observe it, the spin axis will now be vertical to the Earth's surface again but, end B will now be pointing upwards.

www.part66.co.uk

24 hours from the start, the gyro will have returned to its original vertical position with end 'A' uppermost, having apparently rotated 360°.

The rotation of the spin axis at 15° per hour is called *Apparent Drift* and this illusion of movement is due to the Earth's rotation.

Gyroscope 3

This gyroscope has its spin axis AB tilted away from the Earth's spin axis NS. Study the illustration carefully and you should see that this gyroscope would also display *apparent drift* to an observer as the Earth rotates.

Gyroscope 4

Examine this gyroscope at the North and South Poles and see that its spin axis AB in each case is aligned exactly with the Earth's spin axis NS. As the Earth rotates, this gyro will not display any apparent movement of its spin axis.

Transport Wander

Now for something completely different! We are going to travel by air from the South Pole to the North Pole with gyroscope 4 mounted in an aircraft. The spin axis was vertical at the South Pole with end B uppermost. As we travel North the spin axis appears to rotate to the horizontal position in the aircraft by the time we reach the Equator.

It then appears to rotate back to the vertical position by the time we reach the North Pole, but with end 'A' now uppermost. End A is, of course, pointing at the same region in space as it did from the start. We simply transported it around a curved path.

This apparent rotation of the spin axis as we travelled, in this case, North is known as *Transport Wander* and is the result of transporting a free gyro over the Earth's surface.

Now look at gyroscope 2, it would also show transport wander if we moved it East or West. If we transported it North or South it would also be under the influence of the Earth's rotation during the journey and show apparent drift as well. Gyroscope 3 would also display transport wander if we transported it in any direction.

The only exception seems to be if we transported gyroscope 1 either due East or West with its spin axis AB aligned exactly with the Earth's spin axis. If you examine the illustrated gyros carefully, taking the Earth's rotation into consideration during any journey, you will see that all free gyros other than the exception given will suffer from transport wander when travelling on East or

West tracks and transport wander and apparent drift whilst travelling on North or South tracks. The latter courses cause a conical drift motion over 24 hours.

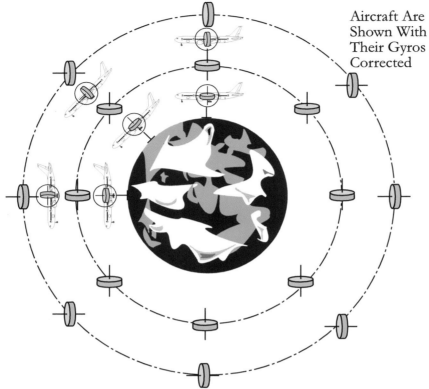

Aircraft Are Shown With Their Gyros Corrected

Figure 2.100 - Transport Wander

Real Drift

Apparent drift is a result of the Earth's rotation and transport wander results from changing a gyro's geographic location. These apparent movements are illusions as it is the frame of the gyro that is actually doing the moving not the spin axis. Some gyros do suffer another form of drift, which are real and where the spin axis does move.

Friction, wear, out of balance moments or stiffness in the gimbal or rotor bearings can cause the spin axis to drift. This form of drift is called *Real Drift* and its cause is mechanical. The only way to reduce this problem is to improve the mechanical construction of the gyroscope.

Earth (Tied) Gyroscopes

Gyroscopes can be converted into useful devices for indicating aircraft attitude and direction changes and also the magnitude of such changes and the rate or speed at which these take place. To achieve this the gyro spin axis has to be continuously corrected for apparent drift and transport wander. Once that is achieved, a gyro spin axis will remain in the same position relative to the aircraft until the aircraft itself changes its attitude or course.

Gyros that are corrected in this way are called *Earth* or *Tied* gyros as opposed to free or space gyros.

Gyros that give indications of the direction and magnitude of aircraft attitude or course changes are called *Displacement* Gyros. Those that give indication of the rate or speed of such changes are called *Rate Gyros*.

Displacement Gyro

Displacement gyros have two axes of freedom and use their rigidity to maintain the spin axis position during aircraft manoeuvres. Gimbals allow the gyro casing to move with the aircraft whilst the gyro spin axis remains fixed. The relative movement between the casing and the rotor is detected as aircraft movement.

Normally there are two instruments in an aircraft that use displacement gyroscopes.

The *Attitude Direction Indicator (ADI)* and the *Horizontal Situation Indicator (HSI)*.

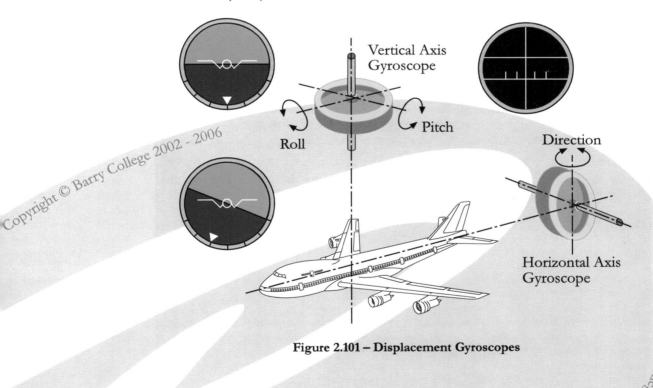

Figure 2.101 – Displacement Gyroscopes

Attitude Direction Indicator

This instrument used to be known as the artificial horizon and gives indications of *Pitch* and *Roll*.

Picture an Earth gyro mounted in an aircraft so that its spin axis is vertical in relation to the aircraft when it is straight and level.

The gyro frame will be securely fixed to the aircraft and the gimbal rings will permit relative movement between the gyro rotor and its frame.

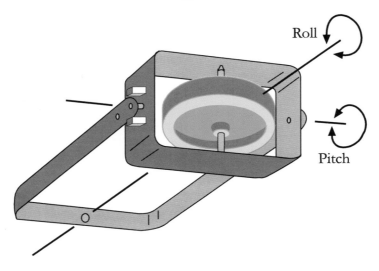

Figure 2.102 – Attitude Gyroscope

If the aircraft were to pitch or roll it would do so relative to the gyro rotor. This would remain vertical with respect to the Earth's surface.

Horizontal Situation Indicator

This instrument is really a gyrocompass and gives an indication that the aircraft has yawed to port or starboard. Now picture a gyro mounted with its spin axis horizontal and aligned with the lateral axis of an aircraft flying straight and level. The frame is again fixed to the aircraft. The gimbal ring would permit the frame to rotate horizontally relative to the gyro rotor. If the aircraft were to yaw to port or starboard it would do so relative to the rotor. This would remain in its original plane of rotation.

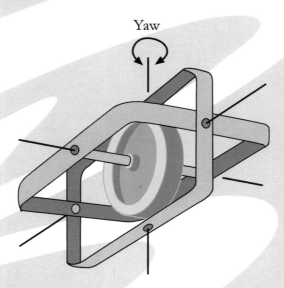

Figure 2.103 – Directional Gyroscope

www.part66.co.uk

Rate Gyro

Rate gyros are given one axis of freedom and use precession. The greater the precession the greater is the rate of aircraft movement in the direction being monitored by the instrument.

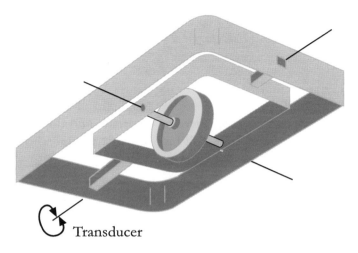

Transducer

Figure 2.104 – Rate Gyro

Rate gyros are used to indicate either roll, pitch or yaw rates. They can also be used to indicate aircraft turn and slip.

The precession of the gyro rotor is resisted by an electrical transducer that measures the precessionary force and converts the signal into an indication of rate of movement.

Friction

Friction is a force that resists any sliding movement between two contacting surfaces. It is a force that can be turned to our advantage, as we would notice when we apply the brakes on a vehicle or, try to walk on a smooth surface.

The force of friction can also be irritating when it reveals itself in seized machinery and worn out bearings.

Every type of surface generates different frictional forces. High friction material is used in brake pad manufacture and this generates a high retarding force when pressed into contact with smooth steel brake discs. When the pads wear out and steel contacts steel, we would notice a dramatic reduction in the frictional force. The material used on the soles of our shoes also reacts in contact with different surfaces to give varying frictional forces.

If you were to put a supposedly smooth surface under a microscope you would be surprised to see it looking like the mountains of the Moon. When this

219

surface is pressed into contact with another surface, the irregularities cause the two surfaces to lock up. The force required to overcome this and slide one surface over another is what determines the frictional force. You could, however reduce the force by separating the surfaces with a lubricant.

You may have noticed that it takes a greater force to start two surfaces sliding over each other than it takes to keep them sliding once they are moving. The former force is the *Static Frictional Force* and the latter is the *Dynamic Frictional Force*.

You may ascertain an idea of the frictional values between two given surfaces by obtaining the Coefficients of Static and Dynamic Friction. These are the ratios of the force pressing the surfaces into contact and the force required to slide them over each other. There will be one value to start them moving and another to keep them moving, the latter value being the lowest.

Limiting Friction

Imagine a block of wood placed on a horizontal surface. The weight of the block is acting straight down through its centre of gravity and on to the supporting surface. The surface reacts the weight of the block by pushing upwards with an equal and opposite force. The block is in equilibrium.

Imagine now that we exert a gradually increasing horizontal pull on the block. Initially the block will resist sliding as the horizontal force increased. This means that there must be an equal and opposite force opposing the horizontal pull force. This is the force of friction. It is increasing in line with the pull force and opposing it. It is, of course, a *Static Frictional Force*.

If we keep increasing the pull force, a point is reached where the block will just break free. The value of the pull force at which this occurs is called the Limiting Friction for the two surfaces at the block's weight. If we were to increase the weight of the block, the value of limiting friction would also increase.

If you examine the illustration, you will see that when no pull force was applied, the normal reaction force (N) to the block's weight is vertical. But, when the pull force (P) was applied, a resultant force (R) appeared. This is the resultant of the weight (W) of the block and frictional force (F). As the frictional force (F) increased in opposition to the pull force (P), the resultant (R) sloped rearwards. At the point the block broke free, the resultant (R) would have formed an angle θ with the vertical. The angle θ is called *Limiting Angle of Friction*. It is reached when the limiting friction value (F) is reached.

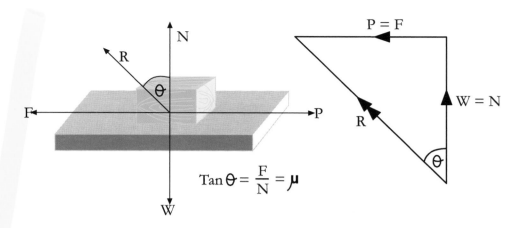

Figure 2.105 - Limiting Friction between Two Contacting Surfaces

If we divide the limiting static frictional force 'F' by the normal reaction force 'N', we will have the *Coefficient of Static Friction (μ)*, which is the tangent of the angle θ.

$$Tan\theta = \frac{F}{N} = \mu$$

Coefficient of Static Friction

Imagine that we now continue with our experiment. We will increase the weight of the block by placing a known weight on top of it. We then increase the horizontal pull force and record the value of the limiting friction. If we do this a number of times, increasing the weight of the block each time we will end up with a set of values that record each block weight against its limiting friction. If we now divide the limiting friction values by their corresponding block weights we will see that we get the same answer each time we do it. This constant value is the coefficient of Static Friction.

Note: That the actual area of the surfaces in contact is of no consequence in determining frictional forces).

$$\therefore \text{ Coefficient of Static Friction } (\mu) = \frac{\text{Friction Force (F)}}{\text{Normal Reaction (N)}}$$

$$\therefore \text{ Frictional Force } F = \mu N$$

Coefficient of Dynamic Friction

We have not finished yet! Continuing the experiment, we now measure the frictional force when the block is actually moving across the surface. This is the *Dynamic Frictional Force*. We will do this for each incremental increase in block weight. You would notice that the horizontal pull force required to keep the block moving was less than the force required to break it free, the limiting friction. If we now divide the friction force by the weight of the block for each incremental increase in weight we will find that another constant value emerges. This time we have found the *Coefficient of Dynamic Friction (μ)*. The value of dynamic coefficient is always smaller than the static coefficient.

Note that the area of surfaces in contact is not considered or, the speed at which the surfaces are sliding over each other. They do not affect the force of friction. The only time the sliding speed would matter is if the friction caused sufficient heat to alter the nature of the surfaces in contact. For example, if they became charred.

Angle of Friction

The angle (θ) that the resultant (R) makes with the normal reaction (N) is known as the *Angle of Friction*. The angle at the limit of static friction is larger than when the block is actually moving. This means that the resultant moves forward, reducing the angle as soon as the block slid. The tangents of each angle will be the same value as the respective coefficients.

Effect of Lubrication

Interposing a lubricant between solid surfaces keeps them out of direct contact with each other. Oils, of various kinds, are the best lubricants for lightly loaded surfaces but for heavy loads, greases of selected viscosity are used and these resist the tendency to be squeezed out. The selected lubricant depends on factors such as the pressure between the surfaces, the speed of the moving surfaces and heat generated.

For dry solid surfaces the frictional force:

1.   Depends on the nature of the surfaces in contact

2.   Is independent of the area of the surfaces in contact

3.   Is independent of the speed of sliding

Inclined Forces

If we were to incline the pulling force (P) with the horizontal, we would notice that the value of the limiting friction would reduce.

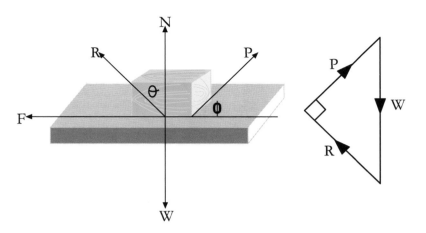

Figure 2.106 – Inclined Pulling Force

As we increase the inclination of force (P), the limiting friction will reduce to a minimum value.

When this happens, the limiting angle of friction will be the same value as the angle at which the pull force is inclined to the horizontal. Additionally, the angle between the resultant (R) and the pull force (P) will be a right angle.

Frictional Forces on Inclined Planes

If we now continue the experiment and incline the surface to an angle that still allows the block to remain stationary we will discover from an examination of the lines of action of the forces that:

1.   The component of the force of gravity acting down the plane and parallel to it is being opposed by the static frictional force acting up the plane and parallel to it

2.   The normal reaction is inclined upwards at right angles to the plane

3.   The lines of action of the four forces act through one point and are in equilibrium

4.   The weight of the block acts vertically downwards.

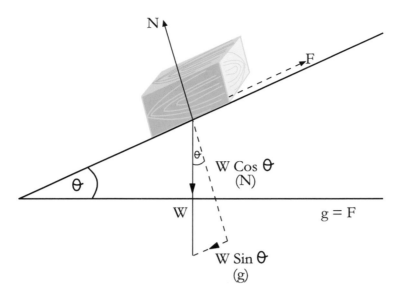

Figure 2.107 – Frictional Forces on Inclined Planes

If we examine the diagram of the inclined plane, we can deduce that the force of gravity 'g' acting to pull the block down the plane must equal the frictional force 'F' acting up the plane if the block is to remain stationary.

If we continue the experiment with the block by inclining the plane, gradually increasing the slope, a point will be reached where the block will just slip. This will occur when the angle of the plane equals the limiting angle of friction. As the block slides, the frictional force will reduce to the dynamic value so the block will continue sliding easily down the plane under the influence of the gravitational force.

Finally, if we increase the angle of the plane further and place the block on the plane and hold it stationary by a spring balance we can do two further checks. If we gradually release the holding pull exerted by the spring balance until the block just breaks free we can note the force reading at which this occurs. If we now pull the block up the plane at a constant speed using the spring balance, we can note the force required. On comparing the two readings we will see that the force required just to hold the block is much lower than the force required to pull it up the plane at constant speed.

The reasons for this are:

1.   With the block stationary, the sum of the force of friction and the pull force exerted by the spring balance is opposing the gravitational force

2.   When the block is pulled up the plane, the frictional force reverses direction and together with the force of gravity opposes the pull on the spring balance

www.part66.co.uk

To prove this, let us look at a worked example:

The block has a mass of 2½kg (24.525N), the plane is angled at 40°, the just holding force is 8N and the pull up force is 23N. Assume the coefficient of static friction between the surfaces is 0.4 and the coefficient of dynamic friction is 0.38.

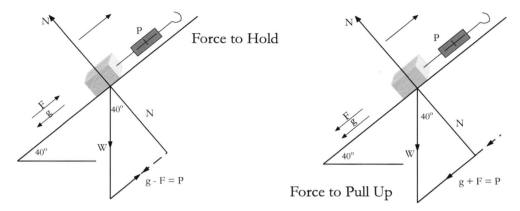

Figure 2.108 –Example of Forces on Inclined Plane

With reference to figure 2.108

Force of Gravity (g) = WSin40° = 25.525 x 0.643 = 15.77N

Normal Reaction (N) = WCos40° = 24.525 x 0.766 = 18.786N

Static Frictional Force just holding block (F) = μN = 0.4 x 18.786 = 7.5N

Dynamic Frictional Force is: F = μN = 0.38 x 18.786 = 7.138N

Therefore readings on spring balance are:

Force just to hold block = g - F (static) = 15.77 - 7.5 = 8N

Force to pull block up plane = g + F (dynamic) = 15.77 + 7.138 = 23N

In summary, the following statements are the basic laws of friction:

- The frictional force is always in such a direction as to oppose relative motion

- The force is always tangential to the surfaces in contact

- The frictional force is independent of the areas of the surfaces in contact

- The frictional force depends on the nature of the surfaces in contact

- Its limiting value is directly proportional to the normal reaction between the surfaces

The formulae you need to remember are:

Friction Force (F) = Coefficient of Friction (μ) × Normal Reaction (N)

$$F = \mu N$$

$$\text{By transposition: } \mu = \frac{F}{N}$$

$$\text{Also: } \mu = \tan\theta$$

Calculations

Example 1

A wooden crate weight 500N sits on a horizontal concrete floor. If the coefficient of static friction between the wood and the concrete is 0.5, what horizontal pull force is required to just move the box?

$$F = \mu N = 0.5 \times 500N = 250N$$

Example 2

A man weighs 800N. He intends to pull a wooden crate along a concrete floor. The coefficient of static friction between his shoes and the floor is 0.5 and the coefficient of static friction between the wood and the concrete is 0.25. What is the heaviest crate he can move?

μN (Man) = μN (Crate). To just move crate before he slips.

0.5 x 800N = 0.25 x N

N = 1600N

Example 3

A 500N crate is being pulled across a level concrete floor with a constant horizontal pull of 250N. What is the coefficient of dynamic friction between the wood and the concrete?

$$\mu = \frac{F}{N} = \frac{250N}{500N} = 0.5$$

These are examples of what can be asked that could be worked out without a calculator. Very few questions are actually in the form of calculations. For example, you could be questioned on the formulae, the relative values of the different coefficients.

Types of Friction

As already mentioned above, friction will depend on several factors and consequently there are many different types of friction.

Dry friction

A simple example of dry friction is that when dry, clean surfaces rub together their surface roughness causes a resistance to movement. Under a microscope, even polished surfaces display peaks and troughs. There is a tendency for each surface to shear the tips of the peaks of the other. Since it is only the peaks that are in contact, the area of true contact is very much less than the apparent area. At average loads, the area of true contact is proportional to the load applied and is almost independent of the apparent area. Therefore, the friction force is proportional to the load applied and the ratio of friction force to load is a constant.

However, for extreme loads, the proportional relationship starts to break down as true contact area may increase more rapidly. In addition, as the surfaces become worn, the value of the constant will change.

Dry friction can be reduced to some extent by making the surfaces smoother but only to a point. As the surfaces become smoother, the true area of contact increases and a problem of the attraction between the molecules of each surface develops, called *Cohesion*, which tends to bind the surfaces together.

The greater the area of true contact, the greater the cohesive force, which will lead to ultimate seizure. Two dry, highly polished metal surfaces will seize together rapidly under load, because of cohesive forces.

Fluid or Viscous Friction

If there is an excess of lubricant present between two solid surfaces, they may become separated by a film of fluid so that friction depends entirely on the fluid and not the nature of the two surfaces. The force required to produce motion will now be the force required to shear the fluid film. Fluid friction force increases with the velocity of sliding. As opposed to dry friction, fluid friction is proportional to the apparent area of contact. Fluid friction will only exist when there is motion, as the fluid will be squeezed out from between stationary surfaces when loads are applied. It is desirable that all surfaces running in contact have a film of lubricant between them.

Boundary Lubrication

Unless surfaces are specially cleaned, they will usually have a very thin greasy film that can prevent surface-to-surface contact. Cohesion takes place between the surface molecules and the weaker grease molecules and the coefficient of friction now depends on the nature of the grease and the surfaces, which will be a lower value than for dry friction. Under heavy loads or low sliding speeds, machinery that appears to be correctly lubricated may in fact be operating on boundary lubrication, which can break down allowing contact between high spots producing high temperatures that can lead to fusion of the surfaces.

Rolling Resistance

When a wheel rolls on flat surface there would be no frictional resistance as long as there was no slip between the wheel and the surface. If, however, the surface was being deformed by the weight of the wheel, and the wheel itself experienced some deformation, rolling resistance would be felt.

As the wheel advanced the deforming surface would ripple up in front of the wheel. This would produce a horizontal component of force, which would oppose the wheel.

The resistance cannot be reduced by lubrication, as there is no sliding motion. Rolling resistance is directly proportional to the load. The ratio of the rolling resistance force to the load between the surfaces is called the Coefficient of Rolling Resistance (μ). It is calculated in the same way as dry friction.

For example: $\mu = F/N$. This coefficient is much smaller than the coefficient of sliding friction. Because of this, designers would prefer to use roller and ball bearings rather than sliding surfaces.

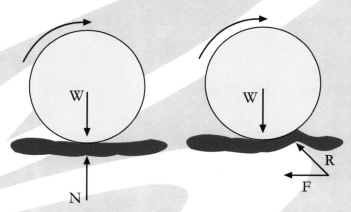

Figure 2.109 – Rolling Resistance

www.part66.co.uk

When determining the total rolling resistance of a wheel on a surface, the axle friction would be added. The value of the coefficient of rolling resistance would depend on the nature of the materials of the wheel and the surface. Hard materials would deform least and offer less resistance.

Another fact of the deformation of the rolling surface is that the surface is stretched. This means that the actual linear distance travelled by the wheel in one revolution could be shorter than the circumference of the wheel.

Rolling Friction during Take-Off and Landing of Aircraft

During take-off, the rolling resistance an aircraft experiences is small compared to the thrust of the engines and the aerodynamic drag forces. Rolling resistance will depend on the weight of the aircraft and the nature and texture of the tyres and runway surface. On landing, the retarding forces include the friction developed in the wheel brakes, the thrust reverse force, the aerodynamic drag and the rolling resistance.

Revision

Dynamics

Questions

1. A mass of one metric tonne is equivalent to:

    A. 500kg

    B. 1000kg

    C. 1200kg

2. A mass of one kilogram is equivalent to:

    A. 98.1N

    B. 981N

    C. 9.81N

3. A force of 100N applied to a mass of 50kg will accelerate it at:

    A. 2m/s²

    B. 0.5m/s²

    C. 5m/s²

4. A mass of 2Mg is accelerated at 5m/s². The force required was:

    A. 10mN

    B. 10kN

    C. 400N

5. A set of aircraft steps is pushed 20m across level ground with a force of 500N. If it takes 20s to complete the move, the power used was:

    A. 500W

    B. 200W

    C. 500J

$$s = 20$$
$$F = 500$$
$$t = 20$$
$$P = \frac{Fs}{t} = \frac{500 \times 20}{20}$$

6. An aircraft mass 100 tonne has a touch down velocity of 25m/s. Its kinetic energy at touch down will be:

    A. 31.25MJ

    B. 25MJ

    C. 2.5MJ

$$ke = \tfrac{1}{2}mv^2$$
$$100\,000 \times 62{,}500{,}000$$
$$31.250{,}000$$

7. An aircraft mass 10Mg is flying at 1000m. Its potential energy at this height will be approximately:

    A. 100GJ

    B. 10MJ

    C. 100MJ

$$P = hgm$$
$$1000 \times 10\,000\,000 \times 10 =$$
$$100{,}000{,}000{,}000$$
$$= 100\,MJ \qquad 1kg = 1J$$

8. A car mass 500kg is travelling at 10m/s. Its momentum is:

    A. 25,000kg m/s

    B. 5000kg m/s

    C. 50,000kg m/s

$$mom = mv$$
$$500 \times 10$$
$$5000{,}000$$

9. When two inelastic bodies collide:

    A. Neither momentum or kinetic energy are conserved

    B. Momentum is conserved but not kinetic energy

    C. Kinetic energy is conserved but not momentum

231

10. A truck mass 1 Mg travelling West at 50m/s collides head on with another truck mass 2Mg which is moving East at 10m/s. If the trucks stick together after collision, they will:

   A. Move West at 10m/s

   B. Move East at 10m/s

   C. Move West at 23m/s

11. A space vehicle total mass M moving with velocity v separates from its landing module. The mass m of the remainder of the space vehicle remains stationary. The landing module will travel on at a velocity v equal to:

   A. mv/M – m

   B. Mv/M – m

   C. Mv/M + m

12. An electric drill produces 3kW power when driving a drill. If the drill motor absorbs 4kW its efficiency will be:

   A. 25%

   B. 95%

   C. 75%

13. A flywheel mass 100kg has a radius of gyration of 100mm. The torque required to accelerate it at a rate of 0.2rad/s is:

   A. 0.2Nm

   B. 2Nm

   C. 4Nm

14. Impulse is the product of:

   A. Mass × Velocity

   B. Force × acceleration

   C. Force × time

15. A hammer mass 1kg is swung at 10m/s and hits a nail, coming to rest in 0.1s. The force on the nail will be:

   A. 100N

   B. 10N

   C. 1000N

$1 \times 10 = 10 \, kgm/s$

$F = \dfrac{10 \, kgm/s}{0.1} = 100N$

16. The Imperial energy equivalent of a British Thermal Unit is:

   A. 1055 ft lb

   B. 550 ft lb

   C. 778 ft lb

17. Precession in a gyro is:

   A. Proportional to speed and proportional to torque

   B. Inversely proportional to speed and proportional to torque

   C. Proportional to speed and torque

18. The apparent drift of a free gyro is caused by:

   A. Friction in the gimbal bearings

   B. Moving the gyros location

   C. The Earth's rotation

19. A gyro that is continuously corrected is known as a:

   A. Rate gyro

   B. Tied gyro

   C. Free gyro

20. **A gyro used to detect aircraft yaw would have its axis:**

    A. Mounted horizontally

    B. Mounted vertically

    C. Mounted either way

21. **A spinning free gyro that is left in one undisturbed position will appear to change its spin axis position by 90° in:**

    A. 12 hours

    B. 6 hours

    C. 3 hours

22. **When viewed looking down at the North Pole, the Earth rotates:**

    A. Clockwise around its NS spin axis at 15°/hr

    B. Anti-clockwise around its NS spin axis at 15°/hr

    C. Anti-clockwise around its EW spin axis at 10°/hr

23. **A rate gyro is constructed to be sensitive to:**

    A. Drift

    B. Angular velocity

    C. Precession

24. **Rolling resistance can be reduced by:**

    A. Lubrication

    B. Load reduction

    C. Slip

25. **The coefficient of dry sliding friction is:**

    A. A lower value than the dry static coefficient

    B. A higher value than the dry static coefficient

    C. The same as the dry static coefficient

www.part66.co.uk

Revision

Dynamics

Answers

1. **B**

2. **C**

3. **A**   F = Ma therefore: a = F/M = 100N/50kg = 2m/s²

4. **B**   F = Ma = 2000kg × 5m/s² = 10,000N = 10kN

5. **A**   Power = (F x d) /t = 500N × 20m/20s = 500W

6. **A**   KE = ½ mv² = ½ ×100t × 25m/s × 25m/s = 31.25MJ

7. **C**   PE = mgh = 10Mg × 9.81m/s² × 1000m = 100MJ

8. **B**   Mom'n = mass × velocity = 500kg ×10m/s = 5000kgm/s

9. **B**

10. **A**   (M1 × V1) − (M2 ×V2) = (Total M × v) = 10m/s West

11. **B**   Mv = (M − m)v therefore: v = Mv/M − m

12. **C**   Eff =OUTPUT/INPUT ×100. 3KW/4KW ×100 = 75%

13. **A**   I = mk² = 100kg × 0.01m² = 1kg/m². T = Iα = 0.2Nm

14. **C**

15. **A**   Impulse = Mass ×change in v = 1kg ×10m/s = 10kgm/s.

     Impulse = force ×time.

     Therefore force = impulse/time = 10kgm/s/0.1 = 100N

16. **C**

17. **B**

18. **C**

19. **B**

20. **A**

21. **B**

22. **B**

23. **C**

24. **B**

25. **A**

www.part66.co.uk

Mechanics-Fluid Dynamics

Density

Mass is defined as the quantity of matter contained in a body and is identified by the SI unit the kilogram (kg). Density identifies the mass of material that is contained in a given volume, that is kilograms per cubic metre (kg/m^3). If you divide the mass of a body by its volume you will determine its density. *The density of a material is defined as its mass per unit volume.*

$$\text{Density} = \frac{\text{Mass}}{\text{Volume}}$$

If you were to compare equal volumes of different materials you would find that their densities vary. The density of aluminium is $2700kg/m^3$, which is fairly low when compared with say, tungsten, which is $19300kg/m^3$. When you compare either of these with air at $1.225kg/m^3$ you can see that it could be useful to know the density of the material you are dealing with. In formulae, density is identified by the Greek letter rho(ρ).

Relative Density

When you are dealing with very high values for density it is sometimes easier to express them as a simpler number. We can do this by comparing the density of a given substance with the density of an equal volume of water. Fresh water has a convenient density of $1000kg/m^3$.

So, if you wish to express the density of Tungsten at $19300kg/m^3$ as a simpler figure you can divide it by the density of water at $1000kg/m^3$. This will give you a figure of 19.3. The figure is the *Relative Density* of tungsten and because it is a ratio, it has no units. Be careful, you cannot use relative density in calculations. You must multiply it by $1000kg/m^3$ to convert it into actual density. *The relative density of a material is the ratio of the mass of any volume of it, divided by the mass of an equal volume of pure water.*

$$\text{Relative Density} = \frac{\text{Mass of any volume of a substance}}{\text{Mass of equal volume of water}}$$

Specific Gravity

The mass of a body is directly proportional to its weight. A kilogram exerts a force due to gravity of 9.81N on this planet. So, we can determine relative density by using the ratio of the weight of a volume of substance to the weight of an equal volume of pure water.

$$\text{Relative Density} = \frac{\text{Weight of any volume of a substance}}{\text{Weight of equal volume of water}}$$

Because we can use the ratio of weights, the relative density can also be referred to as the **Specific Gravity (SG)**. However, relative density is the term most commonly accepted today. Do note that the relative density, and thus specific gravity, of fresh water is 1. You are expected to know this in exams. You would also have to remember that this represents 1000kg/m^3.

Be aware that you might be asked to convert relative density or specific gravity to a unit other than kg/m^3. An SG of 0.5 for example could be 0.5gm/cm^3.

Examples

1. Sea water has a mass of 1030kg/m^3. Its relative density is 1.03.

2. Lead has a mass of 11400kg/m^3. Its relative density is 11.4.

3. Gold has a relative density of 19.3. Its density is 19300kg/m^3.

4. Kerosene has a SG of 0.8. Its density is 800kg/m^3.

5. Mercury has a relative density of 13.6. Its density is 13.6gm/cm^3 or 13600kg/m^3.

Measurement of the Relative Density of a Solid

We can determine the relative density of a solid using *Archimede's Principle*.

This states that: *'When a body is wholly or partly immersed in a fluid it experiences an up-thrust equal to the weight of fluid displaced'*.

Weigh the solid in air and then weigh it again whilst it is immersed in fresh water. Subtract its weight in water from its weight in air to find its apparent loss of weight in water. If we now divide the weight of the solid in air by its apparent loss of weight in water we will have its relative density.

This method is based on the fact that an immersed solid displaces its own volume in water. The weight of this displaced volume of water equals the upthrust on the solid when it is immersed.

$$\text{Relative Density} = \frac{\text{Weight of solid in air}}{\text{Weight of an equal volume of water}}$$

or

$$\text{Relative Density} = \frac{\text{Weight of solid in air}}{\text{Apparent loss of weight of solid in water}}$$

Measurement of the Relative Density of a Liquid

If we have a liquid of unknown density we can determine its relative density and from this its real density. Take a solid of known weight and weigh it whilst it is first immersed in the liquid and then again whilst it is immersed in fresh water. We can then determine the loss of weight of the solid in the liquid and the loss of its weight in fresh water. We can find the relative density by dividing the two as follows:

$$\text{Relative Density} = \frac{\text{Apparent loss of weight of solid in liquid}}{\text{Apparent loss of weight of solid in water}}$$

Measurement of the Relative Density of a Floating Solid

Attach the solid to a light cord and hang a sinker from the end of the cord.

Step 1 Immerse the sinker into water and record the combined weight of the immersed sinker with the solid still suspended in air.

Step 2 Fully immerse the solid with the sinker still attached and again record the combined weight. The difference in weight between step one and two is the upthrust on the solid and thus the weight of the volume of water it displaced.

Step 3 Weigh the solid in air and divide this by the weight of the volume of water displaced.

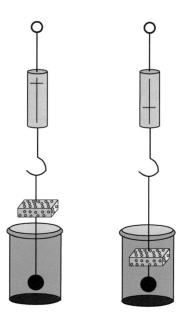

Figure 2.110 –Finding the Relative Density of a Floating Solid

Measurement of the Relative Density of a Powder

This is best achieved using a density bottle, which must first be weighed empty. It is then weighed again while filled to about one third with the test powder. Subtracting the two readings gives the weight of the powder.

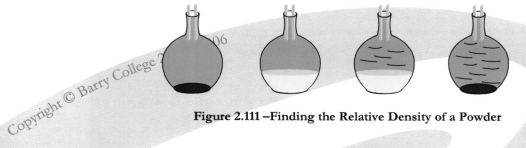

Figure 2.111 –Finding the Relative Density of a Powder

We now fill the bottle containing the powder with water and weigh it again. Finally, the bottle is emptied and cleaned out, filled with water and weighed again. Subtracting the weight of the empty bottle from the weight of the bottle filled with water gives the weight of water. If we now subtract the weight of the bottle that is part filled with the powder from the weight of the bottle filled with powder and water, we will get the weight of water displaced.

For example,

$$\text{Relative Density} = \frac{\text{Mass of any volume of powder}}{\text{Mass of equal volume of water displaced}}$$

www.part66.co.uk

Density of Air

The density of the air we breathe at sea level is 1.225kg/m³ when the air temperature is 15°C and the air pressure is 101.3kPa.

Then why does the air density reduce as we leave the ground? To understand this, imagine a column of air with a cross-section one-metre square rising from the ground to the edge of space. That's a lot of air and it is under the influence of Earth's gravity. If you tried to balance a column of bricks on your head you could not fail to notice the pressure they exerted on you. The pressure between the top two bricks, however, would be small compared to that between the bottom two bricks. Air is no different apart from one aspect. It can be compressed!

Imagine our column of air divided up into blocks, each a cubic metre in volume. There would be a lot more air in the cubic metre at the bottom of the column than in the one at the top. Hence the density of air reduces as altitude increases. At 18000ft the density is about a half its sea level value. At 33000ft it halves again and halves again at around 48000ft.

Imagine that the bottom cubic metre in the column is warmed by the earth's surface. Once its temperature has stabilised it will pass some of its heat up to the next block and, in turn, to the next and so on. Heat passes up the column in a gradually reducing quantity. The temperature of the air reduces at 1.98°C per thousand feet up to 36,000ft this is called the *Lapse Rate*. Above this it remains constant at -56½°C up to around 65000ft.

Reducing air temperature up to 36000ft causes the air to contract, partially recovering a little of the density loss. As altitude increases above 36000ft, the density falls more sharply. Reducing temperature can no longer compensate for it.

From this you should see that air density is affected by temperature and pressure. It is proportional to air pressure and inversely proportional to air temperature.

Due to daily variations in ambient conditions throughout the world it became necessary to establish a standard so that the performance of equipment relying on air density could be measured. Equipment would include aircraft lift producing surfaces and air breathing engines.

The standard used is the *International Standard Atmosphere*. It gives standard values for air temperature and pressure at different altitudes.

Although the air temperature drops with altitude, the lapse rate is uniform; the drop in air pressure and density is not. This is because as we go higher and air pressure falls the air expands.

The relationship between air pressure, temperature and volume is:

$$\frac{PV}{T} = \text{constant}$$

or

$$\frac{P_1 V_1}{T_1} = \frac{P_2 V_2}{T_2}$$

Example

This example is just to show you the relationship between P, V & T. You would not be expected to calculate this in an exam.

The density of air at sea level is 1.225kg/m^3 when the air temperature is 15°C (288K) and the air pressure is 1013mb. What will the density of the air be at an altitude where the air temperature is –20°C (253K) and the air pressure is 506mb?

$$\frac{P_1 V_1}{T_1} = \frac{P_2 V_2}{T_2}$$

$$\frac{1013\text{mb} \times 1\text{m}^3}{288\text{K}} = \frac{506\text{mb} \times V_2}{253\text{K}}$$

$$V_2 = 1.76\text{m}^3$$

This means that the 1.225kg is now occupying 1.76m^3.

$$\text{Density} = \frac{\text{Mass}}{\text{Volume}} = \frac{1.225\text{kg}}{1.76\text{m}^3} = 0.7\text{kg/m}^3$$

The complete ISA table is reproduced below.

Altitude	(h)	Ambient Temperature		(To)	Ambient Pressure	(Po)	Speed of Sound		(ao)
Feet	Metres	K	Deg. C	Deg. F	lb/sq in	millibar	ft/sec	knots	m/sec
-1,000	-304.8	290.13	+16.98	+62.6	15.24	1050.4	1120.3	663.3	341.5
0	0	288.15	15.00	59.0	14.69	1013.2	1116.6	661.1	340.3
+1,000	+304.8	286.17	13.02	55.4	14.17	977.1	1112.6	658.8	339.1
2,000	609.6	284.19	11.04	51.9	13.66	942.1	1108.7	656.5	337.9
3,000	914.4	282.21	9.06	48.3	13.17	908.1	1104.9	654.2	336.8
4,000	1219.2	280.23	7.08	44.7	12.69	875.1	1100.9	651.9	335.6
5,000	1524.0	278.24	5.09	41.2	12.23	843.0	1097.1	649.6	334.4
6,000	1828.8	276.26	3.11	37.6	11.78	811.9	1093.2	647.8	333.2
7,000	2133.6	274.28	1.13	34.0	11.34	781.8	1089.3	644.9	332.0
8,000	2438.2	272.30	-0.85	30.5	10.92	752.6	1085.3	642.6	330.8
9,000	2743.2	270.32	-2.83	26.9	10.51	724.3	1081.4	640.3	329.6
10,000	3048.0	268.34	-4.81	23.3	10.11	696.8	1077.4	637.9	328.4
11,000	3352.8	266.36	-6.79	19.8	9.72	670.2	1073.4	635.6	327.2
12,000	3657.6	264.38	-8.77	16.2	9.35	644.4	1069.4	633.2	325.9
13,000	3962.4	262.39	-10.76	12.6	8.98	619.4	1065.4	630.8	324.7
14,000	4267.2	260.41	-12.74	9.1	8.63	595.2	1061.4	628.4	323.5
15,000	4572.0	258.43	-14.72	5.5	8.29	571.7	1057.3	626.0	322.3
16,000	4876.8	256.45	-16.70	1.9	7.97	549.1	1053.3	623.6	321.1
17,000	5181.6	254.47	-18.68	-1.6	7.65	527.2	1049.2	621.2	319.8
18,000	5486.4	252.49	-20.66	-5.2	7.34	505.9	1045.1	618.8	318.5
19,000	5791.2	250.51	-22.64	-8.8	7.04	485.6	1040.9	616.4	317.3
20,000	6096.0	248.53	-24.62	-12.3	6.75	465.6	1036.9	613.9	316.1
21,000	6400.8	246.54	-26.61	-15.9	6.48	446.4	1032.7	611.5	314.8
22,000	6705.6	244.56	-28.59	-19.5	6.21	427.9	1028.6	609.0	313.5
23,000	7010.4	242.58	-30.57	-23.0	5.95	409.9	1024.4	606.5	312.2
24,000	7315.2	240.60	-32.55	-26.6	5.69	392.7	1020.2	604.1	310.9
25,000	7620.0	238.62	-34.53	-30.2	5.45	375.9	1015.9	601.6	309.7
26,000	7924.8	236.64	-36.51	-33.7	5.22	359.9	1011.8	599.1	308.4
27,000	8229.6	234.66	-38.49	-37.3	4.99	344.3	1007.5	596.6	307.1
28,000	8534.4	232.68	-40.47	-40.9	4.78	329.3	1003.2	594.0	305.8
29,000	8839.2	230.69	-42.46	-44.4	4.57	314.8	998.9	591.5	304.5
30,000	9144.0	228.71	-44.44	-48.0	4.36	300.9	994.7	588.9	303.2
31,000	9448.8	226.73	-46.42	-51.6	4.17	287.4	990.3	586.4	301.9
32,000	9753.6	224.75	-48.40	-55.1	3.98	274.5	986.0	583.8	300.5
33,000	10058.4	222.77	-50.38	-58.7	3.80	261.9	981.7	581.2	299.2
34,000	10363.2	220.79	-52.36	-62.3	3.63	249.9	977.3	578.7	297.9
35,000	10668.0	218.81	-54.34	-65.8	3.46	238.4	972.9	576.1	296.5
36,000	10972.8	216.83	-56.32	-69.4	3.29	227.3	968.5	573.4	295.2
36,089	11000.0	216.65	-56.50	-69.7	3.28	226.3	968.1	573.2	295.1
37,000	11277.6	Ambient temperature			3.14	216.6	Speed of Sound		
38,000	11582.4	remains constant			2.99	206.6	remains constant		
39,000	11887.2	from thispoint up to			2.85	196.8	from this point up		
40,000	12192.0	65,617 ft.			2.72	187.5	to 65,617 ft.		
45,000	13716.0				2.14	147.5			
50,000	15240.0				1.68	115.9			
55,000	16764.0				1.32	91.2			
60,000	18288.0				1.04	71.7			
65,000	19812.0				0.82	56.4			

www.part66.co.uk

Viscosity

Viscosity is defined as a fluid's resistance to flow and is measured in stokes (St) and centistokes. If it flows easily it is described as having a low viscosity. There are a number of ways of measuring viscosity in liquids. The simplest of these is the time taken for a given volume of the liquid to flow under gravity through a calibrated orifice at a given temperature. A second method is to record the time taken for a ball of given mass and diameter to sink through a given height of the liquid.

Pour Point and Cold Point

The *Pour Point* of a liquid is the lowest temperature at which it will just flow under gravity. The point at which the fluid ceases to flow at all is called the *Cold Point*. Distillate fuels suffer a condition known as Waxing where the fuel becomes cloudy and increases in viscosity as heavier hydrocarbons separate out.

Viscosity Index

The viscosity of liquids is affected by temperature changes. Normally, the lower the temperature is, the higher the viscosity will be.

'The Viscosity Index of an oil is a measure of how small a change in viscosity occurs over a given temperature range'.

The index is established by measuring the viscosity of the liquid at two temperature points. The higher the viscosity index, the less the viscosity of the liquid reduces as temperature rises.

Fluid Friction

Fluid passing through a duct experiences friction through contact with the duct walls. The duct wall surface slows the fluid in contact with it creating a shearing action in the layers of fluid close to the wall. This creates a rearward component of force acting parallel to the flow direction. The higher the viscosity of a fluid the greater the frictional forces will be.

When a liquid lubricant is interposed between two bearing surfaces it will cling to both through molecular attraction. This creates a shearing action in the liquid as the surfaces slide over each other. A rearward component of force is created which acts parallel to and against the direction of sliding. The higher the viscosity of the lubricant, the higher this force will be. If the lubricant has too low a viscosity, however, it will be squeezed out from between the bearing surfaces and they will contact each other.

Fluid friction is proportional to the viscosity of the liquid, the area of the contact surface and the velocity of the fluid or the speed of sliding of two surfaces.

Air Viscosity

The viscosity of air is revealed in the resistance experienced when one layer of air moves over another, or when air moves across a solid surface. Air has a Coefficient of Viscosity represented by the Greek letter Mu (μ). The coefficient can be expressed as a *Kinematic Coefficient* or as an *Absolute Coefficient*. The calculations for these are outside the scope of this syllabus.

Air Resistance

For any fluid, including air, the generation of fluid friction or resistance to flow depends on movement. When air passes over a surface like an aircraft wing there is friction between the surface and the air. This slows the air in contact with the surface, causing shear between adjoining layers of air. This process results in the formation of the *Boundary Layer*. This consists of sub-layers that travel at different speeds from near stationary at the wing surface to the speed of the free-stream air. The shearing action creates a resistance to flow that impedes the forward motion of the wing and is called *Skin Friction*.

The shearing action between the layers creates vortices that eventually cause the layers to break up into a turbulent flow. Up to the point this occurs, the boundary layer is said to have *Laminar Flow*. When the flow breaks up it is said to have *Turbulent Flow*.

A boundary layer that is turbulent is much thicker than its laminar counterpart and the resistance to flow increases. The point where laminar flow changes to turbulent flow is called the *Transition Point*.

All fluids moving in contact with surfaces react similarly. It is possible to ascertain the exact point where flow separates and becomes turbulent. The *Reynold's Number* is a figure that is given for different fluids. If it is ever exceeded, the flow becomes turbulent. For demonstration only, the formula is shown below. Note that increases in air density, velocity or length of the surface will all result in the number being reached earlier. The transition point, for example, will move forward as the air velocity increases.

$$R_n = \frac{\rho v l}{\mu}$$

Where:

ρ is air density

V is the air velocity

l is length of surface

μ is the coefficient of dynamic viscosity for the fluid

Another form of air resistance is found in the aerodynamic force that is exerted on the frontal area of a body. This results from the conversion of the kinetic energy in the airflow converting to pressure potential energy when it strikes the surface in its path. The product of this pressure and the frontal area of the body create a retarding force. This type of resistance is known as *Form Drag*.

Resistance Formula

The two forms of air resistance we have discussed are *Skin Friction* and *Form Drag*. Skin friction creates a resisting force that acts parallel to the surface the air passes over. Form drag creates a retarding force that acts normal to the frontal area of a body in the path of the airflow. Both forms of resistance are influenced by the profile of a body and are thus referred to as *Profile Drag*.

Each body has a resistance coefficient that relates to its shape. A flat plate, for example, would offer more resistance than a sphere. We can determine the total resistance, or profile drag, that a body in airflow experiences by considering:

- The coefficient of resistance (Cd)

- The surface area of the body (S)

- The square of the air velocity (v^2)

- The air density (ρ)

Kinetic energy is calculated using the formula ½ mv^2 which converts to pressure using ½ ρv^2 the formula for Dynamic Pressure. If we multiply this pressure by the surface area we will come up with a force that relates to the force felt on a flat plate at right angles to the airflow. We need to modify this by multiplying this force by the resistance coefficient (Cd) for the shape of the body.

Drag Force=Resistance Coefficient(Cd) $\times$ Dynamic Pressure($\frac{1}{2}\rho v^2$) $\times$ Area(S)

Therefore:

$$\text{Drag Force} = Cd \times \tfrac{1}{2}\rho v^2 \times S$$

Example

1. An aircraft has a total planform wing area of $100m^2$. The coefficient of drag is 0.02. It is flying at airspeed of 100m/s at an altitude where the air density is $0.5kg/m^3$. The profile drag on this aircraft will be:

    $$\text{Drag} = Cd \times \tfrac{1}{2}\rho v^2 \times S$$

    $$\text{Drag} = 0.02 \times 0.5 \times 0.5kg/m^3 \times 100m/s \times 100m/s \times 100m^2 = 5000N$$

Note: The value for S is normally taken to be the planform area.

2. If the airspeed of the aircraft is doubled to 200m/s, the new value for profile drag will be:

    $$0.02 \times 0.5 \times 0.5kg/m^3 \times 200m/s \times 200m/s \times 100m^2 = 20000N$$

Note how the value for drag increased four times when the airspeed doubled. Remember, the drag force is proportional to the square of the airspeed.

Streamlining

A streamline may be defined as the path traced by a particle in a steady fluid flow. Airflow can be represented by streamlines and a body that is so shaped that the streamlines follow the contour of that body with no separation from its surface is said to be streamlined.

Streamlined Shapes

When air flows around a shape, the air swirls into violent eddies or vortices behind it and the streamlines distort and intermingle, finally disappearing.

Reducing Air Resistance

When the air passes smoothly over a surface and the boundary layer flow is firmly attached with no turbulence, the airflow is described as being *Laminar Flow*. Once the flow breaks up into turbulent eddies and vortices, the flow is said to be *Turbulent Flow*. Look again at the formula for the Reynold's Number. If the air density, viscosity and length of surface are considered to be fixed, then the point of transition to turbulent flow depends on the air velocity. As this rises, the transition point from laminar to turbulent flow moves upstream. The friction between the airflow and the surface it contacts increases in the thicker boundary layer caused by turbulent flow. The portion of the total air resistance felt on a body caused by skin friction can be reduced if the surface is made smooth and polished.

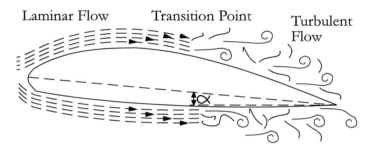

Figure 2.112 – Transition Point

The resistance produced by the shape of a body in pushing the air out of the way as it travels; can also be reduced by modifying that shape. This is important. Look again at the resistance formula. If you doubled the air velocity (v), the resistance would rise four times! If you tripled the air velocity, the resistance would rise nine times! Air resistance is proportional to the square of the air velocity.

Effects of Streamlining

At one extreme, a flat plate will produce maximum resistance with fierce vortices forming behind the plate and high pressure forming in front of it. If you examine the four illustrated shapes you should note that the final shape offers very little resistance to the airflow. The airflow follows the shape in smooth streamlines that do not break away from the surface.

Shapes that give the least resistance and cause the least disturbance to the streamlines are called, rather obviously, *Streamline Shapes*.

www.part66.co.uk

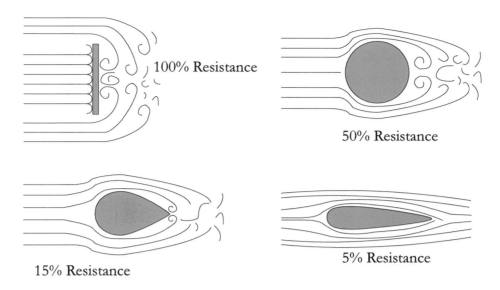

Figure 2.113 – Comparison of Streamlined Shapes

This shape has been found to have a length of between 3 and 4 times its maximum thickness, which occurs one third of the length back from the leading edge. This ratio is known as the *Fineness Ratio,* which produces a shape that incurs the least resistance to flow or *Form Drag*. It is not rocket science! Fish have been using it for millions of years.

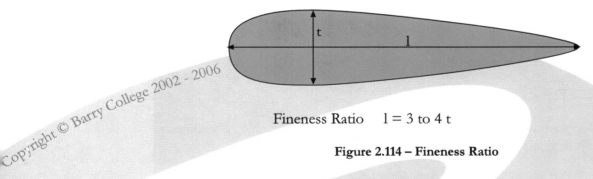

Fineness Ratio   l = 3 to 4 t

Figure 2.114 – Fineness Ratio

Compressibility

When air flows at velocities below the local speed of sound in air it is considered to be *Incompressible Flow*. We can assume that the density of the airflow does not alter when it passes over a body or through ducts.

At airspeeds approaching the local speed of sound in air and above it the compressions and expansions that occur will cause the air density to alter. When this occurs, the flow is described as being *Compressible Flow*.

Mach No.

This is a ratio of the true airspeed to the local speed of sound in air. It is determined by dividing the *True Air Speed* by the *Local Speed of Sound in Air*.

Airflow States

The airflow velocity range is divided up into the following bands:

Subsonic Flow:

This band covers airflow velocities below Mach 1. It is sub-divided in low subsonic and high subsonic. Low subsonic flow is considered to be incompressible flow.

Transonic Flow:

This band covers the situation where a mixture of velocities occurs within the flow, some above Mach 1 and some below. This may be present in aircraft that are flying at airspeeds below Mach 1 but have localised airflow velocities over curved surfaces that reach Mach 1 or above. The flow would be considered compressible in this band.

Supersonic Flow:

This band covers airflow that is over Mach 1 throughout. The flow is considered to be compressible flow.

Hypersonic Flow:

This band is used to identify airflows that are in excess of Mach 5. The flow is most definitely compressible.

Continuity of Mass Flow Equation

When air flows at subsonic velocity through a duct of varying cross-sectional area, the mass airflow rate will remain constant throughout. Simply, the mass of air passing any point in the duct remains constant even though the duct may narrow or widen in places.

As the duct cross-sectional area (A) reduces, the airflow velocity (v) will increase to maintain the mass airflow rate (M). If the duct cross-sectional area (A) increases, the airflow velocity (v) will reduce, again maintaining the mass flow rate (M).

If we were to multiply the cross-sectional area of a duct section by the air velocity in say, metres per second, we could establish the volume of air passing through a given section of the duct.

If we then multiply this product by the air density we would have the mass of air flowing through the duct at a given point in a second. This can be written as:

> Massflow = Density (ρ) x cross–sectional Area (A) x Velocity (v)
> Massflow = $\rho A v$ = a constant

For subsonic airflows, the air density does not alter significantly. So, we can say that if the area is halved, the velocity will double and vice versa. The Equation for the Continuity of Mass Flow for subsonic air flowing through a duct of varying cross-sectional area may be shown, therefore, as:

$$\rho_1 \times A_1 \times v_1 = \rho_2 \times A_2 \times v_2$$

For low subsonic airflow the density ρ (rho) does not alter so, we can say:

$$A_1 \times v_1 = A_2 \times v_2$$

Example

Air flows into the mouth of a convergent duct at a velocity of 100m/s. The area of the entrance mouth is 1m² and the exit area is 0.5m². The airflow velocity at exit will be:

The airflow is low subsonic so density may be considered as constant.

$$A_1 \times v_1 = A_2 \times v_2$$
$$\text{Therefore: } 1\text{m}^2 \times 100\text{m/s} = 0.5\text{m}^2 \times v_2$$
$$v_2 = 200\text{m/s}$$

Incompressible Flow

When air flows at subsonic velocities through convergent and divergent ducts there is an interchange of pressure potential and kinetic energies. The sum of these energies, or the total head pressure, will remain constant throughout. Because the airflow is considered to be incompressible, there will be no noticeable change in air density as these interchanges occur.

Consider air flowing through a convergent section duct. From the equation of the continuity of mass flow we know that the air will increase in velocity. This represents an increase in its kinetic energy. Energy cannot be created so the increase must have come from another source. It came from the pressure potential energy in the airflow, which will reduce as the velocity of the air increases. Some of the heat energy in the airflow will also convert into kinetic energy as well, so the air temperature will also drop. Because the air pressure falls as it passes through the convergent duct it may be considered as expanding through the duct. In subsonic flow, however, the density change is small enough to be ignored.

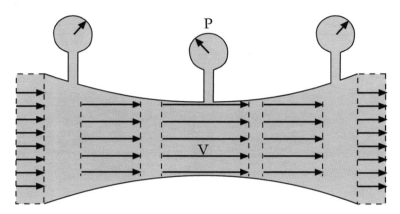

Figure 2.115 – Incompressible Flow

Now consider the air passing through a divergent section duct. According to the equation for the continuity of mass flow, the air velocity will reduce. As kinetic energy is now being lost the pressure potential energy in the airflow will rise, as will the air temperature.

Compressible Flow

Now for something completely different! When high subsonic and supersonic airflows pass through converging and diverging ducts their behaviour is very different. This is due in part to the fact that the air density now alters significantly. It is also due to the fact that the air velocity at the narrow duct sections can reach Mach 1 and choke the duct.

When a compressible flow passes through a converging duct, the increase in velocity will cause a reduction in pressure and air density. This causes the air to expand so, to keep the mass flow constant we must not reduce the cross-sectional area as much as we could have if the flow were subsonic. If we ignore this, the air will accelerate and choke the narrowing section of the duct. This will cause the air to compress and decelerate. So, we have a situation where the airflow passing through a convergent duct is reducing in velocity and increasing in pressure. This is the opposite behaviour of subsonic flow.

Now consider that the airflow passes from the converging section of the duct into a diverging section. The air is compressed and needs to expand. As it passes through the divergent section it will expand and accelerate through the widening duct, its pressure dropping as this occurs. Again, this is the opposite to the behaviour of subsonic airflow passing through a divergent duct.

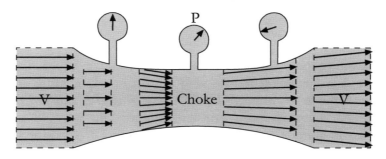

Figure 2.116- Compressible Flow

The point at which the narrow throat of the duct chokes coincides with the flow velocity reaching Mach 1 at this point.

Let us sum up the behaviour of incompressible and compressible airflows through convergent and divergent ducts.

Duct Section	Incompressible Flow (Sub-sonic)	Compressible Flow (Super-sonic)
Convergent	V Increases P Decreases	V Decreases P Increases
Divergent	V Decreases P Increases	V Increases P Decreases

The Speed of Sound in Air

The speed that sound travels in air is 331m/s at sea level when the air temperature is 0°C. Sound travels about four times faster in water and up to fifteen times faster in metals. From this you would imagine that air density would affect the speed of sound in air. Strangely, it does not. The reason is found in the relationship that the velocity of sound in air has with the ratio of air pressure and air density.

Velocity of Sound in air is proportional to: $\sqrt{\dfrac{\text{Pressure}}{\text{Density}}}$

If the air pressure were to rise, so would the air density. In fact, if you doubled the pressure, the density would also double. The ratio does not alter. So, the velocity of sound is unaltered when air pressure and density vary. However, this would only be true for air that was at a constant temperature.

If air temperature were to reduce at constant pressure it would increase the air density. In this case, the air temperature can alter the air density without altering its pressure – the ratio changes.

Looking again at the ratio of pressure and density above, you will see that the speed of sound in air would reduce with a drop in temperature and increase with a rise in temperature. Simply, the *Speed of Sound in Air is Proportional to Absolute Air Temperature*. Air temperature falls by 1.98°C for every 1000ft increase in altitude, so it follows that the speed of sound in air will also reduce as altitude increases. At high altitudes, Mach 1 is reached at lower true air speeds than at sea level.

Shock Waves

If you clap your hands, sound waves travel away from you in all directions at the speed of sound in air. Imagine that you are running fast in one direction when you clap your hands. You will be chasing the sound wave radiating away in front of you and running away from the wave radiating away behind you.

Now imagine you are running at the speed of sound! If you clap your hands, the sound wave in front of you will be travelling at the same speed as you. It cannot get away from you. Keep clapping your hands and an equal number of sound waves will build up right in front of your nose! They will all be travelling with you at the same speed as you. You have formed a shock wave.

A shock wave consists of tightly compressed sound waves and is about one ten thousandth of an inch thick. Sound waves are actually pressure waves. Up to the point you reached the speed of sound, these sound waves warned the air ahead that you were approaching. Once you reached the speed of sound yourself, no such advance warning could occur. Nobody can hear you approaching!

If you were to increase your speed to above the speed of sound in air, you would then leave the sound waves behind you in the form of a shock wave. If you were to pass a stationary observer at this speed they would hear you approaching some time after you had passed by!

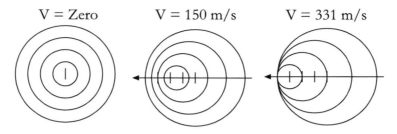

Figure 2.117 – Formation of a Shock Wave

I would like you to now imagine that you are travelling in an aircraft. Here we have a problem. Air accelerates over curved surfaces and aircraft have lots of them, the wings for example. This means that an aircraft flying below the speed of sound, say Mach 0.75, could already have air velocities reaching Mach 1 on its curved surfaces. In this case shock waves will form at these points even though the aircraft speed is below Mach 1.

The aircraft Mach No at which shock waves will form on any curved surface is called the *Critical Mach No.* for that aircraft or, its *Mach Crit* for short.

Finally, your aircraft reaches Mach 1. Now we will have shock waves formed at the nose and leading edges of the wings, tail plane and fin.

All the shock waves so far formed will be at right angles or *Normal* to the path of the airflow causing them. As the speed of the aircraft increases over Mach 1, the shock waves in front of the leading edges, for example, should make contact with them. If the leading edges are blunt, contact cannot occur.

As the aircraft pushes forward to make contact with a shock wave, a blunt leading edge will compress the air in the space between it and the shock wave. This raises the air temperature in this region, which is called the *Stagnation Zone*. A rise in air temperature raises the value of the speed of sound in air so the wave will continue to stay ahead of the leading edge.

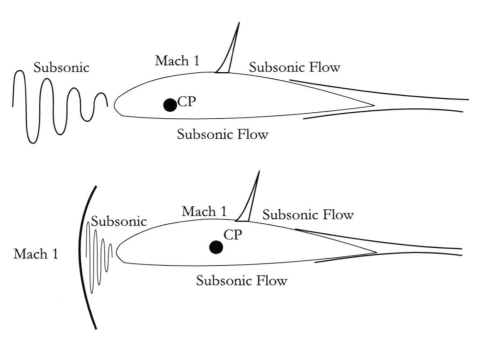

Figure 2.118 – Stagnation Zone

This is a problem. The air resistance or drag felt on an aircraft when generating these normal shock waves is up to six times the sub-sonic value!

The dramatic rise in pressure behind the normal shock wave causes the boundary layer to thicken and increase the skin friction drag. The compression between the leading edge and the shock wave acts on the blunt leading edge producing **Wave Drag**. '*A steep increase in drag is a major effect of the compressibility of airflow*'. If the leading edge is made sharp, the wave drag can be reduced.

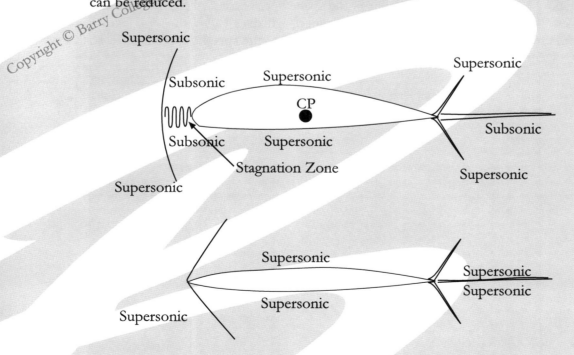

Figure 2.119 – Oblique Shock Wave Formation

This is the so-called sound barrier. An aircraft in this situation would not be able to produce enough engine power to go any faster. The drag would just keep increasing. However, if the aircraft can make contact with the waves, they will slope back and become *Oblique* waves.

The drag would then reduce to below three times the sub-sonic value. Worth doing if you really want to fly at speeds above Mach 1. It is for this reason that supersonic aircraft have sharp noses and leading edges.

As you have probably now guessed, there are two types of shock wave, normal and oblique. They each have a different effect on the airflow.

Normal Shock Wave

The normal shock wave always forms at right angles to the path of the airflow that causes it. The air ahead of the wave will be travelling at Mach 1. As the air passes through the wave it will decelerate to below Mach 1. This is a pretty dramatic drop as it occurs in a distance of around one ten thousandth of an inch, the thickness of the shock wave. This creates turbulence and an increase in air pressure and temperature behind the wave.

If the normal wave is positioned on the cambered surface of, or in front of the wing; the rise in pressure can destroy lift behind the wave.

Aircraft experience a rearward movement in the *Centre of Pressure* or *centre of lift* as they hit this situation. The nose of the aircraft drops and the aircraft dives unless it has been specifically designed to trim out this potentially fatal tendency that is appropriately called *Tuck Under*.

Oblique Shock Wave

This type of wave is formed at an angle to the path of the airflow causing it. It is often the result of a normal shock wave contacting a sharp edge and sloping back. Air ahead of the wave will be above Mach 1. As the air flows through the wave it decelerates but remains above Mach 1. There will be a rise in air pressure and temperature behind the wave. This will be less dramatic than that experienced behind a normal shock. The airflow will change direction as it passes through the wave and will follow the contour of the surface behind it.

Expansion Waves

These are not shock waves. When a supersonic compressible airflow changes direction over a surface like a wing its speed increases and its static pressure falls. As the air density also falls the air expands forming an expansion wave which is normal to the point where the flow direction changed.

Kinetic Heating

High velocity air flowing over the skin of an aircraft generates frictional heat in the boundary layer. Concorde experiences skin temperatures approaching 120°C during supersonic flight. Kinetic heating may also be called *Aerodynamic Heating*.

Sonic Airflow

When air is flowing at speeds below Mach 1 it is sub-sonic flow. When travelling at Mach 1 it is sonic flow. When the airspeed is in excess of Mach 1 it is called supersonic flow.

Sub-sonic Flight

Aircraft flying at airspeeds below Mach 0.75 are deemed to be sub-sonic. This is because all the air flowing over the aircraft is below Mach 1. The airflow is considered to be incompressible.

Transonic Flight

An aircraft flying at airspeeds between Mach 0.75 and Mach 1.2 may have normal shock waves forming on its curved surfaces. If these occur, there will be Mach 1 flow ahead of the waves and sub-sonic flow behind the waves. The air flowing over the aircraft is not fully sub-sonic or fully supersonic so the term transonic is used. There is a mixture of compressible and incompressible flow.

Supersonic Flight

Aircraft flying at speeds above Mach 1.2 will have firmly attached oblique shock waves. As the flow ahead and behind these waves is above Mach 1 the airflow over the whole aircraft will be fully supersonic.

Mach Cone

When aircraft are flying at supersonic speeds they are leaving their sound waves to radiate away behind them. This is a continuous process. If you imagine the pattern made by these radiating waves, you can draw lines from the nose of the aircraft to touch each radiant wave pattern as a tangent to it. As we are dealing with three dimensions this line is in fact the surface of a cone.

The angle at the apex of the cone is called the Mach Angle and the cone is called the Mach Cone. As an aircraft's Mach No. increases, the Mach angle gets smaller. The surface of the Mach cone is actually an expansion wave.

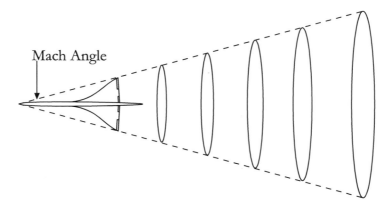

Figure 2.120 – Mach Cone

Design for Transonic Flight

Commercial aircraft fly at speeds of 0.85 – 0.9 Mach without encountering shock stall. The reason for this lies in the swept wing design and the reduced camber, or curvature of their wing aerofoil sections. The swept wing configuration causes the relative airflow 'V', to have two component directions of movement as it passes over the wing. One component V_1 is chord wise and the other V_2 is span wise.

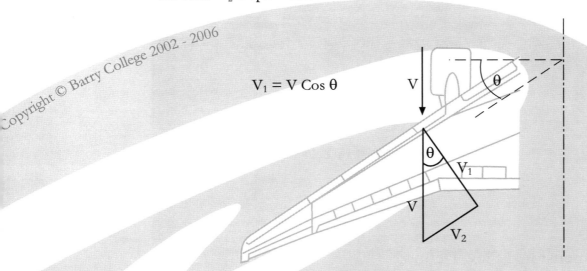

Figure 2.121 – Typical Swept Wing Arrangement

Shock waves always form normal to the direction of the sonic flow, which is the chord wise flow. If the wings were not swept, the chord wise flow velocity on the upper curved surface of the wing would reach Mach one (1) long before the aircraft itself reached this speed. By angling or sweeping the wings, the chord wise airflow velocity is significantly reduced, which delays the onset of shock wave formation allowing the aircraft to safely cruise at a higher mach number. The wings of modern commercial jet aircraft have sweep angles of approximately 30° - 35°. This angle is formed between the lateral axis of the aeroplane and a line drawn at the quarter wing chord position, figure 2.121.

Onset of shock wave formation can be further delayed by reducing the curvature of the wing aerofoil sections, which again reduces the chord wise air velocity.

The speed of sound in air is 331 m/s at sea level at 0°C. This value reduces as air temperature reduces, which means that at very high altitudes, aircraft are more at risk of approaching their critical mach number; shock waves will form on curved surfaces of the aircraft at this Mach number. A warning system, called M_{MO}, which is an abbreviation for *Maximum Mach Operating*, is provided to alert aircrew to the aircraft's close proximity to this critical Mach speed.

The span wise airflow on swept wing aircraft travels over a greater length of the wing surface and, due to the friction in the boundary layer, can slow and become turbulent. This makes swept wing aircraft more prone to wing tip stalling. Devices like wing fences, extended leading edge sections and vortex generators are used to protect against this unfortunate characteristic.

It is possible to calculate the chord wise air velocity given the speed of the relative airflow and the wing sweep angle as illustrated in the following worked example.

Worked Example

A jet aircraft cruising at 280 m/s has a wing sweep of 34° and so the chord wise airflow velocity will be:

$$\cos 34° = \frac{V_1}{V}$$

$$\therefore V_1 = V \cos 34° = 280 \times 0.829$$

$$\therefore V_1 = 232 m/s$$

One-Dimensional Flow Defined

To define one-dimensional flow, we need to imagine air passing through a duct of varying cross-sectional area, called a *Venturi*.

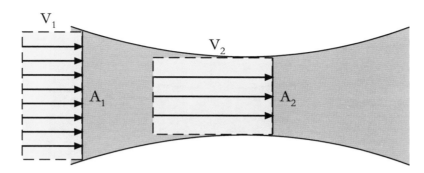

Figure 2.122 – Simple Venturi

If we imagine the air passing through the venturi as a series of streamlines and we take a length-wise section through the duct, we could draw this onto a flat sheet of paper; but the drawing would only have two dimensions, length and height.

If we now consider that any velocity changes will only affect the streamlines and so there are no sideways changes, then we are considering length only. This gives us the term *One-dimensional Flow*.

Bernoulli's Theorem

At the start of this section you will have examined the *Continuity Equation* that is related to the mass flow of air passing through a duct. This equation underpins many principles in fluid dynamics, including Bernoulli's theorem.

Using the equation we can look at the relationship between the pressure potential and kinetic energies that exist in airflow. We will assume that the sum of pressure potential and kinetic energies is the total energy in the flow.

Bernoulli's theorem states that the total energy contained in an incompressible flow of air through a venturi will remain constant. For example, if the kinetic energy were to increase, the pressure potential energy would decrease to maintain the sum of the two energies at a constant figure.

As the air flows through the converging section of the venturi it must increase in velocity in accordance with the continuity equation. This increase in kinetic energy will cause a drop in the static pressure in the duct.

Bernoullis theorem deals with potential & kinetic energies

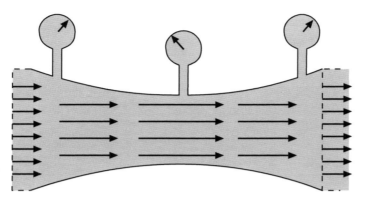

Figure 2.123 – Airflow in a Simple Venturi

The air velocity will reach a maximum at the throat of the venturi and the static pressure will reach a minimum. The sum of the two at this point will still equal the sum of the energies when the air first entered the mouth of the venturi.

As the air then passes out through the diverging section of the venturi it will reduce its velocity, again in accordance with the continuity equation. As the kinetic energy reduces, the static pressure will rise.

At all points in its passage through the venturi the total energy of the air remains constant. The kinetic and potential energies interchange but will always add up to the same figure.

It is interesting to note that the air will also contain heat energy. We have ignored this but it does take part in the interchanges. As the kinetic energy increases in the converging section the static pressure and the temperature of the air drops. Temperature drops to its lowest value in the throat of the venturi and then starts to rise again in the diverging section.

In the resistance formula we used $\frac{1}{2}\rho V^2$ to determine the dynamic pressure of air, which equates to its kinetic energy at constant density. The static pressure P is the pressure potential energy. Using these we can represent Bernoulli's theorem as a formula:

Static Pressure (P) + Dynamic Pressure ($\frac{1}{2}\rho v^2$) = a constant

or

$$P_1 + (\tfrac{1}{2}\rho v^2)_1 = P_2 + (\tfrac{1}{2}\rho v^2)_2$$

Example

A venturi has an entrance of cross-sectional area $4m^2$, a throat area of $2m^2$ and an exit area of $4m^2$. The air enters the venturi at $100m/s$ at a static pressure of $100kPa$. Assuming the air density remains constant at $1.225kg/m^3$ the air velocity, dynamic pressure and static pressure at the throat will be:

www.part66.co.uk

Using the continuous equation:

$$A_1 \times v_1 = A_2 \times v_2 = A_3 \times v_3$$

$4m^2 \times 100m/s = 2m^2 \times v_2$ $V_2 = 200m/s$

$2m^2 \times 200m/s = 4m^2 \times v_3$ $V_3 = 100m/s$

Dynamic px at entry $= \tfrac{1}{2}\rho v^2 = 0.5 \times 1.225 \times 100 \times 100$ $= 6kPa$

Dynamic px at throat $= \tfrac{1}{2}\rho v^2 = 0.5 \times 1.225 \times 200 \times 200$ $= 24.5kPa$

Static px at throat:

Using Bernoulli's theorem: $p_1 + (\tfrac{1}{2}\rho v^2)_1 = P_2 + (\tfrac{1}{2}\rho v^2)_2$

$100 \times 10^3 Pa + (0.5 \times 1.225 \times 100^2) = p_2 + (0.5 \times 1.225 \times 200^2)$

$P_2 = 81.5kPa$

Note: Total energy at entrance is   100kPa+6kPa = 106kPa

         Total energy at throat is 24.5kPa+81.5kPa = 106kPa

The Aerofoil

If we examine the cross sectional view of an aerofoil we will notice that the top surface is curved whilst the lower surface is relatively straight. You may also have noticed that the aerofoil is presented to the relative airflow so that its chord line makes an angle to it, called the *Angle of Attack (AoA)* represented by the Greek letter Alpha (α).

When the aerofoil meets the relative airflow, the air divides, some passing over the top surface and the rest passing beneath the aerofoil.

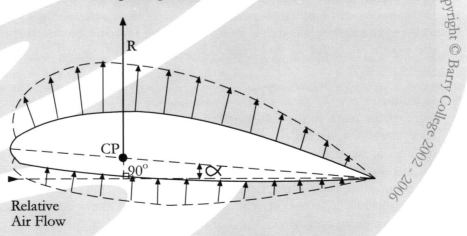

Figure 2. 124 – Airflow over an Aerofoil

The air passing over the top curved surface behaves similarly to airflow passing through a venturi throat, (it accelerates). This increase in air velocity reduces the static pressure in the region over the curved surface.

The air passing beneath the aerofoil meets the angled flat surface and loses velocity, increasing its static pressure to above ambient. Once this occurs, a pressure difference develops across the aerofoil, which results in an upward thrust on it. This upward force is called *Lift* and is the sum of forces that act normal to the surface of the wing in a vertical direction. All the forces can be represented by vectors which, when added, produce a resultant force that acts through the *Centre of Pressure (CP)*.

There are many different aerofoil sections, each having different lift characteristics. To enable a calculation to be made for lift, each aerofoil is given a Lift Coefficient (Cl).

The aerodynamic force experienced by a wing is only derived from moving through the air so the aerodynamic force is a function of dynamic pressure, ie $\frac{1}{2}\rho v^2$, and planform surface area (S), modified by the lift coefficient (Cl) for the aerofoil. The lift formula is therefore:

$$\text{Lift} = \text{cl} \times \tfrac{1}{2}\rho v^2 \times S$$

Airspeed Measurement

We have referred to airspeed on many occasions but so far, we have not explained how it can be measured. The principle, however, has been established that air in motion possesses both kinetic and potential energy and that the sum of these in a one-dimensional fluid flow remains constant. The question is, how can we measure the airspeed? If we tried to measure the kinetic energy in the airflow at various points through the venturi tube, we would also be measuring the potential energy, so our reading would not vary through the venturi even though we know that the velocity is changing. We must therefore find a way of separating the two energies in order that we may measure one of them. At this point, it is better if we refer to the kinetic energy as being the airflow's dynamic pressure, i.e. the pressure due to its motion, and the potential energy as being the static pressure of the air, i.e. the ambient gauge pressure of the air.

If we imagine a flat plate in still air, then static pressure exists equally on both sides of the plate so the thrust, (pressure × area), is equal on both sides. If we now imagine a stream of moving air striking one side of the plate, it is not difficult to see that the plate experiences an increase in thrust on the side facing the airflow. As static pressure still exists on both sides as before, the increase in thrust on one side must be due to the dynamic pressure of the airflow. Unfortunately, a lot of air would spill around the sides of the plate so this would not be an accurate method of measuring dynamic pressure.

The Pitot Static Tube

The flat plate method of measuring dynamic pressure is far too crude, the Pitot Static Tube is an accurate alternative and is almost universally used on aircraft. It consists of two tubes mounted so that they are facing the airflow. One tube, the Pitot tube, has an open end facing directly into the airflow. The other tube, the Static Tube, is closed at its ends but has holes or slits cut into its sides that do not face the airflow.

On some aircraft, the Pitot tube is concentric with the static tube. Whilst on others, the static tube is replaced by a flat plate, called a Static Vent, with holes in it mounted so no airflow can enter the holes.

If we consider the Pitot tube, the airflow entering it has both static pressure and dynamic pressure. When considering the static tube or vent, the air in it possesses only static pressure. The airspeed indicator cancels the static pressure and reacts only to the dynamic pressure. The Pitot pressure enters the flexible capsule while static pressure surrounds the capsule.

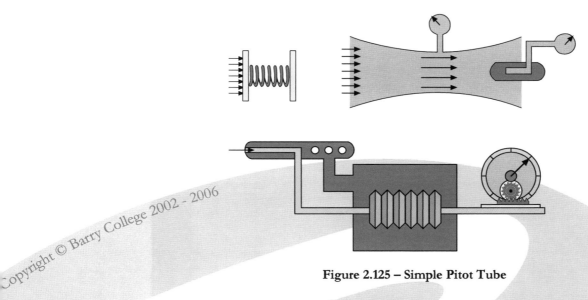

Figure 2.125 – Simple Pitot Tube

As we now have static pressure, both inside and outside the capsule it cannot react to it. So the capsule moves only as a result of changing dynamic pressure, which is the true velocity of the airflow. We can say that:

Pitot pressure = Dynamic pressure + Static pressure

Dynamic pressure = Pitot pressure – Static pressure

www.part66.co.uk

Indicated and True Air Speed

The Pitot static method of measuring airspeed is dependent on the air density. As we now know, air density reduces with increasing altitude, which means that at altitude, the air speed indicator is not showing the true speed of the aircraft and so this reading is called the *Indicated Air Speed (IAS)*. Once the IAS is known, it is easy to calculate the *True Air Speed (TAS)* providing we know the original air density for which the indicator was calibrated, and the density of the air at the height we are concerned with.

Example

At a height of 6000m the IAS reads 204 knots, in other words 105 m/s, which means that the pressure registered by the Pitot tube is the same as would be produced at a speed of 105 m/s at sea level where the density of air is 1.225 kg/m^3. However, this pressure is calculated from $\frac{1}{2}\rho v^2$, $(0.5 \times 1.225 \times 105^2)$, but the density at 6000 m is 0.66 kg/m^3, from the ISA table, and so the pressure will be the same, but at $0.5 \times 0.66 \times v^2$. Therefore, we can say that ρv^2 at 6000 m is the same as ρv^2 at sea level and so:

$$0.66 \times v^2 = 1.225 \times 105^2$$

$$\therefore v = \sqrt{\frac{1.225 \times 11025}{0.66}}$$

$$\therefore v = 143\text{m/s}$$

Therefore, the IAS is 105 m/s but the TAS is 143 m/s.

Remember, the indicated airspeed (IAS) at altitude will be less than the true airspeed (TAS))!

Revision

Fluid Dynamics

Questions:

1. The density of a substance is:

    A. Mass/Volume

    B. Volume/Mass

    C. Weight/Volume

2. The 'Relative Density' of a substance with density 13,600kg/m^3 is:

    A. 1.36

    B. 13.6×10^3

    C. 13.6

3. The density of the atmosphere at standard sea level conditions is:

    A. 0.147kg/m^3

    B. 1.013kg/m^3

    C. 1.225kg/m^3

4. The density of the atmosphere at sea level is approximately halved at an altitude of:

    A. 36,000ft

    B. 18,000ft

    C. 10,000ft

5. Viscosity is a measure of:

A. Mass flow

B. Flow resistance

C. Specific gravity

6. The transition point where flow changes from laminar to turbulent flow in a boundary layer on a surface will:

A. Move rearwards as flow velocity increases

B. Be unaffected by changes in flow velocity

C. Move forwards as flow velocity increases

7. Stream-lining is mainly concerned with:

A. Laminar flow

B. Shape

C. Friction

8. The 'Fineness Ratio' of an ideal stream-lined body is:

A. 1:3

B. 3:1

C. 1:1

9. The air resistance felt on a flat plate presented perpendicular to the air flow may be calculated using:

A. Mass flow x density × air velocity × area of plate

B. Dynamic pressure × area of plate

C. Dynamic pressure + static pressure × area of plate

10. **As altitude increases, the air friction force on a body will:**

    A. Increase

    B. Decrease

    C. Remain unaltered

11. **As altitude increases 'Indicated Air Speed' will:**

    A. Always be the same as True Air Speed

    B. Read higher than True Air Speed

    C. Read lower than True Air Speed

12. **The Mach Number is found by:**

    A. Dividing the indicated air speed by the local speed of sound in air

    B. Dividing the local speed of sound in air by the true air speed

    C. Dividing the true air speed by the local speed of sound in air

13. **As an aircraft climbs at constant airspeed, the Mach Number will:**

    A. Increase

    B. Decrease

    C. Remain constant

14. **Air flow through a divergent duct at sub-sonic velocity will:**

    A. Increase in velocity, decrease in pressure and temperature

    B. Decrease in velocity and increase in pressure and temperature

    C. Decrease in velocity and pressure and increase in temperature

269

15. **Air flowing through a convergent duct at sonic velocity will:**

    A. Increase in velocity and decrease in pressure

    B. Increase in velocity and pressure

    C. Decrease in velocity and increase in pressure

16. **In sonic airflow conditions, any increase in velocity through a venturi duct will:**

    A. Decrease air density and cause the air to expand

    B. Increase air density and cause air to contract

    C. Not affect air density

17. **As air flows through a venturi duct the energy in the air:**

    A. Increases from entry to exit

    B. Remains constant

    C. Drops on entry and recovers at exit

18. **As air flows through a duct of changing cross-sectional area the mass flow of air will:**

    A. Be directly proportional to the cross-sectional area

    B. Be inversely proportional to the cross-sectional area

    C. Remain constant irrespective of cross-sectional area

19. **As the dynamic pressure of sub-sonic air-flow increases through a venturi, the static pressure will:**

    A. Reduce

    B. Increase

    C. Remain constant

20. **Bernoulli's theorem deals with the sum of:**

A. Static pressure and potential energy

B. Static pressure, dynamic pressure and potential energy

C. Air velocity, air pressure and density

21. **Airspeed is measured by:**

A. Subtracting static from pitot pressure

B. Adding pitot to static pressure

C. Subtracting dynamic pressure from pitot pressure

22. **When supersonic airflow changes direction over an aerofoil and increases in velocity as a result, the effect will be:**

A. An increase in pressure and density causing air to contract

B. A decrease in pressure and density causing an expansion wave

C. Constant pressure and density with no effect on flow

23. **When air flow velocity reaches Mach one on any curved surface of an aircraft the result will be:**

A. Normal shock wave forms and air pressure and density rise in its wake

B. Normal shock wave forms and air pressure and density reduce in its wake

C. Oblique shock wave forms and air pressure and density reduce

24. **Transonic flow is defined as:**

A. Airflow over a body is sub-sonic

B. Airflow over a body is sonic

C. Airflow over a body is both sub-sonic and super-sonic

25. **The local speed of sound in air is:**

A. Inversely proportional to absolute temperature

B. Proportional to absolute temperature

C. Not affected by air temperature

Revision

Fluid Dynamics

Answers:

1.   **A**
2.   **C**
3.   **C**
4.   **B**
5.   **B**
6.   **C**
7.   **A**
8.   **A**
9.   **B**
10. **B**
11. **C**
12. **C**
13. **A**
14. **B**
15. **C**
16. **A**
17. **B**
18. **C**
19. **A**
20. **B**
21. **A**
22. **B**
23. **A**
24. **C**
25. **B**

Thermodynamics

Introduction

Energy is defined as the capacity to do work. In the branch of physics we call *Thermodynamics* we are going to study the relationship between *Heat Energy* and work. We will be looking at how the internal energy of matter can be raised by work and heat. We will also look at how this internal energy may be used to produce some useful work as it depletes back to thermal equilibrium again. Before we embark on this, we need to be able to describe heat energy and know the difference between heat and temperature. We will also need to be familiar with the laws that govern thermodynamics.

Heat

Heat is defined as the transfer of energy from a hot place to a cooler place when a temperature difference exists between them.

Heat can transfer in any of three ways. These are *Conduction, Convection and Radiation*. The SI unit of heat is the *Joule (J)* which is the unit used for energy and work.

Temperature

Temperature is merely a figure used to represent the degree of hotness or coldness of a body. The measurement of temperature is usually carried out with a thermometer that uses one of the numbers of scales available that enable a measurement to be made in degrees.

The temperature of a body bears no relationship to the heat energy it contains. A bath full of warm water may have a much lower temperature than a glowing hot plate but it contains more energy in its greater mass.

Internal Energy

Matter contains constantly moving molecules. Pure metals being non-molecular exhibit this movement in their atoms. The particles may be vibrating about fixed positions or moving around with velocities that depend on

273

www.part66.co.uk

whether their host matter is solid, liquid or gaseous. Since the particles have mass, their movement produces kinetic energy.

The internal energy of a body is the sum of the kinetic energies contained in its particles. The application of external heat and work on a body will increase the kinetic energy in its particles, which in sum will increase its internal energy.

Matter also contains potential energy locked up in the forces that binds its molecules and atoms together. For calculating the internal energy of matter, this is not considered.

Laws of Thermodynamics

First Law

Energy cannot be created or destroyed. It can only be converted from one form into another. When energy converts from one form into other forms the total quantity of energy remains the same.

Second Law

Heat can only transfer from a high temperature region to a lower temperature region. It cannot naturally transfer the other way.

Third Law

The transfer of energy from matter becomes increasingly difficult as its temperature approaches absolute zero. It is considered impossible at absolute zero.

Thermometers

The instrument used to measure temperature is called a thermometer. These instruments can be based on a number of principles.

Many rely on the expansion of a suitable *Thermometric Liquid* when it is heated. These types have a glass bulb connected to a graduated glass stem. The expanding liquid rises in the stem and its level indicates the temperature reading to be taken.

Other types of thermometer utilise a bi-metal strip composed of two metals with different coefficients of expansion. The distortion of the strip during heating is mechanically signalled to a means of indicating a related temperature.

Other types employ the *Thermoelectric Principle*. This relies on the production of a milliamp current when a junction of two different metal wires is heated. This type of thermometer is commonly referred to as a *Thermocouple*.

Resistance thermometers use the principle that the electrical resistance of a metal wire will change with temperature. Platinum is a favoured material in these. Another type, commonly called a *Thermistor*, uses a semi-conducting material that changes its electrical resistance with temperature.

Thermometric Liquids

The choice of liquid to be used in a thermometer is really determined by the temperature range you wish to measure. Mercury will freeze at around -40°C and boils at around 360°C. Mercury thermometers would be a bit of a problem in the Polar region where the temperatures regularly drop below –40°C.

Alcohol freezes at –115°C so it would be suited to use in low temperature regions. Industrial and scientific processes often incur temperatures much lower than this and use has to be made of fluids that may be gases at room temperature like Pentane and Helium. For high temperature work, pressurised thermometers will raise fluid boiling points but for very high temperatures, the resistance type thermometer would be used.

The coefficient of expansion of the chosen fluid is important to accurate reading. Alcohol expands at six times the rate of mercury but it too has drawbacks. Mercury does not cling to glass but alcohol does.

This means that alcohol can give falsely low readings as temperature falls and a film remains stuck to the glass above. Alcohol vaporises which can also lead to inaccurate readings. It is colourless so it has to be dyed to show up. Mercury is a much better conductor of heat than alcohol and reacts faster to temperature changes.

From this you can see that mercury would be a favoured liquid in thermometers. Water on the other hand would be completely unsuited as it boils at 100°C and has an anomalous expansion at and below 4°C.

Fixed Temperature Points

The scales used in thermometers have a range that is generally based on two easily understood points. The steam point of water and the melting point of pure water ice are commonly used. The upper fixed point, or steam point, is established with the thermometer placed in steam in an apparatus called a *Hypsometer*. The lower fixed point, or ice point, is established by immersing the thermometer in pure water ice shavings that are melting. The calibration is carried out under standard sea level ambient conditions of 15°C, 14.7psi.

Temperature Scales

The upper and lower fixed points of the *Celsius scale* are divided into 100 equal degrees, the ice point is called 0°C and the steam point 100°C.

The *Fahrenheit scale*, which is in common use in the USA, is more complex as the scale is divided into 180 equal degrees. As a result, the ice point is 32°F and the steam point 212°F. Therefore, 1.8°F is equivalent to 1°C.

The *Kelvin* or *Absolute Scale* is not based on any arbitrary fixed points but on the absolute zero of temperature, (the point where internal energy is zero). This point is called 0K. The scale is called the *Thermodynamic Temperature Scale*. The useful feature of this scale is that 1K is equivalent to 1°C. Absolute zero Kelvin is equivalent to –273°C and so on this scale, the ice point is 273K and the steam point is 373K.

The *Rankine scale* is another absolute temperature scale but this time related to the Fahrenheit scale and so is used more commonly in the USA for thermodynamic temperature measurement. Converting Fahrenheit to Rankine is made by adding 459.67°.

Figure 3.1 shows the Celsius, Fahrenheit, Kelvin and Rankine temperature scales on comparable thermometers.

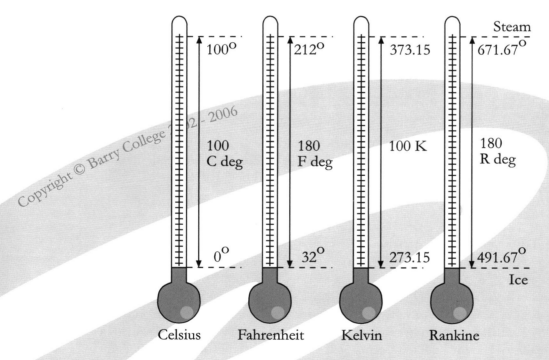

Figure 3.1 – Temperature Scales

www.part66.co.uk

Temperature Conversion

Degrees Centigrade to degrees Fahrenheit	$°C \times \frac{9}{5} + 32$
Degrees Fahrenheit to degrees Centigrade	$°F - 32 \times \frac{5}{9}$
Degrees Centigrade to Kelvin	$°C + 273.15$
Degrees Kelvin to degrees Centigrade	-273.15
Degrees Fahrenheit to degrees Rankine	$°F + 459.67$
Degrees Rankine to degrees Fahrenheit	-459.67

Heat Definition

You have already read that heat is energy that flows from one place to another because of a temperature difference existing between them. The internal energy of a body is denoted by the symbol *(U)* and the SI unit used to measure it is the *Joule (J)*.

The first law of thermodynamics stated that energy can convert from one form into others but the sum of these energies will remain constant. If *Work (W)* is done on a substance or, *Heat (Q)* is added to it, the *Internal Energy (U)* will rise by an amount equal to the sum of the work done and the heat added.

The substance may do work, similar to what a gas may do in expanding and forcing a piston down a cylinder. The substance may lose heat by radiation, conduction or convection. The sum of the work done by the substance and the heat lost by it will equal the fall in the internal energy of the substance.

Change in Internal Energy (U) = Heat input (Q) + Work input (W)

There can be a number of variations to this, for example, heat may flow in and work may be put out. You have to watch the signs. Input will have a positive sign and output will have a negative sign.

The second law of thermodynamics stated that heat can only flow naturally from a high temperature region to a lower temperature one. This should be easy to understand.

A red-hot lump of metal will gradually cool as its heat energy flows out to the atmosphere. We cannot imagine a situation where a cold lump of metal gradually became red hot whilst the room got colder.

The second law is a natural law and can only be reversed if we burn fuel to provide the energy to raise temperatures.

The third law stated that the internal energy of matter decreases to a theoretical zero at absolute zero temperature (-273K). This is where all molecular or atomic movement is predicted to cease. It is emphasised that this is a theoretical prediction, as the point has never been reached.

Heat Capacity

A body's *Heat Capacity* is defined as the heat required to raise its temperature by 1°C. The SI unit of heat is the *Joule/degree Celsius (J/°C)*.

Specific Heat Capacity

A substance's *Specific Heat Capacity*, signified by the lower case letter 'c', is defined as the heat required to raise a unit mass of it through 1°C. The SI unit for specific heat capacity is the *Joule/kilogram degree Celsius (J/kg°C)*.

Take 1kg samples of two substances that are at equal temperature, like aluminium and copper for example. Let's say we heat them both equally in an oven for a minute. We notice that the temperature of the aluminium has gone up by 10°C in that time whilst the temperature of the copper has risen by 20°C in the same time. Think about this, the copper has the lower heat capacity. The joules of energy given to both samples was the same but the joules required to raise the temperature of the kilogram of copper by 1°C were less than for the aluminium.

When describing the heat capacities of different substances the term specific heat capacity is used as the word *specific* refers to unit quantity. Water, for example, has a specific heat capacity of 4200 J/kg°C, which is also 4.2kJ/kg°C.

Worked Example

An ingot of copper mass 2kg is to be heated to raise its temperature from 40°C to 100°C. The specific heat capacity of copper is 400J/kg°C. The heat required will be:

www.part66.co.uk

$$\text{Heat Energy required} = \text{Mass (kg)} \times \text{SHC (J/kg°C} \times \text{Temperature Change)}$$
$$= mc(\theta_2 - \theta_1)$$
$$= 2\text{kg} \times 400\text{J/kg°C} \times (100°C - 40°C) = 48\text{kJ}$$

The symbols used in the equation above are:

m = mass in kg

c = specific heat capacity in J/kg°C

θ_2 = higher temperature in °C

θ_1 = lower temperature in °C

Example Calculations

Example 1

2kg of hot water at 80°C are thoroughly mixed with 4kg of cool water at 10°C. The specific heat capacity of the water is 4200J/kg°C. The final temperature of the water will be:

$$\text{Heat lost} = \text{Heat gained}$$
$$mc(\theta_c - \theta_1) = mc(\theta_2 - \theta_c)$$
$$2\text{kg} \times 4200\text{J/kg°C} \times (80 - \theta_1) = 4\text{kg} \times 4200\text{J/kg°C} \times (\theta_2 - 10)$$

Divide both sides by 4200
$$2\text{kg}(80 - \theta_1) = 4\text{kg}(\theta_2 - 10)$$
$$160 - 2\theta = 4\theta - 40$$

$$\theta = \frac{200}{6} = 33.3°C$$

You will not be expected to work such an example in the IR Part-66 examination. It is shown here to demonstrate the use of the formulae. The next example is more likely to be used.

Example 2

1kg of hot water at 70°C is mixed with an equal mass of cold water at 30°C. The final temperature of the water is: (You can do this mentally, look).

$$1kg \times 4200J/kg°C \times (70 - \theta) = 1kg \times 4200J/kg°C \times (\theta - 30)$$

If you divide both sides by 4200 the equation is easy

$$70 - \theta = \theta - 30$$
$$70 + 30 = \theta + \theta$$
$$100 = 2\theta$$
$$\frac{100}{2} = \theta$$
$$\theta = 50°C$$

With equal masses of the same substance, the heat lost must have equalled the heat gained, so the final temperature will lay halfway between 70°C and 30°C, (50°C).

Heat Transfer

Heat transfers by convection, radiation or conduction. Each of these processes works in a different way.

Convection

When gas or liquids are heated, they will expand increasing their volume. When this occurs their densities will reduce. Hot liquid, for example, will rise in a colder surrounding liquid because it will have buoyancy. The movement of the fluid in this situation is called convection. Conversely, cold liquid will sink in warmer surrounding liquid.

The convective movement within liquids and gases sets up currents where heat is carried from one place to another by the liquid or gas itself.

Radiation

All matter emits radiation. It is electro-magnetic radiation and it does not require any medium in which to travel. The Sun emits huge amounts of radiation at different wavelengths. Some reaches us as visible light but there is also radio, infrared, ultra-violet, X-ray, gamma and cosmic radiation. All this travels from the Sun through a vacuum at the speed of light to reach us in just eight minutes.

Radiant heat is electro-magnetic radiation that travels at the speed of light and can move through a vacuum. It transfers to a body and excites its particles increasing their kinetic energy. It can be reflected and focussed just as light can. It can be absorbed more in some materials than others and can be reflected to different degrees by colours. Light coloured materials will reflect heat whilst darker colours absorb it.

The degree to which a body will radiate or absorb heat will depend on its internal energy, surface area and the nature and colour of its material. All matter has internal energy and will radiate heat.

Conduction

The 'cloud' of free electrons in metals is called conduction electrons. Where a temperature difference exists in a metallic substance, the electrons in the hotter regions quickly gain kinetic energy and diffuse into the cooler regions. This is why heat appears to travel so fast in a metal. It is a good conductor.

Non-metals, on the other hand, are very poor conductors of heat. The covalent nature of their atomic bonds is very strong and there are no free electrons.

The molecules vibrate and pass the vibration through their neighbours to cooler regions. The process is slow and non-metals are described as being good insulators.

Expansion

With very few exceptions, all matter will expand if it is heated, and contract if it is cooled.

Different materials do not expand or contract to the same degree. The degree to which a material will expand when heated is identified by its *Coefficient of Expansion*. When expansion occurs, the dimensions of the substance will increase. For solids, this means their length, breadth, width, area and volume will all increase. Liquids and gases will increase in volume.

To sort out what we are dealing with there are special terms to describe the expansion. Increase in length is called *Linear Expansion*. Increase in area is called *Superficial Expansion* and increase in volume is called *Volumetric Expansion* when we talk of liquids and gases, and *Cubical Expansion* when we talk of solids.

Coefficient of Linear Expansion

A substance's *Coefficient of Linear Expansion*, represented by the Greek letter Alpha (α), is the fraction of its original length by which a rod of the substance expands per degree rise in temperature.

$$l_2 = l_1 + l_1\alpha\theta$$
or
$$l_2 = l_1(1 + \alpha\theta)$$

For example, let l_1 be the original length of a rod and α be the coefficient of linear expansion. For a rise in temperature, θ, the expansion will be $l_1\alpha\,\theta$ and the new length l_2 will be the sum of the original length and the expansion.

Coefficient of Superficial Expansion

The coefficient of superficial expansion, represented by the Greek letter Beta β is the fraction of the original area by which a plate will increase in area when its temperature rises by 1°C. The coefficient is twice the coefficient of linear expansion.

$$A_2 = A_1(1 + \beta\theta)$$

A_1 is the original Area. θ is the temperature change and β is the coefficient of superficial expansion. The expansion will be the increase in area $A_1\beta\,\theta$. The new area A_2 will be the sum of the original area and the increase in area. The coefficient of superficial expansion is twice the coefficient of linear expansion.

Coefficient of Cubical Expansion

The coefficient of cubical expansion, represented by the Greek letter Gamma (γ), is the fraction of the original volume by which a body will expand for a temperature rise of 1°C. The coefficient is three times the coefficient of linear expansion.

$$V_2 = V_1(1 + \gamma\theta)$$

www.part66.co.uk

V_1 is the original volume. θ is the temperature change and γ is the coefficient of cubical expansion. The expansion will be the increase in volume $V_1 \gamma \theta$. The new volume V_2 will be the sum of the original volume and the increase in volume. The coefficient of cubical expansion is three times the coefficient of linear expansion.

Expansion of Liquids

Liquids have no fixed dimensions other than volume. A problem arises when attempts are made to heat a liquid and then measure its increase in volume. The problem lays in the fact that the container it is in will also expand giving a false impression that the liquid has not expanded as much as predicted.

Liquids are given two coefficients for their expansion. First, the *coefficient of Apparent Expansion*, which is the fraction of the liquid's original volume by which it appears to expand per 1°C rise in temperature when it is heated in a container that expands.

The second is the *Coefficient of Real Expansion*, which is the fraction of its original volume by which it really expands by a 1°C rise in temperature.

Expansion of Water

We already know from previous reading about changes in the state of matter that the density of water actually starts to decrease as its temperature falls below +4°C. This means that as water is heated at 0°C it will actually contract as the temperature rises up to +4°C. This behaviour is said to be *Anomalous*. If we continue to heat the water above +4°C, it will then expand. When water freezes, expansion takes place and ice takes up a bigger volume, this causes it to float on water.

Cubic Expansion of Gas

For solids and liquids, the coefficient of cubical expansion is so small that no appreciable error is made by assuming the initial volume to be at or near room temperature. However, gases have a much larger coefficient so it is important to be precise in the definition.

The *Coefficient of Cubic Expansion of Gas* is the amount by which a unit volume of the gas at 0°C increases when the temperature is increased 1°C with the pressure remaining constant. When a gas remains at constant pressure, the variation in volume for 1°C variation in temperature is:

$$\frac{1}{273} \text{ per } °C$$

This relationship was established using the absolute temperature scale. It assumes that a gas would theoretically occupy zero volume at a temperature of absolute zero. This point is –273°C. The expansion of the gas is then assumed to take place in direct proportion to the temperature rise. The result, it expands at 1/273rd of its volume at 0°C for each degree absolute temperature rise (K). Note that 1K is the same as 1°C.

Example Calculations

Example 1

An ingot of steel has a coefficient of linear expansion of 10 x 10^{-6}/°C. If the ingot is a perfect cube with 1 m sides, what will its new volume be, if its temperature is raised by 1000°C?

Coefficient of cubical expansion ($\gamma = 3\alpha = 0.00003$)
$V_2 = V_1(1 + \gamma\theta) = 1m^3(1 + 0.00003 \times 1000°C) = 1.03m^3$

Example 2

A litre of gas at 27°C is heated whilst at constant pressure to raise its temperature to 177°C. Its new volume will be:

Initial absolute temperature at 27°C = 300K

Final absolute temperature at 177°C = 450K

Volume of gas at 127°C = 1 litre x $\frac{450K}{300K}$ = 1.5 litres

First Law of Thermodynamics

The laws of thermodynamics were given to you at the beginning of this section. To remind you, the internal energy of a system is a sum of the work done on the system and the heat supplied to it.

The formula we used was:

Change in Internal Energy (U) = Heat input (Q) + Work input (W)

Try an example that could be a typical IR Pat-66 type question.

During the compression stroke of a petrol engine, the work done on the gas in the cylinder is 70kJ/kg and the heat leaving the gas through the cylinder walls is 40kJ/kg. The change in internal energy of the gas per unit mass is:

U = Q + W therefore U = -40kJ/kg + 70kJ/kg = 30kJ/kg

Systems

An example of a system is a mass of gas contained in an engine cylinder, the boundary of which is drawn by the cylinder walls, the cylinder head and the piston crown. Assuming the valves to be closed, the system we have described is a *Closed System*, figure 3.2.

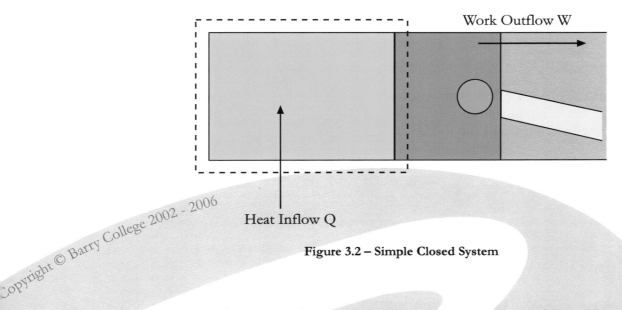

Work Outflow W

Heat Inflow Q

Figure 3.2 – Simple Closed System

The boundary is continuous and no matter can enter or leave. However, energy may pass across the boundary of a system. When this happens it will always be in the form of heat or work. For example, the cylinder head may be heated with the valves closed.

The heat will pass through the head and heat the gas, which will expand and do work in pushing the piston along the cylinder. A system may also exist with breaks in it through which matter may enter or leave. Such an arrangement is called an *Open System*, figure 3.3.

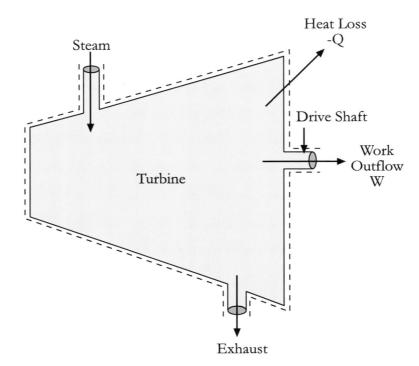

Figure 3.3 – Simple Open System

A steam turbine is a good example of an open system. There is an entrance through which high-pressure steam may pass, and an exhaust port through which low-pressure steam can leave after its passage through the turbine. The boundary of the open system is formed by the turbine casing. If energy passes across the boundary, it will always be in the form of heat or work. Heat may flow off the casing to the surroundings and work may flow along the drive shaft.

Second Law of Thermodynamics

In reality, the second law of thermodynamics is a directional law in that it states that heat transfer will occur naturally of its own accord *down* a temperature gradient. Simply, meaning heat will naturally flow from a hot region to a cooler region but not the other way around.

Heat can be made to transfer up a temperature gradient but not without the aid of some form of external energy being used, fuel burning being the obvious example. Natural heat transfer down the temperature gradient will continue until both temperature regions are equal and so are in thermal equilibrium.

From this second law of thermodynamics it follows that in order to operate any present day engine; fuel must be used to raise the temperature of the working substance. For example, steam or air, up above that of its surroundings. This enables the working substance to transfer energy either by doing work or by heat loss until the temperature of the substance falls to that of its surroundings again.

By virtue of the second law, it is essential that all fuels should be used as efficiently as possible. Once their energy has been degraded by heat transfer down the temperature gradient, further energy can only be obtained by expending more fuel.

Thermal Efficiency

There are two very important facts for you to remember. *Energy cannot be converted into 100% work*. There will always be heat loss through friction in bearings and air resistance. Heat will also be wasted by conduction and radiation through system casings. So, energy will do work but it converts into other less useful forms of energy as well.

Work can be converted into 100% energy. This is true. Work will convert into several forms of energy, some useful, some not. The trick is to get it to convert predominantly into the form of energy you want. A difficult task!

The heat energy that is released from fuel will not all result in useful work. Even the most efficient engines today are very good at using up lots of energy to overcome friction and drive components vital to their own operation before any work appears for you to use. If you divide the useful work output of an engine by the energy released from the fuel it uses you have a measure of the engines thermal efficiency. Car engines today are around 30% thermally efficient and the best aircraft gas turbine engines around barely exceed 40% efficiency.

$$\text{Thermal Efficiency} = \frac{\text{Work produced}}{\text{Energy supplied}} \times 100\%$$

Example

A turbo-jet engine consumes 0.5lb of jet fuel a second. It accelerates 100kg of air a second up to a jet velocity 300m/s. The calorific value of the fuel is 18,500 British Thermal Units (BTU) per lb. One BTU is equal to 1055 Joules.

$$\text{Thermal Efficiency} = \frac{\text{Work produced}}{\text{Energy supplied}} \times 100\%$$

$$\text{Kinetic Energy in the gas stream} = 0.5mv^2$$
$$= 0.5 \times 100kg \times 300m/s^2$$
$$= 4.5MJ$$

$$\text{Fuel Energy released} = 0.5lb \times 18500BTU \times 1055J$$
$$= 9.8MJ$$

$$\text{Thermal Efficiency} = \frac{4.5MJ}{9.8MJ} \times 100\% = 46\%$$

www.part66.co.uk

The Carnot Cycle of Operation

We have just discussed that it is not possible to transfer heat energy into 100% work and we know that it is possible to transfer work into 100% heat. If we imagine that it were possible to transfer heat into 100% work and then transfer that work back into 100% heat energy again, we would have the perfect perpetual motion engine. Imagine we had an engine that consisted of a turbine driving a compressor. Gas at high internal energy enters the turbine and uses all that energy to drive the turbine.

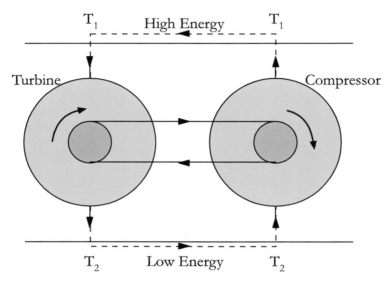

Highest-Efficiency Engine

Figure 3.4 – The Carnot Cycle

The gas exits the turbine at ambient temperature and passes into the compressor. The compressor then works on the gas raising its internal energy back up to its original high value. The gas then passes to the turbine and the cycle continues. If this could be true, we would have discovered perpetual motion. It cannot happen of course. The drive belt has to overcome friction and the compressor, and turbine bearings also generate friction. Add to this pressure losses due to air friction, and heat loss through the casing walls and we have the depressing reality.

The compressor in this example is best described as a '*heat pump*' in that it is taking a fluid in at low temperature and pumping it up to a higher temperature.

The example, illustrated in figure 3.4, is a theoretical one. In reality, we are looking at an engine that would actually have to be continually supplied with heat to replace lost energy.

www.part66.co.uk

Practical Lessons from the Carnot Cycle

The designers of engines will strive to get as near to the perfect Carnot Cycle as possible. They can never reach 100% Carnot efficiency of course. By reducing frictional losses and preventing heat loss through casings, they can make useful improvements. The trick is to put heat in at the highest energy level you can safely achieve and then try to convert as much of it as possible into useful work. Any heat leaving the system should be as close to ambient temperature as you can get it. It is possible to give a prediction of the best Carnot efficiency possible for the heat energy you intend to put in. That does not mean you will achieve it, but it is a useful guide.

$$\text{Carnot Efficiency} = 1 - \frac{288K}{T} \times 100\%$$

Example

An engine takes in heat at 447°C and exhausts it at 15°C. The maximum Carnot Efficiency possible is:

$$1 - \frac{288K}{720K} \times 100\% = 60\%$$

Gases

We are now going to look at the relationships that exist between the volume, pressure and temperature of a gas. These relationships are spelt out for us in three gas laws:

1. The relationship between volume and pressure at a constant temperature; *Boyle's Law*

2. The relationship between volume and temperature at a constant pressure; *Charles' Law*

3. The relationship between pressure and temperature at a constant volume; *Pressure Law*

Boyles constant temper kept the pressure on Charles.

289

Boyle's Law

The volume (V) of a fixed mass of gas at constant temperature is inversely proportional to its pressure (p).

$$p\alpha\frac{1}{V} \text{ or } pV = a \text{ constant}$$

In simple terms, if the pressure is doubled the volume will be halved and vice-versa. When the pressure and volume of a gas are altered, the product of the initial pressure (p_1) and volume (V_1) will equal the product of the new pressure (p_2) and volume (V_2).

This can be expressed in the following way:

$$p_1V_1 = p_2V_2$$

Charles' Law

The volume (V) of a fixed mass of gas at constant pressure is directly proportional to its thermodynamic temperature (T).

To clarify this, the volume of a fixed mass of gas will change by $1/273^{rd}$ of the volume it would be at 0°C for each 1°C change in temperature. Do remember that one degree centigrade is the same as one Kelvin.

$$\frac{V}{T} = a \text{ constant} \quad \text{this can be expressed as:} \quad \frac{V_1}{T_1} = \frac{V_2}{T_2}$$

The Pressure Law

The pressure (p) of a fixed mass of gas at constant volume is proportional to its thermodynamic temperature (T).

To clarify this, the pressure of a fixed mass of gas will change by $1/273^{rd}$ of the pressure it would be at 0°C for every 1°C change in its temperature. To remind you again, one degree centigrade is equal to one degree Kelvin.

$$\frac{P}{T} = a \text{ constant} \quad \text{this can be expressed as:} \quad \frac{P_1}{T_1} = \frac{P_2}{T_2}$$

The Combined Gas Law

The three gas law equations can be combined as:

$$\frac{pV}{T} = R \text{ (the gas constant)}$$

this can be expressed as:

$$\frac{p_1 V_1}{T_1} = \frac{p_2 V_2}{T_2}$$

Note: When dealing with calculations involving the gas laws you must remember to use *Absolute Temperatures* and *Absolute Pressures*.

To remind you, the absolute temperature scale is the Kelvin scale. To convert degrees centigrade to degrees Kelvin just add 273 to the centigrade value. To determine the absolute pressure, just add the ambient pressure to the gauge pressure.

Absolute Pressure = Gauge Pressure + Atmospheric Pressure

Examples

Example 1 - Boyle's Law

Gas in a cylinder at 100kPa absolute pressure is slowly compressed at constant temperature until it reaches one quarter of its original volume. The new gas pressure will be:

Assume the initial volume to be 1m^3.

$$p_1 V_1 = p_2 V_2$$
so: $100\text{kPa} \times 1\text{m}^3 = p_2 \times 0.25\text{m}^3$
therefore: $p_2 = 400\text{kPa}$

Example 2 - Charles' Law

A fixed mass of gas was heated at constant pressure to raise its temperature from 27°C to 127°C when it reached a final volume of 4m^3. The original volume of the gas was:

must use °K

$$\frac{V}{T} = \frac{V}{T}$$

$$\frac{?}{300} \quad \frac{4}{400}$$

$$\frac{4 \times 300}{400} = \frac{1200}{400} = 3\text{m}^3$$

www.part66.co.uk

$$\frac{V_1}{T_1} = \frac{V_2}{T_2}$$

$$\text{so:} \quad \frac{V_1}{300K} = \frac{4m^3}{400K}$$

$$\text{therefore: } V_1 = 3m^3$$

Example 3 - Pressure Law

A tyre pressure check was carried out at an ambient temperature of 27°C and showed the tyre pressure to be 300kPa. The next pressure check was carried out at a route stop where the ambient temperature was -3°C.

Assuming no air was lost en route, the tyre pressure would be:

$$\frac{P_1}{T_1} = \frac{P_2}{T_2}$$

$$\text{so:} \quad \frac{300kPa}{300K} = \frac{P_2}{270K}$$

$$\text{therefore: } P_2 = 270kPa$$

Ideal Gases

An ideal gas can be defined as being one that obeys the equation:

$$\frac{pV}{T} = \text{a constant}$$

The value of the constant depends on the gas we are using and its mass. If we consider there to be 1kg of gas we can express the equation as:

$$\frac{pV}{T} = R$$

'R' in this case is called the *Specific Gas Constant*, because we are relating it to a given mass. The SI unit is the J/kg K.

To express the *Ideal Gas Equation* all we have to do is multiply the gas constant by the mass of the gas.

$$\frac{pV}{T} = mR$$

This is known as the *Characteristic Gas Equation*.

Example 1

A gas has a volume of $1m^3$ at a pressure of 100kPa and a temperature of 27°C. The gas is compressed to a pressure of 400kPa at 327°C.

The new volume is:

$$\frac{P_1V_1}{T_1} = \frac{P_2V_2}{T_2}$$

$$\text{so: } \frac{100kPa \times 1m^3}{300K} = \frac{400kPa \times V_2}{600K}$$

$$\text{therefore: } V_2 = 0.5m^3$$

Example 2

10kg of gas at 27°C and a pressure of 600kPa has a gas constant of 300J/kgK . The volume occupied by the gas will be:

$$\frac{pV}{T} = mR \quad \text{Therefore: } V = \frac{mRT}{p} = \frac{10kg \times 300J/kgK \times 300K}{600 \times 10^3Pa} = 1.5 \, m^3$$

Example 3

A gas bottle has a volume of $1m^3$ and contains gas under 450kPa pressure at 27°C. The specific gas constant is 300J/kg K. The mass of gas is:

$$pV = mRT \quad \text{Therefore: } m = \frac{pV}{RT} = \frac{450 \times 10^3Pa \times 1m^3}{300J/kgK \times 300K} = 5kg$$

Specific Heat Capacity at Constant Pressure and Volume

You are now aware that the *Specific Heat Capacity* of a substance describes the amount of heat required to raise the temperature of a given mass of the substance by one degree centigrade. It is better to call this one degree Kelvin as it reminds us that we are dealing with absolute temperatures. So, we will call the unit used the *J/kg K*.

When a gas is heated, the internal energy of the gas goes up as the molecules gain kinetic energy. If the gas is in a closed container with a fixed volume, the molecules collide with the container walls producing a rise in gas pressure. If the container is open, the gas will expand, losing its new found internal energy in the process of producing the work to expand. A gas will have two values quoted for its specific heat capacity in order to describe its behaviour in either of the two cases we are discussing.

Specific Heat Capacity at Constant Volume (C$_V$)

Consider 1 kg of gas being heated in a closed container, so that no expansion of the gas is allowed. The number of joules required to raise the temperature of 1 kg of the gas through 1K under these conditions is called the *Specific Heat Capacity at Constant Volume (C$_V$)*.

In this case, there is no work of expansion because the gas cannot move, and all the heat supplied is used to increase the internal energy of the gas. The value of C$_V$ for air is 718 J/kg K. See figure 3.5.

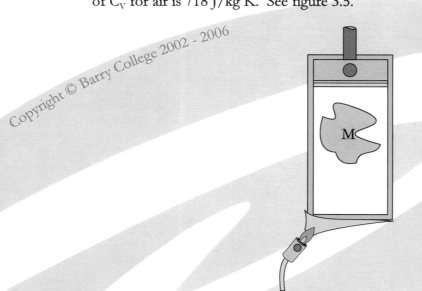

Figure 3.5 – Gas Heated at Constant Volume

Specific Heat Capacity at Constant Pressure (C~P~)

Consider now 1 kg of gas being heated in a cylinder fitted with a moveable piston. When the gas is heated, it will expand. The gas pressure acting on the area of the moveable piston will create a force, which will move the piston through a distance. Force times distance is of course - work. As the work is leaving the system, the internal energy of the gas will fall. If we wish to keep the internal energy constant, we will have to keep on supplying heat to replace the energy being lost as the gas works on the piston to move it.

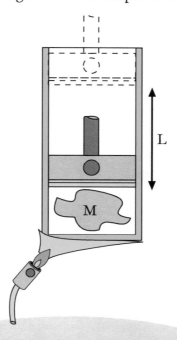

L

M

Figure 3.6 – Gas Heated at Constant Pressure

The joules required to raise the temperature of 1kg of the gas by 1K is the *Specific Heat Capacity at Constant Pressure (C$_P$)*.

The value of the specific heat of a gas at constant pressure will always be greater than that at constant volume by the amount of expansive work done. The value of C$_P$ for air is approximately 1005 J/kg K.

The ratio of C$_P$ to C$_V$ for a particular gas is called its *Specific Heat Ratio* and it is a constant. The symbol used is the Greek letter Gamma (γ). Specific heat ratio for air is 1.4.

$$\frac{C_P}{C_V} = \gamma = \text{constant}$$

Remember, the value of C$_P$ is always greater than the value of C$_V$. It is a frequently used question!

The Relation Between the Specific Heat Capacities of a Gas C_p and C_v

Consider 'm' kg of gas to be receiving heat and expanding at constant pressure in a closed system from temperature T_1 to T_2. Since the heat required to raise the temperature of 1 kg through 1K at constant pressure is C_p then:

$$\text{Heat taken in (Q)} = m \times C_p(T_2 - T_1)$$

When expanding, the gas does external work by forcing the piston outwards against a resisting force and work flows outwards from the system across its boundaries.

Let 'p' be the constant pressure of the gas, which is exerted on a piston of cross sectional area 'A'. Let the piston move through a distance 'L' and heat is added to keep the pressure constant.

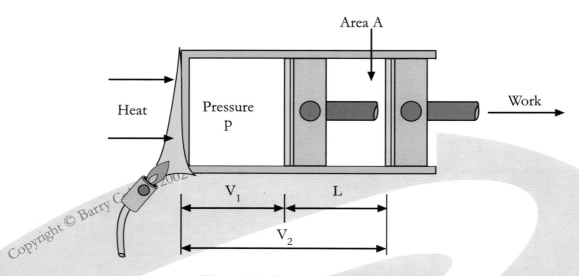

Figure 3.7 – Gas exerting a Pressure on a Piston

Constant force on Piston = Pressure x Area = pA
and
Work done = average force x distance moved = pA x L

AL is also the swept volume and so if we let V_1 be initial volume and V_2 be the final volume then work done will be:

$$\text{Work done} = p(V_2 - V_1)$$

www.part66.co.uk

Before you decide to have a cup of tea, there is one other fact to look at. We have said that the value of C_p is always higher than the value of C_V. If we were to compare these to values for different gases, we would notice that the difference always seems to be the same. There may be an exception or two but these turn out not to be ideal gases. So, we have an interesting link between all the ideal gases. The difference between C_p and C_V for ideal gases appears to be the same as the gas constant R.

$$\text{The ideal gas constant } R = C_p - C_v$$

The value of constant R for air is: 1005J/kgK - 718J/kgK = 287J/kgK.

Example

You are likely to be asked salient facts. Examples would be the comparison of specific heat capacities at constant pressure (C_p) and constant volume (C_V), the specific heat ratio (γ) and the ideal gas constant (R). These are easy to present in multi-choice form. However, try a simple set calculation.

Gas expanding in a cylinder exerts a constant pressure of 500kN on a piston $0.1m^2$ area. The piston moves through a stroke of 0.1m. The heat we would need to supply to keep the pressure constant throughout the stroke would be:

$$\text{Internal energy} = \text{heat} + \text{work}$$

If work leaves the system, we must put in an equivalent amount of heat to keep the internal energy the same.

$$\text{Work done} = \text{Pressure x Area x Distance} = \text{Heat required}$$
$$= (500 \times 10^3 N) \times 0.1m^2 \times 0.1m = 5kJ$$

Flow and Non-Flow Processes

A process can be described as being a *Non-flow Process* when a fixed mass of a substance is confined within a closed boundary and undergoes a change of state. This would describe a gas that was being heated in a closed cylinder. Even if the cylinder has a moveable piston in it, the system is still non-flow as the gas does not cross the boundaries of the system.

A process is described as being a *Flow Process* when the substance can cross the boundary of the system either by entering, or leaving, it. A *Steady Flow Process* is a process where this is happening continuously. A gas turbine engine, for example, has a mass of air flowing into its compressor. The

297

pressure of the air is raised in the compressor. Fuel is added and ignited to expand the air, which then expands through a turbine to do work before being exhausted back to atmosphere. There is a continuous flow of air into the system and out of it. Such a system is a continuous flow process.

The line on the p/v diagram shows the way the state of a gas might change on being heated from state 1 to state 2 so that its pressure increases from p_1 to p_2 and its volume increases from V_1 to V_2.

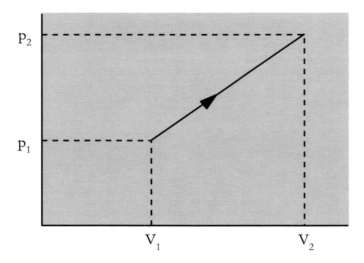

Figure3.8 – Pressure/Volume Diagram

The pressure, volume diagram displays a change of state with a line that represents a change of pressure and volume within the system.

It is often useful to consider part only of a flow process. In which case the part considered might be a non-flow process. For example, if the compression process of a petrol engine is considered separately, the process is non-flow, although the whole action of the engine which takes in air and fuel and rejects exhaust gas is a flow process

Cycle of Operation

A closed system may pass through a series of processes and return to its initial state when it is said to have passed through a cycle. The processes through which the system has passed may be shown on a state diagram.

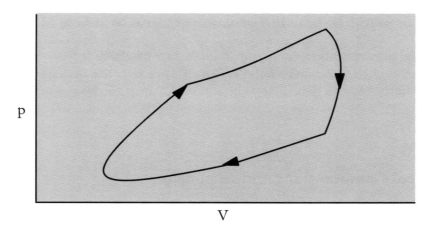

Figure 3.9 – State Diagram

Suppose a system consisted of gas in a cylinder with a moveable piston. If the gas is heated, its pressure will rise so that the gas could force the piston to move as the gas expanded. The gas might then be cooled and the piston drawn in again to the point where the gas is returned to its original pressure and volume. The system would have gone through a cycle.

When a closed system, like the one described, passes through a cycle, its state at the end of the cycle will be precisely the same as its state at the beginning. The system may have received heat, and put out work and heat during the cycle; but at the end of the cycle the internal energy is returned to its initial value.

When a closed system goes through a cycle, the sum of the heat energy taken in is equal to the work put out and any heat wasted.

When an open system undergoes a flow process, the working fluid passes across the boundary into the system and finally passes back out across the boundary. In addition to the work that the system may put out, it also has to work to drive the fluid through the system from the inlet to exhaust.

Before we go any further, it is important to have a look at a few terms used to describe processes and to understand their meanings.

Isothermal

An *Isothermal Expansion* or *Isothermal Compression* of a gas is one in which the gas's temperature remains constant throughout the process. In practice, an isothermal process is only possible if the operation is carried out very slowly so that heat can enter or leave the gas respectively, to keep the temperature constant.

The Adiabatic Expansion or Compression of a Gas

An *Adiabatic* expansion or compression is one in which no heat flow takes place across the boundaries of the system. In practice, the operation must be carried out quickly so that there is little time for heat to flow in or out of the system.

Practical Compressions and Expansions

Boyle's law solely concerns *Isothermal Processes*. It would only be possible if a gas were compressed or expanded at constant temperature. In real life, this is impracticable. The compression of a gas by a piston in a cylinder would have to be done at a rate that allowed the heat of compression to conduct through the cylinder walls to atmosphere as the compression took place. This would be a very slow process. Conversely, if the gas were allowed to expand, the expansion would have to be slow enough to allow heat from the atmosphere to conduct through the walls and into the gas to keep the temperature constant.

The *Adiabatic Process* relies on heat not crossing the boundaries. When a gas is compressed by a piston in a cylinder its temperature will rise. No heat has to come in from outside to do this. Conversely, when a gas expands, its temperature will drop. No heat leaves the system when this occurs. Of course, no system is perfectly insulated and some heat will conduct through the cylinder walls, (both during compression and expansion). So, the perfect adiabatic process is impracticable as well.

The truth is, all compressions and expansions lay somewhere between being adiabatic and isothermal. In a car engine for example, the compressions and expansions happen so quickly that there is little time for conducted heat to leave or enter. This makes the processes close to being perfectly adiabatic.

Let us have a look at a cylinder containing a mass of gas, and see what occurs when we first compress the gas and then let it expand again.

In the first diagram, the piston is going to compress the gas at two different rates. Firstly, it moves very slowly to reduce the volume from V_1 to V_2. The pressure rises from p_1 to p_2 in a purely isothermal compression. The temperature of the gas does not change throughout the compression.

www.part66.co.uk

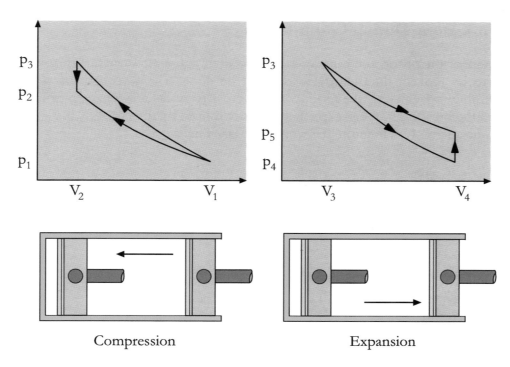

Compression   Expansion

Figure 3.10 – Isothermal & Adiabatic Compression & Expansion

If we had moved the piston quickly, heat would be produced during the compression and the pressure would rise to p_3 as a result. If we then held the piston in this position, the heat would slowly conduct away through the cylinder walls and the pressure would gradually fall to p_2.

The area under the pV graph actually represents the work required to carry out the compression. Notice that there is a bigger area under the upper, or adiabatic, line than under the lower, isothermal line. This tells you that it requires more work to compress a gas adiabatically than to compress it isothermally.

If you examine the second diagram, you will see that the compressed gas is being allowed to expand and push the piston along the cylinder. If this is allowed to happen quickly, the gas temperature will drop. The pressure will drop from p_3 to p_4 as the volume increase from V_3 to V_4. If the piston is now held in this position, heat will conduct in through the cylinder walls and the pressure will slowly rise to p_5. If the expansion had been conducted very slowly, the pressure would have dropped from p_3 to p_5 and the temperature would not have changed. This time the area under the graph represents the work done by the piston as it moves. Notice that more work is done during the isothermal expansion than during the adiabatic expansion

Work Done During Compression

Consider the piston and cylinder arrangement in figure 3.10 again. If the piston is to be moved, then clearly work must be done. The force on the piston resisting movement is the product of the cross sectional area of the piston (A) and the pressure in the gas (p). The distance moved by the piston is the length of the stroke 'L'. Therefore the work done must be:

Work done = Pressure (p) x Cross-sectional area (A) x length of Stroke (L)

or

pAL

However, area (A) $\times$ length (L) is the same as the swept volume of the cylinder and therefore:

$$\text{Work} = p \times (V_2 - V_1)$$

Where V_1 is the volume of the cylinder prior to the piston moving and V_2 is the volume of the cylinder after the piston has moved. $(V_1 - V_2)$ is therefore, the volume swept by the piston.

Ignoring the pressure rise in the gas, the diagram in figure 3.11 shows that the area enclosed under the graph is pV = Work Done.

If we examine the areas under the curves in figure 3.10, for the isothermal and adiabatic compression and expansion, we should see that less work is required for the isothermal compression than for the adiabatic compression. Similarly, more work may be extracted from the piston during the isothermal expansion than from the adiabatic expansion.

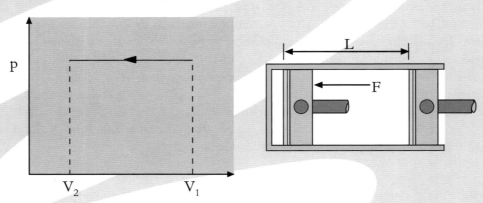

Figure 3.11 – Graph of Work Done

Heat Flow at Constant Volume

If the piston is locked in position to keep the volume constant and heat then flows in to the gas, the pressure will rise in a vertical line. Equally, if the heat flows out, the pressure will fall in a vertical line.

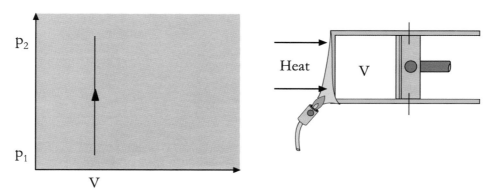

Figure 3.12 – Heat Flow at Constant Volume

Working Cycles

When a gas expands in a cylinder, the piston moves and so external work may be done. However, before this expansion takes place, the gas must be prepared by compression and the addition of heat energy. Since the work from a single expansion is small, a series of expansions are needed to produce a significant amount of work. In order for this chain of events to repeat, the gas must be returned to its original state each time. To achieve this, every pressure rise must be matched by a pressure drop elsewhere in the cycle and every decrease in volume matched by an increase in volume elsewhere.

The Constant Volume Cycle

As we should see from the pV diagram in figure 3.13, heat addition and heat rejection both take place at constant volume in the cycle.

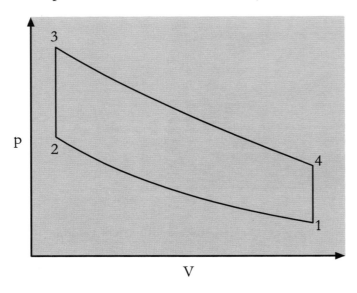

Figure 3.13 – pV Graph

This theoretical model forms the basis for the operation of all reciprocating spark ignition engines.

The phases that make up the cycle are:

1 - 2   Adiabatic compression

2 - 3   Heat addition at constant volume

3 - 4   Adiabatic expansion

4 - 1   Heat rejection at constant volume

The Otto Cycle

The four-stroke cycle takes its name from the number of single piston strokes that are necessary to complete a complete cycle.

The cycle is called the Otto Cycle and because heat is added only at the top of the compression stroke while the piston is momentarily stationary it is a Constant Volume Cycle. The cycle is repeated continuously while the engine is running.

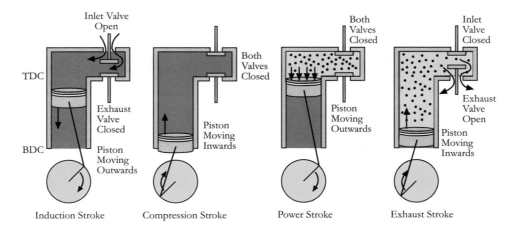

Figure 3.14 – The Otto Cycle in an Engine

Induction Stroke

The piston moves from *Top Dead Centre (TDC)* to *Bottom Dead Centre (BDC)*. During this movement, the inlet valve is open. A depression forms in the cylinder and atmospheric pressure at inlet forces air mixed with the required quantity of fuel into the cylinder.

Compression Stroke

The piston returns to TDC with both valves closed and compresses the charge into the combustion space.

Power Stroke

An electric spark ignites the charge at TDC and pressure rises in the cylinder combustion space because of the heat energy from combustion.

This acts on the cross sectional area of the piston to produce a force which then drives the piston down to BDC doing external work in the process. The expansion is adiabatic.

Exhaust Stroke

The piston moves from BDC to TDC with the exhaust valve open and discharges the spent gas to atmosphere at constant pressure.

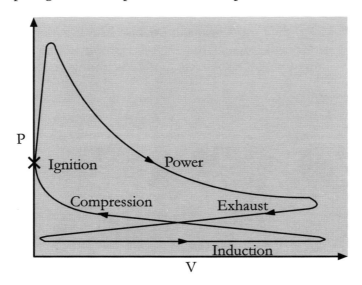

Figure 3.15 – The Otto Cycle

Note: The four-stroke cycle only produces one power stroke in two revolutions of the crankshaft. Part of the available work from this stroke must be used to drive the engine through the three idle strokes.

The Modified Four-Stroke Cycle

Four stroke engines are not the simplest form of piston engine but they have a higher thermal efficiency and are therefore more economical than most configurations. You should appreciate that the power output of an engine will depend on the pressure acting of the piston during the power stroke. It means that the more fuel air mixture that can be induced, the higher the pressure will be. The mixture should be fully burnt as near as possible to the start of the power stroke to maintain the expansion throughout the stroke. Modifications were introduced to the Otto Cycle in both ignition and valve timing to achieve these two aims.

Ignition Timing

The fuel/air mixture in a cylinder does not explode on ignition and so the combustion is not instantaneous. For an engine running at 3000 rpm, the time of one power stroke will be 0.01 sec, which means that complete combustion must occur in 0.0016 sec.

This combustion time does not vary over the range of engine speeds whereas the time taken for a power stroke will. In order to ensure maximum cylinder pressure straight after the piston passes TDC, the ignition point must be progressively advanced, i.e. happen earlier, as the engine accelerates up to maximum rpm and be progressively retarded, i.e. happen later, as the engine decelerates again.

Valve Timing

Air moving through a duct possesses inertia and this fact can be used to improve engine performance. Also the piston movement is not constant, it stops at the end of each stroke before reversing direction, accelerating and decelerating throughout each stroke.

Consider the last part of the power stroke; the piston is starting to slow and the gas pressure is at a low value. To prevent this pressure causing resistance at the start of the exhaust stroke, the exhaust valve is opened before the end of the power stroke. This is called *exhaust valve lead* and the exhaust gases accelerate out of the exhaust duct.

The loss to the power stroke is minimal as the crankshaft to connecting rod angle is very small near the end of a stroke so little turning moment is lost. Due to the inertia of the exhaust gases during the exhaust stroke, the exhaust valve is allowed to remain open into the first part of the induction of suction stroke. This is called *exhaust valve lag*. This allows the inertia of the exhaust gases to scavenge the combustion space causing a slight depression that assists the new mixture to enter in through the inlet valve.

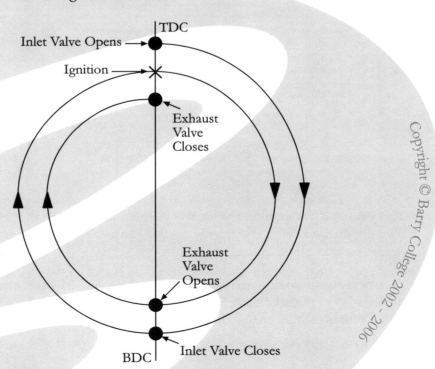

Figure 3.16 – Theoretical Valve Timing Diagram

On the induction stroke, the piston travels from TDC with the inlet valve open. The inlet valve is opened prior, (*inlet valve lead*), to the end of the exhaust stroke to enable the mixture to accelerate into the depression caused by the outgoing exhaust gases. During the first half of the induction stroke, the incoming mixture is accelerating along the inlet duct. The inertia it gains tends to keep the mixture moving in, even though the piston slows on approach to BDC and continues to enter the cylinder after BDC, on the first part of the compression stroke. Therefore, the inlet valve is allowed to remain open, (*inlet valve lag*), for the first part of this stroke.

In the timing diagram in figure 3.17, you should notice that at the end of the exhaust stroke and into the beginning of the induction stroke, both the inlet and exhaust valves are open together; this is called *valve overlap*.

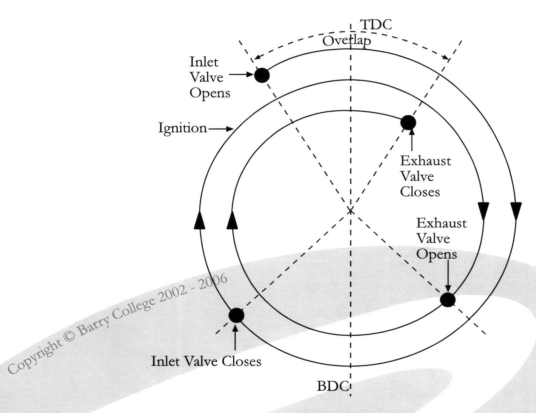

Figure 3.17 – Modified Valve Timing

This caused a problem on some early piston engines when the throttle valve in the inlet duct was closed suddenly resulting in a deep depression caused by the engine suction on this valve.

This depression could cause exhaust gas to be sucked back into the cylinder then across to the inlet duct. This was referred to as *boost reversal* and caused rough running as the engine decelerated to idle.

www.part66.co.uk

The un-swept volume of the cylinder is of the greatest importance. It is essential that exhaust gases be scavenged completely whilst the space must then be completely filled with new air fuel mixture. On later engines, the mixture is forced in under pressure from a supercharger to gain the maximum mass of mixture in this space.

Remember, the petrol engine Otto Cycle is a Constant Volume Cycle. You will be asked this. There is no attempt made to replace the gas internal energy being converted to work during the power stroke. As the piston is driven down, the gas pressure and temperature both reduce.

Heat flow at Constant Pressure

Consider a cylinder and piston arrangement where the expanding gas is working to move the loaded piston. As the gas expands, work is leaving the system, but we are continually supplying heat to replace it and maintain a constant pressure in the gas. The volume will increase but the pressure does not change.

The direction of the process on a pV diagram, figure 3.18, should be instantly recognisable, the area under the line being the work done.

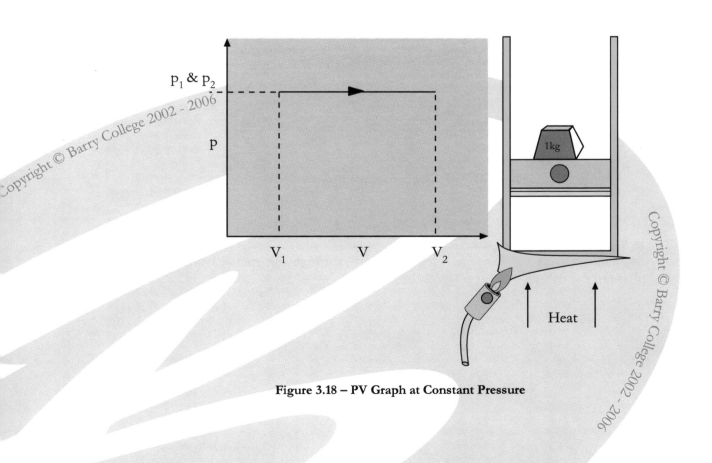

Figure 3.18 – PV Graph at Constant Pressure

The Constant Pressure Cycle

This cycle forms the basis of the of the gas turbine engine and is called the *Brayton Cycle*. If we examine the pV diagram for this cycle, figure 3.19, the following phases occur:

1 - 2	Adiabatic compression
2 - 3	Heat addition at constant pressure
3 - 4	Adiabatic expansion
4 - 1	Heat rejection at constant pressure

Note that in both cases, the cycle starts from point 1 at the beginning of the compression phase and the gas proceeds clockwise around the diagram.

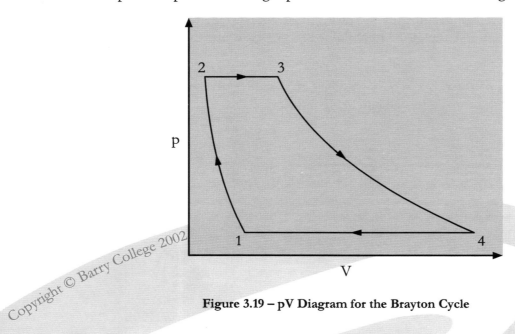

Figure 3.19 – pV Diagram for the Brayton Cycle

In a gas turbine engine, the cycle is continuous, all phases being in operation simultaneously as the fluid passes continuously through the engine from one phase to the other.

The Gas Turbine Engine – Constant Pressure Cycle

The gas turbine engine is an internal combustion engine using air as its working medium. In the piston engine, the four strokes of the working cycle are all carried out in one assembly unit, i.e. the cylinder. As the cylinder can only do one thing at a time, there is a power stroke followed by three idle strokes. The gas turbine, on the other hand, has a separate unit for each of the phases of the cycle, which is continuous in operation with a continuous power output.

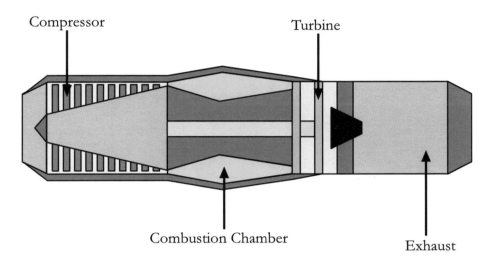

Compressor   Turbine

Combustion Chamber   Exhaust

Figure 3.20 – Simple Gas Turbine Engine

The simplest gas turbine engine consists of a compressor, a combustion chamber, a turbine and an exhaust unit.

Air at ambient atmospheric conditions enters the intake. The intake directs air evenly into the compressor where the air stream undergoes compression. From the compressor, the air stream passes to the combustion section where the high-pressure air is heated by the burning of fuel. The hot gases accelerate out of the combustion section, are guided into the turbine section. Here the hot gas expands and so provides a work output from the turbine to drive the compressor and the engine accessory components. On leaving the turbine, the gas stream enters the exhaust system. Further expansion takes place taking the gas pressure down to atmospheric pressure again as it discharges through the exhaust nozzle. Any pressure or heat remaining in the gas after this will be dissipated in the atmosphere as wasted energy. The velocity of the discharging mass of gas being much higher than the air velocity at intake provides thrust by virtue of the reaction to the acceleration of the mass airflow through the cycle.

The Practical Gas Turbine Cycle

The thermodynamic phases that make up the practical cycle of the simple engine in figure 3.20 are illustrated in figure 3.21.

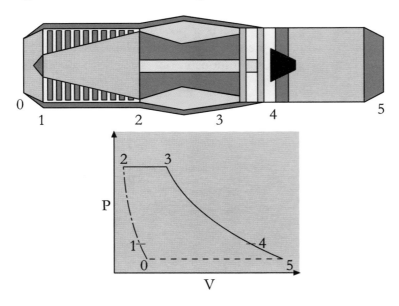

Figure 3.21 – Practical Gas Turbine Cycle

In words, the gas turbine cycle is:

0 - 1   Adiabatic compression with friction in the air intake

1 - 2   Adiabatic compression with friction in the compressor

2 - 3   Heat addition with slight pressure loss in the combustion system

3 - 4   Adiabatic expansion with friction in the turbine

4 - 5   Adiabatic expansion with friction in the exhaust nozzle

5 - 0   Heat rejection at constant pressure in the atmosphere

Refrigerators

Introduction

The second law of thermodynamics states that heat can only flow naturally from a region of high temperature to one of lower temperature. We are now going to consider reversing this. Naturally, we cannot expect heat to flow from a low temperature area to a higher one so we are going to have to make it happen. We could say that we are going to 'pump' the heat up to a higher temperature. This will require work and the energy to produce work.

A refrigeration cycle is one in which heat is absorbed from a low temperature region, such as a food cabinet, and is then transferred to atmosphere. In order that we may understand how this occurs, we need to gather some facts on the vapour pressures of fluids, latent heat and boiling points.

Vapour Pressure

We have learnt in the kinetic theory of matter that molecules are in a continual state of movement, their velocity depending very much on temperature. Liquids evaporate because the molecules at the surface jump clear into the air space above the liquid. Some fall back in again and others are swept away by air currents.

If we put a liquid in a sealed container, molecules would escape into the airspace above it. They would continue to do this until the rate at which molecules enter the air space equals the rate at which molecules are falling back into the liquid again. At this point, the air space is said to be *Saturated*.

The molecules create a pressure in the air space above the liquid. The pressure existing at the time saturation is reached is called the *Saturated Vapour Pressure* of the liquid for the temperature it is at. At this pressure the molecules have to work to enter the air space and lose their energy so they fall back into the liquid. If we increase the temperature of the liquid the molecules gain velocity and the air space will reach saturation at a higher pressure. A liquid will have a precise saturation vapour pressure to match a given temperature.

Now for the important point of all this! If any liquid is exposed to an air pressure that is the same as, or less than, its saturation vapour pressure for the temperature it is at, it will instantly vaporise. Simply, it boils.

We could even make water boil at room temperature if we put it in a container and started sucking the air out. As the pressure in the container fell to the saturation vapour pressure of the water at that temperature, it would boil. Now, we need to examine another fact.

Latent Heat

When a liquid turns into a vapour, it needs heat to sustain the process. As molecules leap clear of the liquid, they are taking their kinetic energy out of the liquid and this would drop the liquid temperature. So, a continuous supply of heat is required to keep the process going. This is called *The Latent Heat of Vaporisation*. Let me give you a graphic example. If you lick the back of your hand and wait for a second you will feel the area on your hand going cold. The evaporation is taking heat from your hand to keep going. Now, put a drop of a more volatile liquid on the back of your hand, the drop in temperature is much more noticeable.

313

Now consider the reverse. As gas molecules lose their kinetic energy they will fall back into liquid form in a process called condensation. You cannot make this energy disappear so it turns into heat. A gas must give out heat in order that it may condense into a liquid.

Here's another graphic example: If you are unfortunate enough to put your hand in the steam from a boiling kettle you will be scalded. Why is the burn so severe? The steam gives out a huge amount of heat as it condenses on your hand. This is the heat it had taken in order to vaporise. It has to lose it before it can go back into being a liquid. This is called *The Latent Heat of Condensation*.

Refrigerants

Now we are getting to the method by which we can remove heat from a low temperature area. Imagine you had a liquid that had a very high saturation vapour pressure at room temperature. Let's say the vapour pressure is around 60psi or 400kPa. Well, atmospheric pressure at sea level is just under 15psi which is way below the saturation vapour pressure of the liquid. If you exposed this liquid to the air in the room it would instantly vaporise taking heat from anywhere it could. It is in fact, boiling at room temperature.

Think about this. If the liquid's saturation vapour pressure is up around 60psi its boiling point must be much lower than room temperature. It will be. An example for such a liquid would be around –200°C.

Imagine that you now compress the vapour to a pressure above 60psi. The vapour would want to return into a liquid form. It has to dump its latent heat to do this. We let it. Now you can see how we can move heat from a low temperature area and transfer it to atmosphere. Where is the catch? We had to use energy to compress the gas in a compressor. What kinds of liquid have the properties we are talking about? Liquefied gases fit the description.

Ammonia has a saturation vapour pressure of 1013kPa at 26°C. This is ten times higher than atmospheric pressure at sea level. Its boiling point is –33°C. *Tetrafluoromethane*, known commercially as *Freon*, has a very high saturation vapour pressure and a boiling point of –128°C. These are both excellent refrigerants. *Dichlorodifluoromethane* is one of a group of halogenated hydrocarbons developed for use as refrigerants in smaller plants. What makes a good refrigerant?

Suitable Refrigerants

Fluids suitable for use as refrigerants are normally compressed liquefied gases that have a *High Saturated Vapour Pressure* and a *Low Boiling Point*. Other considerations are corrosive effects, flammability and toxicity. Methyl Bromide for example, boils at 3°C and has a fairly, high vapour pressure. A fairly good refrigerant - yes. You would need to be careful though as it attacks aluminium and is highly toxic. Water would be no good as its saturation vapour pressure is low and its boiling point too high. Carbon Dioxide on the other hand looks a good bet but it does not exist in liquid form.

The Refrigeration Cycle

The simplest example of this cycle may be seen in a domestic refrigerator. A *Refrigerant* liquid under high pressure is drawn through an expansion valve into the tubes of an *Evaporator*.

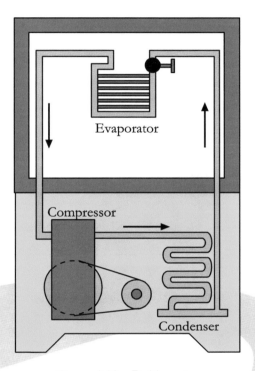

Figure 3.22 – Refrigerator

The evaporator experiences low pressure as it is situated on the inlet side of an electrically driven *Compressor*. As the refrigerant passes through the evaporator, it is exposed to a pressure well below its *Saturation Vapour Pressure*. The refrigerant vaporises and absorbs heat from the air surrounding the evaporator tubing. The refrigerant leaves the evaporator in gaseous form and is drawn into the *Compressor* where its pressure and temperature are raised to well above the saturation vapour pressure. The gas now wants to revert to liquid form but cannot do so unless it can reject its latent heat and the heat added during compression. As the refrigerant passes through the *Condenser*, the gas is able to liquefy and reject its heat to the ambient air surrounding the condenser. The cycle is continuous as long as the compressor is kept running to maintain the low and high-pressure sides of the system. The refrigerator takes heat from the low temperature region of the food cabinet and boosts it by adding work before rejecting to atmosphere.

When examining the pressure volume graph for this cycle, take note of the fact that the directional arrows run in the opposite direction to that of a heat engine. In the illustration shown below, the graph you will see that 50 Joules of heat energy has been extracted from the food cabinet. 20 Joules of work is then added to this in the compressor. 70 Joules of heat is being rejected out of the condenser. This is a heat pump. It reverses the second law only by providing work to pump the heat up to a higher value. It could not occur naturally.

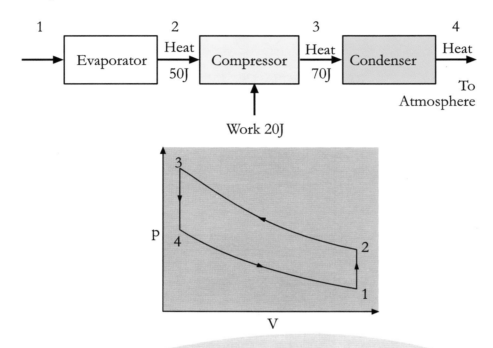

Figure 3.23 – Refrigeration Cycle

1 – 2   Heat is extracted from air. Gas temperature rises.

2 – 3   Gas temperature rises again as work is added.

3 – 4   Heat is rejected to atmosphere. Gas temperature falls.

4 – 1   Cycle returns to start air temperature again.

The refrigerator can be described as being a heat engine working in reverse. Heat is extracted from the air and work is then added in compression before the heat is rejected at high temperature. If you feel the condenser tubes on the back of a refrigerator, you may be surprised at the heat. Imagine, heat is transferring from the chilly region of the food cabinet up to the high temperature of the condenser. The second law has been reversed.

Refrigerators work better in the warm summer months than in winter. If the food cabinet is warm then heat transfers to the evaporator more efficiently than it would if the cabinet were too cold. It is just a matter of temperature difference.

www.part66.co.uk

A warm summer can cause a problem though. If the air surrounding the condenser is warm then the heat does not transfer to atmosphere as efficiently as if it were cooler. If this is a problem then a blower fan is used to force air through the fins of the condenser. This usually solves the problem but increases the energy requirement in that the fan has to be driven.

Vapour Cycle Cooling

The vapour cycle air conditioning system used on some aircraft operates on the same refrigeration cycle as the mechanical domestic refrigerator used to cool food. A refrigerant changes its state from a liquid into a vapour, and in doing so, absorbs heat from the cabin air. This heat is taken outside the aircraft and is given off to the atmosphere as the refrigerant returns to the liquid state (again).

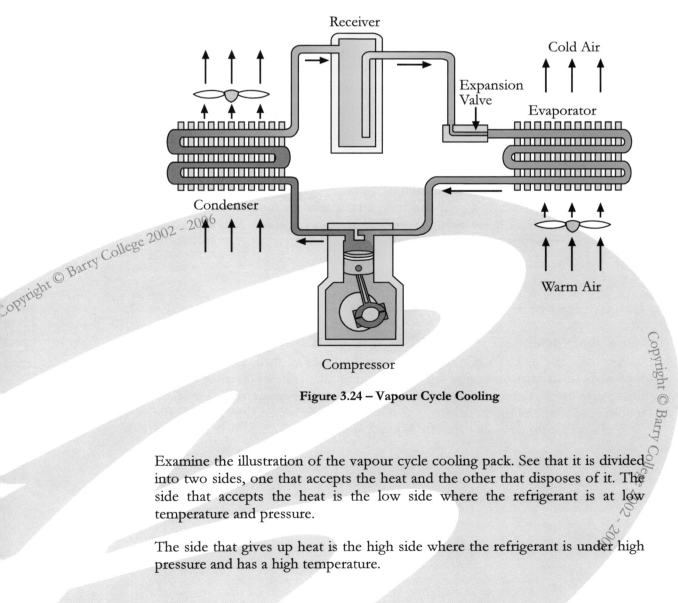

Figure 3.24 – Vapour Cycle Cooling

Examine the illustration of the vapour cycle cooling pack. See that it is divided into two sides, one that accepts the heat and the other that disposes of it. The side that accepts the heat is the low side where the refrigerant is at low temperature and pressure.

The side that gives up heat is the high side where the refrigerant is under high pressure and has a high temperature.

Heat Pumps

A heat pump takes in heat and boosts it up to a higher temperature by adding work. It then rejects the heat to atmosphere at high temperature. This is the reverse of a heat engine, which does work and then tries to reject heat to atmosphere at the lowest temperature.

The refrigerator was an example of a heat pump. The principle is used in other applications. A heat pump can be used in a central heating system. If there was a convenient lake, or river, near your house the heat pump can extract heat from the water into an evaporator. The condenser in this case would be in your house. The cycle would not be as efficient in the winter though as the water would be cold and the heat transfer to the evaporator would be less efficient.

Latent Heats of Fusion and Evaporation

We should learn the meaning of the different terms used to describe change of states. *Solidification* is an easy one. It describes the process when a substance turns into a solid form. *Fusion* is the term used to describe the process when a substance melts. *Vaporisation* is the process whereby a substance turns into a gas. Condensation is the process of turning from a gas into a liquid.

When a substance changes from a solid into a liquid and then into a gas, it requires to take in *Latent Heat* at each of these two phases. When a substance changes from a gas into a liquid and then into a solid, it requires to give out latent heat at each of these two phases. The latent heat taken in is the same value as that given out.

Latent Heat of Fusion

When the temperature of a solid substance reaches its melting point the temperature rise pauses while the substance continues to melt. It is absorbing heat without its temperature going up. The amount of heat it absorbs during this pause is the latent heat of fusion. The actual amount of latent heat required will depend on the nature and the mass of the substance. The SI unit used to express the *Specific Latent heat of Fusion* is the *J/kg*.

The specific latent heat of fusion of a substance is the quantity of heat required to convert a unit mass of the substance from a solid to a liquid state without change of temperature.

Latent Heat of Vaporisation

When the temperature of a liquid rises to its boiling point the temperature rise pauses as the liquid vaporises. You might have noticed this when you boil a kettle. The water turns into steam as heat is continuously applied to the kettle but, the temperature remains at 100°C. The heat taken in by the liquid during this temperature pause is the latent heat of vaporisation. The actual amount of heat absorbed will depend on the liquid and its mass. The SI unit used to express the *Specific Latent Heat of Vaporisation* is the *J/kg*.

The specific latent heat of vaporisation of a substance is the quantity of heat required to change a unit mass of the substance from a liquid to a vapour state without a change of temperature.

Fusion

We need to examine the process of fusion a little more to understand why latent heat is required. You have read that the molecules in a solid are in a constant state of vibration. The total internal energy of a solid is the sum of the kinetic energy produced by this movement and the potential energy. This exists, as a result, of the forces of attraction that hold the molecules together. Whilst the kinetic energy relates to temperature, the potential energy relates to the attractive and repulsive forces existing between the molecules.

When a solid turns into a liquid form, the molecules have to increase their range of movement. A rise in kinetic energy is required to achieve this state and this accounts for the latent heat taken in by the solid as it melts. Conversely, you can see that in order that a liquid may turn back into a solid form it has to give up this latent heat as the range of movement of its molecules reduces

Vaporisation

We now need to examine what is occurring when a liquid vaporises and why it requires latent heat. We have read the simple explanation that the energised molecules must move even further apart. This requires an increase in kinetic energy. It does not end there. The gas also has to expand against atmospheric pressure and this requires work. The sum of the increase in kinetic energy required and the work to push against ambient pressure accounts for much of the latent heat requirement. You can see that when the gas finally condenses back into a liquid, it will first have to give up this extra energy in the form of latent heat expelled.

You may now understand why the boiling point of a liquid reduces if you drop the air pressure over it and vice versa. This is why water boils at only 60°C at the summit of Everest and why the water in the pressurised radiator of your car does not boil when its temperature is at 130°C and instantly boils the

www.part66.co.uk

second you remove the cap. The boiling point of a liquid is proportional to the pressure existing over its surface.

Example Calculations

We need to be in possession of some data on the substance we are going to examine, in this case water.

The specific heat capacity of ice	$= 2.1$kJ/kg°C (2.1J/gm°C)
The specific latent heat of ice	$= 336$kJ/kg. (336J/gm)
The specific heat capacity of water	$= 4.2$kJ/kg°C (4.2J/gm°C)
The specific latent heat of steam	$= 2260$kJ/kg (2260J/gm)

Example 1

Determine the heat required to change 1kg of ice at –4°C into steam at 100°C.

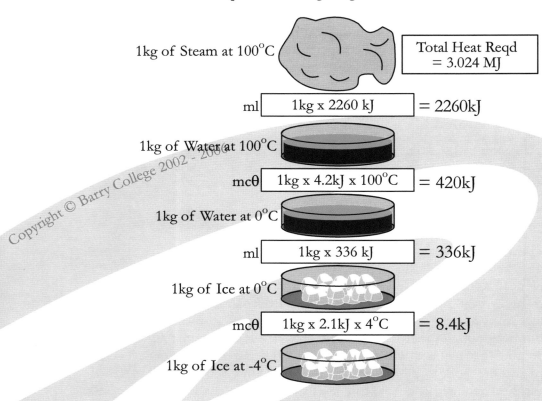

Figure 3.25 – Heat Required to turn Ice to Steam

Example 2

One kilogram of a metal initially at a temperature of 15°C is completely melted. The melting point of the metal is 330°C. The specific heat capacity is 150J/kg°C and the specific latent heat of fusion for this metal is 270kJ/kg. The heat required would have been:

Heat to raise temperature from 15°C to 330°C
$$mc\theta = 1kg \times 150J/kg°C \times 315°C$$
$$= 47.25kJ$$

Heat required to melt metal
$$ml = 1kg \times 270kJ$$
$$= 270kJ$$

Total heat required $= 47.25kJ + 270kJ$
$$= 317.25kJ$$

Saturation Vapour Pressure (SVP)

You will have encountered this during your study into refrigeration. We need to examine the subject a little further. To recapitulate, if a liquid is placed in a sealed container and heated to a given temperature, molecules of the liquid escape into the airspace until no more can be accepted. We called this the *Saturation Point*. The molecules in the air space, are moving at increased energy levels and collide with the walls of the container and each other. This causes a pressure, which we called the *Saturation Vapour Pressure (SVP)* for the liquid at the given temperature. If the liquid, at that temperature, is ever exposed to a pressure at or below its saturation vapour pressure, it will vaporise.

Liquids that have high vapour pressures are described as being *Volatile*. Some highly volatile liquids will vaporise at sea level ambient pressure and temperature.

The fuel carried in aircraft tanks has to be protected against this process. Gasolene, for example, has an SVP of 7psi at 30°C. This is the ambient pressure at 18000ft. If gasoline at 30°C were exposed to this pressure, it would vaporise in the fuel tanks and pipelines. With the rates of climb of some modern aircraft, the pressure/temperature conditions for the fuel's SVP could easily be met. Kerosene has an SVP of 0.1psi at 30°C. This pressure is not encountered until 62000ft. Suction on the inlet side of fuel pumps could however; produce the required conditions for vaporisation. For this reason, the airspaces in aircraft fuel tanks are always kept at a pressure above ambient.

Evaporation

Most liquids will evaporate when exposed to air, some more than others. The more volatile a fluid is, the faster the rate of evaporation. The process is based on the kinetic theory of matter.

The molecules of liquid at the surface of the liquid gain sufficient heat energy from their surroundings to jump clear of the liquid. Some fall back in again but, if there are air currents over the liquid, some molecules are carried away. As the energised molecules leave the liquid the total internal energy level of the remaining liquid falls. The result is that the liquid gradually cools as evaporation takes place. We rely on this process to keep ourselves cool during hot weather. The perspiration on our skin evaporates by extracting heat from our bodies. If you stand in a breeze during the process, you may feel quite cold.

Thermal Energy

You should be more than familiar with the idea that heat is energy. You should also be aware that it can flow naturally from a high temperature region to a lower temperature region by either, conduction, convection or radiation. We can also make it flow the other way by raising energy levels either by burning fuels or doing work. It is a fair assumption that all forms of energy, including work, eventually reveal themselves as heat. Hence the generic SI unit for energy and work is the Joule.

Heat energy can be locked up in fuels waiting to be released by chemical reaction. The amount of energy contained in a unit quantity of fuel is a measure of the fuel's *Calorific Value*.

Heat of Combustion

Combustion is simply a chemical reaction that produces heat as a by-product. The heat of the Sun is the result of the nuclear fusion of hydrogen atoms into helium. Closer to earth, we combine hydrocarbon fuels with oxygen at high temperature to produce carbon dioxide and water. The process releases a quantity of heat that depends on the fuel being used.

The *Calorific Value* of a fuel is determined by measuring the amount of heat given out by a unit quantity of the fuel when it is burnt. The ***British Thermal Unit (BTU)*** is often used to express the calorific value of aviation fuels. The SI unit for calorific value is the *Calorie*.

One British Thermal Unit (BTU) is defined as the heat required to raise 1lb of water through 1°F. The heat energy equivalents for the BTU are:

$$\text{One BTU} = 1.0554kJ \text{ or } 778ft\ lb$$

One Calorie is defined as the heat required to raise the temperature at 1gm of water through 1°C. The heat energy equivalents for the Calorie are:

$$\text{One Calorie} = 4.186J \text{ or } 3.09ft\ lb$$

Example 1

Aviation jet-fuel has a calorific value of 18500BTU per pound. The energy contained in a pound of this fuel will be:

$$1lb \times 18500BTU \times 1.0554kJ = 19.5MJ$$

Example 2

Aviation jet-fuel has a calorific value of 40800BTU per kg. The energy contained in one kilogram of the fuel would be:

$$1kg \times 40800BTU \times 1.0554kJ = 43MJ$$

Chemistry of Combustion

Crude oil is the base for the production of aviation fuels by fractional distillation. The fuels are hydrocarbons. When these fuels are mixed with oxygen at a high temperature, they combine with the oxygen to produce carbon dioxide and water.

The equation for the combustion of the carbon is:

$$C + O_2 = CO_2$$

The equation for the combustion of hydrogen is:

$$2H_2 + O_2 = 2H_2O$$

323

Revision

Thermodynamics

Questions:

1.   **Heat is defined as the:**

    A. Temperature changes resulting from work done

    B. Energy transfer due to molecular motion

    C. Energy transfer resulting from temperature difference

2.   **The freezing point of pure water in degrees absolute is:**

    A. 273 K

    B. -273 K

    C. 32°F

3.   **10°Centigrade converted to °Fahrenheit is:**

    A. 18°F

    B. 50°F

    C. 42°F

$$\frac{10 \times 9}{5} \quad \frac{90}{5} = 18 + 32 = 50$$

4.   **Heat is measured in:**

    A. Degrees on a temperature scale

    B. Joules

    C. Newtons

5. Specific heat capacity is defined as:

    A. Heat required to raise the temperature of a substance by 1°C

    B. The time a substance can maintain a given temperature

    C. The heat required to raise the temperature of a given mass of a substance by 1°C

6. The heat given out when a mass of 0.5kg, specific heat capacity 500 J/kg°C, cools from 40°C to 30°C is:

    A. 10 kJ

    B. 2 ½ kJ

    C. 25 kJ

$mc\theta$

$0.5 \times 500 \times 10 = 2500$

$2.5kJ$

7. The transmission of heat through a substance by the movement of free electrons is called:

    A. Conduction

    B. Radiation

    C. Convection

8. Heat energy from the sun transfers to earth by:

    A. Radiation

    B. Electron flow

    C. Convection

9. A litre of gas at 27°C is heated to 67°C, the pressure remaining constant, the new volume will be:

    A. 0.88 litre

    B. 1.4 litre

    C. 1.13 litre

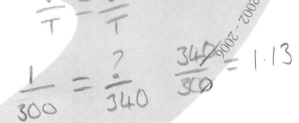

USE °K

$\dfrac{V}{T} = \dfrac{V}{T}$

$\dfrac{1}{300} = \dfrac{?}{340}$

$\dfrac{340}{300} = 1.13$

www.part66.co.uk

10.   The coefficient of cubical expansion of a material having a coefficient of linear expansion $10 \times 10^{-6}/°C$ is:

A. $33 \times 10^{-6}/°C$

B. $30 \times 10^{-6}/°C$

C. $1000 \times 10^{-6}/°C$

11.   A block of light alloy, forming a perfect cube (1m sides) is heated to raise its temperature by 500°C. Assuming the coefficient of cubical expansion to be 0.0001/°C, the new volume will be:

A. 1.02 m^3

B. 1.15 m^3

C. 1.05 m^3

$1 + 1 \times 500 \times 0.0001$

$1 + 0.05 = 1.05 \text{ m}^3$

12.   During the compression stroke of a four-stroke piston engine, the work done on the air is 70 kJ/kg and the heat wasted is 40 kJ/kg. The change in internal energy of the air will be:

Change heat in + Work Out

A. 30 kJ/kg

B. 110 kJ/kg

$-40 + 70 = +30$

C. −30 kJ/kg

13.   Which of the following statements is true:

A. Energy can be converted into 100% work

B. Work cannot be converted into energy

C. Work can be converted into 100% energy

www.part66.co.uk

14.   A process which takes place with no heat entering or leaving the system is called:

A. Isobaric

B. Isothermal

C. Adiabatic

15.   Assuming no heat energy is lost, a temperature of 50°C could be obtained by mixing:

A. Equal masses of ice and boiling water

B. Equal masses of water at 20°C and 80°C

C. Equal masses of ice and steam

16.   A gas occupies 30 litres volume at 27°C and 100kPa pressure. The volume it will occupy at 0°C and 273kPa will be:

A. 10 litres

B. 11 litres

C. 27 litres

$$\frac{P_1 V_1 T_2 = P_2 V_2 T_1}{P_2 T_1}$$

$$\frac{100 \times 30 \times 273}{273 \times 300} = \frac{3000}{300} = 10$$

17.   150 litres of gas at 100kPa pressure is compressed to occupy a 25-litre volume. Assuming no change in temperature occurs, the final pressure will be:

A. 600 kPa

B. 500 kPa

C. 700 kPa

$$\frac{P_1 V_1 = P_2 V_2}{V_2}$$

$$\frac{150 \times 100}{25} = \frac{15000}{25} = 600$$

18.   The heat energy required to turn water at room temperature into steam is:

A. The same as that required to raise its temp to 100°C

B. Less than that required to raise its temp to 100°C

C. More than that required to raise its temp to 100°C

To turn to steam must use latent heat

www.part66.co.uk

19. A turbo-fan engine has an inlet diameter of 2m. A speed sensor on the inlet indicates that the speed of air entering the engine is 200 m/s. If the density of air is 1.2 kg/m^3, the mass flow rate is:

A. 480 kg/s

B. 720 kg/s

C. 960 kg/s

Handwritten: $d = 2 \therefore r = 1$

$\pi r v$ density =

$3 \times 1 \times 200 \times 1.2 = 600 \times 1.2 = 720$

20. 1 kg of gas is contained in a closed cylinder 0.5m^3. If the pressure of the gas at 27°C is 420 Kpa, its specific gas constant will be:

A. 1005 J/kg K

B. 700 J/kg K

C. 290 J/kg K

Handwritten: $\dfrac{PV}{mt} = R$

$\dfrac{420000 \times 0.5}{1 \times 300} = \dfrac{210000}{300} = 700$

21. The specific heat capacity of water is 4 KJ/°C and the specific latent heat of fusion of ice is 300 KJ/kg. The heat energy required to change 10 kg of ice into water at 10°C is:

A. 3.4 mJ

B. 18.24 mJ

C. 1.8 mJ

Handwritten: $mc\theta$ $10 \times 4 \times 10 = 400$

ml $10 \times 300 = 3000$

22. The specific heat capacity of a fluid being heated at constant pressure will be:

A. Lower than if it were heated at constant volume

B. Higher than if it were heated at constant volume

C. The same as if it is heated at constant volume

Handwritten: $\dfrac{Cp}{Cv}$ is constant   Cp is always greater then

23. **One British Thermal Unit (BTU) has an energy value of:**

A. 1.0554 kJ

B. 18, 300 J

C. 80 kJ

24. **An effective refrigerant will have:**

A. Low saturated vapour pressure and a high boiling point

B. Low saturated vapour pressure and a low boiling point

C. High saturated vapour pressure and a low boiling point

25. **The equations for the combustion of a hydrocarbon fuel are:**

A. $C + 0_2 = C0$ and $2H_2 + 0_2 = 2H_20$

B. $C + 0_2 = C0_2$ and $2H_2 + 0_2 = 2H_20$

C. $C + 0_2 = C$ and $2H_2 + 0_2 = H_20$

Revision

Thermodynamics

Answers:

1. **C**

2. **A**

3. **B** $10°C \times 9/5 + 32 = 50°F$

4. **B**

5. **C**

6. **B** $mc\,\theta = 0.5kg \times 500J/kg°C \times 10°C = 2.5kJ$

7. **A**

8. **A**

9. **C**   Convert to absolute. $340K/300K = 1.13$ litre

10. **B**   Cubical is $3 \times$ linear

11. **C** $V_2 = V_1 (1 + \gamma\,\theta) = 1m^3 \times (1 + 0.0001 \times 500) = 1.05m^3$

12. **A** $U = -Q + W = -40kJ/kg = 30kJ/kg$

13. **C**

14. **C**

15. **B**   Heat lost = heat gained. $80 - 30 = 20 + 30$

16. **A** $(p_1V_1/T1 = p_2V_2/T_2)$ $100kPa \times 30$ ltr$/300K = 273kPa \times$ $V_2/273K$ $V_2 = 100kPa \times 30$ltr $\times 273K/273kPa \times 300K = 10$ litre

17. **A** $(p_1V_1 = p_2V_2)$ $100kPa \times 150$ltr $= p_2 \times 25$ ltr   p2=600kPa

18. **C**

19. **B**   Flow in kg/sec $= \pi$ x $1m^2 \times 200/sec \times 1.2kg/m^3 = 720kg/s$

20. **B** $pv = mRt.$ $R = pv/Mt.$ $420,000pa \times 0.5m^3/1kg \times 300k = 700$

21. **A** $mc\theta + ml$ $(10kg \times 300KJ/kg) + (10kg \times 4kJ/°C \times 10°C)$ $= 3.4mJ$

22. **B**

23. **A**

24. **C**

25. **B**

     www.part66.co.uk

Light - Optics

Nature of light

Light consists of minute packets of energy called *Photons* that travel in a stream at *186,000 miles or 300,000 kilometres a second* in a vacuum. Light is a part of the *Electromagnetic Spectrum* occupying a narrow frequency band between infra red at 10^{14}Hz and ultra-violet at 10^{15}Hz. Its wavelength varies around 10^{-6}m decreasing in length from red through the visible light spectrum to violet. Light behaves both as an *Electromagnetic Wave* and as a particle. It can travel through a vacuum and is affected by gravitational forces. Its behaviour is often referred to as the *Duality of Light*.

Visible Spectrum

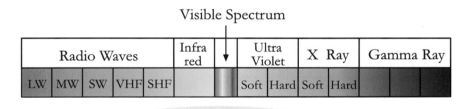

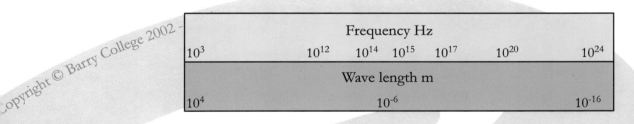

Figure 4.1 – The Electromagnetic Spectrum

Light waves can be reflected by shiny surfaces and focussed by lenses. Some materials will absorb light at different frequency values and reflect it at others. The main source of the light we see is the Sun, its light takes eight minutes to make the 93 million mile journey to earth. The sun's light is also reflected off the planets and moons in our Solar System making them visible to us. All the stars we see in the night sky are actually distant suns emitting light that can take tens or even thousands of light years to reach us. The light from distant galaxies travels to us over millions of light years.

The speed that light travels is slightly reduced as it passes through our atmosphere. It is significantly reduced when it passes through water and glass.

www.part66.co.uk

The materials through which light can travel and its speed depend on the *Optical Density* of the material.

Changes in the velocity of light as it enters or exits different mediums cause the light rays to *Refract* or bend. Light obeys the *Inverse Square Law* for electromagnetic radiation in that its intensity from a point source in space is inversely proportional to the square of the distance from the source.

Light Waves

Light radiates out from a point source as an expanding sphere. To enable us to represent a ray of light we imagine that the light comes to our eye in a straight line from the source.

For light, it is usual to draw a straight line representing the particular direction in which light is travelling in relation to an observer rather than drawing the wave fronts.

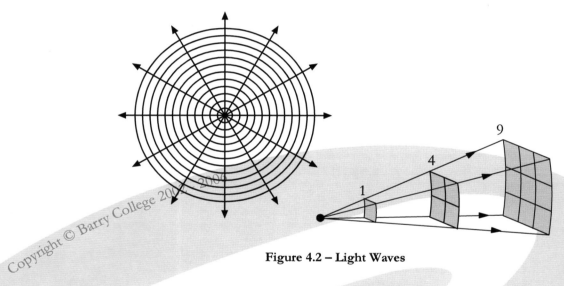

Figure 4.2 – Light Waves

Ray Diagrams

If we draw straight lines to represent light rays we are producing a ray diagram. We often have to exaggerate the angles between these lines in order to interpret what is happening. Light rays from a distant source enter the eye almost as parallel lines.

The actual variation in the divergence of rays entering the eye with respect to changing distance is very small. Your brain can interpret these minute changes into accurate judgements for distance. To draw the actual ray paths would be an impossible task so we exaggerate their angles in ray diagrams.

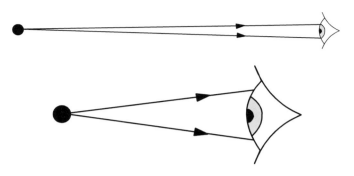

Figure 4.3 – Light Rays in Diagrammatic Form

Laws of Reflection

A ray of light striking a reflecting surface is called an *Incident Ray*. The light ray reflecting off the surface is called the *Reflected Ray*.

The angle between the incident ray and a line drawn perpendicular to the reflecting surface is known as the *Angle of Incidence (i)*. The angle between the reflected ray and a line drawn perpendicular to the reflecting surface is called the *Angle of Reflection (r)*.

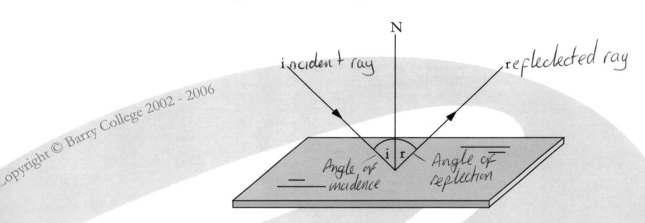

Figure 4.4 – Reflected Light Ray

There are two (2) laws of reflection and these are:

1. The angle of incidence (**i**) equals the angle of reflection (**r**).

2. The incident ray, the reflected ray and the perpendicular from the point of incidence, are coplanar. *i.e all lined up.*

Reflection in Plane Mirrors

Plane mirrors have flat surfaces. The image you will see in a plane mirror will be:

- Laterally inverted

- The same size as the object being reflected

- The same distance behind the mirror as the object is in front of it

- A virtual image that cannot be formed on a screen

When you look into a mirror you will see that your image is the same height as you and is laterally inverted. Your left hand has become your right hand in the reflection. You will also see that your image is positioned a similar distance behind the mirror as you are in front of it. Step backwards and your image recedes by a similar distance. The image you see cannot be projected onto a screen so it is described as being a virtual image.

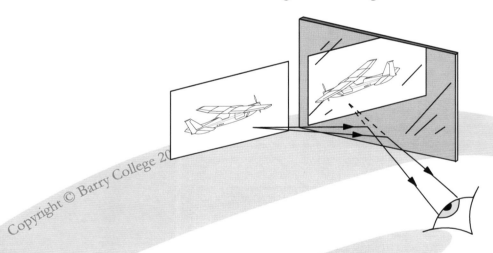

Figure 4.5 – Lateral Inversion

Look at the ray diagram of a pencil reflected in a plane mirror, figure 4.6. You see the image in an apparent cone of rays IPQ entering the eye from the image. The portion IRS of the cone behind the mirror does not exist. The real portion PQRS of the cone in front of the mirror is the result of light coming from the object down the cone ORS. You actually see the image through the reflected cone ORSPQ.

The distance ON of the object from the mirror is equal to the distance IN of the image behind the mirror.

www.part66.co.uk

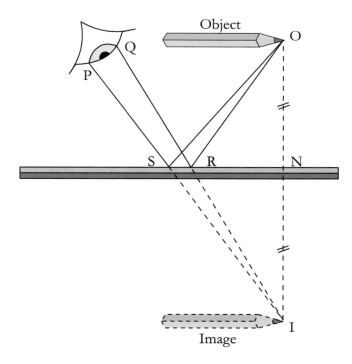

Figure 4.6 – Reflection in a Plane Mirror

Two Mirrors at Right Angles

If two mirrors are placed at right angles to each other to view the reflection of a single object you will see three images

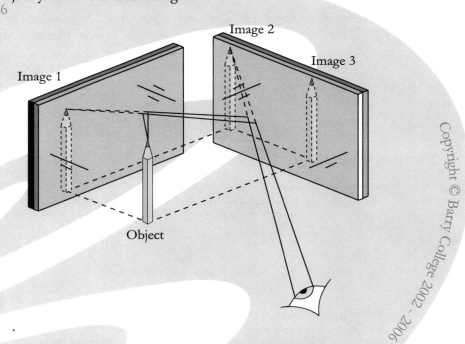

Figure 4.7 – Images in Two Mirrors at 90°

Parallel Mirrors

If you put an object between two parallel mirrors you will see an infinite number of images. They will all be in a line with the object at right angle to the plane of the mirrors.

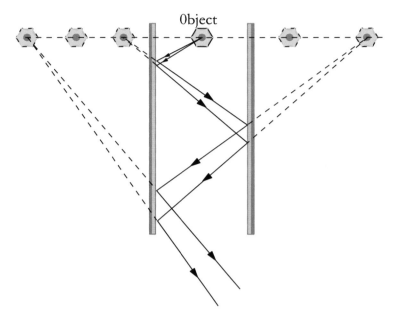

Figure 4.8 – Parallel Mirrors

The Periscope

This instrument comprises two opposing plane mirrors positioned at 45°. A distant object forms an image in the upper mirror, which then acts as a virtual object to produce another image in the lower mirror.

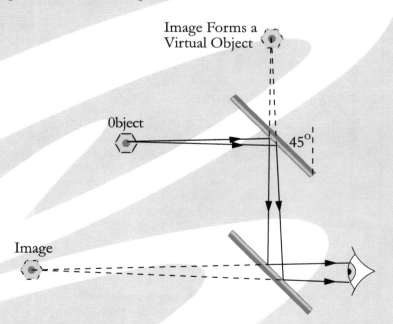

Figure 4.9 - Periscope

www.part66.co.uk

The Kaleidoscope

This instrument comprises two opposing plane mirrors positioned at an angle of 60° to each other in a viewing tube. Light enters through a ground glass plate at the bottom of the tube. When a small object is placed between the mirrors five images are seen and the object. Each will be in one of six symmetrical segments.

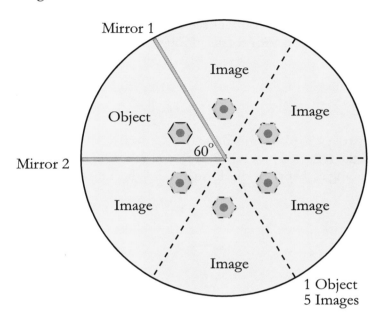

Figure 4.10 – The Kaleidoscope

Diffuse Reflection

Surfaces that appear to be smooth and polished may in fact be quite rough when examined through a magnifying glass. High quality mirrors should have very smooth surfaces. When light reflects off a surface it will be affected by the nature of that surface.

Light incident on a smooth surface will reflect away at the same angles as the incident rays. This is known as *Regular Reflection*.

Light incident on a rough surface will form varying angles of incidence with the surface irregularities. Rays will reflect off in different directions as *Diffuse Reflection*.

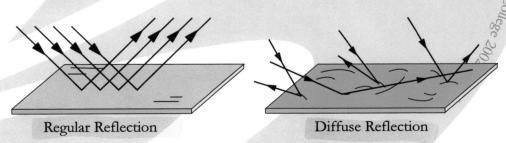

Figure 4.11 – Diffuse Reflection

Rotation of a Reflected Ray

If a ray of light strikes a mirror its angle of incidence will equal the angle of reflection (r). Imagine that we rotate the mirror through an angle (θ). The angle the incident ray makes with the perpendicular from the mirror will either increase by θ or, decrease by θ, dependent on which way the mirror is rotated. The reflected ray will also change by θ.

If you study the diagrams, you will see that the reflected ray rotates through twice the angle that the mirror rotates through.

Example

A light ray strikes a plane mirror and is reflected. The angle between the incident and the reflected rays is 30°. If the mirror is rotate through 20° in each direction the angles between the incident and the reflected rays in each case are:

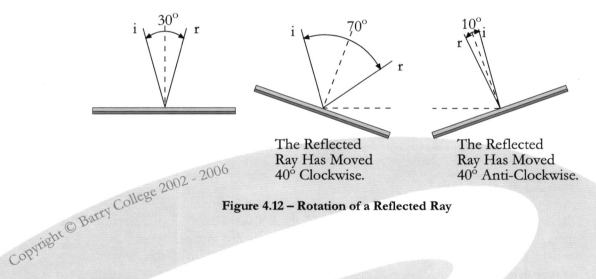

The Reflected Ray Has Moved 40° Clockwise.

The Reflected Ray Has Moved 40° Anti-Clockwise.

Figure 4.12 – Rotation of a Reflected Ray

Spherical Mirrors

Spherical mirrors are a segment of a hollow sphere. They are manufactured in silvered glass. When the glass is silvered on the outside of the curvature, the mirror is *Concave* or *Converging*. When silvered on the inside of the curvature, the mirror is *Convex* or *Diverging*.

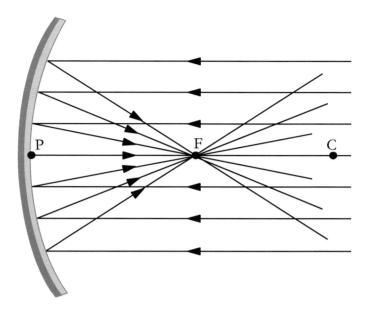

Figure 4.13 – Concave Mirror

The principal axis of the mirror is a line, which connects the Centre of Curvature (C) of the mirror with the Pole (P). The centre of curvature is the centre of an imaginary sphere that has the mirror on its surface. The pole is the centre of the mirror. The radius of curvature is CP. The centre of curvature is in front of a concave mirror and behind a convex mirror.

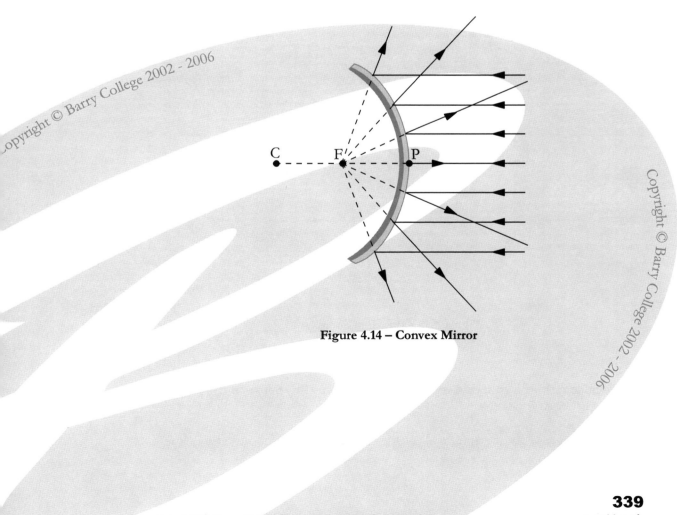

Figure 4.14 – Convex Mirror

Principal Focus

When parallel rays of light strike a spherical concave mirror they are reflected so that all the rays converge and pass through the *Focus (F)*. If the incident rays are parallel to the principal axis of the mirror they will reflect and pass through a point midway between the pole (P) and the centre of curvature (C). This point is called the *Principal Focus*.

When incident rays of light that are parallel with the principal axis fall onto a convex mirror, they are reflected as diverging rays that appear to be diverging from a virtual, or imaginary, principal focus behind the mirror.

A *Concave* mirror has a *Real Principal Focus* in front of the mirror.

A *Convex* mirror has a *Virtual Principal Focus* behind the mirror.

Definitions

You will find it useful to remember these definitions in respect of spherical mirrors:

The principal focus (F) of a spherical mirror is the point on its principal axis where all incident light rays that are parallel to the principal axis will reflect and converge through in a concave mirror. Or, from where the reflected rays will appear to diverge from in a convex mirror.

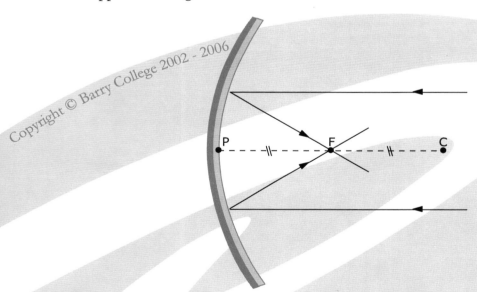

Figure 4.15 – Principal Focus

The focal length of a spherical mirror is the distance (PF) between the pole (P) and the principal focus (F).

The focal length (PF) of a spherical mirror is half the radius of curvature (PC).

When constructing ray diagrams for spherical mirrors it is useful to remember the following rules:

1. An incident light ray passing through the centre of curvature along the principal axis is reflected back along its own path.

2. Incident rays parallel to the principal axis will reflect through the principal focus.

3. An incident light ray that first passes through the principal focus will reflect from the mirror parallel to the principal axis.

4. An incident light ray striking the pole of a mirror will reflect at the same angle as the incident angle.

Real and Virtual Images

A real image is formed by the actual intersection of light rays through a real focal point. A virtual image is formed by the apparent intersection of light rays when they are projected backwards through a theoretical focal point.

A real image can be formed on a screen whilst a virtual image cannot. Convex mirrors always give virtual images. Concave mirrors will give real images unless the object is placed between the focus and the pole of the mirror. We will examine some ray diagrams to get you familiar with the variety of images that can be given by spherical mirrors. The IR Part-66 examination has contained questions on these so it is worth studying them.

Images formed by a Concave Mirror

The examples that follow will demonstrate the images formed by a concave mirror when the object is placed at different distances from it.

Example 1

In this example, the object is placed between the principal focus (F) and the pole of the mirror (P).

Note that the image is:

- Virtual

- Formed behind the mirror

- Larger than the object

- Erect

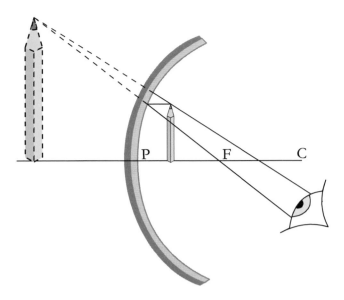

Figure 4.16 – Object between P and F

Example 2

In this example, the object is placed on the principal focus (F).

Note that the image will be at infinity.

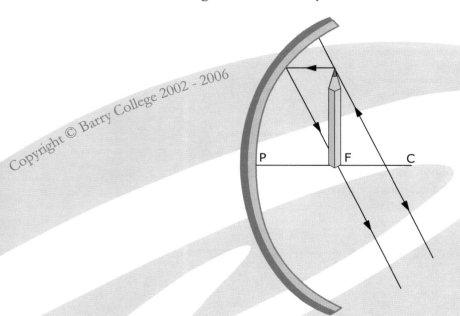

Figure 4.17 – Object at Principal Focus

Example 3

In this example, the object is placed between the principal focus (F) and the centre of curvature (C).

www.part66.co.uk

Note that the image is:

- Real

- Inverted

- Larger than the object

- Beyond the centre of curvature

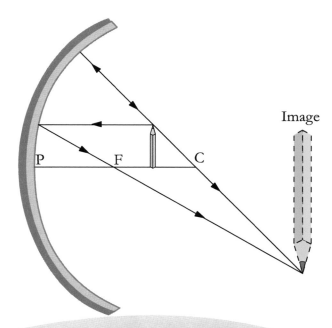

Image

P   F   C

Figure 4.18 – Object between F and C

Example 4

In this example, the object is placed at the centre of curvature (C).

Note that the image is:

- Real

- Inverted

- The same size as the object

- At the centre of curvature

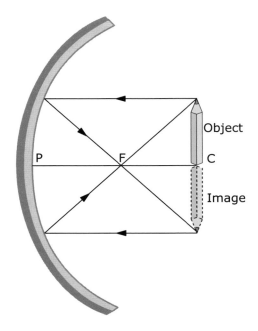

Figure 4.19 – Object at Centre of Curvature

Example 5

In this example, the object is placed beyond the centre of curvature (C).

Note that the image is:

- Real

- Inverted

- Smaller than the object

- Positioned between the principal focus and the centre of curvature.

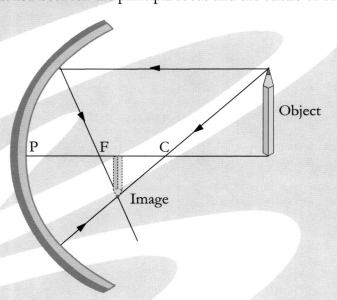

Figure 4.20 – Object beyond Centre of Curvature

www.part66.co.uk

Example 6

In this example, the object is placed at infinity.

Note that the image will be:

- Real

- Inverted

- Smaller than the object

- Positioned at the principal focus (F)

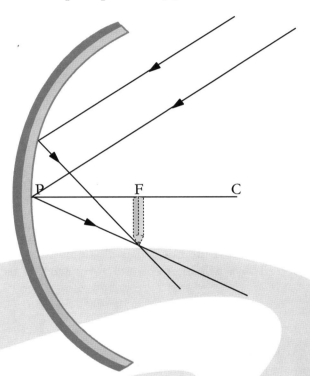

Figure 4.21 – Object at Infinity

Parabolic Mirrors

We often have a need to produce a wide parallel beam of light. Car headlights are a good example. If a light source is placed at the principal focus of a concave spherical mirror, the light rays will reflect away from the mirror as a narrow parallel beam. If the mirror is parabolic, the beam will be wider as well as being parallel.

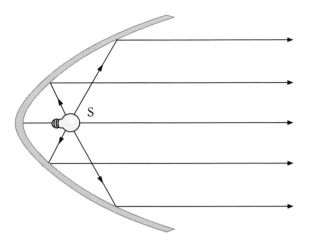

Figure 4.22– Parabolic Mirror

The light source can be made bright by using a halogen type bulb. The image produced by the bulb would be projected at infinity providing it is placed at the principal focus of the mirror.

Large Aperture Hemispherical Mirrors

Parallel light rays incident on a concave mirror will produce a point source of light at the principal focus. If the mirror is truly hemispherical and has a large aperture, the reflected rays will intersect and form what is called a *Caustic Curve.*

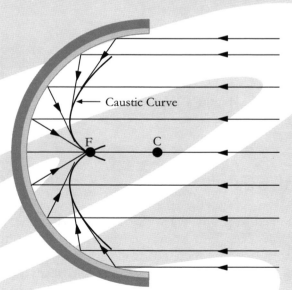

Figure 4.23 – Hemispherical Mirror

You may have observed this when light reflects inside a drinking mug or glass. At times, you may see the whole curve or, just the bright centre portion.

The Reflecting Telescope

This instrument was designed for viewing distant objects. Light enters in parallel rays and reflects off the concave mirror to converge through the principal focus.

A small plane mirror angled at 45° is positioned at the focus. This reflects the rays so that they enter the telescope eyepiece. Large aperture concave mirrors have a considerable light gathering capability and will detect faint light sources.

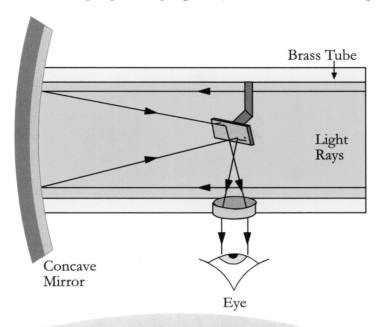

Figure 4.24 – Principle of the Reflecting Telescope

Images formed by Convex Mirrors

Convex mirrors will only give a virtual image. They are particularly useful as they give a widened field of view and an erect image. You often find them used as car rear view mirrors for this reason. It can be difficult to judge distance in them because the image is always smaller than the object.

Note that the image is always:

- Virtual

- Erect

- Smaller than the object

- Positioned between the pole of the mirror and the principal focus.

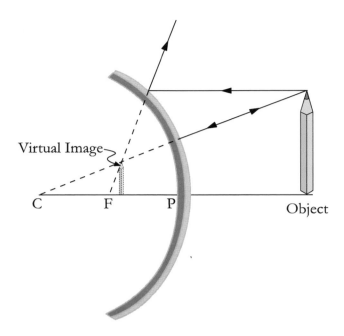

Figure 4.25 – Image formed by a Convex Mirror

Magnification

You will have noticed by now that the images formed in concave and convex mirrors vary in size when compared with their objects. We can determine the magnification of an image using either the respective heights of the object and image or, their distances from the mirror.

$$\text{Magnification (m)} = \frac{\text{Height of image}}{\text{Height of object}}$$

$$\text{Magnification (m)} = \frac{\text{Distance of image from mirror}}{\text{Distance of object from mirror}}$$

Mirror formula

The following formula may be used to determine the image distance, object distance or the focal length of a concave or convex mirror.

f = focal length

v = distance of image from mirror

u = distance of object from mirror

$$\frac{1}{f} = \frac{1}{v} + \frac{1}{u}$$

www.part66.co.uk

When using this formula it is important to establish whether the image will be formed behind or, in front of the mirror. To make it possible to identify the image position we need to adopt a system of signs for values entered into the formula.

There are two sign conventions in existence. You need only choose to use one. Both are shown here so that you are aware of the two systems.

Real-Is-Positive

This is the convention most often used. Using this system all distances are from the mirror, the signs used are:

Distances of real images and focal points have positive (+) signs.

Distances of virtual images and focal points have negative (-) signs.

When you use this system, you will discover that *Concave* mirrors will have positive focal lengths and will be thus *Real Focal Points*.

You will also discover that *Convex* mirrors will have negative focal lengths and be thus *Virtual Focal Points*.

Example 1

An object is positioned 30cm in front of a concave mirror that has a focal length of 15cm. The type of image formed, and its distance from the mirror will be:

$$\frac{1}{15} = \frac{1}{v} + \frac{1}{30}$$

therefore: $\quad \dfrac{1}{v} = \dfrac{1}{15} - \dfrac{1}{30} = \dfrac{1}{30}$

if $\quad \dfrac{1}{v} = \dfrac{1}{30} \quad$ then v = 30cm

The sign for v is positive so the image is a real image and it is positioned 30cm in front of the mirror.

Have you noticed something here? Look at the illustrations for image positions in concave mirrors. The object in the example has been placed at the centre of curvature (C) of the mirror. Does that tell you something about the image? It will be inverted. Well done if you saw that!

Example 2

Now we will try a calculation for a convex mirror.

An object is placed 20cm in front of a convex mirror and produces a virtual image 10cm behind the mirror. The focal length of this mirror will be:

$$\frac{1}{f} = \frac{1}{-10} + \frac{1}{20}$$

$$\text{therefore: } \frac{1}{f} = \frac{-2 + 1}{20} = \frac{-1}{20}$$

$$f = -20\text{cm}$$

The value of f is negative so the focus is 20cm behind the mirror and is virtual. Did you note that images in convex mirrors always appear between the pole of the mirror and the principal focus?

New Cartesian

This is another sign convention, which can be used in mirror formulae. The rules are given here merely to show you that there are two ways. Stick to real is positive or you will get yourself confused. The rules for this system are:

All distances measured against the incident light are negative.

All distances measured with the incident light are positive.

In this convention, real focal lengths will have a negative sign and virtual focal lengths will have a positive sign. The system is useful when visualising graphical representations of mirrors. Don't panic, the real is positive convention will serve you well.

Optical Density

The optical density of a material bears no relationship with its mass or volume. It is related only to the speed at which light will travel through it. The higher the optical density of a material, the slower light travels through it. The materials do have to be transparent though; light will not travel through materials that are opaque.

Refraction

Change of speed occurs first

The speed of light in a vacuum is 3×10^8 m/s but this reduces slightly as light passes into mediums that have a higher optical density. For example, light passing from space into the atmosphere and then into water will reduce in velocity. It will reduce again if it passes into clear glass. This change in velocity causes the light to alter direction as it enters or leaves mediums of different optical density. The change of direction is called *Refraction*.

You may have noticed some of the optical illusions that are caused by refraction. When you look into a swimming pool it looks shallower than it actually is; a common hazard for young children or people who cannot swim. Another illusion occurs if you immerse a straight stick into a clear water pool; it appears to bend upwards. All fishermen will tell you that fish appear to be closer to the surface than they actually are, a common hazard for cats!

We need to get to know some terms that are connected to refraction. The angle between an incident light ray and a line-drawn at right angles to the surface which we will call, the normal, is the *Angle of Incidence (i)*. The angle between the refracted light ray and the normal is known as the *Angle of Refraction (r)*.

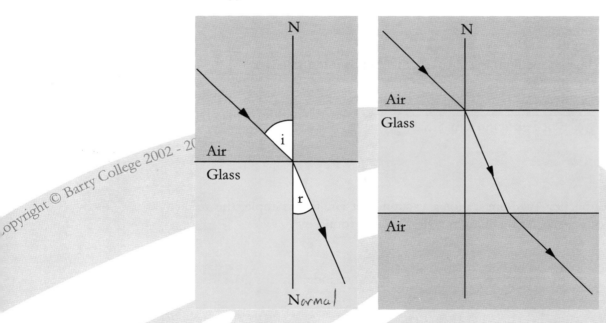

Figure 4.26 – Refraction

When a light ray passes from a medium of low optical density to one of a higher optical density it will bend towards the normal. On the other hand, if the ray passes into a medium of lower optical density it will bend away from the normal.

Snell's Law

The incident and refracted rays sit on opposite sides of the normal drawn through the point of incidence and all three are coplanar. With this in mind, Snell's Law states that:

The ratio of the sine of the angle of incidence (i) to the sine of the angle of refraction (r) is a constant.

Refractive Index

The value of the constant for light passing from a vacuum into another medium is the Absolute Refractive Index (n) of the medium. For light that, for example, passes from air into glass, the constant is the Refractive Index (n) of the second medium, in this case the glass.

$$\frac{\sin i}{\sin r} = \text{a constant} = \text{refractive index}$$

Where the first medium is a vacuum, this can be interpreted as:

$$\frac{\text{speed of light (c) in a vacuum}}{\text{speed of light(c) in a material}} = \text{Abs refractive index of material}$$

Where the first medium is not a vacuum but air, for example, the refractive index of the second medium, say glass, can be found by:

$$\frac{\text{speed of light (c) in air}}{\text{speed of light(c) in glass}} = \text{refractive index (n) for glass}$$

$$\text{or:} \quad \frac{\sin i}{\sin r} = \text{refractive index (n) of glass}$$

The refractive index for fresh water is 1.33. Crown glass is 1.5 and ordinary glass is about 1.65.

Example

The speed of light in glass, refractive index 1.5, is:

$$1.5 = \frac{\text{speed of light (c) in a vacuum}}{\text{speed of light(c) in glass}}$$

$$1.5 = \frac{3 \times 10^5 \text{km/s}}{\text{c (glass)}} \qquad \text{therefore: c (glass)} = 2 \times 10^5 \text{km/s}$$

This is an easy question to ask in a multi-choice examination.

Effects of Refraction

When you immerse a stick into clear water the rays of light from the end of the stick will refract away from the normal as they leave the water and enter the air before passing to your eye. The light rays entering your eye will appear to be coming from point Y. This point is the image of the end of the stick X, which has apparently moved because of refraction. You see the immersed portion of the stick as YZ rather than the actual immersed portion XZ.

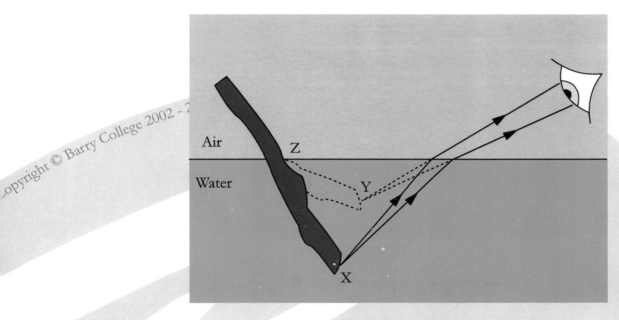

Figure 4.27 – Effects of Refraction

Another example of the effects of refraction can be seen if you place a thick plate of clear glass over a printed page. The print seems to be raised. The light rays from the print are being refracted away from the normal as they pass out of the glass and into the air giving you the impression that the print under the glass is at a higher level than the page.

Figure 4.28 – Refraction through Thick Glass

Real and Apparent Depth

A swimming pool seems to be only three quarters of its real depth when viewed from above. The thick plate of glass would only appear to be three quarters of its true thickness when you look down on it. When you look straight down, the light rays from point 0 at the bottom of the pool are refracted away from the normal when they pass into the air on their way to your eye. The rays appear to be coming from point I that is the virtual image of point 0.

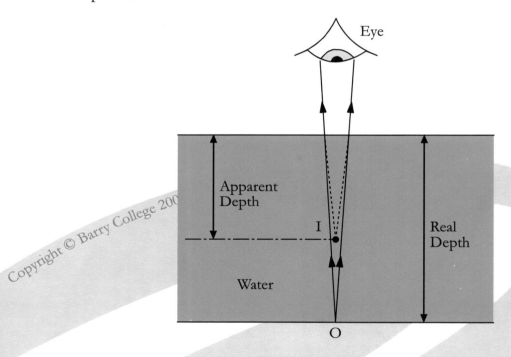

Figure 4.29 – Real & Apparent Depth in Water

Refractive Index Related to Real & Apparent Depth

The refractive index of transparent materials can be determined by using the real and apparent depths.

$$\text{Refractive Index (n)} = \frac{\text{Real Depth}}{\text{Apparent Depth}}$$

Reversibility of Light

Light rays entering water or glass can be reflected and pass back into the air again. We need to differentiate between these paths if we are looking to find the refractive index. We can do this by giving the refractive index (n) a prefix and a suffix to indicate the direction.

For example, consider a light ray passing from air into glass and vice versa.

$$\text{Air to Glass ang} = \frac{\sin i}{\sin r}$$

$$\text{Glass to Air gna} = \frac{\sin r}{\sin i}$$

$$\text{Put these together and we can get: gna} = \frac{1}{\text{ang}}$$

So, you can find the refractive index of glass or air in this example.

Example

If light passes from air into glass that has a refractive index gna of 1.5 then the value of the refractive index gna for light passing from glass into air will be:

$$\text{Refractive Index gna} = \frac{1}{1.5} = 0.66$$

Do you recall that we established that the speed of light in glass, refractive index 1.5, was 2×10^5 km/s?

Using the refractive index for glass to air of 0.66 recurring that we have determined above lets establish the speed of light in a vacuum.

$$\text{Speed of light} = \frac{\text{Speed of light in glass}}{\text{Refractive index air na}}$$

$$= \frac{2 \times 10^5 \text{km/s}}{0.66 \text{ recurring}} = 3 \times 10^5 \text{km/s}$$

Total Internal Reflection – The Critical Angle

This subject introduces you to a very important principle underlying fibre optics. This is a favourite topic for IR Part-66 questions!

When light passes into a more optically dense medium we know it will refract towards the normal. Now consider that the light has passed through a glass block and has reached the interface between the glass and the air again. The light will refract out of the block, bending away from the normal this time. But, some of the light will reflect weakly at the interface and pass back into the block. The angle of reflection will equal the angle of the incident ray. The reflected ray will be weak and the exiting refracted ray will be strong

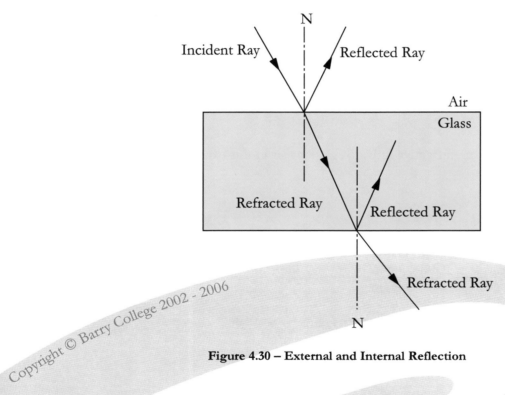

Figure 4.30 – External and Internal Reflection

If you were to increase the angle of incidence then the angle of the exiting refracted ray would also increase. The refracted ray would weaken and the internally reflected ray would get stronger.

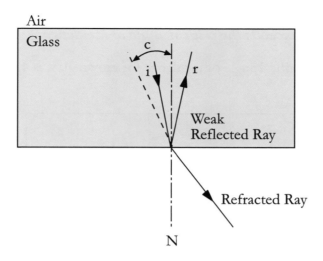

Figure 4.31 – Below the Critical Angle (c)

If the angle of incidence continues to increase, a point will be reached where the exiting refracted ray will be at a right angle to the normal.

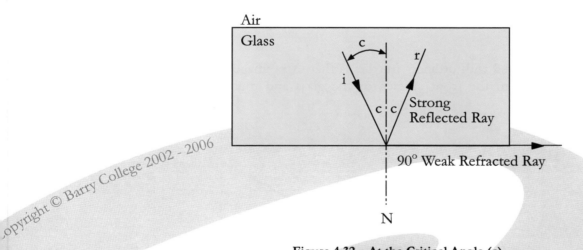

Figure 4.32 – At the Critical Angle (c)

It will lay parallel to the surface of the glass block. The internally reflected ray will now be very strong. The angle of incidence at which this occurs is called the *Critical Angle (c)*.

It is impossible to have a refracted ray greater than 90° to the normal. If the angle of incidence is increased again, the critical angle will have been exceeded. The incident ray will now experience *Total Internal Reflection*. The reflected ray will be very strong as there is now no refracted ray.

The critical angle of incidence is defined as the minimum angle of incidence where total internal reflection can occur.

Total internal reflection of an incident light ray will occur if the angle of the incident ray exceeds the critical angle of incidence.

For example, the critical angle of incidence for crown glass is 42°.

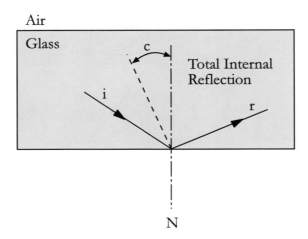

Figure 4.33 – Above the Critical Angle (c)

Multiple Images

A problem encountered with ordinary mirrors is that extra images are formed due to reflection from the front surface of the glass and multiple internal reflections.

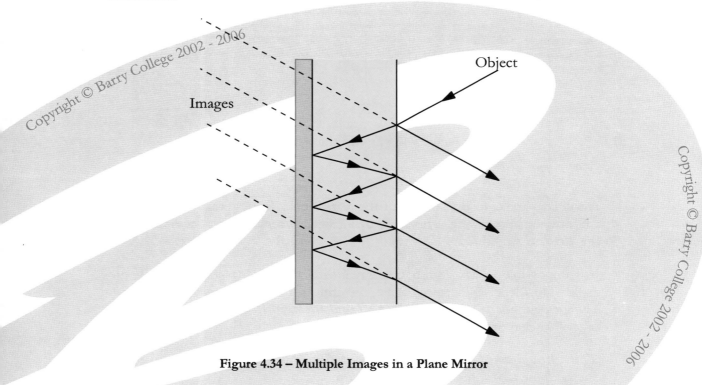

Figure 4.34 – Multiple Images in a Plane Mirror

Because these additional images are often quite weak, we may not notice them. The problem becomes a nuisance when plane mirrors are used in reflecting telescopes. To reduce the nuisance, these mirrors are often aluminised on their front surfaces so extreme care is needed when handling these to avoid scratches.

Total Internal Reflection in Prisms

A method used to ensure one image only, is to employ a prism instead of mirrors. Right-angled glass prisms can be used for a variety of applications.

Light enters the face of the prism so that it strikes the hypotenuse internal face at an incident angle of 45°. Total internal reflection will occur because the critical angle for glass is about 42°. This will reflect the ray out of the adjacent face of the prism. If the ray is allowed to enter a second prism in similar fashion, we have a system useful for periscopes.

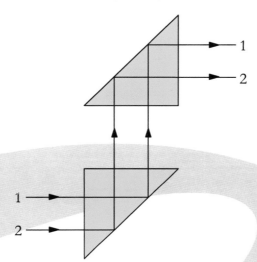

Figure 4.35 – Periscope

A second application of the right-angled prism is its use as an erecting prism. If light enters a face parallel to the hypotenuse face, refraction and reflection will invert the image.

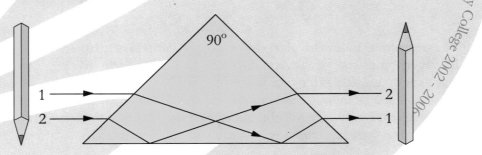

Figure 4.36 – Erecting Prism

www.part66.co.uk

A third application is the use of prisms in prismatic binoculars that enable the overall length of the binocular to be reduced by making the light travel three lengths.

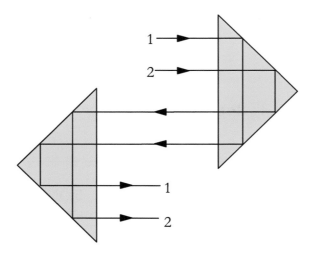

Figure 4.37 – Prismatic Binocular

Triangular Prisms and Dispersion

The rectangular prism, in other words cube shaped, simply displaces emergent light parallel to its incident direction. However, a triangular prism causes light to be deviated. The angle of deviation is the angle between the incident and emergent rays.

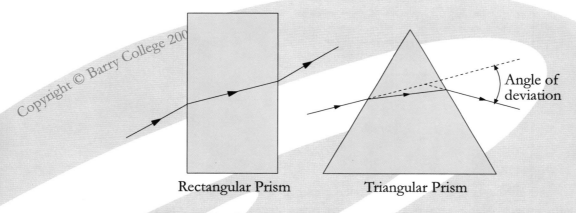

Rectangular Prism   Triangular Prism

Figure 4.38 – Deviation and Displacement of Light through Prisms

The refractive index of glass is based on light rays that are white. Light, however, consists of seven different colours, each having a different wavelength and the refractive index of glass is different in respect of each of these colours. Because a triangular prism will deviate light by refraction, then it is possible to receive white light and cause it to deviate into each of the colours of the white light spectrum because each colour is refracted at a different angle.

360
www.part66.co.uk

The colours are violet, indigo, blue, green, yellow, orange and red. Violet has the shortest wavelength and precedes ultra-violet and red has the longest wavelength following infrared.

Violet is deviated most in the prism and red the least. The separation of white light into the component colours is called *Dispersion*.

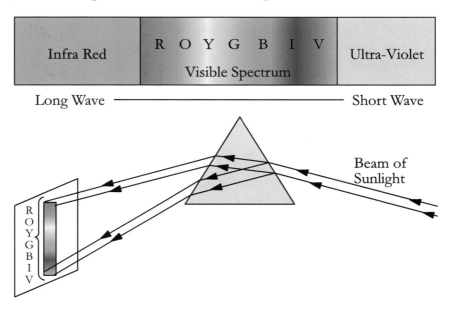

Figure 4.39 – The Light Spectrum

The Spectrometer

The *Spectrometer.* is an instrument that is used to analyse the spectra of gases. The gases may be the product of substances that are deliberately burnt in an electric arc. One familiar use of this instrument will be found in the *Spectrometric Oil Analysis Programme (SOAP)*. The light spectra emitted gives an indication of metallic trace elements present in engine oils.

The light source is positioned at the principal focus of a convex lens. This creates a parallel beam of light, which is then refracted through a prism as separate parallel rays of colour. The rays leaving the prism, are then individually focussed by a second lens and projects an image of the spectra onto a screen. The process of producing parallel light rays is called *Collimation* and any device in an instrument that is used to do this is called a *Collimator.*

Recombination of Spectrum Colours

The colours of the spectrum may be recombined back into white light by forming the spectrum on a row of plane mirrors. By careful adjustment of the mirrors, the incident light on each one can be made to reflect onto one place on a screen and a patch of white light will be seen. The same effect can be obtained by painting the colours of the spectrum onto a disc which is then spun at high speed, the result is that we will observe the disc as being stationary and a greyish white colour. The grey tinge is because we cannot recreate pure colours using paints.

Colour of Objects

All the objects we see around us absorb and reflect light in different combinations. Some will not absorb any light and will reflect all the spectrum colours and appear to be white. At the other extreme, some objects will absorb all the spectrum colours and not reflect any. These objects appear to be black.

Most objects will absorb some colours and reflect others. The colour of the object will depend on the mix of colours being reflected. Grass appears green because it reflects only green and absorbs other colours. A sheet of white paper reflects all the colours and appears to be white.

When an object absorbs coloured light its internal energy rises and it gets warmer. This is much the same as sunbathers absorbing 'rays'. They get hot, even burnt. It is common knowledge that dark coloured objects will absorb heat, and light coloured objects will reflect it.

Primary, Secondary and Complementary Colours

If we deal in the pure colours found in the light spectrum we find that we cannot create red, blue or green light by mixing other coloured lights together. For this reason, **Red, Blue** and **Green** are called the *Primary Colours*. If you mix the primary colours together, they produce white light. Now look at the colours we can produce. Yellow colour results from mixing red and green. Magenta results from mixing red and blue. Cyan results from mixing green and blue. **Yellow, Magenta** and **Cyan** are known as the *Secondary Colours*.

White light can be produced by mixing the primary colours and the secondary colours together in the following combinations: Red and cyan, green and magenta, blue and yellow. These pairs are called *Complementary Colours*. When mixing paints you will find that you can produce green from mixing yellow and blue paint. This is possible only because the colours of paints are not pure. You read above that recombining painted spectrum colours on a spinning disc only produces grey, not white, light.

Lenses

A lens is a piece of glass with curved surfaces. If you examine the construction of a lens you could imagine that it is made up of prisms. The angles of the sides of the prisms reduce from the edge of the lens to its centre. This means that light is deviated more at the edges of the lens and less at its centre. The result of this is that light rays passing through the lens are brought to a focal point. The focus will be real for a converging or convex lens and virtual for a diverging or concave lens.

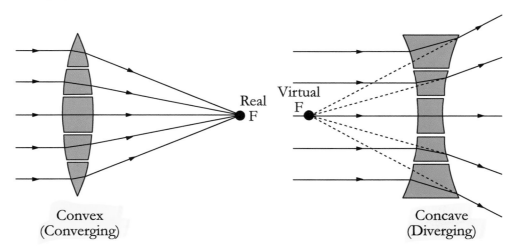

Figure 4.40 – How a Lens Achieves a Focal Point

There are two groups of lenses. The first group contains the *Convex* lenses which are often referred to as a converging lens. These have real focal points. The images and magnifications will depend on the position of the object.

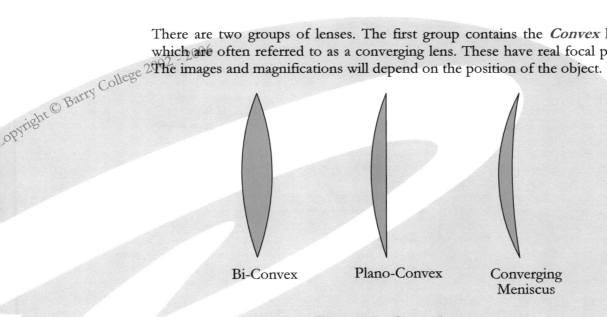

Figure 4.41 – Convex Lenses

The second group contains the *Concave* lenses. These are often referred to as diverging lenses. These have virtual focal points and always give diminished and erect virtual images that are positioned between the object and the lens.

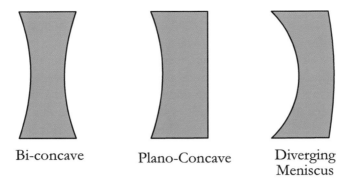

Bi-concave   Plano-Concave   Diverging
                                       Meniscus

Figure 4.42 – Concave Lenses

The Principal Focus

The principle focus of a lens lies on its principal axis and is the point where all the light rays entering the lens parallel to its axis converge to or diverge from. Light rays parallel to the axis and entering a convex or converging lens will converge to form a real focal point on the principal axis. Light rays parallel to the axis and entering a concave or divergent lens will spread out after passing through the lens as if they were diverging from an imaginary or virtual point.

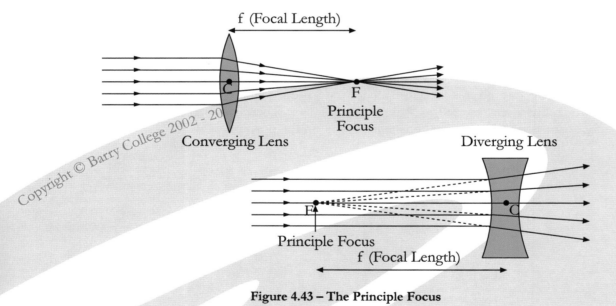

Figure 4.43 – The Principle Focus

The focal length of a lens is the distance measured from the Optical Centre (C) of the lens to the Principal Focus (F). The optical centre of the lens is the very centre of the lens where light rays will pass straight through without any deviation.

Because light rays can pass through a lens from either side there will be two Principal Foci, each being equidistant from the optical centre on either side of the lens along the principal axis.

www.part66.co.uk

Formation of Images by Converging Lenses

The examples that follow will demonstrate the image (I) formed by a convex lens when the object (0) is placed at different distances from it.

Example 1

In this example, the object (0) is placed between the principal focus (F) and the optical centre (C) of the lens. This would be suitable for a magnifying glass

Note that the image (I) is:

- Virtual

- Behind the object

- Magnified

- Erect

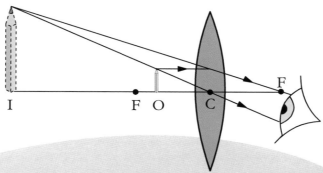

Figure 4.44 – Object between C and F

Example 2

In this example, the object (0) is placed on the principal focus (F)

- Note that the image will be at infinity.

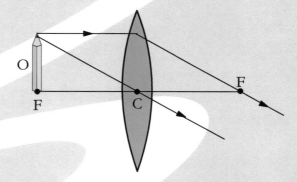

Figure 4.45 – Object at Principal Focus

Example 3

In this example, the object (0) is placed between the principal focus (F) and a point equal to twice the focal length (2F). This would suit a projection lens where a magnified image could be projected onto a screen. Note that the projected image would be inverted.

Note that the image (I) is:

- Real

- At a distance more than 2F

- Magnified

- Inverted

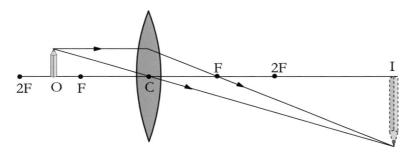

Figure 4.46 – Object between F and 2F

Example 4

In this example, the object (0) is placed at a distance equal to two focal lengths from C.

Note that the image (I) is:

- Real

- At a distance equal to 2F

- Same size as object

- Inverted

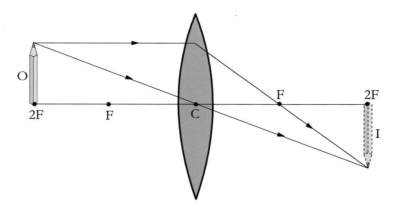

Figure 4.47 – Object at Twice Focal Length

Example 5

In this example, the object (0) is placed at a distance more than twice the focal length of the lens. This would suit a camera where a small inverted image of a distant object can be projected onto a film.

Note that the image (I) is:

- Real

- Between F and 2F

- Smaller than the object

- Inverted

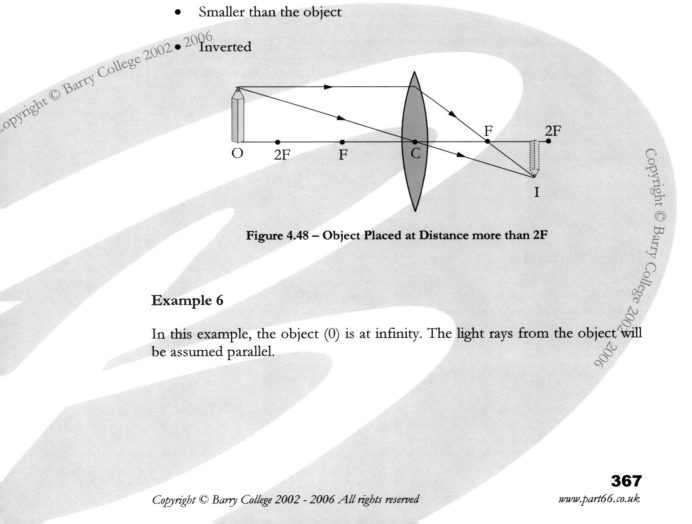

Figure 4.48 – Object Placed at Distance more than 2F

Example 6

In this example, the object (0) is at infinity. The light rays from the object will be assumed parallel.

Note that the image (I) is:

- Real

- At the principal focus

- Smaller than the object

- Inverted

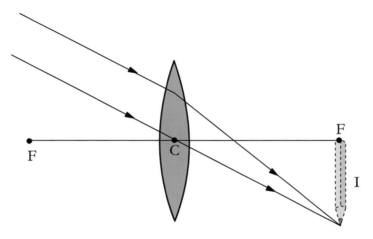

Figure 4.49 – Object Placed at Infinity

Light Rays and Lenses

It is worth remembering some facts about the path of light rays through lenses.

1. Light rays that pass through the optical centre (C) do not deviate.

2. Light rays parallel to the principal axis will pass through the principal focus when refracted through a converging lens.

3. Light rays that first pass through the principal focus will emerge parallel to the principal axis after refraction through a converging lens.

Image Formed by a Diverging Lens

Concave, or diverging, lenses produce virtual images (I) that have similar properties regardless of the position of the object (0).

Example

The object (0) has been placed at a randomly chosen position.

www.part66.co.uk

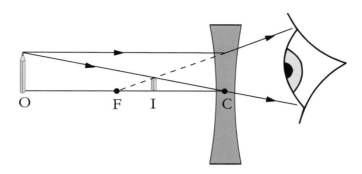

Figure 4.50 – Image Formed by a Diverging Lens

Note that the image is:

- Virtual

- Between the object and the lens

- Smaller than the object

- Erect

Magnification

As with mirrors, you may have noticed that the images formed in convex and concave lenses vary in size when compared to their respective objects. We can determine the magnification of an image using the respective heights of the object and image or, their distances from the lens.

$$\text{magnification (m)} = \frac{\text{Height of Image}}{\text{Height of Object}}$$

$$\text{magnification (m)} = \frac{\text{Distance (v) of Image from Lens}}{\text{Distance (u) of Object from Lens}} \quad \text{or} \quad \frac{v}{u}$$

Lens Formula

When using the lens formula the correct signs must be applied to object distances, image distances and focal lengths according to the convention chosen. There are two conventions as with the mirror formula. Both are shown for convenience.

The following formulae may be used to determine the image distance, object distance or, the focal length of converging or diverging lenses. Do take note that for lenses there are two formulae, each depends on the sign convention you choose to use. This is unlike the mirror formula where there is only one formula for both conventions.

$$\frac{1}{f} = \frac{1}{v} + \frac{1}{u} \qquad \text{(Real is positive convention)}$$

$$\frac{1}{f} = \frac{1}{v} - \frac{1}{u} \qquad \text{(New Cartesian convention)}$$

f = focal length

v = distance of image from lens

u = distance of object from lens

Again similar to the mirror formula, it is important to establish whether the image will be formed behind or, in front of the lens. To make it possible to identify the image position we adopt a system of signs for values entered into the formula.

We have already discussed the fact that there are two sign conventions in existence. Both are described here so that you are aware that there are two, you need only use one of them.

Real is Positive

This is the convention most often used. Using this system all distances are taken from the optical centre (C) of the lens. The signs used are:

$$\text{The lens formula used is: } \frac{1}{f} = \frac{1}{v} + \frac{1}{u}$$

Distances of real images and objects have positive (+) signs.

Distances of virtual images and objects have negative (-) signs.

Focal lengths of converging lenses have positive (+) signs (Real).

Focal lengths of diverging lenses have negative (-) signs (Virtual).

www.part66.co.uk

Example 1

An object is placed 40cm from a converging lens that has a focal length of 20cm. The type of image formed and its distance from the lens will be:

$$\frac{1}{20} = \frac{1}{v} + \frac{1}{40} \qquad \text{therefore:} \quad \frac{1}{v} = \frac{1}{20} - \frac{1}{40} = \frac{1}{40}$$

$$\text{if} \quad \frac{1}{v} = \frac{1}{40} \quad \text{then } v = 40\text{cm}$$

The sign for v is positive so the image is a real image and is positioned 40cm from the lens.

Have you noticed? The object was placed at two focal lengths (2F) from the lens. Look at the illustrations for images formed in converging lenses. The image is positioned at 2F on the opposite side of the lens from the object, it is real; the same size as the object and is inverted. Well done if you saw that!

Example 2

Now we will try a calculation for a diverging lens.

An object is placed 30cm from a diverging lens and produces a virtual image 15cm from the lens. The focal length of the lens is:

$$\frac{1}{f} = \frac{1}{-15} + \frac{1}{30} \qquad \text{therefore:} \quad \frac{1}{f} = \frac{-2+1}{30} = \frac{-1}{30} \quad \text{so } f = -30\text{cm}$$

The value of f is negative so the focus is virtual and on the same side of the lens as the object. Did you note that images formed in diverging lenses always appear between the object and the lens?

Did you also note that the object was placed at the virtual focal point of the lens? If you study the illustration for an image formed in a diverging lens you will see that the image is smaller than the object, virtual, on the same side as the object and is erect.

New Cartesian

This is the other sign convention, which can be used in lens formulae. The rules are given here merely to show you that there are two ways. Stick to real is positive or you may get yourself confused. The rules for the New Cartesian system are:

371

The lens formula used is: $\dfrac{1}{f} = \dfrac{1}{v} - \dfrac{1}{u}$

All distances are measured form the optical centre (C) of the lens. All distances measured against the incident light are negative. All distances measured with the incident light are positive.

In this convention, objects are placed to the left of the lens so:

Distances to the left of the lens are negative. Distances to the right of the lens are positive.

In this convention, real focal lengths will have a negative sign and virtual focal lengths will have a positive sign. The system is useful when checking graphical illustrations of lenses. Don't panic, the real is positive convention will continue to serve you well.

Uses of Lenses

Lenses are used in slide and film projectors. The light source is usually a carbon arc lamp.

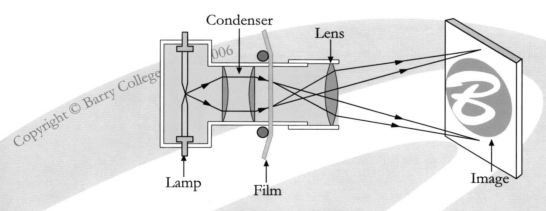

Figure 4.51 – Projector

Camera

The lens to film distance can be adjusted to produce sharp images on the film. A variable speed shutter is used to permit light from the object to reach the film. An iris is used to adjust the aperture and thus the light gathering capability of the camera.

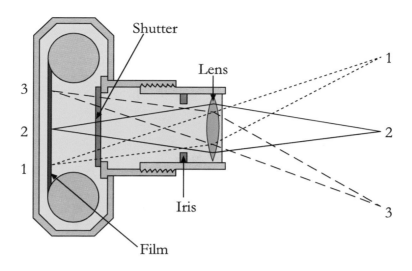

Figure 4.52 - Camera

Astronomical Telescope

Light rays entering the objective lens from very distant objects are near enough parallel. A real image is formed at the focal point of the object lens, which is also the focal point of the eyepiece lens. The image formed by the object lens is the object for the eyepiece lens. A second, virtual, inverted and magnified image is thus formed at infinity.

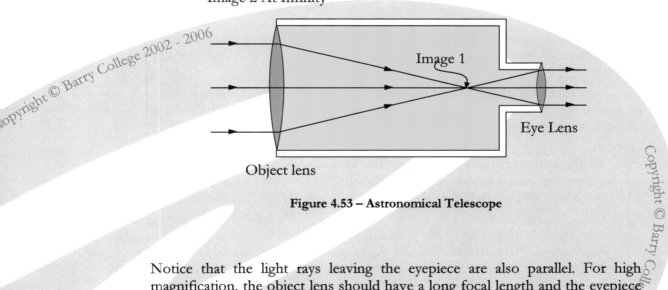

Figure 4.53 – Astronomical Telescope

Notice that the light rays leaving the eyepiece are also parallel. For high magnification, the object lens should have a long focal length and the eyepiece should have a short focal length.

Microscope

The object and the eyepiece lenses have short focal lengths. The object lens forms a real, magnified, inverted image of the small object on the slide. This image forms the object for the eyepiece lens that produces a highly magnified virtual second image.

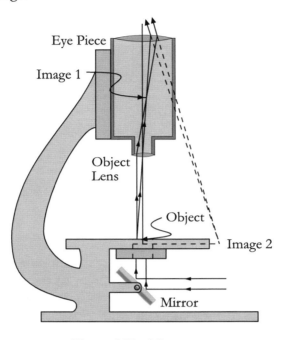

Figure 4.54 – Microscope

The Eye

The *lens* in the eye forms an image on the light sensitive *retina*, which transmits signals to the brain by way of the optic nerve. The image is inverted so the brain corrects this. The *iris* can adjust the aperture of the pupil and so alter the light gathering capability of the eye. The *ciliary muscles* adjust the shape of the lens and thus its focal length. This creates sharp images on the *retina*. The *cornea* is a transparent shield in front of the lens and is part of the *sclerotic* which is a tough casing surrounding the eye. The space between the cornea and the lens is filled with a clear liquid called the *aqueous humour*. The cavity between the lens and the retina is filled with a viscous jelly called the *vitreous humour*. The *choroid* behind the retina is a dark coloured layer that prevents internal reflections in the eye.

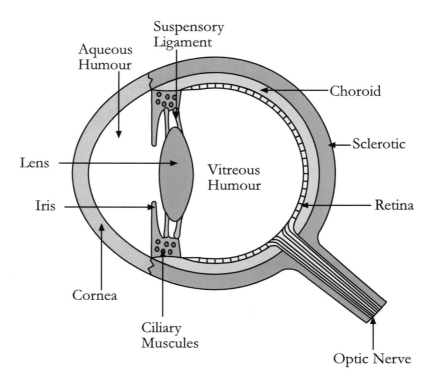

Figure 4.55 – The Eye

Normal Sight

When you look at a distant object the lens in the eye is adjusted by being stretched until it is thin. If you then look at a near object the lens is squeezed and thickens to bring the object into focus on the retina.

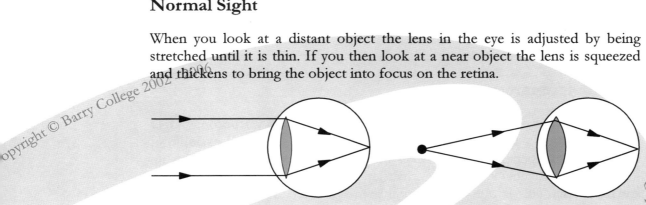

Figure4.56 – Normal Sight

Short Sight

If your range of clear vision is limited to seeing, only near objects then you are short sighted. Your eye is longer than normal. The retina is too far away from the lens. Distant objects are focussed in front of the retina instead of on it. You would need spectacles with *Diverging Lenses* to correct the problem. These lenses diverge the light rays enough to make it seem as though they are coming from a nearer point.

375

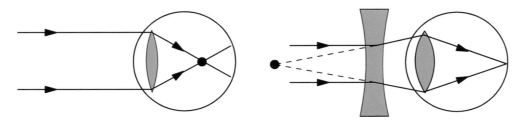

Figure 4.57 – Short Sight

Long Sight

If your eye is shorter than normal, you are unable to focus near objects. The retina is too close to the lens and is in front of its focal point. Even distant objects would require the lens in your eye to squeeze and thicken. The problem can be corrected with spectacles having Converging Lenses. These lenses converge the light rays enough to make it seem that they are coming from a more distant point.

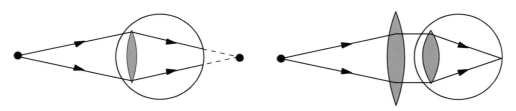

Figure 4.58 – Long Sight

Angular Magnitude

You may have noticed that distant objects look very small yet become larger the closer you get to them. An avenue of trees presents a good example of what artists call perspective. The trees may be all the same actual height but their apparent heights seem to be inversely proportional to the distance they are from you. This is due to their angular magnitudes, which are the angles they subtend at your eye.

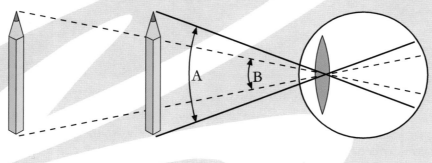

Angluar Magnitude (m) = $\dfrac{A}{B}$

Figure 4.59 – Apparent Heights of Similar Objects

Parallax

If you have observed the scenery from the side window of a moving vehicle you may have noticed that objects appear to be moving relative to each other. A tree in the foreground may appear to be to the right of a distant house but apparently moves to the left of it. Neither object has moved. The apparent displacement is called parallax and it is governed by the fact that you are moving. Parallax can cause problems when you observe analogue instruments. These are instruments that require you to align something, such as a needle on a gauge. The gauge and the needle may be stationary but if you move, they appear to change their alignment. This can cause you to make an error in your reading, which will be positive or negative dependant on your position.

Shadows

When an object is exposed to a large light source the dark shadow it throws seems to be surrounded by a border of partial shadow. The dark shadowed area is called the *Umbra* and the border of partial shadow is called the *Penumbra*. If a point source of light is used, the dark shadowed Umbra is sharp edged and there is little or no Penumbra. Large light sources allow light rays to pass the edges of the object at differing angles, point light sources do not.

Fibre Optics

Introduction

Optical fibres are strands of very pure silica glass that are thinner than a human hair. Using total internal reflection they receive and transmit light by reflecting it millions of times through the fibre with minimum attenuation or loss of intensity. The high frequency range of light makes it possible to simultaneously transmit huge amounts of digital information along a fibre.

A light emitting diode converts information data from electrical to light signals which are then transmitted along the fibre to a photo sensitive diode for conversion back to electrical signal form.

Optical fibres are used extensively in the telecommunications industry and in computer networks. They are gradually replacing traditional electrical cables in a number of aircraft internal data transmission systems. One further use that you should be familiar with is in the borescopes used to conduct visual inspections in inaccessible places.

Total Internal Reflection

You will have studied the principle of internal reflection earlier in this chapter when we discussed refraction. Revisit the topic if you are at all unsure of this. If you are sure then the brief revision here will suffice. You will recall that when light passes from one material to another with a different refractive index the light rays bend. If the material they pass into is less optically dense the rays bend or refract away from the normal.

Imagine that light is passing from glass out into air. As the angle of incidence with the normal increases, the angle of the refracted ray increases also. At a given angle of incidence, the refracted ray will be at 90° to the normal. As the refracted ray is now theoretically running along the surface of the glass you can see that it is no longer in air, it is reflecting along the surface of the glass.

The angle of incidence where this occurs is called the *Critical Angle*. For pure glass, this critical angle of incidence is 42°. Any increase in the angle of incidence will cause the light ray to totally reflect back into the glass. Light travels approximately 33% slower in glass than in air. The speed of light in air is in turn slower than it would be in the vacuum of space.

To remind you:

$$\text{Refractive index (n)} = \frac{\text{Speed of light in a vacuum}}{\text{Speed of light in material}}$$

Now we can look at how the optical fibre exploits this.

Operation of an Optical Fibre

The series of illustrations accompanying this section should be studied together with this text.

Ideally, light would enter the end of a glass fibre at 90° to the end surface and travel straight through it. If the glass were of very high purity, little intensity would be lost. Of course, that limits us to an almost impossibly narrow light beam. If the light enters the fibre end at any angle, it will refract towards the normal. Light rays will be entering at all angles so their passage through the fibre will be governed on whether we can cause them to internally reflect as they strike the first glass to air interface in the fibre.

In our first illustration the light ray enters the fibre at a high angle of incidence, refracts towards the normal and then strikes a glass to air interface in the fibre at an incident angle θ of less than 42°. Because this is less than the critical angle, the light passes out into the air, refracting away from the normal. All is lost! This ray will not have reflected and cannot be transmitted through the fibre.

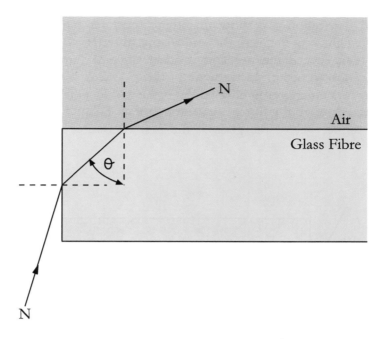

Figure 4.60 – Critical Angle θ Not Reached

In the second illustration, the light ray enters the end of the fibre at a lower angle of incidence, refracts and strikes the first glass to air interface at an incident angle θ of over 42°. As 42° is the critical angle, total internal reflection occurs and the light ray reflects back through the glass to strike the opposite glass to air interface. The reflection process now continues right through the fibre.

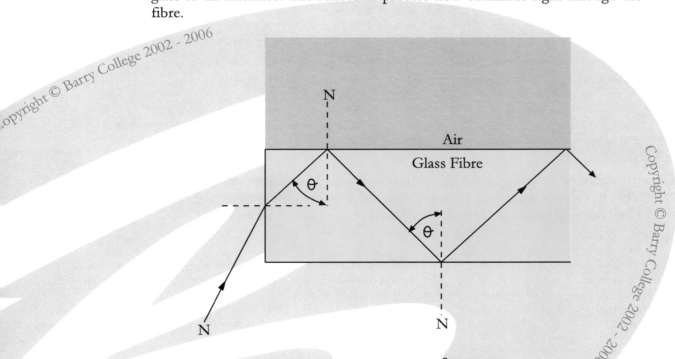

Figure 4.61 – Critical Angle θ Exceeded

In our third illustration, we show that there must be a maximum angle of incidence for light rays entering the end of the fibre. If we exceed this angle, we cannot then exceed the necessary critical angle at the first interface for internal reflection to occur. As we work in three dimensions, you can imagine that the light rays entering the fibre end must lie within a given cone if they are to be reflected through the fibre. Incident light rays falling outside of this cone will merely refract out of the glass at the first encounter with a glass to air interface.

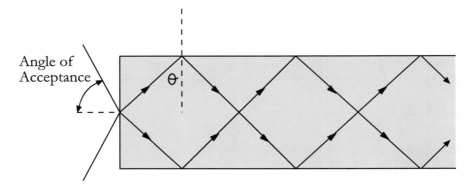

Figure 4.62 – Angle of Acceptance

The cone we have just described is called the *Cone of Acceptance*. The light rays entering the fibre end must fall within the required incidence angle with the fibre end normal, which is actually the axis of this cone. Therefore, we refer to the maximum incident acceptance angle of light rays as being the *Cone Half Angle*. (Half the angle of the apex of the cone).

The Angle of Acceptance is therefore the *Cone Half Angle*. Light rays exceeding this angle will fall outside the cone of acceptance and will not reach the critical angle of incidence required for reflection to take place.

Cladding

If the optical fibre consisted of just glass, problems would occur. If the fibre were to touch any material en route that had a higher optical density than the fibre, the light rays could refract out of the fibre and into the material.

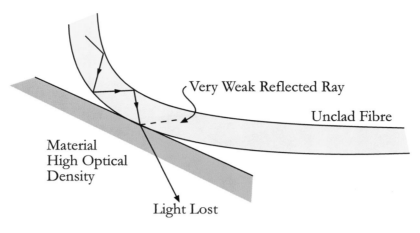

Figure 4.63 Light Loss from Unclad Fibre

An unprotected glass fibre would also be at risk from chafing and inadvertent impacts. If the unprotected fibre were to run across an irregular surface, the fibre may be distorted and form small radius bends, called *Microbends*. These would interfere with the passage of the light rays.

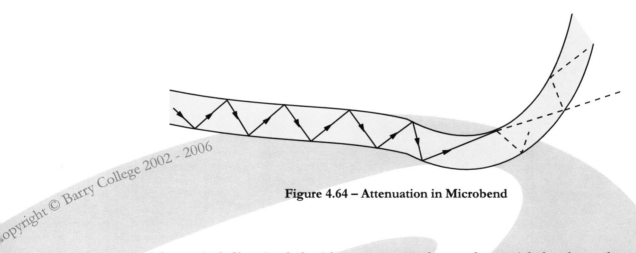

Figure 4.64 – Attenuation in Microbend

The optical fibre is clad with a concentric layer of material that has a lower refractive index (n) than the glass in the fibre. The *Cladding* is a dielectric material made of plastic or lower purity glass. For extra protection, the cladding is covered in a further layer of material called the buffer layer. The *Buffer* is made of elastic material and protects the fibre optic from chafing and from being distorted.

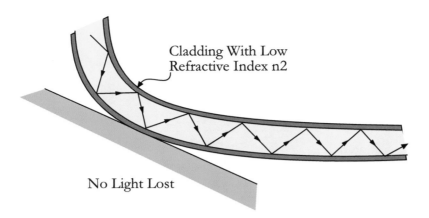

Figure 4.65 – Clad Fibre

Angle of Confinement

This is the largest angle that can be reached between a light ray and the fibreglass to air interface without refraction occurring. In fact, it is the complementary angle to the critical angle of incidence. If you were to exceed the angle of confinement, you would create an angle of incidence lower than the critical angle and light would refract out of the fibre.

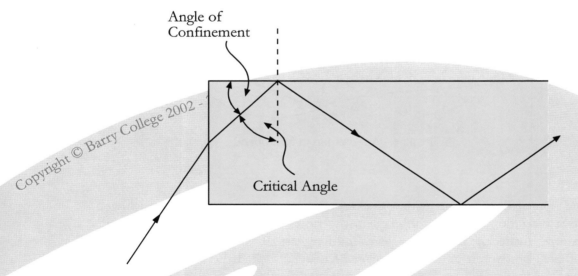

Figure 4.66 – Angle of Confinement

Attenuation

When light passes through an optical fibre the light intensity diminishes. This is called attenuation and it happens for a number of reasons. The quality of an optical fibre depends on how little attenuation occurs. The degree of attenuation over a distance does vary with the wavelength and the type of fibre used.

www.part66.co.uk

Light is electro-magnetic radiation and as such obeys the inverse square law. This states that its energy will diminish in inverse proportion to the square of the distance travelled. Looking how far light can travel in a second, we can completely ignore this law when dealing with Earth bound optical fibres!

The silica glass used is very high purity but there is always the risk of impurities or inclusions in any material. When a light ray strikes an inclusion in the glass it can be deflected or even absorbed by it. The surface finish of the fibre is also important in maintaining the correct angles of reflection. Light rays striking a rough glass to cladding interface will diffuse rather than reflect cleanly. This can cause light to either be absorbed into the cladding or be scattered. The scattering of light is called *Backscatter*.

The absorption of light by impurities or into the cladding is called, rather predictably, *Absorption*. Backscatter and absorption are the two chief causes of attenuation in optical fibres.

Small radius bends in the optical cable referred to earlier as *Microbends* cause light to scatter and refract into the cladding. In most cases, the light signal is completely lost. Microbends should not exist and a properly routed cable will not have them.

Structure of a Fibre Optic Cable

A cable usually consists of three main parts. The *Core*, the *Cladding* and the *Buffer*.

The core is in the optical fibre and it is made from high purity silica glass or sometimes, plastic. Typical optical fibres have diameters measured in micro-metres and are as thin, if not thinner than a strand of hair. The glass is so pure that if the seas were as pure you would be able to see the seabed clearly anywhere in the world!

Plastic fibres are more flexible than glass and cheaper to produce. They suffer greater attenuation than glass fibres and are usually restricted to short runs. Plastic fibres can be made from polycarbonate, polystyrene or polymethylmethacrylate.

The choice of fibre used is governed by:

1.   Frequency bandwidth and capacity.

2.   The ease of joining up cable runs.

3.   Attenuation

4.   Flexibility required in routing.

The cladding is a dielectric material. This has a lower refractive index than the core. The cladding is used to:

1.   Reduce loss of light from the core.

2.   Reduce light scatter at the surface of the core.

3.   Protect the fibre core from contamination.

4.   Strengthen the cable.

The buffer is the elastic covering that prevents abrasion of the core and cladding. It also stiffens the cable sufficiently to avoid the formation of micro-bends when the cable runs over uneven surfaces.

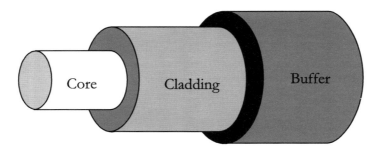

Figure 4.67 – Structure of Optical Fibre (Step Index)

Types of Fibre Optics

You will need to remember these - they are favourite questions! There are two main types of fibre optic cables. The *Step Index* and the *Graded Index*

Step Index

This consists of a fibre core having a refractive index n1, which is covered in a concentric cladding that has a lower refractive index n2. A problem that can occur with the step index cable is that the light may travel along a number of different paths. It is for this reason that step index cables are referred to as *Multi mode* cables. If light energy travels along different paths, the respective rays are transmitted over minutely different times. This gives rise to multi-mode dispersion. There is a limit to data or pulse rate that can be carried and to the frequency bandwidth. At this time, the bandwidth is limited to around 25MHz over a distance of one kilometre.

www.part66.co.uk

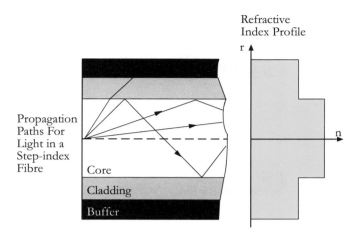

Figure 4.68 – Step Index

If the fibre core diameter is reduced to less than 3.2 times the wavelength of the light then the light can be made to travel along a single path. This type of step-index cable is called a *Single mode* cable.

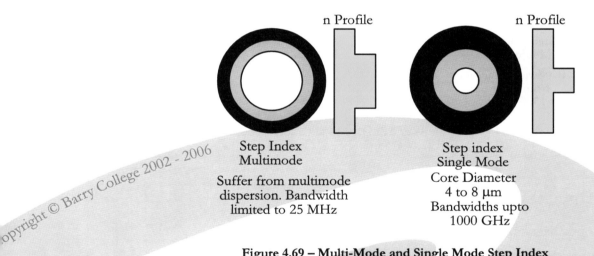

Figure 4.69 – Multi-Mode and Single Mode Step Index

Graded Index

The graded index cable has a fibre core that has a variation in refractive index, decreasing from the centre to the circumference. Graded index cables do not require cladding as the light rays are progressively bent or refracted across the radius of the fibre. By the time the light rays reach the interface they are reflecting back into the fibre. Clever idea! The effect is that the further the light is from the centre of the fibre, the faster it travels. This reduces the tendency for multi-mode dispersion and allows greater bandwidths. Bandwidths will be in the region of 200 to over 1500MHz over a one kilometre distance.

385

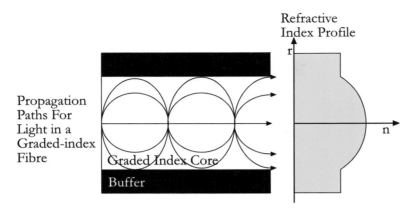

Figure 4.70 – Graded Index

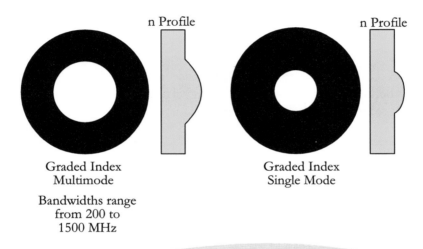

Figure 4.71 – Multi-Mode and Single Mode Graded Index

Fibre Optic Data Link System

A fibre optic data link system must have three basic parts:

1. A transmitter to receive an electrical signal from a sensor and convert it into a light signal for transmission into the cable.

2. A suitable cable to transmit the signal by light reflection.

3. A receiver that accepts the light signal and converts it back into an electrical signal for onward transmission to the equipment requiring it, (a computer).

www.part66.co.uk

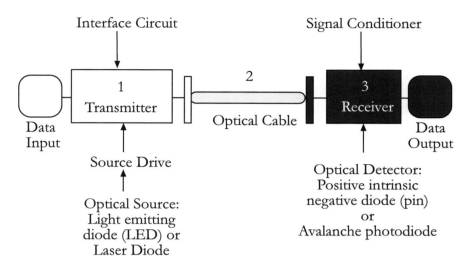

Figure 4.72 – Fibre Optic Data Link System

Transmitter

The transmitter converts the input signal from a sensor into an optical signal suitable for transmission and consists of two parts; an interface circuit and a source drive circuit. The transmitter's drive circuit converts the electrical signals to an optical signal by varying the current flow through the light source. There are two (2) types of optical sources; *Light Emitting Diodes (LED)* and *Laser Diodes*. The transmitter contains a frequency oscillator, a buffer and a modulator.

Receiver

The receiver converts the optical signal exiting the fibre back into an electrical signal and consists of two parts:

1.   The optical detector
2.   The signal conditioning circuits

The receiver amplifies and processes the optical signal without introducing noise or signal distortion. Noise is any disturbance that obscures or reduces the quality of the signal, which could cause distortion of the receiver's output signal. An optical detector can be either a semi-conductor *Positive-Intrinsic-Negative (PIN Diode)* or an *Avalanche Photo-Diode (APD)*. The receiver contains an amplifier.

Power

Both the transmitter and receiver require electrical power for their operation. Some sensors may also require power for their operation particularly where the signals have to be amplified. The optical fibre itself, however, does not require electrical power to transmit the light except where an active connector, or driver, may be used to boost the light signal.

Connections

Fibre optic connections can be splices, connectors or couplings. They are used to link cables to components, to join cables together, to connect several cables to a single cable or vice versa.

Splices

A splice makes a permanent join between two fibres or groups of fibres. They are intended to be permanent connections and are only used where there is no intention to dismantle them. There are two types of splice, *Mechanical Splices* and *Fusion Splices*.

Alignment of the fibres in a mechanical splice is achieved by crimping ferrules. These align the fibres under compression.

Fusion splices are made by melting the glass at the joint to fuse the fibres together permanently.

Connectors

These connections are designed for repeated disconnection and reconnection. The connectors maintain the alignment of fibres and have a known attenuation value. They are also proof against dust and moisture.

The main feature of compression type connectors lay in a flexible ferrule. When the connection is being made, the bushing compresses the ferrule automatically aligning the fibres in the connector. They are often referred to as *self-aligning* compression connections.

The cable buffer material has to be stripped back when connections are to be made. Epoxy resin is used to fix the fibre into the ferrule. The exposed ends of the fibres are then polished to a mirror finish prior to connection.

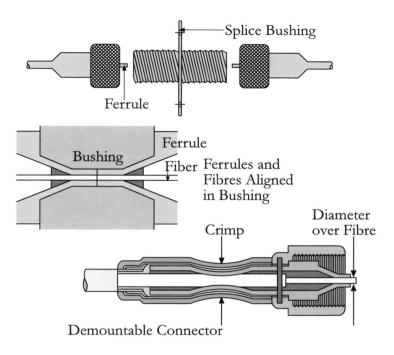

Figure 4.73 – Fibre Optic Connections

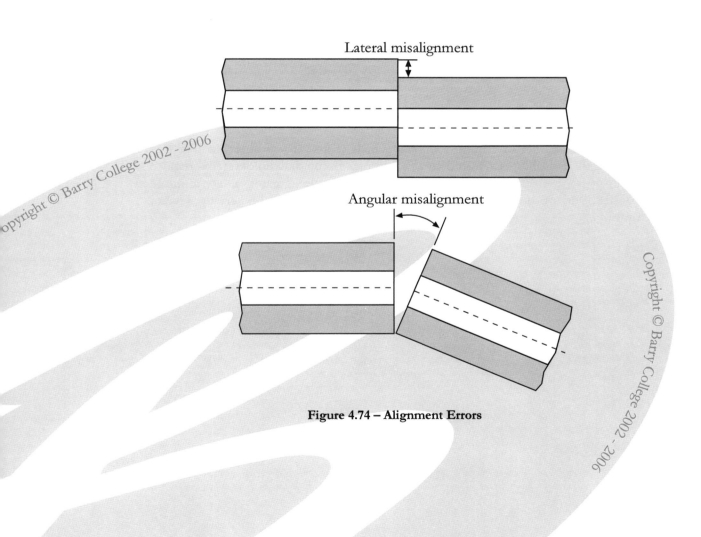

Figure 4.74 – Alignment Errors

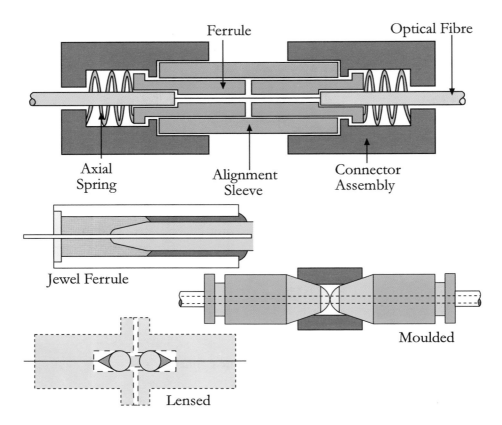

Figure 4.75 – Fibre Optic Connectors

Couplers

Couplers distribute or combine optical signals from several fibres. Where this is done the coupling is referred to as a splitter. Some data link systems require multi-port connections. The attenuation tends to be greater when multiple connections are being made because one input signal will be serving several outputs.

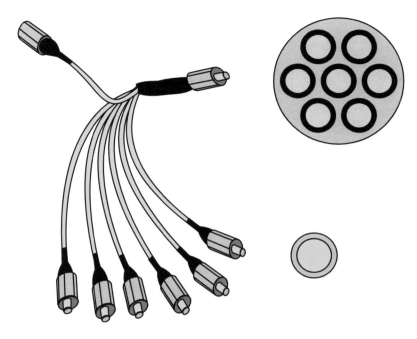

Figure 4.76 – Seven Way Splitter

Fibre optic couplers can be either active or passive. Active couplers are electronic components that split or combine signals electrically using light sensors and output signal sources to transmit the light. Passive couplers just redistribute the light signal without any light to electrical conversion.

The hardest connections to make are those between single mono-mode fibres and integrated optical channel wave-guides. The optical fibre has a circular profile whilst the optical wave-guide has a strip-like profile. Two methods that are used to achieve these connections are End-fire Coupling and Evanescent field Coupling. The essential idea is to butt the core of the optical fibre against the end of the optical wave-guide and once alignment is achieved, fix the elements in place. The end of the fibre has to be polished to produce an accurate mirror finished flat face. The coupling will self align the faces under compression.

A development of the end-fire method is to provide alignment grooves in the coupling to achieve even greater alignment accuracy.

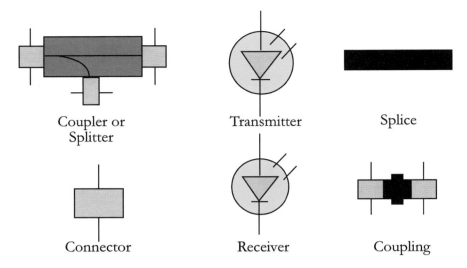

| Coupler or Splitter | Transmitter | Splice |
| Connector | Receiver | Coupling |

Figure 4.77 – Fibre Optic Cable Symbology

Testing Fibre Optics

Testing is required after the fitment of fibre optic cables and components. Splices, connectors and splitters have attenuation limits. Every time a splice or a connection is made or disturbed, the system must be tested for optical integrity. You may be surprised that this topic is included in the physics module but experience has shown that questions are being asked about the test equipment used.

Optical Power Meter (OPM)

This instrument measures the resistance to light transmission in an optical cable in decibels/metre before and after fitment. This gives a comparison upon which you can ascertain the integrity of connections or splices. The instrument is capable of measuring attenuation levels within a range of wavelengths.

It is similar in operation to a voltmeter. The optical power of the light signal received from an installed cable is then compared with the power received through the fibre prior to installation.

Optical Time-Domain Reflectometer (OTDR)

This instrument is much more reliable than the optical power meter and relies on measuring reflection. The instrument measures the reflective 'backscatter' in the optical fibre, known as '*Rayleigh Scatter*'. It then compares this with the loss of optical power in a theoretically perfect fibre. The results are displayed graphically on a cathode ray tube showing the loss of reflective power in dB over distance. The display accurately identifies the position of any source of loss in a fibre and also identifies the reason for the loss.

Reasons can include reflection from splices, loss through a bad connection, reflection from the end of a fibre or, reflection from breaks in the fibre. These will be displayed along with distances from the point at which the OTDR is connected.

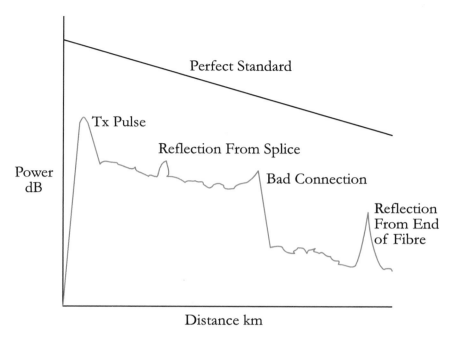

Figure 4.78 – Optical Time Domain Reflectometer Display

The OTDR can be used to compare the loss per unit length of fibres before installation and after installation. This will highlight any problems stemming from installation such as sharp bends. It is also used to check the integrity of individual splices and connectors.

The optical time-domain reflectometer is usually connected at the transmitter end of the optical fibre, replacing the transmitter during installed checks.

Revision

Light – Optics

Questions:

1.   **The speed of light in a vacuum is:**

 (A.) 3×10^5 km/s

 B. 3×10^8 km/s

 C.   300 m/s

2.   **The distance light will travel in one microsecond is:**

 A.   300,000m

  300.000.000   Per second

 B.   3000m

 (C.) 300m

3.   **Light is transmitted as:**

 A.   A longitudinal wave

 B.   A compression wave

 (C.) An electro-magnetic wave

4.   **As light passes from space into our atmosphere its velocity:**

 A.   Increases

 (B.) Decreases

 C.   Is unaltered

www.part66.co.uk

5.   **The intensity of light from a point source is:**

A. Proportional to the distance from the source

B. Inversely proportional to the distance from the source

C. Inversely proportional to the square of the distance from the source

6.   **When light passes from air into glass, its velocity:**

A. Increases

B. Decreases

C. Is unaltered.

7.   **The wave length of light:**

A. Increases from blue to red

B. Increases from red to blue

C. Decreases from violet to green

8.   **When light reflects off a plane surface:**

A. The angle of incidence is double the angle of reflection

B. The angle of reflection is double the angle of incidence

C. The angle of incidence is equal to the angle of reflection

9.   **The image seen in a plane mirror is:**

A. Real and the same size as the object

B. Virtual and the same size as the object

C. Virtual and half the size of the object

10.   The image seen in a plane mirror is:

   A.   The same distance behind the mirror as the object is in front

   B.   At the plane of the mirror

   C.   At the focal point of the mirror

11.   A concave mirror has :

   A.   A virtual principal focus behind the mirror

   B.   A real principal focus in front of the mirror

   C.   A real principal focus behind the mirror.

12.   A convex mirror has:

   A.   A virtual principal focus in front of the mirror

   B.   A real principal focus behind the mirror

   C.   A virtual principal focus behind the mirror.

13.   The focal length of a spherical mirror is:

   A.   Equal to its radius of curvature

   B.   Double its radius of curvature

   C.   Half its radius of curvature

14.   When a concave spherical mirror reflects an object that is at infinity, the image will be:

   A.   Real, inverted and smaller than the object

   B.   Virtual, upright and larger than the object

   C.   Real, upright and the same size as the object

www.part66.co.uk

15. **Convex, spherical mirrors give images that are:**

   A. Real, inverted and smaller than the object

   B. Virtual, upright and smaller than the object

   C. Virtual inverted images, the same size as the object

16. **When light passes from air into glass it will refract:**

   A. Away from the normal

   B. Towards the normal

   C. Parallel to the normal

17. **Refraction of light is primarily caused by:**

   A. Change of light velocity

   B. Change of light intensity

   C. Change of material mass or volume.

18. **The refractive index of light is:**

   A. sin r/sin i

   B. sin i/sin r

   C. sin i − sin r

19. **When light passes from air into glass, the refractive index Sin i/Sin r will be that of:**

   A. The air

   B. The air and glass

   C. The glass

20. When a stick is held in water, it appears to:

    A. Bend downwards

    B. Bend upwards

    C. Be straight

21. When you look into a swimming pool the water appears:

    A. Deeper than it is

    B. Shallower than it is

    C. At its correct depth

22. When light passes from glass to air and the angle of incidence is increased to exceed the 'critical angle', the light will be:

    A. Totally refracted in to the glass

    B. Passed totally out of the glass

    C. Totally reflected back into the glass

23. An object is placed 48cm in front of a concave mirror of focal length 12cm. The nature and position of the image is:

    A. Real image 16cm in front of mirror

    B. Virtual image 12cm behind the mirror

    C. Real image 36cm in front of mirror

24. The magnification of the concave mirror in Q23 is:

    A. 3×

    B. 0.3×

    C. 0.75×

www.part66.co.uk

25. **The speed of light through glass of refractive index 1.5 is:**

    A. 400m/microsecond

    B. 300m/microsecond

    C. 200m/microsecond

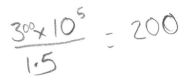

$$\frac{300 \times 10^5}{1.5} = 200$$

26. **A converging lens focuses light to a point because:**

    A. Light deviates more through its centre than its edges

    B. Its sides are not spherical

    C. Light deviates more through its edges than its centre

27. **The image formed by a diverging lens will be:**

    A. Real, inverted and larger than the object

    B. Virtual, erect and smaller than the object

    C. Real, erect and smaller than the object

28. **If an object is positioned between a convex lens and its principal focus, the image will be:**

    A. Virtual, erect and larger than the object

    B. Real, inverted and smaller than the object

    C. Virtual, inverted and smaller than the object.

29. **A slide being projected onto a screen through a convex lens will be:**

    A. Fitted upright in the projector behind the lens

    B. Fitted upside down in the projector behind the lens

    C. Fitted upright in the projector in front of the lens

399

30. Images projected onto the retina of the eye are:

   A. Inverted and diminished in size

   B. Upright and diminished in size

   C. Inverted and magnified

31. The 'critical angle' for Crown glass is approximately:

   A. 22°

   B. 42°

   C. 72°

32. Light passes through a fibre optic cable:

   A. In a straight line

   B. As a sinusoidal wave

   C. By internal reflection

33. The acceptance angle of a fibre optic cable is:

   A. Equal to the cone angle   *half*   *Page 380 Para 3*

   B. Less than the cone half angle

   C. Greater than the cone half angle

34. Attenuation in fibre optic cables is primarily caused by:

   A. Length of cable

   B. Absorption and back-scattering

   C. Microbends and scattering

35. The refractive index of a fibre optic cable's cladding is:

   A. Greater than the core's index.

   B. Less than the core's index

   C. The same as the core's index.

36. **A fibre optic cable core that has a refractive index that gradually decreases as its radius increases is called:**

   A. Step index

   B. Multimode index

   C. Graded index

37. **The transmitter in a fibre optic system converts electrical signals to light signals using a:**

   A. Photodiode

   B. Light emitting diode (LED)

   C. Positive intrinsic negative diode (PIN)

38. **A Step index cable consists of:**

   A. A core covered by a cladding of lower optical density

   B. A core covered by a cladding of higher optical density

   C. A core with no cladding

39. **A frequency oscillator, buffer and modulator are fitted in a fibre optic data link system in the:**

   A. Transmitter

   B. Receiver

   C. Sensor

40. **Breaks in a fibre optic core can be detected using:**

   A. An optical detector

   B. An Avalanche photodiode

   C. A time domain reflectometer.

Revision

Light – Optics

Answers:

1.	**A**		21.	**B**
2.	**C**		22.	**C**
3.	**C**		23.	**A**
4.	**B**		24.	**B**
5.	**C**		25.	**C**
6.	**B**		26.	**C**
7.	**A**		27.	**B**
8.	**C**		28.	**A**
9.	**B**		29.	**B**
10.	**A**		30.	**A**
11.	**B**		31.	**B**
12.	**C**		32.	**C**
13.	**C**		33.	**B**
14.	**A**		34.	**B**
15.	**B**		35.	**B**
16.	**B**		36.	**C**
17.	**A**		37.	**B**
18.	**B**		38.	**A**
19.	**C**		39.	**A**
20.	**B**		40.	**C**

www.part66.co.uk

Wave Motion and Sound

Wave Motion

If you have ever observed raindrops falling into a puddle of water or maybe thrown a pebble into a village pond, you will have seen wave motion. The ripples that spread out in circular patterns across the surface are good examples of circular wave fronts. You may also have observed the effects of several wave patterns colliding and crossing each other. There are distinct similarities with the behaviour of these waves and waves occurring in other media such as vibrating strings, springs, sound, radio, light. The list is considerable!

When we look at the list of possible candidates for wave motion, we can make two distinctions. Some waves required a medium through which to travel. For example, sound waves and water waves and vibrating strings. These are referred to as *Mechanical Waves*. Other waves, for example, light, radio and X-rays, do not depend on a medium to travel in. They can travel through a vacuum if required. These are referred to as being *Electromagnetic Waves*.

We can now look at a further distinction between waves. Sound waves consist of a series of pulses or pressure fronts. These are called *Longitudinal Waves*. A vibrating string on the other hand, forms a sinusoidal shape. Imagine shaking one end of a rope up and down to picture this. These are called *Transverse Waves*. Electromagnetic waves are all transverse waves but mechanical waves can consist of either type.

Figure 5.1 – A Transverse Wave set up on a Spring

Figure 5.2 – A Longitudinal Wave set up on a Spring

Finally, waves can move like the spreading ripples on a pond, or they can be stationary. If they are moving distributing energy as they travel, they are known as *Progressive Waves*. If they are stationary, they are called Standing Waves. All waveforms can become either progressive or standing waves.

We have introduced you to a few new descriptive words in this introduction. We need to examine each of these in more detail, but before doing this you will need to acquaint yourself with a few definitions; some of which you have already encountered in periodic motion. Waves are periodic in nature so it is important to do this.

Wave Velocity (v)

The velocity of a wave is represented by the symbol v and is the product of the wave frequency (f) and the wavelength (λ).

$$v = f\lambda$$

Periodic Time (T)

This is the time taken in seconds or, parts of a second for a wave to complete one cycle or oscillation.

Frequency (f)

This is the number of complete cycles occurring in one second. It is measured in *Hertz (Hz)* and is represented by the symbol f.

$$f = \frac{1}{T} \quad \text{and} \quad f = \frac{v}{\lambda}$$

Amplitude (a)

The amplitude of a wave is the distance from its mid or rest point to the point of maximum displacement.

Wave-length (λ)

This is the distance measured along the path of the wave between two similar points that are in the same phase and moving in the same direction. Wavelength is represented by the Greek letter Lamda (λ).

$$\lambda = \frac{v}{f}$$

Wave-Front

A line drawn through a progressive wave that joins all particles that are in similar phase is called a wave front. It is like a single ripple on a pond.

Transverse Waves

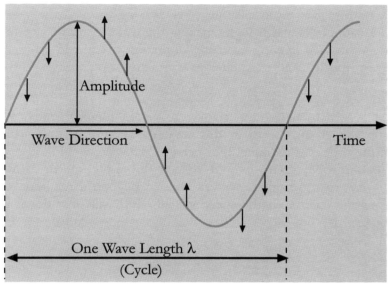

(F) Frequency = N^O of Cycles per Sec = $\dfrac{1}{T}$ = Hertz

(T) Periodic Time = Time to complete one cycle

Figure 5.3 – A Transverse Wave

You have read that transverse waves are sinusoidal. The wave pattern resembles a sine wave. The forward motion of the wave is accompanied by sideways motion. This waveform exists at varying wavelengths in all parts of the electromagnetic spectrum. This includes radio, infrared, visible light, ultra-violet, X-ray, gamma and cosmic radiation. Do not forget that radiant heat is also electromagnetic in nature. All electromagnetic waves are capable of travelling at the speed of light through a vacuum. They do not depend on a medium to travel in, as their displacement is due to electrical and magnetic fields as opposed to elastic energy.

The radiant heat and the light from the Sun, for example, travel through ninety three million miles of space at the speed of light to reach us in eight minutes. Electromagnetic waves will slow down as they enter denser mediums and will refract just like light.

A simpler example of the transverse wave can be witnessed by shaking the free end of a rope. Of course, this mechanical transverse wave does require a medium in which to travel.

www.part66.co.uk

Imagine that the rope particles at the end you are shaking are exerting a pull on the adjoining particles and cause them to oscillate as well. The process will continue along the rope until all the rope particles are oscillating up and down. Each particle oscillates slightly later than the one preceding it so the rope eventually takes up the shape of a series of equally spaced crests and troughs that appear to move forwards. Obviously, the rope particles are not moving along the rope, the wave is passing through it at the wave velocity.

Now imagine waves in the sea. This is the same process. The water is not moving forwards, it is the oscillating wave passing through the water that is causing alternate peaks and troughs making the water appear to be moving. If the water was actually moving forwards all the sea would end up in a heap on the land! In mechanical transverse waves, the wave passes through the medium.

The speed at which mechanical transverse waves travel through a medium depends on the elastic forces in the medium. If you were to increase the tension in the rope, for example, the speed of the wave would increase. If you used a heavier rope, inertia would reduce the wave speed. However, do remember that electromagnetic waves do not rely on a medium. They can travel through a vacuum at the speed of light and will slow down in denser materials.

Longitudinal Waves

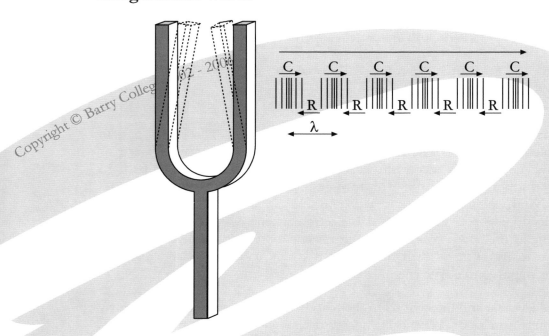

Figure 5.4 – A Longitudinal Wave

www.part66.co.uk

This type of wave consists of a series of compressions and rarefactions. The particles oscillate in the same path as the wave and not at right angles to it. This waveform exists in sound waves and shock waves. If you were to hit a solid object with a hammer, the shock wave would travel through it as a longitudinal wave.

We often describe these types of shock waves as seismic waves and they are longitudinal in nature. If you were to shake the free end of a vertically suspended spring up and down you would induce a longitudinal wave through it. Sections of the spring would alternately compress and then extend as rarefactions, the equally spaced compressions and rarefactions appearing to travel along the spring. The speed of the wave would depend on the elastic energy between each particle in the spring.

Longitudinal waves are mechanical waves. They need a medium to travel in. Sadly, the explosions and engine noises you hear in 'Star Wars' movies are bogus. Sound cannot travel in a vacuum. You may see the light but not hear the sound unless it has something made of matter to connect it to your eardrum.

Longitudinal waves travel through the medium. The matter in the material oscillates back and forth but does not progress forward. If it did you would probably suffocate as soon as you spoke! The local Philharmonic Orchestra would create a hurricane in the concert hall! Longitudinal sound waves travel at the speed of sound in air, which is 331m/s at standard sea level conditions. They increase in velocity in denser materials. Sound waves travel four times faster in water and about fifteen times faster in steel.

Wave Fronts

If you were to drop a pebble into a pond of still water, you would see ripples spreading out in concentric circles. If you assume one of the ripples to represent a wave front then the direction of the wave can be assumed to be at right angles to it.

407

www.part66.co.uk

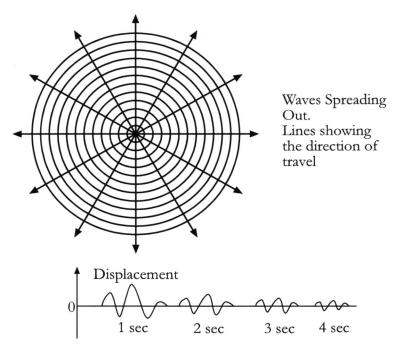

Figure 5.5 – Ripple Caused by a Pebble Dropped into a Pond

You might also notice that the amplitude of the ripples near the impact site of the pebble is large and decreases steadily as the radius increases. The energy in a ripple or wave is proportional to the square of its amplitude. Energy is gradually lost to the surrounding water and the amplitude falls. A ripple 4cm high has sixteen times the energy of a ripple 1cm high.

Intensity

The energy contained in a wave will reduce the further it travels. If we first consider an electromagnetic wave travelling in free space, we will find that it obeys the *Inverse Square Law*. This law states that:

The intensity of an electromagnetic wave emanating from a point in free space is inversely proportional to the square of the distance from its source.

$$\text{Intensity (I)} = \frac{\text{Wave energy (E)}}{\text{Distance from source}^2 \ (d^2)}$$

Electromagnetic waves travel out in all directions from a point source like an inflating sphere. This means that the wave energy is progressively spread over a larger area as the radius of the sphere increases.

www.part66.co.uk

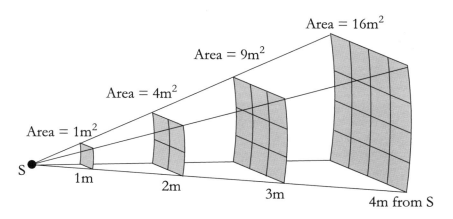

Figure 5.6 – Electromagnetic Wave Inverse Square Law

When electromagnetic waves travel through a medium such as air or glass, for example, some wave energy is also absorbed by the material. This is called *Attenuation* and is a loss of intensity in addition to that lost through the inverse square law. Now let us have a look at the intensity of mechanical waves. These are proportional to the square of their amplitude.

$$\text{Intensity (I)} = \text{Amplitude}^2$$

A water wave, 3 metres high, will have nine times the energy of a wave one metre high. The wave gives up its energy to the medium it travels through in a process of attenuation. As the wave front spreads out its energy is spread over an increasing area. If you could imagine the wave to be in free space, it would also obey the inverse square law. This is an additional loss to the attenuation it experiences in an earthbound medium. The law is modified for mechanical waves because of the additional losses incurred by attenuation.

Displacement

The displacement of a progressive wave can be illustrated as either distance travelled or, time taken. The wave cycle starts at zero displacement and moves to a maximum amplitude as the crest passes. The wave then reduces back to zero again before displacing to maximum amplitude as the trough passes. The wave then returns to zero and the cycle is complete. The distance travelled in one complete cycle would represent the *Wavelength* (λ). The time taken for one complete cycle would represent the *Period (T)*. From this information, we can derive the **frequency (f)** and the wave *velocity (v)*.

We have shown a distance base graph where the wave completes one cycle in 5m. The wavelength is clearly 5 metres.

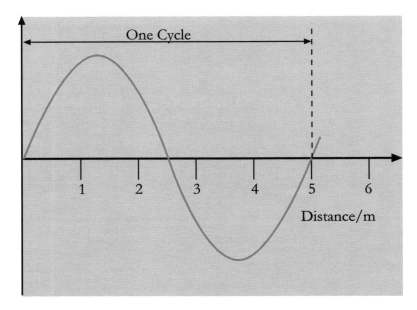

Figure 5.7 – Graph of Displacement in Terms of Distance

We now show the same wave on a time-base graph. We can see that the wave displaces one cycle in 5 seconds. The period is clearly 5 seconds.

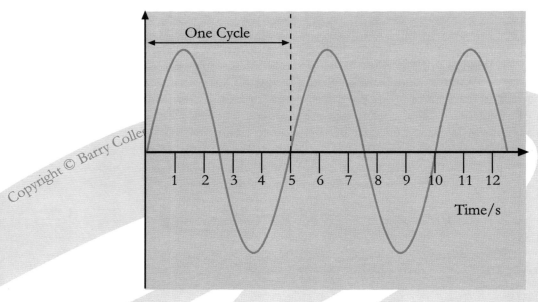

Figure 5.8 – Graph of Displacement in Terms of Time

Let us see what we can gain from this information

$$\text{Frequency (f)} = \frac{1}{T} = \frac{1}{5s} = 0.2\text{Hz}$$

$$\text{Wave velocity (v)} = f\lambda = 0.2\text{Hz} \times 5\text{m} = 1\text{m/s}$$

www.part66.co.uk

Reflection of Waves

You should now be familiar with the laws of reflection in regard to light waves. What you may not appreciate at this time is that reflection can also occur in all waves including water waves, sound waves etc.

You need to picture the propagation of different waves. Water waves, for example, spread out in concentric circles from a point source. This could be the proverbial pebble dropped in the pond.

Sound waves and light waves propagate out from a point source as a sphere. In both cases, as the radius of propagation increases the wave fronts gradually become to all intents and purposes, straight. A series of wave fronts could then be assumed to be parallel.

We can now look at a few examples where waves are incident on plane and curved surfaces. Water waves striking harbour walls for example. In each case, we look at parallel incident waves and then circular waves propagating from a point source disturbance in front of a wall.

Example 1

In the first illustration we can observe parallel waves incident on a plane wall that is angled at 45° to their path. Note that the angle of incidence equals the angle of reflection, just like in a plane mirror.

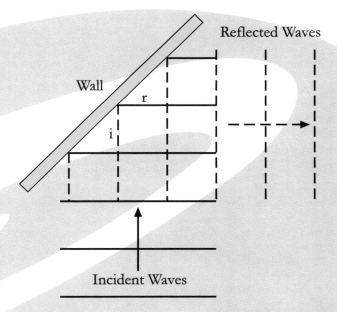

Figure 5.9 – Straight Wave Reflection off a Plane Wall

Example 2

Here we illustrate curved wave fronts propagating from a point source in front of a plane wall. Note how the waves reflect back in curved form.

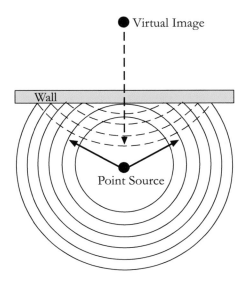

Figure 5.10 – Curved Wave Reflection off a Plane Wall

If we were to find the virtual centre where these reflected waves appeared to diverge from we would see that it lay behind the wall at a distance equal to that of the point source disturbance in front of the wall. It is in effect the position of a virtual image behind the wall.

Example 3

In our third illustration, parallel waves are incident on a concave wall. Note that in the case of parallel incident wave fronts the waves reflect off the concave wall in curved form. The real centre where the reflected waves appear to diverge from lies in front of the wall and is, in fact, the focal point. Just like a concave spherical mirror.

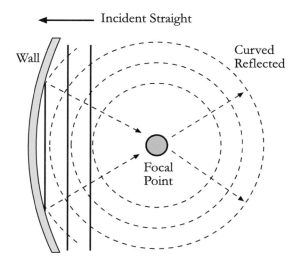

Figure 5.11 – Straight Waves Reflect off Concave Wall

Example 4

In this illustration, the curved incident waves are propagating from a point source in front of a concave wall just where the focal point would be. They strike the wall and reflect back as parallel lines.

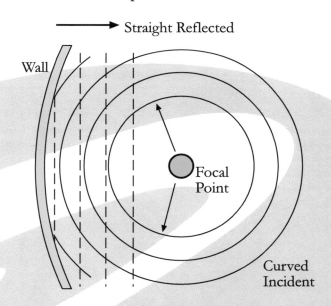

Figure 5.12 – Curved Waves Reflect off Concave Wall
(Point Source at Focal Point)

Example 5

If we now position the point source disturbance between the focal point and the pole of a concave wall, we will see that the reflected waves are curved.

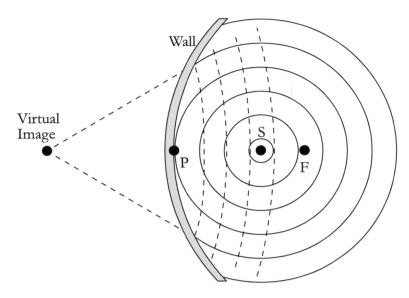

Figure 5.13 – Wave Source(s) between Focus (F) and Pole (P)

The virtual centre where the reflecting waves seem to diverge from will lay behind the wall and would be the position of a virtual image if this were a spherical mirror.

Example 6

In our final example for a concave wall, we have positioned the point source disturbance in front of the wall and out beyond the centre of curvature of the wall. Note how the reflected waves converge to a point between the focal point and the centre of curvature of the wall. This would be the image if this were a mirror. Having passed through the image point, the reflected waves then diverge away.

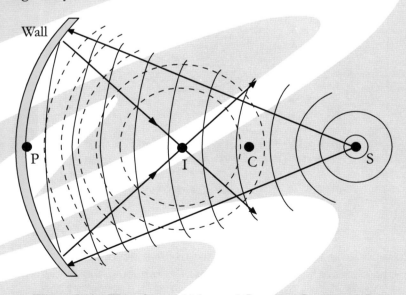

Figure 5.14 – Wave Source(s) beyond Centre of Curvature (C)

Example 7

We will now look at parallel waves incident on a convex wall.

Note how they reflect away in curved form. The virtual centre of the curvature lies behind the wall and is the virtual focal point.

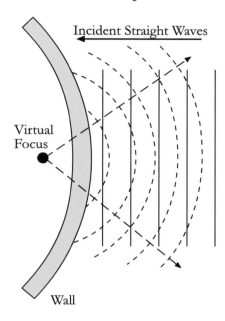

Figure 5.15 – Straight Waves Reflecting off Convex Wall

Example 8

Finally, we will look at curved waves incident on a convex wall that is propagating from a point source disturbance. Note that the reflected waves are again curved and once again appear to be diverging from a virtual image point behind the wall.

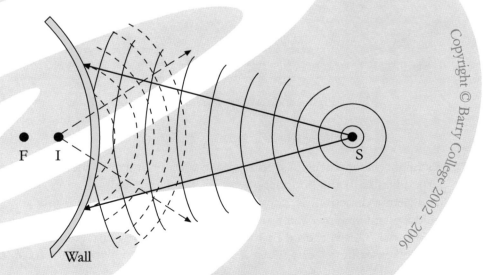

Figure 5.16 – Curved Waves Reflecting off Convex Wall

You should now be aware that all waves reflecting off plane and curved surfaces behave in a similar fashion to light rays incident on mirrors.

Refraction of Waves

You have already encountered the refraction of light in the previous chapter. You should be aware that it is the change in wave velocity that causes the refraction. Light is not the only wave medium that refracts. To illustrate this we shall take a simple example of water waves approaching a beach.

When straight water waves pass over a shelving seabed, they alter their wavelength and wave velocity. If the waves pass from deep to shallow water their wavelength and wave velocity decrease. Because both wavelength and velocity decrease, the frequency of the waves does not alter. You can see this by:

$$\text{Frequency (f)} = \frac{\text{Wavevelocity}}{\text{Wavelength}} = \frac{v}{\lambda}$$

Wave Length (λ) and Velocity (V) Decrease.
No Change in Frequency (F).

$$F = \frac{V}{\lambda}$$

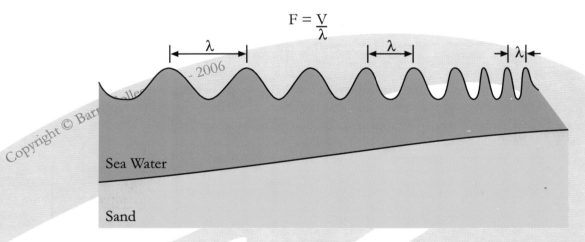

Figure 5.17 – Waves Passing into Shallow Water

If straight water waves pass in to shallow water at a zero incident angle, that is perpendicular to the boundary between deep and shallow water, they continue in the same direction. If, however, the waves approach the boundary between the deep and shallow water at an angle to the normal, they will refract towards the normal. This is caused by the change of wave velocity. Remember that light also decreases in velocity when it passes from air to glass and refracts towards the normal.

www.part66.co.uk

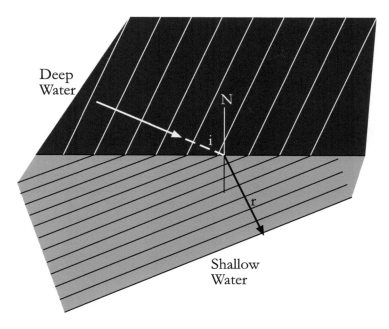

Figure 5.18 – Refraction of Waves

Waves that are incident at a boundary at an angle to the normal that experience a change in velocity will refract. If they slow down, they will refract towards the normal. If they speed up they will refract away from the normal. Sound waves, for example, speed up when they pass from air into water. They will refract away from the normal. Light, on the other hand, slows down when passing from air into water. It refracts towards the normal.

$$\text{Refractive index (n)} = \frac{\text{Velocity in first medium}}{\text{Velocity in second medium}} = \frac{\text{Sin i}}{\text{Sin r}}$$

Diffraction of Waves

We will now have a look at another property of waves. Again, straight water waves stand as a good example but the effect may be observed in other mechanical and electromagnetic waves when they meet plane surfaces.

Imagine that a harbour wall has an opening in it. Assume the opening is wider than the wavelength of straight waves that are striking the wall at zero incidence-angle. The waves will pass through the opening to the inner harbour as parallel straight waves. You may observe a slight curvature at the ends of each wave after it has passed through the gap in the wall. This curvature is called *Diffraction*.

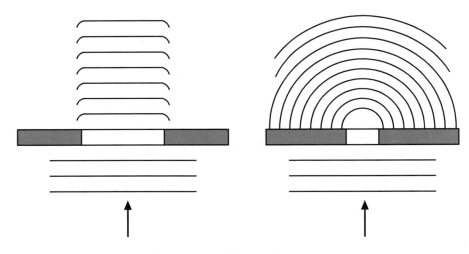

Figure 5.19 – Wave Diffraction

Now imagine that the gap in the harbour wall is the same width or less than the wavelength of the straight waves. The waves will emerge through the gap into the inner harbour as circular waves that will radiate out in all directions across the inner harbour. This curvature of the emergent waves is a clear example of Diffraction.

Substitute the harbour wall for an opaque filter in front of a light source and imagine that the filter has a slit cut across it. If the slit is wide, the light will pass through it and project onto a screen as a sharp edged image of the slit. If the slit is very narrow, you will observe that the image of the slit on the screen has fuzzy edges. The diffraction of light is not so noticeable because of the short wavelength of the light. The slit in the filter would have to be very narrow indeed to produce it.

If you increased the wavelength of the light by using a red or orange source, the effect may become slightly more noticeable.

Interference Phenomena

Now we are going to make life complicated. We have been looking at waves that emanate from a single point source. Now, we will look at the waves emanating from more than one source and what occurs when they cross each other's paths. Maybe you would like to have a cup of coffee first!

I would like you to go back to our harbour wall again. It is the easiest example. Imagine that the wall now has a number of equally spaced gaps in it. Each of the gaps is at or less than the wavelength of straight water waves striking the wall at zero incidence-angle. You now know that the waves will emerge through each gap into the inner harbour as circular wave fronts. The problem is, each radiating circular pattern will run across the neighbouring patterns. The gaps are acting as individual point sources of waves.

www.part66.co.uk

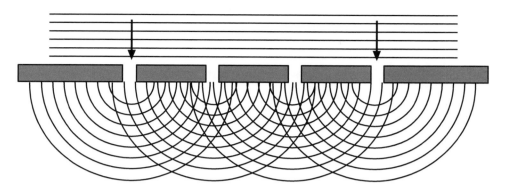

Figure 5.20 – Waves Diffracting from Several Points

When you stand on the wall and look into the inner harbour you will observe that there appears to be regions of rough and smooth water and that these regions seem to have some kind of line symmetry. Your eyes are not fooling you. You are observing a good example of wave interference phenomena!

As each wave front spreads out and crosses its neighbours, there will be points where the crest of one wave coincides with the crest of a neighbouring wave. There will also be points where the trough of one wave coincides with the trough of a neighbour. In both cases the coinciding wave fronts cause increased disturbance or **Constructive Interference** and the points where this occurs are called *Antinodal Points*.

Following this through, there will be points where the crest of one wave will coincide with the trough of a neighbouring wave. This will effectively cancel the wave by *Destructive Interference*. The points where this occurs are called *Nodal Points*.

The lines of rough and smooth water, you are observing are caused by *Antinodes* and *Nodes*. This is the effect of wave interference.

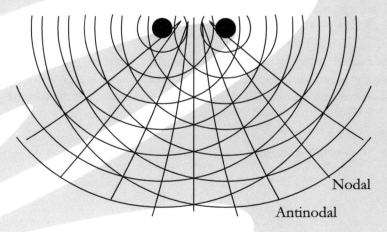

Nodal

Antinodal

Figure 5.21 – Interference of Two Wave Patterns

Let's look at other waveforms. Go back to the opaque filter with the light source behind it. Now we have a series of very narrow equidistant slits across the filter. Diffraction will occur through each slit and the emergent light waves will interfere with each other. The image you will now observe on the screen will be that of light and dark bands. Have you guessed it? The bright light bands are the *Antinodal* points and the dark bands are the *Nodal points*. What you are observing are called *Interference Fringes*.

Gaps in walls or slits in filters are not the only way to create this phenomenon. The examples we are using conveniently create this phenomenon. These examples also conveniently create several point sources. Two or more independent light sources or, two or more pebbles dropped into our village pond will do the same.

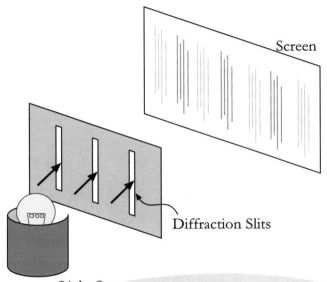

Figure 5.22 – Interference Fringes

Let us go to yet another example, sound waves. Imagine the local Pop Group is holding a Gig on the stage of the Summer Rock festival. Two loudspeakers are placed close together and are radiating similar sounds at the same time. As the waves radiate away from each speaker they will cross each other creating regions of increased and decreased disturbance. These regions will actually run in radial lines called *Antinodal lines* and *Nodal lines*. Quite whether you are going to be affected by where you stand will naturally depend on other sound sources. But you get the idea.

www.part66.co.uk

Figure 5.23 – Interference from Two Point Sources

Before we move on, let us sum up what we have learnt about interference so far. If waves emanating from two point sources cross each other, they will experience interference. When the crest of one wave coincides with the crest of a neighbouring wave or, trough coincides with trough, the interference is said to be *Constructive*. The coincident points are *Anti-nodes*. The wave energy intensifies at these points.

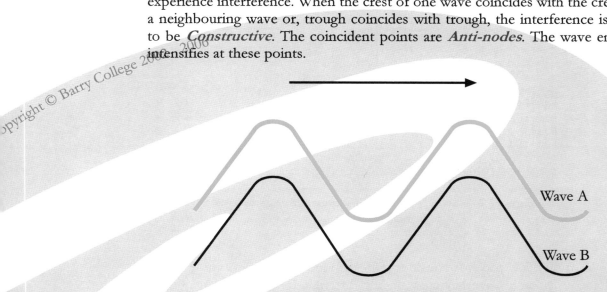

Figure 5.24 – Crest on Crest. Trough on Trough. Constructive (Anti-nodal)

When the crest of a wave coincides with the trough of a neighbouring wave, the interference is said to be *Destructive*. The coincident points are then said to be *Nodes*. The wave energy is cancelled out at these points.

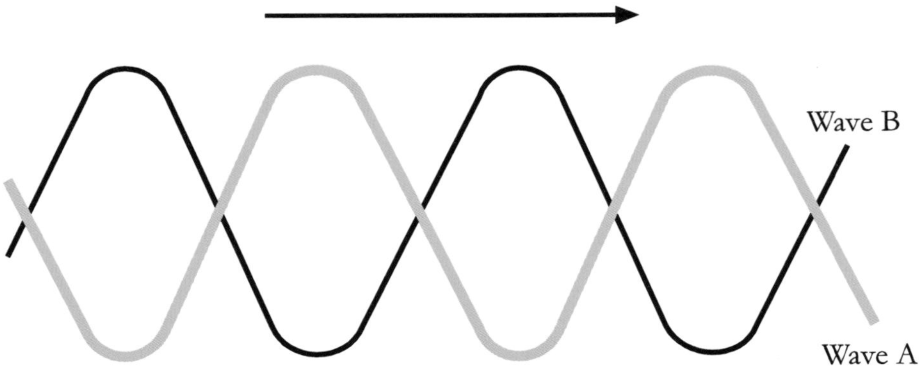

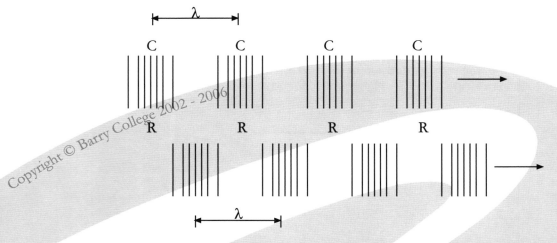

Figure 5.25 – Crest on Trough. Destructive (Nodal)

Consider two identical sound waves, each having the same wavelength, amplitude and frequency. Say the waves are emitted from a source at slightly different times, so that they superpose on each other exactly one half a wavelength out of alignment. What would you hear?

The answer is nothing. The two waves would cancel each other out because of destructive interference. The compressions would align with the rarefactions destroying the wave energy.

Figure 5.26 – Sound Waves Half Wavelength Apart

I would now like you to consider two sound waves that are emitted simultaneously, each wave having a slightly different frequency. Imagine that the waves are superposed on each other and are travelling in the same direction. What would you hear? You would hear a regular rise and fall in the intensity of the sound. When the compressions of each wave align, the sound gets louder. When the compressions align with the rarefactions, the sound disappears. The regular rises and falls in the sound you hear are called Beats. The waves start in alignment but because they are at slightly different frequencies they periodically misalign and then re-align again.

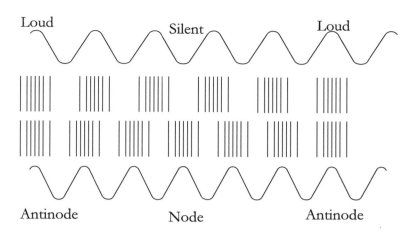

Loud   Silent   Loud

Antinode   Node   Antinode

Figure 5.27 – Production of 'Beats'

I have illustrated this for you by showing you both longitudinal and transverse waves. Although sound waves are longitudinal, they are often graphically represented by transverse waves for convenience. By showing you both forms you should have no trouble identifying how 'Beats' occur

Standing Waves

So far, we have been examining waves that are progressive and travelling in the same direction. I would now like you to consider two similar progressive waves having the same amplitude and frequency that are superposed on each other whilst travelling in opposite directions. When this occurs they combine to form a *Standing Wave*, sometimes referred to as a *Stationary Wave*. The positions of the crests and troughs of the waves appear to be stationary.

A good example for you would be a violin string. When it is bowed, a transverse waveform is produced in the vibrating string that travels to the bridge of the violin where it is then reflected back along its path. Another example of would be water waves striking a wall and reflecting straight back along their original path. The incident and reflected waves then combine to form a stationary, or standing wave.

Imagine a guitar string vibrating between the two bridges. The amplitude will be at a maximum (Anti-node) in the centre of the string and zero (Node) at the ends of the string.

423

www.part66.co.uk

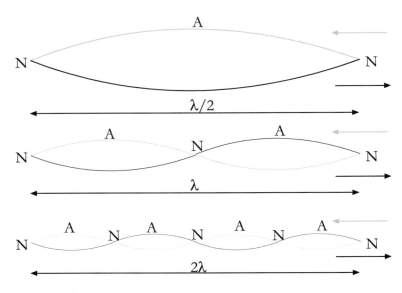

Figure 5.28 – Standing Waves

If I were to place my finger at the centre of the vibrating string, the string would then vibrate in two segments. I would now have three nodal points, one at each end of the string and one in the centre. I would also have two anti-nodal points, one at the centre of each segment.

Standing waves can be produced in all waveforms. For example, two identical sound waves each having the same frequency and amplitude and travelling over each other in opposite directions will form a standing wave. You can reproduce this by blowing over the mouth of an empty bottle. The wave reflects off the bottom and travels back over its path.

Study the illustration and identify that the distance between two nodal points in a stationary wave is equal to a half wavelength. In one wavelength, you would have three nodal points and two anti-nodal points.

Sound

The majority of sound waves that you hear are transmitted through the medium of air. However, sound waves can travel through liquids and solids. The *sound wave* is *a longitudinal wave* comprising a series of *Compressions* and *Rarefactions.* The velocity of a sound wave is governed by the elasticity and density of the medium it is travelling through. Sound waves cannot travel through a vacuum.

The speed of sound in air is determined to be 331½ m/s at 0°C. This is equivalent to 1087ft/s, 741mph, or 644kts. Liquids are better transmitters of sound and sound waves will travel approximately four times faster in water than in air. The speed of sound in solids is even greater. Sound travels through steel, for example, at 5000m/s, which is fifteen times faster than it travels in air.

The velocity changes from one medium to another causing the sound waves to refract. Sound waves will also reflect off interfaces between two mediums, for example, air and a wall.

Factors affecting the Speed of Sound in Air

The loudness, or intensity, of sound waves has no effect on their speed. The pitch of sound waves is proportional to their frequency but neither has any effect on the velocity of the sound in air. If you hear music playing in the distance you hear all the notes in exactly the right order so, they must all be travelling at the same speed. Although $v = f \lambda$ the value of v is fixed by the speed of sound in air and that, as we shall see, is fixed by the absolute temperature of the air alone.

Changes in air pressure and density do not affect the speed of sound in air. This can be simply explained by studying Boyles's Law. If the pressure of air is doubled at constant temperature, its volume will be halved and its density will double. The velocity of sound is proportional to the square root of pressure, divided by density as follows:

$$\text{Velocity of Sound in air is proportional to: } \sqrt{\frac{\text{Pressure}}{\text{Density}}}$$

It follows that, if the pressure changes, the density also changes by a similar proportion, so there is no overall change in sound velocity.

Temperature, however, can alter the density of air without altering its pressure. Consequently, if the air temperature changes at constant pressure the velocity of sound will be affected. Let us sum this up:

The speed of sound in air is proportional to its absolute temperature.

What does this mean? The speed of sound in air is only affected by the absolute temperature of the air. If the temperature rises, the speed of sound in air rises also. If the air temperature falls, the speed of sound in air falls also.

This effectively means that the speed of sound in air at altitude is less than it would be at sea level. A good way of remembering this is to consider why attempts at the World land speed record are always carried out in very hot climates. The car designers and drivers are not always sure of the effects that shock waves will have if they form on the cars. Therefore, they drive them in hot climates where the value of the local speed of sound in air is higher than the speed they are attempting. It's a way of remembering the relationship that air temperature has with sound velocity. The speed of sound in air rises by approximately 61cm/s or 2ft/s for every degree Centigrade rise in temperature.

www.part66.co.uk

Production of Sound

You have already read that sound waves are longitudinal waves. A simple example can be made if you imagine a vibrating tuning fork. It will send out a sound wave. As one prong of the fork moves one way, it will compress the air molecules in contact with it, **Compression**. This compression pulse will be transmitted through the adjoining air molecules ahead of it.

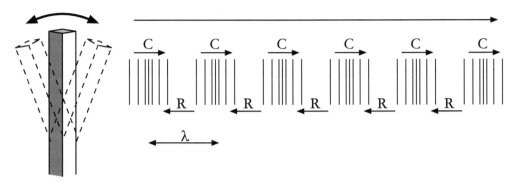

Figure 5.29 – Production of a Sound Wave

As the prong moves in the opposite direction, it gives a reverse compression called a **Rarefaction**. If you were to be able to see these pulses, you would see that the compressions pulse in the direction of the wave whilst the rarefactions pulse in the opposite direction. The distance between the centres of two compressions or, two rarefactions, is equal to one wavelength (λ).

Frequency Ranges

The human voice has a frequency range between 85Hz and 1.1kHz. The human hearing range is between 20Hz and 20kHz. Frequencies above 20kHz are in the ultra-sound range that extends up as high as 10MHz

Reflection of Sound

The rules governing the reflection of sound are similar to those governing other waveforms including light. Incident sound waves will reflect off plane and curved surfaces and total internal reflection will occur at a given critical angle. Sound waves refract when their velocity changes. Sound waves entering water or a solid material from air will increase in velocity and refract away from the normal

When airborne sound waves strike a hard plane surface like a wall they will reflect in the form of an Echo. If you were to clap your hands in the vicinity of a wall you may detect an echo. The time taken for the sound wave to return to you will depend on the distance that you are standing away from the wall. Remember, the wave has to first travel to the wall, reflect, and then travel back to you. Both journeys will occur at the local speed of sound in air.

Example

You are standing at a distance of 99m from a large, flat, vertical surface. You clap your hands and record that a sound echo occurs 0.6s later. You then calculate the local speed of sound in air as being:

Time for sound wave to travel from you to surface is 0.3s

Distance of surface from you is 99m

Local speed of sound in air $= \dfrac{\text{Distance}}{\text{Time}} = \dfrac{99\text{m}}{0.3\text{s}} = 330\text{m/s}$

Note: that this is quite easy to set as a multi-choice question.

For you to hear an echo clearly, it must be at least 0.1sec behind the originating source, (your handclap for example). As sound travels at 331 ½ m/s at zero degrees Centigrade at sea level, you would have to be at least 17 meters away from the reflecting surface to ensure that time separation. If you were closer than this, you would only be conscious of an extended clapping sound. This prolonging of sounds when you are close to reflecting surfaces is called *Reverberation*. It is a common phenomena that is often encouraged in concert halls where musical notes seem to 'hang in the air' for a moment.

Excessive reverberation is, however, undesirable as it results in the confusion of sounds as one note runs into the other. This can occur when a sound wave reflects off multiple internal surfaces at different distances from the source. The notes from an organ in a large, empty Cathedral, for example, can reverberate for five or six seconds. Architects often use sound absorbent and reflective panels to adjust this phenomenon that governs the Acoustic properties of a building.

The intensity of a reflected wave is governed by the nature of the reflecting surface. If the surface is hard, the reflected sound intensity is high. This becomes a problem for people who act on a stage. During rehearsals, the sound is reflecting off a multitude of hard surfaces in the theatre. Voices seem to be clear and loud as far as the speaker is concerned. When an audience is present, the sound waves are being absorbed into a mass of soft clothing and the reflected sound intensity can be lost causing speakers to think their voices are weak.

Intensity

The intensity of a sound wave, often loosely referred to as 'loudness', is the energy of the wave. It is proportional to the square of its amplitude. It is also proportional to the density of the medium and the square of the frequency but the most important relationship it has is to its amplitude.

Sound intensity is proportional to the square of Amplitude

427

In simple terms this means, for example, that if the amplitude of a sound wave is doubled, the intensity will increase fourfold. If the amplitude is trebled, the intensity will rise nine times.

Loudness does depend on intensity but your hearing only operates within a given frequency range. For example, you cannot hear ultra-sound. For this reason, loudness is not always proportional to the square of the amplitude but intensity is. Both intensity and loudness do obey the inverse square law in that they are inversely proportional to the square of the distance from the source.

The amplitude of a sound wave is the maximum displacement of an oscillating particle from its rest position. We know that the compressions and rarefactions in the wave oscillate as they move in the wave direction.

Pitch

The pitch of a sound can be best described as its position on the musical scale. You would instantly recognise high and low pitch sounds. The pitch of a sound wave is proportional to its frequency. (The higher the frequency, the higher the pitch.) You will remember that the frequency of a wave is the number of complete cycles occurring in one second and that it is measured in Hertz (Hz).

Pitch of a sound wave is proportional to frequency

Quality

You may need another cup of coffee before getting into this topic, unless you are a musician, of course. IR Part-66 papers have a habit of probing into this.

Imagine that the same musical note is played first on a piano, then on a guitar and then on a violin. It is exactly the same note that is being played in each case. I bet you would recognise each instrument that played it though. It is the quality of the sound being played that differentiates between them.

If you were to pluck a perfect harp string on a perfect harp to produce a single musical note, the string would vibrate at a frequency called the *Fundamental Frequency*. The note emitted would be a characteristic of the string vibrating at that frequency on that instrument. It is the strongest note the string can produce. However, no instrument is perfect and other frequencies are set up in the instrument that then overlay the fundamental frequency. These are called *Overtones* and it is these that determine the quality of a musical sound. In fact the fundamental frequency of an instrument gives sound that is not always particularly pleasant to listen to. Instrument makers deliberately create selected overtones to give an instrument its quality of sound. Now you know how Stradivarius did it.

www.part66.co.uk

We need to examine the topic of the quality of sound further as a number of related questions appear in the examination papers. Do remember this:

The quality of a musical sound is governed by its overtones.

Vibrating Strings

A *Sonometer* is a sounding board with a *single-tensioned string*. It will serve us well to explain the production of musical tones from a vibrating string. The ranges of frequencies that can be present in a vibrating string are called Harmonics and they produce frequencies ranging from the fundamental frequency to frequencies producing overtones. We need to examine these and their relationship with overtones. You can be asked about these.

If the string is plucked or bowed, it will vibrate and the transverse wave in the string will reflect back off the bridges to give us a standing wave. In its most simple form the string will vibrate in one segment only, which is the fundamental frequency, and the sonometer will emit a single note called the *Fundamental*. This is the *first harmonic*.

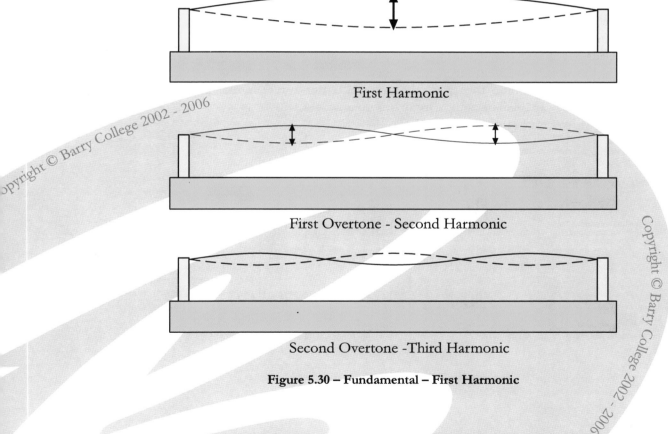

First Harmonic

First Overtone - Second Harmonic

Second Overtone -Third Harmonic

Figure 5.30 – Fundamental – First Harmonic

If you now touch the centre of the vibrating string, it will start to vibrate in two segments and produce an overtone. The note emitted is now the *Octave* of the fundamental, which is the *second harmonic* and the *first overtone*.

If you were to now make the string vibrate in three segments you would produce the third harmonic, which is the second overtone.

You should have the idea now. Musical instruments play a complex number of overtones and this is where the quality of what you are hearing comes from. The frequency of a vibrating string will depend on its length, the tension in the string and the mass of the string. The frequency of a string is:

- Inversely proportional to its length.

- Proportional to the square root of its tension.

- Inversely proportional to its mass.

Pipes

Imagine that a sound wave is created in a pipe that has one end closed. This can be done by blowing across the open end or, by holding a tuning fork over the open end. As the air particles in the closed end of the pipe cannot move, a nodal point will occur there. If the pipe is a quarter wavelength long an anti-node forms at the open end. This will be the first Resonant Position. To find the second resonant position you will need a pipe three times longer or, three quarters wavelength. This will again place an anti-node at the open end. You can see that the resonant positions are created, by having pipes with lengths that always place an anti-node at the open end. So, the third resonant position would occur in a pipe that was one and a quarter wavelengths. All waves created in the pipe will be stationary or standing waves.

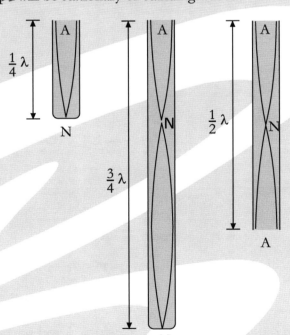

Figure 5.31 – Resonance in Pipes

www.part66.co.uk

Ultra-sound

Ultra-sonic sound frequencies are higher than the range of human hearing. We can hear sounds in the frequency range 20Hz to 20kHz. Above this, ultra-sound frequencies may be found up to 10MHz in industrial use. Ships use 50kHz for sonar to detect submerged obstacles. Much higher frequencies are used for medical scanning equipment. Higher frequencies are used for industrial non-destructive testing. Ultra-sound is a very safe alternative to the use of X-ray and Gamma ray equipment.

Doppler Effect in Sound Waves

When a sound wave is created, it radiates away from the source in all directions. If the source is moving, the sound waves still radiate away from it at the local speed of sound in air. Imagine the source to be a motorbike travelling in a given direction. It is chasing the sound waves ahead of it and distancing itself from the sound waves radiating behind it.

Depending on the speed of the motorbike, the sound waves travelling forward of it will be closer together and will be at a higher frequency than the waves behind it. The waves being left behind will be further apart and at a lower frequency.

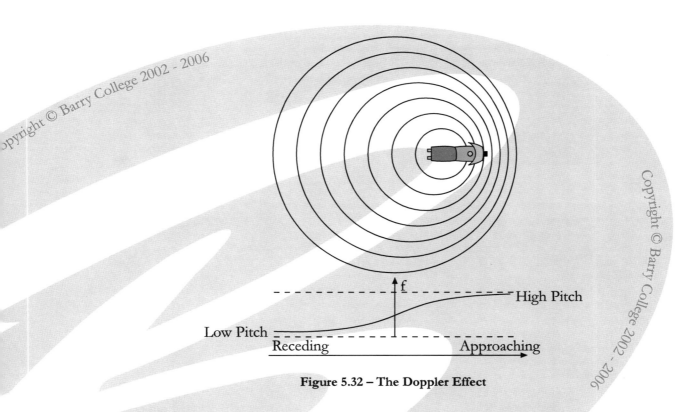

Figure 5.32 – The Doppler Effect

www.part66.co.uk

We have read that the pitch of sound is proportional to its frequency. The effect of this is that if you are standing beside a road when the motorbike is approaching you, the engine note will have a high pitch. As the motorbike passes you and recedes away from you, the engine note will change to a distinctly lower pitch. This change of pitch is the *Doppler Effect*.

Doppler Effect in Light Waves

Although light waves travel at much higher speeds than sound waves they still display the Doppler Effect. Astronomers can determine whether a body is moving towards the Earth or is receding away from it by analysing the light waves they receive from it.

If the body is moving towards us, the light waves reaching us will be at a higher frequency and the light will be in the blue region of the visible spectrum. The faster the closing speed is, the bluer the light will be. This is called *Blue Shift.*

If the body is moving away from us the light we receive from it will be at a lower frequency and will be in the red end of the visible spectrum. The faster the body recedes from us, the redder the light we receive will be. This is called *Red Shift.*

Revision

Wave Motion and Sound

Questions

1. Waves that always require a material substance through which to travel are known as:

    A. Electromagnetic waves

    B. Standing waves

    C. Mechanical waves

2. Sound waves take the form of:

    A. Transverse waves

    B. Longitudinal waves

    C. Sinusoidal waves

3. If two waves of the same amplitude and frequency travelling at the same speed in opposite directions superpose on each other they will:

    A. Form a standing wave

    B. Cancel each other

    C. Reduce in amplitude

4. Sound waves travel:

    A. Slower in water than in air

    B. At the same velocity in water and air

    C. Faster in water than in air

433

5.   The speed of sound in dry air, at sea level, at 0°C is:

A. 3×10^3 m/s

B. 331 m/s

C. 731 m/s

6.   If two identical sound waves are produced, one being exactly half a wavelength behind the other, you would hear:

A. Nothing

B. Beats

C. Double the amplitude

7.   When water waves move across shallower depths:

A. They decrease in velocity and reduce in wavelength

B. They decrease in velocity and increase in wavelength

C. They increase in velocity and wavelength

8.   Which statement is true:

A. Radio, light and sound waves will all travel in a vacuum

B. Radio and light waves will both travel in a vacuum

C. Sound and radio waves will both travel in a vacuum

9.   If a loudspeaker emits sound at a frequency of 200Hz and the speed of sound in air is normal for sea level, 0°C, the wavelength in metres is approximately:

A. 3.65m

B. 1.65m

C. 0.6m

10. If two sound waves of identical frequency are produced simultaneously, you would hear:

    A. Beats

    B. Nothing

    C. Two different tones

11. A time period of 10 microseconds is equal to a frequency of:

    A. 10kHz

    B. 1mHz

    C. 100kHz

12. When two radiating wave patterns cross over each other and superpose on each other in the same phase, crest upon crest, they produce:

    A. Antinodal lines giving increased disturbance

    B. Antinodal lines giving decreased disturbance

    C. Nodal lines giving increased disturbance

13. The nodal points in a stationary wave are positioned:

    A. Two wavelengths apart

    B. One wavelength apart

    C. Half a wavelength apart

14. When light waves radiating from two point sources are projected onto a single screen, the series of light and dark bands formed are caused by:

    A. Reflection

    B. Diffusion

    C. Interference

15. A person standing 66m from the foot of a wall claps their hands and hears an echo 0.4 sec later. The speed of the sound wave in these conditions was:

    A. 165m/s

    B. 330m/s

    C. 82.5m/s

16. If a reverberating sound wave has a wavelength of 0.3m, its frequency at sea level will be approximately:

    A. 99Hz

    B. 1.1kHz

    C. 2.2kHz

17. If the frequency of sound is increased the:

    A. Pitch will increase

    B. Pitch will decrease

    C. Pitch will not be affected

18. The intensity of a sound wave is:

    A. Proportional to the square of its frequency

    B. Inversely proportional to the square of its frequency

    C. Proportional to the square of its amplitude

19. The quality of a musical tone is primarily related to:

    A. Intensity

    B. Overtones

    C. The fundamental frequency

20. **The change in direction of water waves travelling into shallower water is caused by:**

    A. Reflection

    B. Diffraction

    C. Refraction.

21. **If a violin string is bowed so as to vibrate in two segments it produces:**

    A. Its fundamental frequency

    B. Two notes

    C. The octave of its frequency

22. **If a motorcycle passes you, the pitch of its sound will be:**

    A. Lower on approach and higher on departure

    B. Higher on approach and lower on departure

    C. The same on approach and departure

23. **The amplitude of a node in a stationary wave is:**

    A. Zero

    B. Halved

    C. Maximum

24. **The intensity of sound being emitted from a distant source is:**

    A. Inversely proportional to the distance

    B. Inversely proportional to the square of the distance

    C. Not affected by distance

25. **The velocity of sound in air is affected by:**

    A. Its pitch

    B. Its frequency

    C. Air temperature

437

Revision

Wave Motion and Sound

Answers

1. **C**
2. **B**
3. **A**
4. **C**
5. **B**
6. **A**
7. **A**
8. **B**
9. **B**
10. **A**
11. **C**
12. **A**
13. **C**
14. **C**
15. **B**
16. **B**
17. **A**
18. **C**
19. **B**
20. **C**
21. **C**
22. **B**
23. **A**
24. **B**
25. **C**

THE BOOK ®

Triumph Triples & Fours
Service and Repair Manual

Penny Cox and Matthew Coombs

Models covered
(2162-208-7V1)

750 Trident. 748cc. UK August 1991 through 1995
750 Daytona. 748cc. UK July 1991 through Spring 1993
900 Trident. 885cc. UK August 1991 through 1995, US 1995
900 Trophy. 885cc. UK July 1991 through 1995, US 1995
900 Daytona. 885cc. UK December 1992 through 1995, US 1995
900 (Trident) Sprint. 885cc. UK January 1993 through 1995, US 1995
900 Daytona Super III. 885cc. UK January 1994 through 1995, US 1995
900 Speed Triple. 885cc. UK February 1994 through 1995, US 1995
900 Thunderbird. 885cc. UK January 1995, US 1995
900 Tiger. 885cc. UK January 1993 through 1995, US 1995
1000 Daytona. 998cc. UK April 1991 through Spring 1993
1200 Trophy. 1180cc. UK April 1991 through 1995, US 1995
1200 Daytona. 1180cc. UK January 1993 through 1995, US 1995

ISBN **1 56392 162 6**

British Library Cataloguing in Publication Data
A catalogue record for this book is available from the British Library

ABCDE
FGHIJ
KLMNO
PQ

Library of Congress Catalog Card Number **95-81647**

Printed by **J. H. Haynes & Co. Ltd., Sparkford, Nr Yeovil, Somerset, BA22 7JJ, England**

Haynes Publishing
Sparkford, Nr Yeovil, Somerset BA22 7JJ, England

Haynes North America, Inc
861 Lawrence Drive, Newbury Park, California 91320, USA

Editions Haynes S.A.
147/149, rue Saint Honoré, 75001 PARIS, France

Contents

LIVING WITH YOUR TRIUMPH

Introduction

Daily (pre-ride) Checks

MAINTENANCE

Routine maintenance and Servicing

Contents

REPAIRS AND OVERHAUL

Engine, transmission and associated systems

Chassis components

Fairing and bodywork components

Electrical components

Wiring diagrams

REFERENCE

Index

A Phoenix from the ashes by Julian Ryder

Where is the most modern motorcycle factory in the World? Tokyo? Berlin? Turin, maybe? No, it's in Hinckley, Leicestershire. Improbable as it may seem, the Triumph factory in the Midlands of England is a more advanced production facility than anything the mighty Japanese industry, German efficiency or Italian flair can boast. Still more amazingly, the first motorcycle rolled off the brand new production line in July 1991, nine years after the last of the old Triumphs had trickled out of the old Meriden factory.

It's important to realise that the new Triumph company has very little to do with the company that was a giant on the world stage in the post-War years when British motorcycle makers dominated the global markets. It is true that new owner John Bloor bought the patents, manufacturing rights and, most importantly, trademarks when the old factory's assets were sold in 1983, but the products of the old and new companies bear no relation at all to one another. Apart, of course, from the name on the tanks. Bloor's research-and-development team started work in Collier Street, Coventry and in 1985 work started on the ten-acre green-field factory site which was occupied for the first time the following year.

The reborn Triumphs

The R & D team soon dispensed with the old Meriden factory's project for a modern DOHC, eight-valve twin known within the factory as the Diana project (after Princess Di) but shown at the NEC International Bike Show in 1982 as the Phoenix. The world got to see the new Triumphs for the first time at the Cologne Show in late 1990. The company was obviously anxious to distance itself from the old, leaky, unreliable image of the traditional British motorcycle, but it was equally anxious not to engage in a head-on technology war with the big four Japanese

factories. The new motto was "proven technology", the new engines were in-line threes and fours with double overhead camshafts and four valves per cylinder. They were all housed in a universal steel chassis with a large-diameter tubular backbone, and interestingly the new bikes would all carry famous model names from Triumph's past. If you were looking to compare the technology level with an established machine, you'd have to point to the Kawasaki GPZ900R launched back in '84. Do not take this as a suggestion, current in '91, that the new Triumphs were in some way Kawasakis in disguise because the cam chain was sited on the right side of the motor rather than between the middle cylinders. Yes, of course Triumph had looked at the technology and manufacturing of the Japanese companies and naturally found that an in-line multi-cylinder motor was the most economical way to go. It's just the same in the car world, the straight four is cheaper than the V6 because it uses fewer, simpler parts. In fact the layout of the new motor would seem to indicate that designers from the car world had been brought in by John Bloor. If anyone still harbours the belief that Triumph copied or co-operated with Kawasaki, try and find a contemporary Kawasaki that uses wet liners (cylinder liners in direct contact with coolant as opposed to sleeves fitted into the barrels).

But if Triumph's technology wasn't exactly path-breaking it was certainly very clever. The key concept was the modular design of the motor based around long and short-throw crankshafts in three and four-cylinder configurations. Every engine used the common 76 mm bore with either 55 or 65 mm throw cranks so that the short-stroke engine would be 750 cc in three-cylinder form and 1000 cc as a four. Put the long-stroke crank in and you get a 900 cc triple and a 1200 cc four. The first, six-bike range

consisted of two 750-3s, two 900-3s, a 1000-4 and a 1200-4. The first bike to hit the shops was the 1200 Trophy, a four-cylinder sports tourer which was immediately competitive in a very strong class. There was also a 900 cc, three-cylinder Trophy. The 750 and 1000 Daytonas used the short-stroke motor in three and four-cylinder forms in what were intended to be the sportsters of the range. The other two models, 750 and 900cc three-cylinder Tridents, cashed in on the early-'90s fad for naked retro bikes that followed the worldwide success of the Kawasaki Zephyr.

Even though it was lumbered with the retro label, the Trident was in no way harking back to the good old days. Retro bikes were supposed to look like they'd stepped out of a 1970s time warp with wire wheels, twin shock absorbers and a sit-up-and-beg riding position, but the first Trident was clearly a modern bike that simply didn't have a fairing. It was fairly obviously a Trophy with some glass fibre removed.

The reborn Triumphs were received with acclaim from the motorcycle press - tinged with not a little surprise. They really were very good motorcycles, the big Trophy was a match for the Japanese opposition in a class full of very accomplished machinery. The fact it could live with a modern day classic like the Yamaha FJ1200 straight off the drawing board was a tribute to John Bloor's designers and production engineers. The bike was big, fast, heavy and quite high, but it worked and worked well. And it didn't leak oil or break down, it was obvious that whatever else people were going to say about Triumphs they weren't going to able to resurrect the old jokes about British bangers leaving puddles of lubricant under them.

Six months into production, I surveyed a group of 1200 Trophy owners and found the only problem had been rust attacking a welded seam between the exhaust pipe and

The 1200 Trophy model

The 1200 Daytona model

the hanger bracket that attached it to the chassis. For a brand new design to be so reliable was quite outstanding and gave the lie to the impression current in several countries that British industry could no longer produce a top-quality engineered product. John Bloor does not give interviews, but it is thought that his major motivation in spending a large chunk of his considerable personal fortune in setting up the Triumph factory was simply to prove that a British factory could still turn out high-tech products that could succeed in world markets. He succeeded.

As the rest of the range arrived and tests of them got into print, the original impression was underlined and the star of the show emerged; it was the long-stroke, three-cylinder, 900cc motor. It didn't matter how it was dressed up, the big triple had that indefinable quality - character. It was the motor the Japanese would never have made, very torquey but with a hint of vibration that endears rather than annoys. Somewhere among the modern, water-cooled, multi-valve technology, the 900-triple had the genes of the old air-cooled, OHV Triumph Tridents that appeared in 1969 and stayed in production until '75. If there was an under-achiever in the

range it was the Daytona. With hindsight it is easy to see that taking on the Japanese on their own territory - something Triumph said they never intended to do - was not a good idea, up against the cutting edge race-replicas of the day the Daytonas couldn't live up to their billing as sportsters.

Model development

The range stayed basically unchanged for two years, until the Cologne Show of '92. Looking back at the first range it is now easy to see - hindsight again - that the identity of all the models were far too close. The sports tourer Trophys were reckoned to be a little too sporting, the basic Tridents still had the handlebar and footrest positions of faired bikes. Triumph management later agreed that the first range evinced a certain lack of confidence, that was certainly not the case of the revamped 1993 range.

Visitors to the Cologne Show in September '92 agreed that the Triumphs were the stars, any lack of confidence there may have been two years before was completely gone. The only short-stroke motor left in the range was in the 750 Trident which, like its 900cc big brother, got a total cosmetic revamp. Any shyness the

management may have felt about the Triumph name's past was shaken off as the new Tridents went retro style. Footrests were lowered and bars raised, the engine's cosmetics were tidied up and the motor and exhausts got a black finish. The engine styling was important as the original Tridents looked very much like faired bikes with the bodywork off, such was the plumber's nightmare of hoses and cables open to view. But most strikingly, these new Tridents unashamedly drew on the old Triumph heritage in their colour schemes with two-tone tanks featuring gold pinstriping - and all in very classic colours.

The original Trident wasn't totally abandoned though, it metamorphosed into the Trident Sprint, a 900 Trident with the addition of a striking twin-headlight half-fairing but retaining the sporty riding position of the first models. The two Daytona models quietly changed into one, this time with the 900 triple motor rather than the short-stroke three or four-cylinder motors. A slightly lower screen, new side panels and upswept silencers gave the bike a much sportier look, the lines were good enough to win a British Design Council Award for the bike's styling. The Trophys' identity as sports tourers was

The 750 Trident model

The 900 Sprint model

The 900 Speed Triple model

The 900 Daytona Super III model

emphasised by more relaxed riding positions with higher bars and lower footrests for both rider and pillion. The only real criticism of the 1200 Trophy - that it could do with more braking power - was answered with new four-piston calipers on the front discs. Its long distance credentials were underlined with better mirrors, a higher screen option and a clock.

Overall, the identities of the original bikes became more individual and more obviously separated; the Trophys became more touring oriented, the Daytona more sporty looking and the Tridents more traditional. The factory even had the confidence to put small Union Jacks on the side panels of each model, no more apologising for the imagined shortcomings of British engineering. Despite this spreading of the range's appeal, all these bikes were still built on the original modular concept. All the 900 triples made 100 PS (74 kW), the 750 Trident 97 PS (71 kW) and the 1200 Trophy 110 PS (80 kW). Note that the smaller Trident made nearly as much peak power as the 900, but the bigger motor made over 25% more torque for astounding mid-range punch. There was, however, an exception to this rule of uniformity in the

shape of a brand new bike, the Tiger 900. This model was in the enduro/desert-racer style much favoured on Continental Europe but not at all popular at home in the UK. Here was a Triumph with a 19-inch front tyre, wire wheels and a lower power output than the other 900s, 85 PS (63 kW). Both the chassis and engine parts were slightly different from the rest of the range, the Tiger got a higher seat and longer wheelbase and a retuned - the factory would not like the word detuned - motor with a massive spread of power and torque traded off against a loss of top-end power and speed, not the most important requirements on a bike of this type. This retuning was accomplished by internal changes to such things as camshaft lift and timing and set the precedent for what was to come. Lack of ultimate performance compared to some of the opposition hadn't handicapped the first Triumphs and it hasn't held the Tiger back, especially in the important German market where it is a top seller.

Judging their market as cleverly as ever, the factory held back another new model for the International Bike Show at the Birmingham NEC. This was the Daytona 1200, an out and out speed machine with a hidden political

agenda. Its high-compression, 147 PS engine gave it brutal straight-line performance in much the same way as the big Kawasakis of the mid-'80s, and like them it wasn't too clever in the corners because of its weight and length. The bike was built as much to show that Triumph could do it as to sell in big numbers, it also had the secondary function of thumbing the corporate nose at the UK importers' gentlemen's agreement not to bring in bikes of over 125 PS.

Next year's NEC show saw two more new Triumphs, both reworkings of what was now regarded as a modern classic, the 900 triple. The Speed Triple was a clever reincarnation of the British café racer style, complete with clip-on handlebars and rear-set footrests. The big three-cylinder engine in standard tune got an all-black finish with black chrome pipes and silencers for the appropriately mean look. Black wheel rims and new bodywork completed a superbly styled bike available with black or yellow bodywork, the Speed Triple was the star of the show, a bike with an attitude. A one-make race series with generous prize money helped give the factory's products some race-track credibility that would otherwise have been impossible to come by.

The 900 Tiger model

The 900 Thunderbird model

Ian Cobby in action at the Bol d'Or

The Speed Triple Challenge went international in 1995 - riders from all over the world met at the Bol d'Or

The other newcomer was a more radical project, the Daytona Super III. Externally the motor looked like the usual 900 cc three, but a lot of work by Cosworth Engineering was hidden under the cases, notably reworked heads, ports and cam profiles. The result was 115 PS as opposed to the standard 900 Daytona's 98. New six-piston calipers built and designed by Triumph, not bought in, stopped the plot which was a couple of kilos lighter thanks to judicious use of lightweight materials like the carbon-fibre look silencers.

But the new Triumphs aren't really about out-and-out performance, as Rolls Royce like to say power is "adequate" and quite enough for real world motorcycling as evidenced by commercial success in demanding markets like Germany where Triumph's strict quality control and top-quality finish are paying dividends. One German magazine, MO, ran an early Trident for 100,000 km with hardly a problem. When it was stripped for inspection at the Hinckley factory the engine was found to be as good as new, a tribute to the original design and production engineering.

Triumphs in America

Triumph's next big step is into the US market, where the old company was so strong in the post-War years when the only competition was Harley-Davidson and where there is considerable affection for the marque. The name Triumph chose to spearhead this new challenge is Thunderbird, a trademark sourced in Native American mythology. This time the famous name adorns yet another version of the 900 triple but this time heavily restyled and in a retro package. This is the first of the new-generation Triumph motors designed to be looked at without a fairing covering most of it. Dummy cooling fins give it the look of an air-cooled motor, the logo is cast into the clutch cover, there are soft edges and large expanses of polished alloy. Inside those restyled cases, the motor is retuned even more than the Tiger's to

give 70 PS for a very user friendly dose of low-down punch and mid-range power - maximum torque is at just 4800 rpm as opposed to the 900 Trident's 6500 rpm. The cycle parts have been given an equally radical redesign, although the retro style stopped short of giving the Thunderbird twin rear shock absorbers. But everything else, the shape of the tank, the chrome headlight and countless other details, harks back to the original Thunderbird and nothing does so as shamelessly as the "mouth-organ" tank badge, a classic icon if ever there was one.

But the Thunderbird is more than just another new model, it's the start of a whole new marketing game. With one eye on Harley-Davidson's success, Triumph have designed a range of bolt-on accessories for the Thunderbird and a family of Thunderbird derivatives. The first bolt-on goodies offer extra chrome, leather panniers, a windshield, and two-tone front mudguards for the bike and boots, leathers, jackets and helmets for the rider. Sounds familiar? It looks very like the formula that Harley-Davidson used to such effect in their comeback from the commercial grave.

Triumph have had the advantage of starting with a blank sheet of paper, and under the firm hand of the owner the company has done nearly everything right. As confidence has grown they have drawn more and more on the heritage of the marque. In 1990 they said they would take no notice of history, but as the Thunderbird shows we can expect more astute exploitation of the Triumph heritage.

Acknowledgements

Our thanks are due to Riders of Bridgwater who supplied the machines featured in the photographs throughout this manual and to Mel Rawlings A.I.R.T.E. of MHR Engineering who carried out the mechanical work.

Thanks are also due to Julian Ryder for providing the introductory copy, to Kel Edge for the Speed Triple racing

photographs, and to Kyoichi Nakamura for the rear cover action photograph. We would also like to extend thanks to Triumph Motorcycles, Hinckley, for permission to use pictures of the Triumph models. Triumph Motorcycles Limited bears no responsibility for the content of this book, having had no part in its origination or preparation.

NGK Spark Plugs (UK) Ltd supplied the colour spark plug condition photos and the Avon Rubber Company supplied information on tyre fitting.

About this manual

The aim of this manual is to help you get the best value from your motorcycle. It can do so in several ways. It can help you decide what work must be done, even if you choose to have it done by a dealer; it provides information and procedures for routine maintenance and servicing; and it offers diagnostic and repair procedures to follow when trouble occurs.

We hope you use the manual to tackle the work yourself. For many simpler jobs, doing it yourself may be quicker than arranging an appointment to get the motorcycle into a dealer and making the trips to leave it and pick it up. More importantly, a lot of money can be saved by avoiding the expense the shop must pass on to you to cover its labour and overhead costs. An added benefit is the sense of satisfaction and accomplishment that you feel after doing the job yourself.

References to the left or right side of the motorcycle assume you are sitting on the seat, facing forward.

We take great pride in the accuracy of information given in this manual, but motorcycle manufacturers make alterations and design changes during the production run of a particular motorcycle of which they do not inform us. No liability can be accepted by the authors or publishers for loss, damage or injury caused by any errors in, or omissions from, the information given.

Professional mechanics are trained in safe working procedures. However enthusiastic you may be about getting on with the job at hand, take the time to ensure that your safety is not put at risk. A moment's lack of attention can result in an accident, as can failure to observe simple precautions.

There will always be new ways of having accidents, and the following is not a comprehensive list of all dangers; it is intended rather to make you aware of the risks and to encourage a safe approach to all work you carry out on your bike.

Asbestos

● Certain friction, insulating, sealing and other products - such as brake pads, clutch linings, gaskets, etc. - contain asbestos. Extreme care must be taken to avoid inhalation of dust from such products since it is hazardous to health. If in doubt, assume that they do contain asbestos.

Fire

● Remember at all times that petrol is highly flammable. Never smoke or have any kind of naked flame around, when working on the vehicle. But the risk does not end there - a spark caused by an electrical short-circuit, by two metal surfaces contacting each other, by careless use of tools, or even by static electricity built up in your body under certain conditions, can ignite petrol vapour, which in a confined space is highly explosive. Never use petrol as a cleaning solvent. Use an approved safety solvent.

● Always disconnect the battery earth terminal before working on any part of the fuel or electrical system, and never risk spilling fuel on to a hot engine or exhaust.

● It is recommended that a fire extinguisher of a type suitable for fuel and electrical fires is kept handy in the garage or workplace at all times. Never try to extinguish a fuel or electrical fire with water.

Fumes

● Certain fumes are highly toxic and can quickly cause unconsciousness and even death if inhaled to any extent. Petrol vapour comes into this category, as do the vapours from certain solvents such as trichloro-ethylene. Any draining or pouring of such volatile fluids should be done in a well ventilated area.

● When using cleaning fluids and solvents, read the instructions carefully. Never use materials from unmarked containers - they may give off poisonous vapours.

● Never run the engine of a motor vehicle in an enclosed space such as a garage. Exhaust fumes contain carbon monoxide which is extremely poisonous; if you need to run the engine, always do so in the open air or at least have the rear of the vehicle outside the workplace.

The battery

● Never cause a spark, or allow a naked light near the vehicle's battery. It will normally be giving off a certain amount of hydrogen gas, which is highly explosive.

● Always disconnect the battery ground (earth) terminal before working on the fuel or electrical systems (except where noted).

● If possible, loosen the filler plugs or cover when charging the battery from an external source. Do not charge at an excessive rate or the battery may burst.

● Take care when topping up, cleaning or carrying the battery. The acid electrolyte, evenwhen diluted, is very corrosive and should not be allowed to contact the eyes or skin. Always wear rubber gloves and goggles or a face shield. If you ever need to prepare electrolyte yourself, always add the acid slowly to the water; never add the water to the acid.

Electricity

● When using an electric power tool, inspection light etc., always ensure that the appliance is correctly connected to its plug and that, where necessary, it is properly grounded (earthed). Do not use such appliances in damp conditions and, again, beware of creating a spark or applying excessive heat in the vicinity of fuel or fuel vapour. Also ensure that the appliances meet national safety standards.

● A severe electric shock can result from touching certain parts of the electrical system, such as the spark plug wires (HT leads), when the engine is running or being cranked, particularly if components are damp or the insulation is defective. Where an electronic ignition system is used, the secondary (HT) voltage is much higher and could prove fatal.

Remember...

✗ **Don't** start the engine without first ascertaining that the transmission is in neutral.

✗ **Don't** suddenly remove the pressure cap from a hot cooling system - cover it with a cloth and release the pressure gradually first, or you may get scalded by escaping coolant.

✗ **Don't** attempt to drain oil until you are sure it has cooled sufficiently to avoid scalding you.

✗ **Don't** grasp any part of the engine or exhaust system without first ascertaining that it is cool enough not to burn you.

✗ **Don't** allow brake fluid or antifreeze to contact the machine's paintwork or plastic components.

✗ **Don't** siphon toxic liquids such as fuel, hydraulic fluid or antifreeze by mouth, or allow them to remain on your skin.

✗ **Don't** inhale dust - it may be injurious to health (see Asbestos heading).

✗ **Don't** allow any spilled oil or grease to remain on the floor - wipe it up right away, before someone slips on it.

✗ **Don't** use ill-fitting spanners or other tools which may slip and cause injury.

✗ **Don't** lift a heavy component which may be beyond your capability - get assistance.

✗ **Don't** rush to finish a job or take unverified short cuts.

✗ **Don't** allow children or animals in or around an unattended vehicle.

✗ **Don't** inflate a tyre above the recommended pressure. Apart from overstressing the carcass, in extreme cases the tyre may blow off forcibly.

✔ **Do** ensure that the machine is supported securely at all times. This is especially important when the machine is blocked up to aid wheel or fork removal.

✔ **Do** take care when attempting to loosen a stubborn nut or bolt. It is generally better to pull on a spanner, rather than push, so that if you slip, you fall away from the machine rather than onto it.

✔ **Do** wear eye protection when using power tools such as drill, sander, bench grinder etc.

✔ **Do** use a barrier cream on your hands prior to undertaking dirty jobs - it will protect your skin from infection as well as making the dirt easier to remove afterwards; but make sure your hands aren't left slippery. Note that long-term contact with used engine oil can be a health hazard.

✔ **Do** keep loose clothing (cuffs, ties etc. and long hair) well out of the way of moving mechanical parts.

✔ **Do** remove rings, wristwatch etc., before working on the vehicle - especially the electrical system.

✔ **Do** keep your work area tidy - it is only too easy to fall over articles left lying around.

✔ **Do** exercise caution when compressing springs for removal or installation. Ensure that the tension is applied and released in a controlled manner, using suitable tools which preclude the possibility of the spring escaping violently.

✔ **Do** ensure that any lifting tackle used has a safe working load rating adequate for the job.

✔ **Do** get someone to check periodically that all is well, when working alone on the vehicle.

✔ **Do** carry out work in a logical sequence and check that everything is correctly assembled and tightened afterwards.

✔ **Do** remember that your vehicle's safety affects that of yourself and others. If in doubt on any point, get professional advice.

● **If** in spite of following these precautions, you are unfortunate enough to injure yourself, seek medical attention as soon as possible.

VIN (Vehicle Identification Number)

The frame VIN is stamped into the right side of the steering head. It is duplicated on a plate attached to the frame under the seat (UK models) or attached to the steering head (US models). The engine VIN is stamped into the right upper side of the crankcase, directly above the clutch cover. Both of these numbers should be recorded and kept in a safe place so they can be furnished to law enforcement officials in the event of a theft.

The frame and engine VINs should also be kept in a handy place (such as with your driving licence) so they are always available when purchasing or ordering parts for your machine.

Models are identified in the manual by their engine size and model name (eg 1200 Trophy). Where a modification necessitates a different working method, the VIN may be used to indicate early and later models. Owners of the 900 Daytona Super III should refer to information for the 900 Daytona unless specific mention is made of the Super III model.

Buying spare parts

Always provide the model name, engine size and VIN (Vehicle Identification Number) when ordering parts. Providing the VIN will ensure that you obtain the correct part if a modification has been introduced.

Whenever possible, take the worn part to the dealer so direct comparison with the new component can be made. Along the trail from the manufacturer to the parts shelf, there are numerous places that the part can end up with the wrong number or be listed incorrectly.

A Triumph dealer will be able to obtain all parts for your machine, although a motor accessory store is a good source for lubricants, spark plugs etc.

Used parts can be obtained for roughly half the price of new ones, but you can't always be sure of what you're getting. Once again, take your worn part to the breaker for direct comparison.

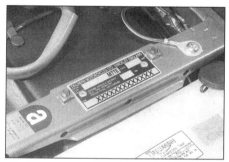

On UK models the frame VIN is also on a plate riveted to the frame under the seat

The engine VIN is located on the upper crankcase

Frame VIN is stamped into right side of steering head

Note: *The daily (pre-ride) checks outlined in the owner's manual (and on the label stuck to the underside of the seat) covers those items which should be inspected on a daily basis.*

1 Engine/transmission oil level

Before you start:

✔ Take the motorcycle on a short run to allow it to reach operating temperature. *Caution: Do not run the engine in an enclosed space such as a garage or workshop.*

✔ Stop the engine and place the motorcycle on its center stand, or hold it upright, for a few minutes to allow the oil level to stabilize. Ensure the motorcycle is on level ground.

The correct oil

● Modern, high-revving engines place great demands on their oil. It is very important that the correct oil for your bike is used
● Always top up with a good quality oil of the specified type and viscosity and do not overfill the engine.

Oil type	API grade SG
Oil viscosity 900 Daytona Super III and 1200 Daytona	Fully synthetic 5W/30 or 10W/30 motor oil
Oil viscosity all other models	Semi synthetic 10W/40 motor oil

Bike care:

● If you have to add oil frequently, you should check whether you have any oil leaks. If there is no sign of oil leakage from the joints and gaskets the engine could be burning oil (see Troubleshooting).

● On early models, the dipsticks are marked 3 and 4 in relation to the number of cylinders; on later models the markings are the same for all engines.

1 On all models except the Thunderbird, (for Thunderbird details see below) the dipstick is integral with the filler cap and is located in the engine sprocket cover. Unscrew it to check the engine oil level.

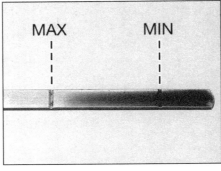

3 Unscrew the dipstick and note the oil level in relation to its markings. The oil level should be between the 'MAX' and 'MIN' marks on the end of the dipstick.

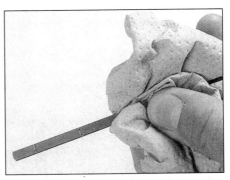

2 Using a clean rag or paper towel remove all oil from the dipstick. Insert the clean dipstick back into the sprocket cover and screw it fully in.

4 If the level is below the lower (minimum) dipstick mark, top up with oil of the recommended grade and type, to bring the level up to the upper (maximum) mark.

Thunderbird models

1 Wipe any road dirt off the oil level sightglass set beneath the crankshaft right cover. The oil level is correct if it lies midway up the sightglass, when the motorcycle is held upright.

2 If topping up is required, use a large flat-bladed screwdriver to unscrew the filler cap from the clutch cover. The cap will be tight so make sure the screwdriver is a good fit to prevent damaging the slot.

3 Top up the oil level using a funnel to prevent spillage. When the level is correct, check the condition of the filler cap seal, then tighten the cap securely.

2 Coolant level

Warning: DO NOT remove the radiator pressure cap to add coolant. Topping up is done via the coolant reservoir tank filler. DO NOT leave open containers of coolant about, as it is poisonous.

Before you start:

✔ Make sure you have a supply of coolant available (a mixture of 50% distilled water and 50% corrosion inhibited ethylene glycol antifreeze is needed).
✔ Place the motorcycle on its centre stand, or hold it upright, whilst checking the level. Make sure the motorcycle is on level ground.
✔ Always check the coolant level when the engine is cold - a false reading will otherwise result.

Bike care:

● Use only the specified coolant mixture . It is important that antifreeze is used in the cooling system all year round, not just during the winter months. Don't top-up with water alone, as the antifreeze will become too diluted.
● Do not overfill the reservoir tank. If the coolant is significantly above the MAX line at any time, the surplus coolant should be siphoned off to prevent it from being expelled out of the overflow hose when the engine is running.
● If the coolant level falls steadily, check the system for leaks as described in Chapter 1. If no leaks are found and the level still continues to fall, it is recommended that the machine be taken to a Triumph dealer who will pressure test the system.

1 On all models except the Thunderbird, the coolant reservoir is located underneath the seat. The coolant level markings are moulded into the right side of the reservoir.

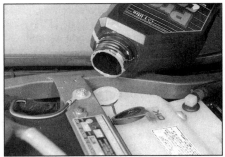

2 If the coolant level does not lie between the MAX and MIN markings, pull off the filler cap and top up with coolant. *(All models except Thunderbird)*

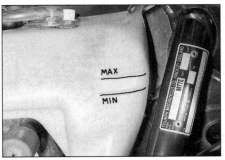

3 On Thunderbird models, the coolant reservoir is located under the fuel tank. It is possible to view the level markings via the front right side of the fuel tank.

4 If the coolant level does not lie between the MAX and MIN markings, remove the fuel tank (see Chapter 4), pull off the filler cap and top up with coolant. *(Thunderbird)*

3 Brake and clutch fluid levels

Warning: Brake and clutch hydraulic fluid can harm your eyes and damage painted surfaces, so use extreme caution when handling and pouring it. Do not use fluid that has been standing open for some time, as it absorbs moisture from the air which can cause a dangerous loss of braking and clutch effectiveness.

Before you start:

✔ Hold the motorcycle upright and turn the handlebars until the top of the master cylinder is as level as possible. If necessary, tilt the motorcycle to make it level.
✔ Make sure you have the correct hydraulic fluid - DOT 4 is recommended.

1 On the front brake and clutch reservoirs, make sure that the fluid level, visible through the sightglass, is above the LOWER level line

2 To top up the front brake and clutch reservoirs, remove the two screws retaining the reservoir cover. Lift off the cover with the diaphragm.

Bike care:

● The fluid in the front and rear brake master cylinder reservoirs will drop slightly as the brake pads wear down.

● If any fluid reservoir requires repeated topping-up this is an indication of a hydraulic leak somewhere in the system, which should be investigated immediately.

● Check for signs of fluid leakage from the hydraulic hoses and components - if found, rectify immediately.

● Check the operation of both brakes and the clutch before taking the machine on the road; if there is evidence of air in the system (spongy feel to lever or pedal), it must be bled as described in Chapter 7 (brake) or Chapter 2 (clutch).

3 After topping up ensure that the diaphragm is correctly folded and install the cap.

4 Remove the right side cover (see Chapter 8) and pull off the air intake tube for improved access to the rear reservoir.

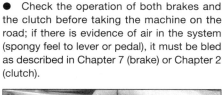

5 To top up the rear brake reservoir, unscrew its cap and remove the diaphragm.

6 Top up the reservoir with the specified fluid. The fluid level must lie between the UPPER and LOWER lines.

7 After topping up, install the diaphragm, plastic ring and cap.

8 The number on the span adjuster wheel must align exactly with the triangular mark on the lever bracket (circled).

4 Tyres

The correct pressures

● The tyres must be checked when **cold**, not immediately after riding. Note that low tyre pressures may cause the tyre to slip on the rim or come off. High tyre pressures will cause abnormal tread wear and unsafe handling.

● Use an accurate pressure gauge.

● Proper air pressure will increase tyre life and ensure stability and ride comfort.

Tyre care

● Check the tyres carefully for cuts, tears, embedded nails or other sharp objects and excessive wear. Operation of the motorcycle with excessively worn tyres is extremely hazardous, as traction and handling are directly affected.

● Check the condition of the tyre valve and ensure the dust cap is in place.

● Pick out any stones or nails which may have become embedded in the tyre tread. If left, they will eventually penetrate through the casing and cause a puncture.

● If tyre damage is apparent, or unexplained loss of pressure is experienced, seek the advice of a tyre fitting specialist without delay.

Model	Front tyre	Rear tyre
750 and 1000 Daytona	36 psi (2.5 Bar)	36 psi (2.5 Bar)
Trophy, 900 and 1200 Daytona	36 psi (2.5 Bar)	42 psi (2.9 Bar)
Trident, Speed Triple, Sprint and Thunderbird	36 psi (2.5 Bar)	42 psi (2.9 Bar)
Tiger	30 psi (2.1 Bar)	33 psi (2.3 Bar)

1 Check the tyre pressures when the tyres are **cold** and keep them properly inflated.

2 Measure the tread depth at the centre of the tyre using a tread depth gauge. The tyre must be replaced when the depth is less than specified.

3 Many tyres incorporate wear indicators (arrow). Replace the tyre when the tread has worn down to the indicator bar.

Tyre tread depth

● At the time of writing UK law requires that tread depth must be at least 1 mm over 3/4 of the tread breadth all the way around the tyre, with no bald patches.

● Readers are advised to adhere to the maker's minimum tread depth (see table).

Front tyre	2 mm minimum
Rear tyre At speeds under 80 mph (130 kph) At speeds above 80 mph (130 kph)	 2 mm minimum 3 mm minimum

5 Other checks

Drive chain
● Check that drive chain slack isn't excessive.
● If the chain looks dry, lubricate it - See Chapter 1.

Suspension and Steering
● Check that the front and rear suspension operates smoothly without binding.
● Check that the suspension adjustment settings are as required.
● Check that the steering moves smoothly from lock-to-lock.

Lighting and signalling
● Take a minute to check that the headlight(s), taillight, brake light, turn signals all work correctly.
● Check that the horn sounds when the switch is operated.
● A working speedometer is a statutory requirement in the UK.

Safety
● Check that the throttle grip rotates smoothly and snaps shut when released.
● Check that the engine shuts off when the kill switch is operated.

● Check that sidestand return spring holds the stand securely up when retracted. The same applies to the centre stand (where fitted).

Fuel
● This may seem obvious, but check that you have enough fuel to complete your journey. If you notice signs of fuel leakage - rectify the cause immediately.
● Ensure you use the correct grade unleaded fuel - see Chapter 4 Specifications

Notes

Chapter 1
Routine maintenance and Servicing

Contents

1

Degrees of difficulty

Easy, suitable for novice with little experience	Fairly easy, suitable for beginner with some experience	Fairly difficult, suitable for competent DIY mechanic	Difficult, suitable for experienced DIY mechanic	Very difficult, suitable for expert DIY or professional

Specifications

Engine

Spark plugs
  Type . . . . NGK DPR9EA-9
  Electrode gap . . . . 0.8 to 0.9 mm
Valve clearances (COLD engine)
  Inlet . . . . 0.10 to 0.15 mm
  Exhaust . . . . 0.15 to 0.20 mm
Engine idle speed . . . . 1000 ± 50 rpm
Carburettor synchronisation vacuum range . . . . 127 to 152 mm Hg
Cylinder numbering (from left side to right side of the bike) . . . . 1-2-3 (3 cylinder), 1-2-3-4 (4 cylinder)
Firing order . . . . 1-2-3 (3 cylinder), 1-2-4-3 (4 cylinder)

Miscellaneous

Brake pad minimum thickness	1.5 mm
Drive chain 20-link length service limit	319 mm

Freeplay adjustments

Throttle grip	2 to 3 mm
Choke shaft	2 to 3 mm

Drive chain

Thunderbird	25 to 30 mm
All other models	35 to 40 mm

Minimum tyre tread depth

Front	2 mm
Rear - at speeds under 80 mph (130 kph)	2 mm
Rear - at speed above 80 mph (130 kph)	3 mm

At the time of writing, UK law requires that tread depth must be at least 1 mm over 3/4 of the tread breadth all the way around the tyre, with no bald patches.

Tyre pressures (cold)	Front	Rear
750/1000 Daytona	36 psi (2.5 Bar)	36 psi (2.5 Bar)
Trophy, 900/1200 Daytona	36 psi (2.5 Bar)	42 psi (2.9 Bar)
Trident, Speed Triple, Sprint, Thunderbird	36 psi (2.5 Bar)	42 psi (2.9 Bar)
Tiger	30 psi (2.1 Bar)	33 psi (2.3 Bar)

Torque settings

Spark plugs	18 Nm
Oil drain plug	48 Nm
Oil filter centre bolt	18 Nm
Valve cover bolts	10 Nm
Coolant drain plugs	13 Nm
Steering stem nut	65 Nm
Steering head bearing adjuster ring pinch bolt (early models)	7 Nm
Steering head bearing adjuster locknut (later models)	40 Nm
Front brake and clutch master cylinder clamp bolts	15 Nm

Top yoke fork clamp bolts

Tiger	18 Nm
All other models	20 Nm

Handlebar clamp bolts

Tiger and Thunderbird	18 Nm
All other models	22 Nm
Rear wheel axle bolt	85 Nm
Drive chain adjuster clamp bolts	35 Nm

Recommended lubricants and fluids

Engine/transmission oil type	API grade SG

Engine/transmission oil viscosity

900 Daytona Super III, 1200 Daytona	Fully synthetic 5W/30 or 10W/30 motor oil
All other models	Semi synthetic 10W/40 motor oil

Engine/transmission oil capacity

Thunderbird	4.0 litres
All 3-cylinder models except Thunderbird	3.75 litres
All 4-cylinder models	3.5 litres

Coolant

Mixture type	50% distilled water, 50% corrosion inhibited ethylene glycol antifreeze

Coolant capacity

3 cylinder engine	2.8 litres
4 cylinder engine	3.0 litres
Front fork oil type and level	see Chapter 6 Specifications
Brake and clutch fluid	DOT 4
Drive chain	Commercial chain lubricant, marked as being suitable for O-ring type chains, or EP80 gear oil
Wheel bearings	High-melting-point grease
Rear suspension bearings	Molybdenum disulphide grease
Cables, lever and stand pivot points	Motor oil
Throttle grip	Multi-purpose grease or dry film lubricant

Note: *The intervals listed below are the shortest intervals recommended by the manufacturer for each particular operation during the model years covered in this manual.*

Daily (pre-ride)
☐ See *"Daily (pre-ride) checks"* at the beginning of this manual.

After the initial 500 miles (800 km)
Note: *A one-off check is usually performed by a Triumph dealer after the first 500 miles (800 km) from new. Thereafter, maintenance is carried out according to the following intervals of the schedule.*

Every 200 miles (300 km)
☐ Lubricate the drive chain (Section 1).

Every 500 miles (800 km)
☐ Check and adjust drive chain freeplay (Section 2).

Every 3000 miles (5000 km)
Carry out all items in the Daily (pre-ride) checks, plus the following:
☐ Check and adjust the idle speed (Section 3).
☐ Drain the airbox (Section 4).
☐ Check the steering head bearing freeplay (Section 5).
☐ Check the front and rear suspension (Section 6).
☐ Check the drive chain for wear or stretch (Section 7).
☐ Check the brake light switches (Section 8).
☐ Check the brake pads (Section 9).
☐ Check the tyre and wheel condition, and the tyre tread depth (Section 10).
☐ Check the battery electrolyte level (or every month) (Section 11).

Every 6000 miles (10 000 km)
Carry out all items in the 3000 mile (5000 km) check, plus the following:
☐ Change the engine oil and filter (Section 12).
☐ Check the valve clearances (Section 13).
☐ Check the condition of the cooling system hoses and connections (Section 14).
☐ Check throttle/choke cable operation and freeplay (Section 15).
☐ Check carburettor synchronisation (Section 16).
☐ Check the fuel system components (Section 17).
☐ Check the condition of the evaporative loss system hoses (California only) (Section 18).
☐ Check the spark plug gaps (Section 19).
☐ Check the tightness of all nuts and bolts (Section 20).
☐ Lubricate all stand and lever pivot points and cables (Section 21).

Every 12 000 miles (20 000 km)
Carry out all items in 6000 mile (10 000 km) check, plus the following:
☐ Change the clutch fluid (or every 2 years, whichever comes first) (Section 22).
☐ Replace the spark plugs (Section 23).

Every 12 000 miles (20 000 km) - continued
☐ Change the front fork oil (Section 24).
☐ Re-grease the steering head bearings (or every 2 years, whichever comes first) (Section 25).
☐ Change the brake fluid (or every 2 years, whichever comes first) (Section 26).

Every 18 000 miles (30 000 km)
Carry out all items in 6000 mile (10 000 km) check, plus the following:
☐ Change the coolant (or every 2 years, whichever comes first) (Section 27).

Every 24 000 miles (40 000 km)
☐ Replace the airbox (Section 28).
☐ Lubricate rear suspension linkage bearings (or every 3 years, whichever comes first) (Section 29).
☐ Lubricate the swingarm bearings (or every 3 years, whichever comes first) (Section 30).
☐ Replace drive chain slider block - Tiger models (or every 2 years, whichever comes first) (Section 31).

Every 2 years
☐ Change the clutch fluid (or every 12 000 miles (20 000 km), whichever comes first) (Section 22).
☐ Replace the clutch master cylinder and release cylinder seals (Section 32).
☐ Change the coolant (or every 18 000 miles (30 000 km), whichever comes first) (Section 27).
☐ Re-grease the steering head bearings (or every 12 000 miles (20 000 km), whichever comes first) (Section 25).
☐ Replace drive chain slider block - Tiger models (or every 24 000 miles (40 000 km), whichever comes first) (Section 31).
☐ Change the brake fluid (or every 12 000 miles (20 000 km), whichever comes first) (Section 26).
☐ Replace the brake master cylinder and caliper seals (Section 33).

Every 3 years
☐ Lubricate the rear suspension linkage bearings (or every 24 000 miles (40 000 km) whichever comes first) (Section 29).
☐ Lubricate swingarm bearings (or every 24 000 miles (40 000 km) whichever comes first) (Section 30).

Every 4 years
☐ Replace the clutch hose (Section 34).
☐ Replace the fuel hose (Section 35).
☐ Replace the brake hoses (Section 36).

1

Component locations on right side (all models except Thunderbird)

1 Coolant reservoir
2 Battery
3 Airbox

4 Rear brake master
  cylinder fluid reservoir
5 Steering head bearings

6 Front master cylinder
7 Throttle cable upper
  adjuster

8 Fork seals
9 Brake pads

10 Rear suspension
   linkage

Component locations on left side (all models except Thunderbird)

1 Idle speed knob
2 Oil filler/dipstick

3 Oil filter
4 Oil drain plug

5 Radiator pressure cap
6 Coolant drain plugs

7 Choke cable adjuster
8 Drive chain

9 Clutch release cylinder

Component locations on right side (Thunderbird)

1 Coolant reservoir
2 Battery
3 Airbox

4 Rear brake master
 cylinder fluid reservoir
5 Steering head bearings

6 Front master cylinder
7 Throttle cable upper
 adjuster

8 Fork seals
9 Brake pads
10 Rear suspension linkage

11 Oil level sightglass
12 Oil filler

Component locations on left side (Thunderbird)

1 Idle speed knob
2 Oil filter

3 Oil drain plug
4 Radiator pressure cap

5 Coolant drain plugs
6 Choke cable adjuster

7 Drive chain
8 Clutch release cylinder

1

Introduction

1 This Chapter is designed to help the home mechanic maintain his/her motorcycle for safety, economy, long life and peak performance.
2 Deciding where to start or plug into the routine maintenance schedule depends on several factors. If the warranty period on your motorcycle has just expired, and if it has been maintained according to the warranty standards, you may want to pick up routine maintenance as it coincides with the next mileage or calendar interval. If you have owned the machine for some time but have never performed any maintenance on it, then you may want to start at the nearest interval and include some additional procedures to ensure that nothing important is overlooked. If you have just had a major engine overhaul, then you may want to start the maintenance routine from the beginning. If you have a used machine and have no knowledge of its history or maintenance record, you may desire to combine all the checks into one large service initially and then settle into the maintenance schedule prescribed.
3 Before beginning any maintenance or repair, the machine should be cleaned thoroughly, especially around the oil filter, spark plugs, valve cover, side panels, carburettors, etc. Cleaning will help ensure that dirt does not contaminate the engine and will allow you to detect wear and damage that could otherwise easily go unnoticed.
4 Maintenance information is printed on decals attached to the motorcycle. If the information on the decals differs from that included here, use the information on the decal.

Every 200 miles (300 km)

1 Drive chain lubrication

Note: *If the chain is extremely dirty, it should be removed and cleaned before it is lubricated (see Chapter 6).*

1 For routine lubrication, the best time to lubricate the chain is after the motorcycle has been ridden. When the chain is warm, the lubricant will penetrate the joints between the side plates better than when cold.
2 Apply the lubricant to the area where the side plates overlap - not the middle of the rollers. After applying the lubricant, let it soak in a few minutes before wiping off any excess.

> **HAYNES HiNT** *Apply oil to the top of the lower chain run - centrifugal force will work it into the chain when the bike is moving.*

Every 500 miles (800 km)

2 Drive chain freeplay check and adjustment

Check

1 A neglected drive chain won't last long and can quickly damage the sprockets. Routine chain adjustment will ensure maximum chain and sprocket life.
2 To check the chain, shift the transmission into neutral and make sure the ignition switch is OFF. Support the bike so that the rear wheel is clear of the ground.
3 Measure freeplay on the chain's bottom run, at a point midway between the two sprockets, then compare your measurement to the value listed in this Chapter's Specifications **(see illustration)**. Since the chain will rarely wear evenly, rotate the rear wheel so that another section of chain can be checked; do this several times to check the entire length of chain. In some cases where lubrication has been neglected, corrosion and galling may cause the links to bind and kink, which effectively shortens the chain's length. If the chain is tight between the sprockets, rusty or kinked, it's time to replace it with a new one. If you find a tight area, mark it with felt pen or paint, and repeat the measurement after the bike has been ridden. If the chain's still tight in the same area, it may be damaged or worn. Because a tight or kinked chain can damage the transmission countershaft bearing, it's a good idea to replace it.

Adjustment

4 Rotate the rear wheel until the chain is positioned with the tightest point at the centre of its bottom run.
5 Slacken the chain adjuster clamp bolt on each side of the swingarm **(see illustration)**.
6 Insert a 12 mm Allen key (as supplied in the tool kit) in the hexagon socket of the chain adjuster on each side of the swingarm, and operating both keys simultaneously, rotate the chain adjusters until the specified chain freeplay is reached **(see illustration)**. Tighten the chain adjuster clamp bolts to the specified torque setting.
7 Following chain adjustment, check the markings on each chain adjuster in relation to the notch on the swingarm **(see illustration)**.

2.3 Measuring drive chain freeplay

2.5 Slacken the chain adjuster clamp bolts on each side . . .

2.6 . . . and rotate the adjusters using the 12 mm Allen key supplied in the tool kit

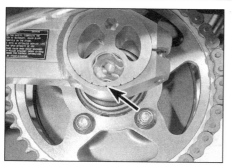

2.7 Wheel alignment can be checked via the alignment marks on the adjusters and swingarm (arrowed)

2.8a Wheel alignment can be adjusted after removing the spring clip from each side of the wheel axle . . .

2.8b . . . and slackening the axle bolt from the right side

It is important that the same mark on each adjuster aligns with the notch; if not, the rear wheel will be out of alignment with the front.

8 If there is a discrepancy in the chain adjuster positions, pick out the spring clip from each side of the wheel axle and slacken the axle bolt from the wheel right side **(see illustrations)**. Slacken the chain adjuster clamp bolt on each side of the swingarm **(see illustration 2.5)**. Using the 12 mm Allen key in the hexagon socket of the chain adjuster, rotate one of the chain adjusters so that its position is exactly the same as the other. Check the chain freeplay and readjust if necessary.

9 Tighten the axle bolt and chain adjuster clamp bolts to the specified torque settings. Secure the wheel axle with new spring clips, making sure they seat correctly.

Every 3000 miles (5000 km)

3 Idle speed check

1 The idle speed should be checked and adjusted before and after the carburettors are synchronised, or if it is obviously too high or too low. Before adjusting the idle speed, make sure the valve clearances and spark plug gaps are correct. Also, turn the handlebars back-and-forth and see if the idle speed changes as this is done. If it does, the throttle cable may not be adjusted correctly, or may be worn out. This is a dangerous condition that can cause loss of control of the bike. Be sure to correct this problem before proceeding.

2 The engine should be at normal operating temperature, which is usually reached after 10 to 15 minutes of stop and go riding. Place the motorcycle on its stand and make sure the transmission is in neutral.

3 Turn the idle speed knob, which is located in a wire guide which extends from the left side of the carburettor assembly, until the idle speed listed in this Chapter's Specifications is obtained **(see illustration)**.

4 Snap the throttle open and shut a few times, then recheck the idle speed. If necessary, repeat the adjustment procedure.

5 If a smooth, steady idle can't be achieved, the fuel/air mixture may be incorrect. Refer to Chapter 4 for additional carburettor information.

4 Airbox draining

1 Trace the drain hose from the base of the airbox and remove the plug from its end **(see illustration)**. Allow any fluid to drain into a container. Install the plug when draining is complete.

5 Steering head bearing freeplay check and adjustment

1 This motorcycle has tapered roller steering head bearings which can become dented, rough or loose during normal use of the machine. In extreme cases, worn or loose steering head bearings can cause steering wobble, which is potentially dangerous.

Check

2 Place the motorcycle on its centre stand. Where only a sidestand is fitted, an auxiliary stand will be needed to hold the motorcycle securely upright and allow the front wheel to be raised off the ground.

3 Point the front wheel straight-ahead and slowly move the handlebars from side-to-side. imperfections in the bearing races will be felt and the bars will not move smoothly.

4 Next, grasp the fork sliders and try to move them forward and backward **(see illustration)**.

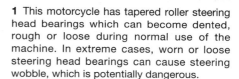

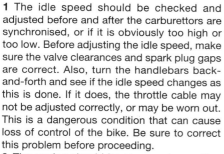

3.3 Idle speed screw is located on left side of carburettor assembly

4.1 Remove plug to drain airbox

5.4 Checking for looseness in the steering head bearings

1

5.8 Bearing adjuster pinch bolt (A) and adjuster ring (B) - early models

Any looseness in the steering head bearings will be felt as front-to-rear movement of the forks. If play is felt in the bearings, adjust the steering head as follows.

> **HAYNES HiNT** *Freeplay in the fork due to worn fork bushes can be misinterpreted for steering head bearing play - do not confuse the two*

Adjustment

Early Trident, Trophy and Daytona models

Note: *On early models, the bearing adjuster incorporates a pinch bolt to clamp it in place. This design was superseded by a separate adjuster nut and locknut on all later machines. It is possible to replace the early type adjuster with the two-piece arrangement used on later models.*

5 Position the bike as described in Step 2.
6 Slacken the fork clamp bolts in the top yoke **(see illustration 5.14)**. Access to these bolts may be restricted by the front brake and clutch master cylinders on certain models; if so, slacken off the master cylinder clamp bolts and rotate the cylinder about the handlebar to provide access. **Caution: Be careful that hydraulic fluid does not escape from the master cylinder reservoirs.** On Daytona models also slacken the handlebar clamp bolts.
7 Slacken off the steering stem nut **(see illustration 5.15)** and bearing adjuster ring pinch bolt.

5.14 Slacken the fork top yoke clamp bolts

8 Rotate the adjuster ring clockwise to take up bearing freeplay and preload the bearings, vice versa to reduce preload **(see illustration)**. The object is to set the adjuster ring so that the bearings are under a very light loading, just enough to remove any freeplay. **Caution: Take great care not to apply excessive pressure because this will cause premature failure of the bearings.**
9 When the setting is correct, tighten the pinch bolt to the specified torque setting to lock the adjuster ring's position. Tighten the fork clamp bolts and steering stem nut to their specified torque settings. On Daytona models, make sure the handlebar abuts the lug on the underside of the top yoke and tighten the handlebar clamp bolts to the specified torque setting.
10 If the brake and clutch master cylinders were disturbed, align the joining line of their clamps with the dot on the handlebars **(see illustration 5.19)**. Tighten the clamp top bolt first, then the lower, to the specified torque setting.
11 Re-check the head bearing adjustment as described in Steps 3 and 4.

All other models

Note: *Adjustment of the bearings with the top yoke in place requires the use of two very slim open-end spanners - these can be obtained under Pt. No. 3880140.*
12 Position the motorcycle as described in Step 2.
13 Remove the fuel tank for easier access to the adjuster nuts (see Chapter 4).
14 Slacken the fork clamp bolts in the top

5.15 Slacken the steering stem nut

yoke **(see illustration)**. Access to these bolts may be restricted by the front brake and clutch master cylinders on certain models; if so, slacken off the master cylinder clamp bolts and rotate the cylinder about the handlebar to provide access. On Daytona and Speed Triple models, also slacken the handlebar clamp bolts. **Caution: Be careful that hydraulic fluid does not escape from the master cylinder reservoirs.**
15 Slacken off the steering stem nut **(see illustration)**. Unclamp the handlebars from the top yoke on Thunderbird and Tiger models to improve access to the steering stem nut.
16 Slacken off the bearing adjuster locknut, then rotate the adjuster nut beneath it to adjust bearing freeplay **(see illustration)**. Turn the adjuster nut clockwise to take up bearing freeplay and preload the bearings, vice versa to reduce preload. The object is to set the adjuster nut so that the bearings are under a very light loading, just enough to remove any freeplay. **Caution: Take great care not to apply excessive pressure because this will cause premature failure of the bearings.**
17 When the setting is correct, hold the adjuster nut with one spanner and tighten the locknut against it with another spanner. **Note:** *The torque setting for the locknut can be applied if using the service tool specified in the Note above; the torque wrench locates in the square machined in the tool (see illustrations).*
18 Tighten the fork clamp bolts and steering stem nut to their specified torque settings. On Daytona and Speed Triple models, make sure

5.16 Back off the locknut (A) and adjust freeplay with the adjuster nut (B)

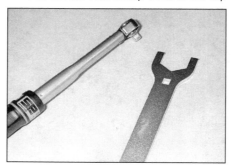

5.17a If the Triumph tool is available (right of photo) . . .

5.17b . . . the locknut can be secured to the specified torque

5.19 If the master cylinders were disturbed, align their clamp top joint with the dot (arrowed) on the handlebar

the handlebar abuts the lug on the underside of the top yoke and tighten the handlebar clamp bolts to the specified torque setting. On Thunderbird and Tiger models, align the punch mark(s) on the handlebar with the mating surfaces of the handlebar clamps and tighten the clamp bolts to the specified torque.

19 If the brake and clutch master cylinders were disturbed, align the joining line of their clamps with the dot on the handlebars **(see illustration)**. Tighten the clamp top bolt first, then the lower, to the specified torque setting.

20 Re-check the head bearing adjustment as described in Steps 3 and 4.

21 Install the fuel tank (see Chapter 4).

6 Suspension checks

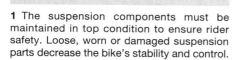

1 The suspension components must be maintained in top condition to ensure rider safety. Loose, worn or damaged suspension parts decrease the bike's stability and control.

Front suspension

2 Carefully inspect the area around the fork seals for any signs of fork oil leakage **(see illustration)**. If leakage is evident, the seals must be replaced as described in Chapter 6. On Tiger models, slacken the gaiter clamp and pull the gaiter up off the fork slider to examine the seals.

Rear suspension

3 Inspect the rear shock for fluid leakage and tightness of its mountings. If leakage is found, the shock should be replaced.

4 Position the motorcycle on its centre stand; where only a sidestand is fitted, position the motorcycle on an auxiliary stand so that the rear wheel is off the ground. Grab the swingarm on each side, just ahead of the axle. Rock the swingarm from side to side - there should be no discernible movement at the rear. If there's a little movement or a slight clicking can be heard, make sure the swingarm pivot bolt is tight. If movement is still noticeable, the swingarm bearings or suspension linkage bearings require attention (see Chapter 6).

6.2 Inspect the area above the fork oil seal for oil leakage

7 Drive chain wear and stretch check

1 Check the entire length of the chain for damaged rollers, loose links and pins and replace if damage is found.

2 If the chain has reached the end of its adjustment, it must be replaced. The amount of chain stretch can be measured by hanging a 10 to 20 kg weight midway between the sprockets on the chain's bottom run. Remove the chainguard for access to the top run of the chain. With the weight applied, measure along the top run the length of 20-links (from the centre of the 1st pin to the centre of the 21st pin) and compare with the service limit **(see illustration)**. Rotate the rear wheel so that several sections of the chain are measured, then calculate the average. If the chain exceeds the service limit it must be replaced (see Chapter 6). **Note:** *It is good practice to replace the chain and sprockets as a set.*

3 Remove the engine sprocket cover (see Chapter 6). Check the teeth on the engine sprocket and the rear wheel sprocket for wear **(see illustration)**.

4 Inspect the drive chain slider on the swingarm for excessive wear and replace if necessary (see Chapter 6). On Tiger models check the condition of the chain slider block mounted to the frame; if the chain slider block is replaced, repeat the chain freeplay check described above.

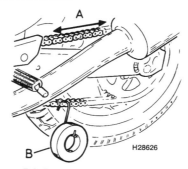

7.2 Drive chain stretch check

A 20-link length B Weight

1 Make sure t the front brak with the rear l brake light switch is adj operate properly, and the fault cannot be traced to the bulbs or wiring, replace the switch with a new one (see Chapter 9).

9 Brake pad wear check

1 It is possible on certain caliper types to view the pads with the caliper installed on the disc. However, it is advised that the caliper be removed to enable the pads to be viewed properly. Remove the two caliper mounting bolts and slide the caliper off the disc.

2 If the friction material has worn down so that the three grooves are no longer visible, ie so that friction material remaining is level with the base of the grooves, both pads must be replaced immediately **(see illustrations)**. **Note:** *If the front brake pads require replacement, note that the pads in both calipers must be replaced at the same time.* The amount of friction material can be measured to determine whether replacement is required (see the Specifications section of this Chapter). Tighten the caliper bolts to the specified torque (see Chapter 7 Specifications).

3 Refer to Chapter 7 for pad replacement.

10 Wheel and tyre checks

1

Tyres

1 Check the tyre condition and tread depth thoroughly - see *"Daily (pre-ride) checks"*.

Wheels

2 The cast wheels used on all models except the Thunderbird and Tiger are virtually

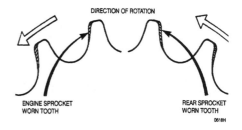

7.3 Check the engine and rear wheel sprockets for wear

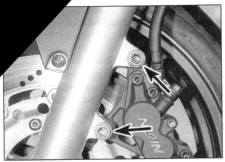

9.2a Remove the two mounting bolts (arrowed) to free the front brake caliper - type A caliper shown

9.2c Remove the two mounting bolts (arrowed) to free the rear brake caliper - type B caliper shown

maintenance free, but they should be kept clean and checked periodically for cracks and other damage. Never attempt to repair damaged cast wheels; they must be replaced with new ones. Check the valve rubber for signs of damage or deterioration and have it replaced if necessary. Also, make sure the valve stem cap is in place and tight.

3 On Thunderbird and Tiger models, visually check the spokes for damage, breakage or corrosion. A broken or bent spoke must be renewed immediately because the load taken by it will be transferred to adjacent spokes which may in turn fail.

4 If you suspect that any of the spokes are incorrectly tensioned, tap each one lightly with a screwdriver and note the sound produced. Properly tensioned spokes will make a sharp pinging sound, loose ones will produce a lower pitch and overtightened ones

11.3b On Thunderbird models, remove the screw ...

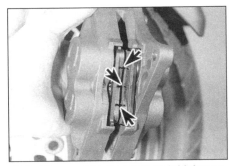

9.2b View pad friction material thickness via caliper mouth. Renew pads if wear grooves (arrowed) are no longer visible

9.2d Inspect the rear caliper pad condition via caliper mouth

will be higher pitched. Unevenly tensioned spokes will promote rim misalignment - seek the help of a wheel building expert if this is suspected.

11.2 Remove the battery negative lead (A) first, then the positive lead (B)

11.3c ... and unclip the side of the battery holder

11 Battery checks

⚠️ *Warning: Be extremely careful when handling or working around the battery. The electrolyte is very caustic and an explosive gas (hydrogen) is given off when the battery is charging.*

1 Remove the seat; on Thunderbird models also remove the right side panel (see Chapter 8).

2 Unhook the battery retaining strap and free the plastic tray. Remove the screws securing the battery cables to the battery terminals; remove the negative cable first, positive cable last **(see illustration)**.

3 On all models except the Thunderbird, lift the battery upwards out of its holder **(see illustration)**. On Thunderbird models, remove the screw and unclip the side of the battery holder, being careful not to strain the fusebox and turn signal relay wiring **(see illustrations)**. Pull the vent hose off the battery and slide the battery out of its holder.

4 The electrolyte level is visible through the translucent battery case - it should be between the UPPER and LOWER level marks **(see illustration)**.

5 If the electrolyte is low, remove the cell caps and fill each cell to the upper level mark with distilled water. Do not use tap water (except in an emergency), and do not overfill. The cell holes are quite small, so it may help

11.3a On all except the Thunderbird, lift the battery out of its holder

11.4 Electrolyte level must be between UPPER and LOWER marks on battery case

11.6 Battery vent tube is routed through hole in base of battery holder (arrowed)

to use a clean plastic squeeze bottle with a small spout to add the water. Install the battery cell caps, tightening them securely.

6 Install the battery in a reverse of the removal sequence, making sure that its vent tube is properly connected and routed **(see illustration)**.

 Warning: It is important that the vent tube is not pinched or trapped at any point, because the battery may build up enough internal pressure during normal charging to explode - always refer to the routing label stuck to the underside of the seat.

7 Reconnect the cables to the battery, attaching the positive cable first and the negative cable last. Make sure to install the insulating boot over both terminals. Install the plastic tray and battery strap.

8 If the machine is not in regular use, disconnect the battery and give it a refresher charge every month to six weeks, as described in Chapter 9.

 Battery corrosion can be minimised by applying a layer of petroleum jelly to the terminals after the cables have been connected.

Every 6000 miles (10 000 km)

12 Engine oil and filter change

1 Consistent routine oil and filter changes are the single most important maintenance procedure you can perform on a motorcycle. The oil not only lubricates the internal parts of the engine, transmission and clutch, but it also acts as a coolant, a cleaner, a sealant, and a protectant. Because of these demands, the oil takes a terrific amount of abuse and should be replaced often with new oil of the recommended grade and type. Saving a little money on the difference in cost between a

good oil and a cheap oil won't pay off if the engine is damaged.

2 Before changing the oil and filter, warm up the engine so the oil will drain easily. Be careful when draining the oil, as the exhaust pipes, the engine, and the oil itself can cause severe burns.

3 Put the motorcycle on its centre stand; where no centre stand is fitted position the motorcycle on an auxiliary stand, or have an assistant hold it upright during the procedure to ensure that oil drains fully. Position a clean drain tray below the engine. Unscrew the oil filler cap to vent the crankcase to act as a reminder that there is no oil in the engine.

4 Next, remove the drain plug from the sump

and allow the oil to flow into the drain tray **(see illustration)**. Discard the sealing washer on the drain plug; it should be replaced whenever the plug is removed.

5 Unscrew the oil filter centre bolt and withdraw the filter assembly from the sump **(see illustration)**. Discard the filter element, but retain all other filter components.

6 Slip a new sealing washer over the drain plug. Fit the plug to the sump and tighten it to the specified torque setting. Avoid overtightening, as damage to the sump will result.

7 Install new O-rings on the centre bolt and cover **(see illustrations)**. Install the centre bolt through the cover, then install the coil spring and washer **(see illustration)**. Work the new oil

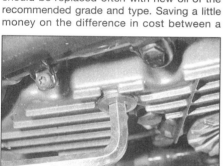

12.4 Engine oil drain plug is located in sump

12.5 Unscrew the oil filter centre bolt to free the filter assembly

Note: It is antisocial and illegal to dump oil down the drain. In the UK, call this number free to find the location of your local oil recycling bank.

0800 66 33 66

In the USA, note that any oil supplier must accept used oil for recycling.

12.7a Install a new O-ring on the centre bolt . . .

12.7b . . . and cover

12.7c Install the coil spring and washer on the centre bolt . . .

1

12.7d ... followed by the new filter ...

12.7e ... and washer

12.7f Install the filter assembly in the sump

filter on the centre bolt, having lubricated the filter seals with engine oil, then install the washer **(see illustrations)**. Install the oil filter assembly on the sump and tighten the centre bolt to the specified torque **(see illustration)**.

8 Refill the crankcase to the proper level with the recommended type and amount of oil and install the filler cap. Start the engine and let it run for two or three minutes (make sure that the oil pressure light extinguishes after a few seconds). Shut it off, wait a few minutes, then check the oil level. If necessary, add more oil to bring the level up to the upper mark (see *"Daily (pre-ride) checks"*). Check around the drain plug and filter for leaks.

9 The old oil drained from the engine cannot be re-used and should be disposed of properly. Check with your local refuse disposal company, disposal facility or environmental agency to see whether they will accept the used oil for recycling. Don't pour used oil into drains or onto the ground.

HAYNES HINT *Check the old oil carefully - if it is very metallic coloured, then the engine is experiencing wear from break-in (new engine) or from insufficient lubrication. If there are flakes or chips of metal in the oil, then something is drastically wrong internally and the engine will have to be disassembled for inspection and repair. If there are pieces of fibre-like material in the oil, the clutch is wearing excessively and should be checked.*

13 Valve clearance check

1 The engine must be completely cool for this maintenance procedure, so let the machine sit overnight before beginning.

2 Remove the valve cover (see Chapter 2). Unscrew the spark plugs to allow the engine to be turned over easier.

3 The engine can be turned over by placing the motorcycle on its centre stand (or an auxiliary stand), selecting a high gear and rotating the rear wheel by hand. Alternatively,

remove the crankshaft right cover; have a drain tray ready in case of oil loss. Rotate the crankshaft using a ring spanner on the large engine turning hexagon **(see illustration)**. If the latter approach is adopted, the fairing right lower panel must be removed on Trophy and Daytona models (see Chapter 8).

4 Make a chart or sketch of all twelve (3 cylinder) or sixteen (4 cylinder) valve positions so that all four valves for each cylinder can be identified.

5 Starting with cylinder No 1, rotate the engine until one pair of valves is completely closed, ie with their lobes pointing diametrically opposite the valve. At this point insert a feeler blade of the correct thickness (see Specifications) between each cam base and shim and check that it is a firm sliding fit **(see illustration)**. If it is not, use the feeler blades to obtain the exact clearance. Record the measured clearance on the chart.

6 Proceed to check all other clearances in the same way, noting that the specification differs for inlet and exhaust valves.

7 When all clearances have been measured and charted, identify whether the clearance on any valve falls outside of that specified. If it does, the shim between the tappet and camshaft must be replaced with one of different thickness.

8 Remove the camshafts to access the shims (see Chapter 2).

9 The shim size (eg 2.60) should be stamped on its face, however, it is recommended that the shim is measured to check that it has not worn **(see illustrations)**. Shims are available in 0.05 mm increments from 2.00 to 3.20 mm.

10 Use the shim selection chart, find where the measured valve clearance and existing shim thickness values intersect and read off the shim size required **(see illustrations)**. Note that the charts differ for inlet and exhaust

13.3 Engine can be rotated with a ring spanner on the hexagon - rotate clockwise

13.5 Measuring a valve clearance. Lobe must point diametrically opposite valve

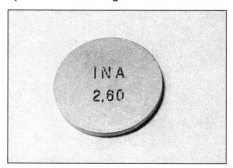

13.9a Shim thickness should be marked on one side of shim

13.9b Shim can be sized by direct measurement

MEASURED INTAKE VALVE CLEARANCE

CORRECT CLEARANCE, NO CHANGE OF SHIM REQUIRED

MEASURED THICKNESS OF FITTED SHIM

H28659

13.10a Intake valve shim selection chart

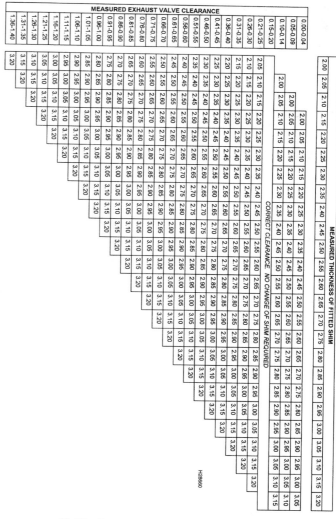

MEASURED EXHAUST VALVE CLEARANCE

CORRECT CLEARANCE, NO CHANGE OF SHIM REQUIRED

MEASURED THICKNESS OF FITTED SHIM

H28660

13.10b Exhaust valve shim selection chart

valves so make sure you are using the correct one. Obtain and install the replacement shim, noting that its size marking should be installed downwards and that the shim should be lubricated with engine oil **(see illustration)**.

11 Install the camshafts as described in Chapter 2.

13.10c Install shim with its size marking downwards, towards the valve

12 Check that the valve clearance is correct (see Step 5).

13 Install all disturbed components in a reverse of the removal sequence.

14 Cooling system checks

> **Warning: The engine must be cool before beginning this procedure.**

1 Check the coolant level as described in *"Daily (pre-ride) checks"*.

2 On Trophy and Daytona models, remove the lower fairing panels as described in Chapter 8. On Thunderbird models, remove the fuel tank (see Chapter 4).

3 A trim cover is fitted over the water pump-to-cylinder block hose on later models; release the cover by removing its two retaining screws **(see illustrations)**. On Speed Triple and later Trident models, the radiator top hose cover screw can be accessed after removing the side cover from the radiator; peel off the reflector and remove the two screws to free the radiator side cover.

4 The entire cooling system should be checked for evidence of leakage. Examine each rubber coolant hose looking for cracks, abrasions and other damage **(see illustration)**. Squeeze each hose at various points. They should feel firm, yet pliable, and return to their original shape when released. If they are dried out or hard, replace them with new ones.

5 Check for evidence of leaks at each cooling system joint. Tighten the hose clips carefully to prevent future leaks.

6 Check the radiator for leaks and other damage. Leaks in the radiator leave telltale scale deposits or coolant stains on the outside of the core below the leak. If leaks are noted, remove the radiator, detach the grille (see Chapter 3) and have it repaired at a

14.3a On later models, release the trim cover . . .

14.3b . . . for access to water pump coolant hose

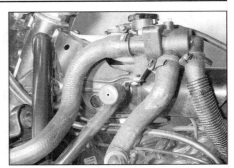

14.4 On Thunderbird models, fuel tank must be removed to check coolant hoses

radiator shop or replace it with a new one. *Caution: Do not use a liquid leak-stopping compound to try to repair leaks.*

7 Check the radiator fins for mud, dirt and insects, which may impede the flow of air through the radiator. If the fins are dirty, force water or low pressure compressed air through the fins from the rear of the radiator. If the fins are bent or distorted, straighten them carefully with a screwdriver.

8 The pressure cap is located in the top left side of the radiator on all models except the Thunderbird, where it locates in the radiator filler neck/thermostat housing **(see illustrations)**. On models with fairings, either reach up underneath the front of the fairing for access or remove the detachable inner panel. Remove the pressure cap by turning it anti-clockwise until it reaches a stop. If you hear a hissing sound (indicating there is still pressure in the system), wait until it stops. Now press down on the cap and continue turning the cap until it can be removed. Check the condition of the coolant in the system. If it is rust-coloured or if accumulations of scale are visible, drain, flush and refill the system with new coolant (see Section 27). Check the cap seal for cracks and other damage. If in doubt about the pressure cap's condition, have it tested by a Triumph dealer or replace it with a new one. Install the cap by turning it clockwise until it reaches the first stop, then push down on the cap and continue turning until it can turn no further.

14.8a Pressure cap is located at top left corner of radiator . . .

9 Check the antifreeze content of the coolant with an antifreeze hydrometer. Sometimes coolant looks like it's in good condition, but might be too weak to offer adequate protection. If the hydrometer indicates a weak mixture, drain, flush and refill the system (see Section 27).

10 Start the engine and let it reach normal operating temperature, then check for leaks again. As the coolant temperature increases, the fan should come on automatically and the temperature should begin to drop. If it does not, refer to Chapter 3 and check the fan and fan circuit carefully.

11 If the coolant level is consistently low, and no evidence of leaks can be found, have the entire system pressure checked by a Triumph dealer **(see Haynes Hint)**.

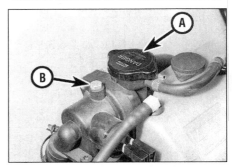

14.8b . . . on Thunderbird it is on thermostat housing (A). Note coolant bleed screw (B)

cable must be replaced. Note that in very rare cases the fault could lie in the carburettors rather than the cable, necessitating the removal of the carburettors and inspection of the throttle linkage (see Chapter 4).

3 With the throttle operating smoothly, check for a small amount of freeplay at the grip **(see illustration)**. The amount of freeplay in the throttle cable, measured in terms of twistgrip rotation, should be as given in this Chapter's Specifications. If adjustment is necessary, adjust idle speed first (see Section 3).

4 Slacken the lockwheel on the cable upper adjuster and rotate the adjuster until the correct amount of freeplay is obtained, then tighten the lockwheel against the adjuster **(see illustration)**. If it is not possible to obtain the correct freeplay with the upper adjuster, it will also be necessary to make adjustment at

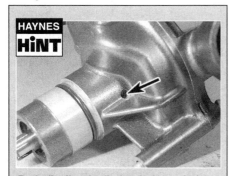

Periodically, check the drainage hole on the underside of the water pump - leakage from this hole indicates failure of the pump's mechanical seal

---

15 Throttle and choke cable checks

Throttle cable

1 Make sure the throttle grip rotates easily from fully closed to fully open with the front wheel turned at various angles. The grip should return automatically from fully open to fully closed when released.

2 If the throttle sticks, this is probably due to a cable fault. Remove the cable as described in Chapter 4 and lubricate it as described in Section 21. Install the cable, routing it so that it takes the smoothest route possible. If this fails to improve the operation of the throttle, the

15.3 Throttle cable freeplay is measured in terms of twistgrip rotation at the grip flange (arrowed)

the lower adjuster, situated on the carburettors (see illustration).

5 To gain access to the lower adjuster remove the fuel tank (see Chapter 4). Prior to making adjustment at the carburettor end of the cable, fully back off the lockwheel on the upper adjuster and screw the adjuster into the throttle housing; this will create more slack in the cable and allow for future cable adjustment to be taken up with the upper adjuster.

6 Where fitted, free the spring clip from the cable adjuster locknut on the lower adjuster. Slacken the adjuster locknut and rotate the adjuster until the correct freeplay is obtained at the throttle grip (see Step 3). When the freeplay is correct, tighten the lower adjuster locknut and where fitted, secure it with the spring clip. Tighten the upper adjuster lockwheel. Install the fuel tank (Chapter 4). **Note:** *Access to the lower adjuster is limited with the carburettors in situ - it is advised that they are detached from the inlet manifolds.*

7 Check that the throttle twistgrip operates smoothly and snaps shut quickly when released. *Caution: Turn the handlebars all the way through their travel with the engine idling. Idle speed should not change. If it does, the cable may be routed incorrectly. Correct this condition before riding the bike (see Chapter 4).*

Choke cable

8 Operate the choke lever whilst observing the movement of the carburettor choke shaft on the left side of the carburettor assembly. There should be a small amount of freeplay (see Specifications) before the choke shaft contacts the choke plunger (see illustration). To make adjustment, remove the fuel tank (see Chapter 4) and locate the in-line adjuster in the choke cable (see illustration). Slacken its locknut and rotate the adjuster body as required; tighten the locknut.

9 If the choke does not operate smoothly this is probably due to a cable fault. Remove the cable as described in Chapter 4 and lubricate it as described in Section 21. Install the cable, routing it so it takes the smoothest route possible. If this fails to improve the operation of the choke, the cable must be replaced. Note that in very rare cases the fault could lie in the carburettors rather than the cable, necessitating the removal of the carburettors and inspection of the choke plungers and choke shaft as described in Chapter 4.

---

16 Carburettor synchronisation

⚠️ *Warning: Petrol is extremely flammable, so take extra precautions when you work on any part of the fuel system.*
Don't smoke or allow open flames or bare light bulbs near the work area, and don't work in a garage where a natural gas-type

15.4a Small adjustments can be made using the throttle cable upper adjuster

15.8a Check for freeplay between the choke shaft and plunger tip (arrowed)

appliance is present. If you spill any fuel on your skin, rinse it off with soap and water. When you perform any work on the fuel system, wear safety glasses and have a fire extinguisher suitable for a Class B type fire (flammable liquids) on hand.

⚠️ *Warning: Take great care not to burn your hand on the hot engine when accessing the gauge take-off points on the inlet manifolds. Do not allow exhaust gases to build up in the work area; either perform the check outside or use an exhaust gas extraction system.*

1 Carburettor synchronisation is simply the process of adjusting the carburettors so they pass the same amount of fuel/air mixture to each cylinder. This is done by measuring the vacuum produced in each cylinder. Carburettors that are out of synchronisation will result in decreased fuel mileage, increased engine temperature, less than ideal throttle response and higher vibration levels.

2 To properly synchronise the carburettors, you will need some sort of vacuum gauge set-up, preferably with a gauge for each cylinder, or a mercury manometer, which is a calibrated tube arrangement that utilises columns of mercury to indicate engine vacuum.

3 A manometer can be purchased from a motorcycle dealer or accessory shop and should have the necessary rubber hoses supplied with it for hooking into the vacuum take-off stubs.

4 A vacuum gauge set-up can also be purchased from a dealer or alternatively, can be fabricated from commonly available

15.4b Lower adjuster is situated on carburettor (arrowed)

15.8b Choke cable adjustment is made using the in-line adjuster (arrowed)

hardware and automotive vacuum gauges.

5 The manometer is the more reliable and accurate instrument, and for that reason is preferred over the vacuum gauge set-up; however, since the mercury used in the manometer is a liquid, and extremely toxic, extra precautions must be taken during use and storage of the instrument.

6 Because of the nature of the synchronisation procedure and the need for special instruments, most owners leave the task to a Triumph dealer.

7 Position the bike on its centrestand; where only a sidestand is fitted, support the bike using an auxiliary stand. Start the engine and let it run until it reaches normal operating temperature, then shut it off.

8 Remove the fuel tank (see Chapter 4).

9 Disconnect the fuel tap vacuum hose from the vacuum take-off stub of No. 3 carburettor (see illustration). **Note:** *This does not apply*

16.9 Disconnect the fuel tap vacuum pipe from No. 3 carburettor (models with vacuum tap)

16.10 Disconnect the caps from vacuum take-off points on the other carburettors

16.15 Synchronising screw locations on 3 cylinder engine (arrowed)

Check

1 Remove the fuel tank (see Chapter 4) and check the fuel hose(s), vacuum hose (where fitted) and breather hose for signs of damage; in particular check that there is no leakage from the fuel hose(s). Replace any hoses which are cracked or deteriorated.

Filter cleaning

2 Although not part of the maintenance schedule, cleaning of the fuel filters is advised after a particularly high mileage has been covered. It is also necessary if fuel starvation is suspected.

3 The fuel tap incorporates a gauze type filter inside the fuel tank **(see illustration)**. Remove the fuel tap as described in Chapter 4 and clean the filter being careful not to tear the gauze.

4 A gauze filter is fitted in the fuel delivery hose T-piece(s) on the carburettors. Remove the fuel tank (see Chapter 4) and disconnect the fuel hose where it joins the T-piece union on the carburettors; note that the Thunderbird and Tiger have a single fuel delivery hose, and all other models have two **(see illustration)**. Remove the gauze filter from the union and clean it **(see illustration)**. Install the filter and secure the hose with its clip. Install the fuel tank (see Chapter 4) and check that there is no leakage from the fuel hose(s).

to Thunderbird or Tiger models which have a gravity-fed fuel tap.

10 On California models, disconnect the evaporative loss system hoses from the vacuum take-off stubs, having labelled them for easy reconnection. On all other models, remove the blanking caps from the vacuum take-off stubs **(see illustration)**.

11 Connect the gauge hoses to the take-off stubs. Make sure there are no air leaks as false readings will result.

12 Arrange a temporary fuel supply, either by using a small temporary tank or by using extra long fuel pipes to the now remote fuel tank on a nearby bench. Turn the fuel tap to the PRI position (the ON position on Thunderbird and Tiger models).

13 Start the engine and make sure the idle speed is correct. If it isn't, adjust it (see Section 3). If the gauges are fitted with damping adjustment, set this so that the needle flutter is just eliminated but so that they can still respond to small changes in pressure.

14 The vacuum readings for all of the cylinders should be the same, or at least within the tolerance listed in this Chapter's Specifications. If the vacuum readings vary, adjust as necessary. Cylinder No. 2 is the base carburettor on 3 cylinder engines, and cylinder No. 3 on 4 cylinder engines. Set the base carburettor using the idle adjuster screw, then balance all other carburettors to its setting as follows using the synchronisation screws.

15 The carburettors are adjusted by the two (3 cylinder engines) or three (4 cylinder

engines) screws situated in-between each carburettor, in the throttle linkage **(see illustration)**. **Note:** *Do not press down on the screws whilst adjusting them, otherwise a false reading will be obtained.* When all the carburettors are synchronised, open and close the throttle quickly to settle the linkage, and recheck the gauge readings, readjusting if necessary.

16 When the adjustment is complete, recheck the vacuum readings and idle speed, then stop the engine. Remove the vacuum gauge or manometer. Install the blanking caps, fuel tap hose and evaporative loss hoses (as applicable).

17 Detach the temporary fuel supply and install the fuel tank (see Chapter 4).

17 Fuel system checks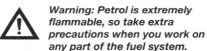

> ⚠ **Warning: Petrol is extremely flammable, so take extra precautions when you work on any part of the fuel system.**
> **Don't smoke or allow open flames or bare light bulbs near the work area, and don't work in a garage where a natural gas-type appliance is present. If you spill any fuel on your skin, rinse it off with soap and water. When you perform any work on the fuel system, wear safety glasses and have a fire extinguisher suitable for a Class B type fire (flammable liquids) on hand.**

18 Evaporative loss system check (California only)

1 This system is installed on California models to conform to stringent state emission control standards. It is explained in greater detail in Chapter 4.

2 To begin the inspection of the system, remove the fuel tank and seat (see Chapters 4 and 8). Refer to the vacuum hose routing diagram on the frame, and trace the hoses between the system components, looking for signs of cracking, perishing or other damage. Any such hoses must be replaced.

3 Check the charcoal canister, mounted beneath the rear mudguard, for damage or fuel leakage.

17.3 Fuel tap incorporates a gauze filter - vacuum tap shown

17.4a Release its clip and pull the fuel hose off the carburettor union

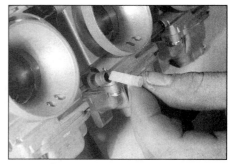

17.4b Slip the fuel filter out of the union

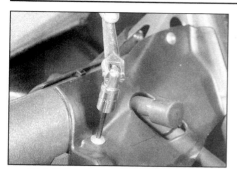

19.4 Valve cover cowls are secured by two screws

19.6a Pull the spark plug caps out of the valve cover

19.6b Use the 12 mm Allen key supplied in the tool kit together with the plug spanner to unscrew the spark plugs

19 Spark plug gap check

1 This motorcycle is equipped with spark plugs that have 12 mm threads and an 18 mm wrench hex. Make sure your spark plug socket is the correct size before attempting to remove the plugs, a suitable one is supplied in the motorcycle's tool kit and is operated by the 12 mm Allen key also contained in the tool kit.

2 Remove the seat and disconnect the battery negative lead.

3 Remove the fuel tank (see Chapter 4).

4 Remove the valve cover cowls on all models except the Thunderbird; they are secured by two screws **(see illustration)**.

5 Clean the area around the valve cover and plug caps to prevent any dirt falling into the spark plug channels.

6 Pull the spark plug caps off the spark plugs, having checked that the cylinder location is marked on each lead, and using a deep socket type wrench, unscrew them from the cylinder head **(see illustrations)**. Lay the plugs out in relation to their cylinder number; if any plug shows up a problem it will then be easy to identify the troublesome cylinder.

7 Inspect the electrodes for wear. Both the centre and side electrodes should have square edges and the side electrode should be of uniform thickness. Look for excessive deposits and evidence of a cracked or

chipped insulator around the centre electrode. Compare your spark plugs to the colour spark plug reading chart. Check the threads, the washer and the ceramic insulator body for cracks and other damage.

8 If the electrodes are not excessively worn, and if the deposits can be easily removed with a wire brush, the plugs can be regapped and re-used (if no cracks or chips are visible in the insulator). If in doubt concerning the condition of the plugs, replace them with new ones, as the expense is minimal.

9 Cleaning spark plugs by sandblasting is permitted, provided you clean the plugs with a high flash-point solvent afterwards.

10 Before installing new plugs, make sure they are the correct type and heat range. Check the gap between the electrodes, as they are not preset. For best results, use a wire-type gauge rather than a flat (feeler) gauge to check the gap. If the gap must be adjusted, bend the side electrode only and be very careful not to chip or crack the insulator nose **(see illustrations)**. Make sure the washer is in place before installing each plug.

11 Since the cylinder head is made of aluminium, which is soft and easily damaged, thread the plugs into the heads by hand. Once the plugs are finger-tight, the job can be finished with a socket **(see Haynes Hint)**. Tighten the spark plugs to the specified torque listed in this Chapter's Specifications; do not over-tighten them.

12 Reconnect the spark plug caps and reinstall all disturbed components.

HAYNES HiNT *Since the plugs are recessed, slip a short length of hose over the end of the plug to use as a tool to thread it into place. The hose will grip the plug well enough to turn it, but will start to slip if the plug begins to cross-thread in the hole - this will prevent damaged threads and the resultant repair costs.*

20 Nuts and bolts check

1 Since vibration of the machine tends to loosen fasteners, all nuts, bolts, screws, etc. should be periodically checked for proper tightness.

2 Pay particular attention to the following:
Spark plugs
Engine oil drain plug
Gearshift pedal bolt
Footrest and stand bolts
Engine mounting bolts
Shock absorber mounting bolts
Handlebar and yoke bolts
Rear suspension linkage bolts
Front axle and clamp bolts
Rear axle bolt
Exhaust system bolts/nuts

3 If a torque wrench is available, use it along with the torque specifications at the beginning of this, or other Chapters.

1

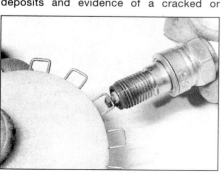

19.10a A wire type gauge is recommended to measure the spark plug electrode gap

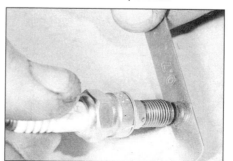

19.10b Using a feeler blade to measure spark plug electrode gap

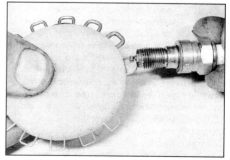

19.10c Electrode gap is adjusted by bending the side electrode

21 Stand, lever pivots and cable lubrication

1 Since the controls, cables and other components of a motorcycle are exposed to the elements, they should be lubricated periodically to ensure safe and trouble-free operation.
2 The footrests, clutch and brake levers, brake pedal, gearshift lever linkage (where applicable) and stand pivots should be lubricated frequently. In order for the lubricant to be applied where it will do the most good, the component should be disassembled. However, if chain and cable lubricant is being used, it can be applied to the pivot joint gaps and will usually work its way into the areas where friction occurs. If motor oil or light grease is being used, apply it sparingly as it may attract dirt (which could cause the controls to bind or wear at an accelerated rate). **Note:** *One of the best lubricants for the control lever pivots is a dry-film lubricant (available from many sources by different names).*
3 To lubricate the cables, disconnect the relevant cable at its upper end, then lubricate the cable with a pressure lube adapter **(see illustration)**. See Chapter 4 for the choke and throttle cable removal procedures.
4 The speedometer cable should be removed from its housing and lubricated with motor oil or cable lubricant. Do not lubricate the upper few inches of the cable as the lubricant may travel up into the speedometer head.

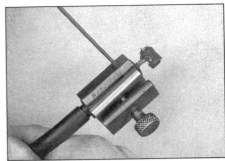

21.3 Lubricating a cable with a pressure lube adapter (make sure the tool seats around the inner cable)

Every 12 000 miles (20 000 km)

22 Clutch fluid change

Or every two years
1 Refer to the clutch bleeding section in Chapter 2, noting that all old fluid must be pumped from the fluid reservoir and hydraulic line before filling with new fluid.

23 Spark plug replacement

See *"Spark plug gap check"* under the 6000 mile (10 000 km) heading for details.

24 Front fork oil change

1 Since oil drain plugs are not fitted, remove the forks from the yokes, then drain and refill with new oil as described in Chapter 6.

25 Steering head bearing greasing

Or every two years
1 Disassemble the steering head for re-greasing of the bearings. Refer to Chapter 6 for details.

26 Brake fluid change

Or every two years
1 Refer to the brake bleeding section in Chapter 7, noting that all old fluid must be pumped from the fluid reservoir and hydraulic line before filling with new fluid.

Every 18 000 miles (30 000 km)

27 Coolant change

Or every two years

⚠ *Warning: Let the engine cool completely before starting. Also, don't allow antifreeze to come into contact with your skin or the painted surfaces of the motorcycle. Rinse off spills immediately with plenty of water. Antifreeze is highly toxic if ingested. Never leave antifreeze lying around in an open container or in puddles on the floor; children and pets are attracted by its sweet smell and may drink it. Check with local authorities about disposing of antifreeze. Many communities have collection centres which will see that antifreeze is disposed of safely. Antifreeze is also combustible, so don't store it near open flames.*

Draining

1 On Trophy, Daytona, Sprint and Tiger models, remove the fairing panels necessary to provide easy access to the radiator pressure cap (see Chapter 8). On Thunderbird models, remove the fuel tank (see Chapter 4).
2 Position a suitable container beneath the water pump, then remove the drain plug and sealing washer from the pump cover **(see illustration and Haynes Hint)**.
3 Remove the pressure cap by turning it anti-clockwise until it reaches a stop. If you hear a hissing sound (indicating there is still pressure

27.2a Coolant drain plug is located in the water pump

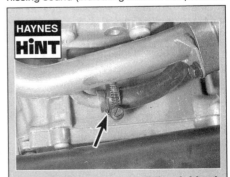

Slacken its clamp and pull the air bleed hose off the metal coolant pipe - this is the lowest point in the system, and will allow the coolant to drain fully

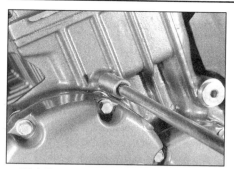

27.4 Remove drain plug from cylinder block to drain coolant from water jacket

in the system), wait until it stops. Now press down on the cap and continue turning the cap until it can be removed. As the cap is removed, the flow of coolant will increase - be prepared for this.

4 Have the container to hand, and remove the water jacket drain plug and sealing washer from the cylinder block **(see illustration)**.

5 Drain the coolant reservoir. Refer to Chapter 3 for reservoir removal procedure. Wash out the reservoir with fresh water and re-install it.

Flushing

6 Flush the system with clean tap water by inserting a garden hose in the radiator filler neck. Allow the water to run through the system until it is clear and flows cleanly out of the drain holes.

7 Clean the drain holes, then install the drain plugs and sealing washers.

8 Fill the cooling system with clean water mixed with a flushing compound. Make sure the flushing compound is compatible with aluminium components, and follow the manufacturer's instructions carefully. Install the pressure cap on the radiator. On Thunderbird models, install the fuel tank, noting that it need only be connected temporarily at this stage.

9 Start the engine and allow it reach normal operating temperature. Let it run for about ten minutes.

10 Stop the engine. Let it cool for a while, then cover the pressure cap with a heavy cloth and turn it anti-clockwise to the first stop, releasing any pressure that may be present in the system. Once the hissing stops, push down on the cap and remove it.

11 Drain the system once again.

12 Fill the system with clean water and repeat the procedure in Steps 9 through 11.

Refilling

13 Fit a new sealing washer to both drain plugs and tighten them to the specified torque.

14 On Thunderbird models, slacken the bleed screw on the thermostat housing.

15 Fill the system with the proper coolant mixture via the radiator filler neck (see this Chapter's Specifications). **Note:** *Pour the coolant in slowly to minimise the amount of air entering the system.*

16 When the system is full (all the way up to the top of the radiator filler neck), install the pressure cap. On Thunderbird models, tighten the bleed screw when coolant runs out of it and the system is full **(see illustration 14.8b)**.

17 Top-up the coolant reservoir to the UPPER level mark. On Thunderbird models, reconnect the fuel tank, noting that it need only be connected temporarily at this stage.

18 Start the engine and allow it to idle for 2 to 3 minutes. Flick the throttle twistgrip part open 3 or 4 times, so that the engine speed rises to approximately 4000 - 5000 rpm, then stop the engine. Any air trapped in the system should now have been expelled.

19 Let the engine cool, then remove the pressure cap as described in Step 10. Check that the coolant level is still up to the radiator filler neck. If it's low, add the specified mixture until it reaches the top of the filler neck. Reinstall the pressure cap.

20 Check the coolant level in the reservoir and top-up if necessary.

21 Check that there are no leaks from the cooling system. If all is well, install the fairing panels on Trophy, Daytona, Sprint and Tiger models (see Chapter 8). On Thunderbird models, install the fuel tank (see Chapter 4).

22 Do not dispose of the old coolant by pouring it down the drain. Instead pour it into a heavy plastic container, cap it tightly and take it into an authorised disposal site or garage - see **Warning** at the beginning of this Section.

Every 24 000 miles (40 000 km)

1

28 Airbox replacement

1 The air inlet system on these machines does not have a replaceable filter element. At the specified interval, the airbox must be replaced. Refer to Chapter 4 for removal and installation procedures.

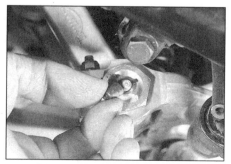

29.1a On all models except the Thunderbird and Tiger, remove dust cap from grease nipples . . .

29 Rear suspension linkage bearing lubrication

Or every three years

1 Identify the grease nipple locations on the suspension linkage pivots and wipe any dirt off them and remove their caps **(see illustrations)**. Using a grease gun and the specified grease, work lubricant into all pivots.

29.1b . . . and force grease into the linkage spindle ends . . .

30 Swingarm bearing lubrication

Or every three years

1 The swingarm is not equipped with grease nipples. Periodically remove the swingarm as described in Chapter 6 for greasing of the bearings.

29.1c . . . linkage arm pivot . . .

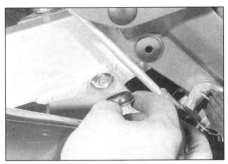

29.1d . . . and connecting rod-to-swingarm pivots

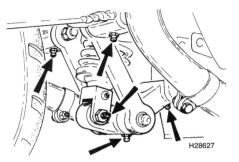

29.1e Grease nipple locations on Thunderbird and Tiger models (arrowed)

31 Drive chain slider block replacement (Tiger model)

Or every two years

1 Unbolt the drive chain slider block from the frame and replace it with a new one. Don't forget the spacer when installing the new block and tighten the nut securely.

2 Always check the chain freeplay after installing a new slider block.

Every two years

32 Clutch release cylinder and master cylinder seal replacement

Refer to Chapter 2 and dismantle the components for seal replacement.

33 Brake caliper and master cylinder seal replacement

Refer to Chapter 7 and dismantle the components for seal replacement.

Every four years

34 Clutch hose replacement

1 Refer to Chapter 2 and disconnect the hydraulic hose from the clutch master cylinder and release cylinder. The hose should be replaced regardless of its condition. Always replace the banjo union sealing washers with new ones.

35 Fuel hose replacement

1 Refer to Chapter 4 and disconnect the single hose (Tiger and Thunderbird) or two hoses (all other models) from the fuel tap and carburettors. The hose(s) should be replaced regardless of its condition.

36 Brake hose replacement

1 Refer to Chapter 7 and disconnect the brake hoses from the master cylinders and calipers. The hoses should be replaced regardless of their condition. Always replace the banjo union sealing washers with new ones.

Chapter 2
Engine, clutch and transmission

Contents

Degrees of difficulty

| **Easy,** suitable for novice with little experience | | **Fairly easy,** suitable for beginner with some experience | | **Fairly difficult,** suitable for competent DIY mechanic | | **Difficult,** suitable for experienced DIY mechanic | | **Very difficult,** suitable for expert DIY or professional | |

Specifications

General

Capacity
   750 models . . . . 748 cc
   900 models . . . . 885 cc
   1000 model . . . . 998 cc
   1200 models . . . . 1180 cc
Bore - all models . . . . 76 mm
Stroke
   750 and 1000 models . . . . 55 mm
   900 and 1200 models . . . . 65 mm
Compression ratio
   Thunderbird . . . . 10.0 to 1
   900/1200 Trophy, 900 Daytona, Speed Triple, 900 Trident,
      Sprint, Tiger . . . . 10.6 to 1
   750/1000 Daytona, 750 Trident . . . . 11.0 to 1
   900 Daytona Super III, 1200 Daytona . . . . 12.0 to 1
Cylinder numbering (from left side to right side of the bike) . . . . 1-2-3 (3 cylinder), 1-2-3-4 (4 cylinder)
Firing order . . . . 1-2-3 (3 cylinder), 1-2-4-3 (4 cylinder)

Camshafts and tappets

Camshaft runout . . . . 0.05 mm maximum
Camshaft bearing oil clearance . . . . 0.12 mm maximum
Camshaft journal diameter - all journals except outrigger . . . . 22.90 to 22.93 mm
Camshaft journal diameter - outrigger journals (cam chain end) . . . . . . 22.923 to 22.936 mm

Camshafts and tappets (continued)

Camshaft bearing bore diameter . . . .   23.000 to 23.021 mm
Tappet OD
    Blue marking . . . .   27.983 to 27.993 mm
    Red marking . . . .   27.980 to 27.986 mm
    White marking . . . .   27.974 to 27.979 mm
Tappet bore diameter . . . .   28.000 to 28.021 mm
Cam chain tensioner spring length . . . .   73.7 mm

Valves, guides and springs

Intake valve stem diameter
    Standard . . . .   5.475 to 5.490 mm
    Service limit . . . .   5.47 mm
Exhaust valve stem diameter
    Standard . . . .   5.455 to 5.470 mm
    Service limit . . . .   5.45 mm
Valve guide bore diameter - intake and exhaust . . . .   5.500 to 5.515 mm
Valve stem-to-guide clearance - intake
    Standard . . . .   0.01 to 0.04 mm
    Service limit . . . .   0.07 mm
Valve stem-to-guide clearance - exhaust
    Standard . . . .   0.03 to 0.06 mm
    Service limit . . . .   0.09 mm
Valve face width . . . .   1.8 to 2.5 mm
Valve seat width
    Standard . . . .   0.9 to 1.1 mm
    Service limit . . . .   1.5 mm

Clutch

Friction plate thickness
    Standard . . . .   3.80 + 0.8 mm
    Service limit . . . .   3.60 mm
Plain plate maximum warpage
    Standard . . . .   0.15 mm
    Service limit . . . .   0.20 mm
Master cylinder bore diameter . . . .   14.0 mm
Release cylinder bore diameter . . . .   33.6 mm

Lubrication system

Oil pressure @ 5000 rpm . . . .   40 psi (2.76 Bars) at 80°C
Oil pump rotor tip-to-outer rotor clearance
    Standard . . . .   0.15 mm
    Service limit . . . .   0.20 mm
Oil pump outer rotor-to-body clearance
    Standard . . . .   0.15 to 0.22 mm
    Service limit . . . .   0.35 mm
Oil pump rotor endfloat
    Standard . . . .   0.02 to 0.07 mm
    Service limit . . . .   0.10 mm

Cylinder liners

Cylinder bore ID
    Bore Nos. 1 and 3 (3 cylinder), Nos. 1, 3 and 4 (4 cylinder) . . . .   76.03 to 76.05 mm
    Bore No. 2 . . . .   76.04 to 76.05 mm
Service limit . . . .   76.1 mm

Pistons

Piston OD (measured 5 mm up from skirt, at 90° to piston pin axis)
    Bore Nos. 1 and 3 (3 cylinder), Nos. 1, 3 and 4 (4 cylinder) . . . .   75.96 to 75.98 mm
    Bore No. 2 . . . .   75.97 to 75.98 mm
Piston pin bore diameter in piston . . . .   19.002 to 19.008 mm
Piston pin diameter . . . .   18.995 to 19.000 mm
Connecting rod small-end diameter . . . .   19.016 to 19.034 mm

Piston rings

Ring-to-groove clearance (top and second rings) . . . .   0.02 to 0.06 mm

Piston rings (continued)

Groove width in piston
  Top and second rings . . . . 1.01 to 1.03 mm
  Oil control ring . . . . 2.01 to 2.03 mm
End gap (installed)
  Top ring . . . . 0.20 to 0.41 mm
  Second ring . . . . 0.35 to 0.56 mm
  Oil control ring side rails . . . . 0.29 to 0.85 mm

Connecting rods and bearings

Connecting rod side clearance . . . . 0.5 mm
Connecting rod big-end bearing oil clearance
  Standard . . . . 0.036 to 0.066 mm
  Service limit . . . . 0.1 mm
Connecting rod big-end journal diameter (Trident, Sprint,
  Thunderbird, Tiger) . . . . 40,946 to 40,960 mm
Connecting rod big-end journal diameter (Trophy, Daytona,
  Speed Triple) . . . . 40.951 to 40.965 mm

Crankshaft and main bearings

Main bearing oil clearance
  Standard . . . . 0.020 to 0.044 mm
  Service limit . . . . 0.1 mm
Main bearing journal diameter (Trident, Sprint, Thunderbird, Tiger) . . . . 37.960 to 37.976 mm
Main bearing journal diameter (Trophy, Daytona, Speed Triple) . . . . . . 37.965 to 37.981 mm

Transmission

Gear ratios (No. of teeth)
  First gear . . . . 2.733 to 1 (41/15T)
  Second gear . . . . 1.947 to 1 (37/19T)
  Third gear . . . . 1.545 to 1 (34/22T)
  Fourth gear . . . . 1.291 to 1 (31/24T)
  Fifth gear . . . . 1.154 to 1 (30/26T)
  Sixth gear (except Speed Triple and Thunderbird) . . . . 1.074 to 1 (29/27T)
Gearshift fork end width
  Standard . . . . 5.8 to 5.9 mm
  Service limit . . . . 5.7 mm
Gearshift fork groove width in gears
  Standard . . . . 6.0 to 6.1 mm
  Service limit . . . . 6.25 mm
Gearshift fork-to-groove clearance . . . . 0.55 mm maximum

Torque settings

Engine mounting bolts . . . . 95 Nm
Swingarm pivot shaft bolt . . . . 85 Nm
Sidestand bracket-to-frame bolt (all models except Thunderbird) . . . . . 22 Nm
Valve cover bolts . . . . 10 Nm
Cylinder head bolts
  Stage 1 . . . . 20 Nm
  Stage 2 (engines with alternator/starter clutch access cover) . . . . . . 35 Nm
  Stage 2 (engines without alternator/starter clutch access cover) . . . 27 Nm
  Stage 3 . . . . Angle-tighten 90°
Cylinder head-to-cylinder block screws . . . . 12 Nm
External oil pipe banjo union bolts
  Upper bolt . . . . 20 Nm
  Lower bolt . . . . 25 Nm
Camshaft sprocket bolts . . . . 15 Nm
Camshaft cap bolts . . . . 10 Nm
Cam chain upper guide screws . . . . 12 Nm
Cam chain tensioner body bolts . . . . 9 Nm
Cam chain tensioner body end bolt . . . . 23 Nm
Cam chain tensioner blade pivot bolt . . . . 18 Nm
Ignition pick-up coil screws . . . . 10 Nm
Ignition rotor bolt . . . . 27 Nm
Crankshaft end cover bolts . . . . 9 Nm
Clutch cover bolts . . . . 9 Nm
Clutch centre nut . . . . 105 Nm
Clutch pressure plate bolts . . . . 10 Nm

2

Torque settings (continued)

Clutch release cylinder bolts	9 Nm
Clutch hose banjo union bolts	25 Nm
Clutch master cylinder clamp bolts	15 Nm
Engine output sprocket nut	132 Nm
Crankcase 6 mm bolts (see text)	12 Nm
Crankcase 8 mm bolts (see text)	28 Nm
Connecting rod nuts	
Stage 1	14 Nm
Stage 2	32 Nm
Stage 3	36 Nm
Crankshaft breather disc screws	
(later 4 cylinder engines and Thunderbird)	8 Nm
Neutral switch	14 Nm
Balancer retaining plate bolts (3 cylinder engines)	9 Nm
Balancer clamp retaining screws (4 cylinder engines)	12 Nm
Balancer shaft pinch bolts (4 cylinder engines)	11 Nm
Alternator driveshaft shock absorber housing and drive gear bolts	25 Nm
Alternator driveshaft/starter clutch access cover bolts (early	
models only)	9 Nm
Starter clutch screws	11 Nm
Starter idler gear shaft retaining bolt	12 Nm
Gearshift drum ball bearing retaining screw	9 Nm
Gearshift detent arm nuts	9 Nm
Gearshift detent cam screw	9 Nm
Gearshift rod retaining plate screw	9 Nm
Gearshift shaft quadrant stopper bolt	28 Nm
Main oil gallery plug	25 Nm
Oil pump mounting screws	12 Nm
Oil pump intermediate gear screw	9 Nm
Oil pressure relief valve	15 Nm
Oil pressure switch	8 Nm
Sump bolts	12 Nm
Oil pipe (internal) banjo bolts	8 Nm
Oil strainer screws	11 Nm
Oil cooler pipe banjo union bolts	25 Nm

1 General information

The engine/transmission is of water-cooled three- or four-cylinder in-line design, fitted transversely across the frame. The twelve (3 cylinder) or sixteen (4 cylinder) valves are operated by double overhead camshafts, chain driven off the right end of the crankshaft. The pistons run in wet liners, surrounded by a water jacket.

The engine/transmission is constructed in aluminium alloy with the crankcase being divided horizontally. The crankcase incorporates a wet sump, pressure fed lubrication system, and houses a gear driven oil pump. An external oil feed pipe supplies oil to the cylinder head and cam components. A single balancer shaft is fitted on 3 cylinder models and is driven directly off a gear on the crankshaft left end. Two balancer shafts are located in the lower crankcase of 4 cylinder engines; drive is taken off the clutch outer drum.

The clutch is of the wet multi-plate type and is gear driven off the crankshaft. An auxiliary gear on the back of the clutch drives the oil pump (and thence the water pump) and the alternator driveshaft.

The transmission is of the six-speed constant mesh type, five-speed on the Speed Triple and Thunderbird. Final drive to the rear wheel is by chain and sprockets.

2 Operations possible with the engine in the frame

The components and assemblies listed below can be removed without having to remove the engine/transmission assembly from the frame. If however, a number of areas require attention at the same time, removal of the engine is recommended.

Valve cover
Cam chain tensioner
Camshafts and tappets
Cam chain and tensioner/guide blades
Cylinder head
Cylinder liners and pistons
Starter motor
Alternator
Water pump
Clutch
Gearshift detent cam and arms
Oil cooler (where fitted)
Sump and pressure relief valve
Alternator/starter clutch drive - early models
Balancer shaft (3 cylinder)
Balancer shafts (4 cylinder) - not advised due to poor access

3 Operations requiring engine removal

It is necessary to remove the engine/transmission assembly from the frame and separate the crankcase halves to gain access to the following components.

Transmission shafts
Crankshaft and bearings
Connecting rod assemblies and bearings
Oil pump
Gearshift mechanism (except detent cam and arms)
Balancer shafts (4 cylinder)
Alternator/starter clutch drive - later models

4 Major engine repair - general note

1 It is not always easy to determine when or if an engine should be completely overhauled, as a number of factors must be considered.

2 High mileage is not necessarily an indication that an overhaul is needed, while low mileage, on the other hand, does not preclude the need for an overhaul. Frequency of servicing is probably the single most important consideration. An engine that has regular and frequent oil and filter changes, as well as other required maintenance, will most likely give many miles of reliable service. Conversely, a neglected engine, or one which has not been run in properly, may require an overhaul very early in its life.

3 Exhaust smoke and excessive oil consumption are both indications that piston rings and/or valve guides are in need of attention, although make sure that the fault is not due to oil leakage.

4 If the engine is making obvious knocking or rumbling noises, the connecting rod and/or main bearings are probably at fault.

5 Loss of power, rough running, excessive valve train noise and high fuel consumption rates may also point to the need for an overhaul, especially if they are all present at the same time. If a complete tune-up does not remedy the situation, major mechanical work is the only solution.

6 An engine overhaul generally involves restoring the internal parts to the specifications of a new engine. The piston rings and main and connecting rod bearings are usually replaced during a major overhaul. Generally the valve seats are reground, since they are usually in less than perfect condition at this point. The end result should be a like new engine that will give as many trouble-free miles as the original.

7 Before beginning the engine overhaul, read through the related procedures to familiarise yourself with the scope and requirements of the job. Overhauling an engine is not all that difficult, but it is time consuming. Plan on the motorcycle being tied up for a minimum of two weeks. Check on the availability of parts and make sure that any necessary special tools, equipment and supplies are obtained in advance.

8 Most work can be done with typical workshop hand tools, although a number of precision measuring tools are required for inspecting parts to determine if they must be replaced. Often a dealer will handle the inspection of parts and offer advice concerning reconditioning and replacement. As a general rule, time is the primary cost of an overhaul so it does not pay to install worn or substandard parts.

9 As a final note, to ensure maximum life and minimum trouble from a rebuilt engine, everything must be assembled with care in a spotlessly clean environment.

5 Engine - removal and installation

Note: *Engine removal and installation should be carried out with the aid of at least one assistant; injury or damage could occur if the engine falls or is dropped. An hydraulic floor-type jack should be used to support and lower the engine to the floor if possible.*

Removal

1 Sit the bike on its centre stand. If no centre stand is fitted, use a motorcycle stand to support the bike securely in an upright position. Work will be made easier by raising the machine to a suitable working height on a hydraulic ramp or a suitable platform.

2 If the engine is dirty, particularly around its mountings, wash it thoroughly before starting any major dismantling work. This will make work much easier and rule out the possibility of caked on lumps of dirt falling into some vital component.

3 Remove the seat and disconnect the battery negative lead.

4 Remove the fairing on Trophy, Daytona, Sprint and Tiger models (see Chapter 8). Where the fairing bolts to a mounting bracket on the cylinder head, it is advisable to detach the bracket from the head to prevent it becoming bent or damaged **(see illustration)**. On Tiger models, also remove the sump guard and free the rear shock absorber reservoir from its bracket on the left of the cylinder head (see Chapter 8).

5 Remove the fuel tank (see Chapter 4).

6 Drain the engine oil and coolant (see Chapter 1).

5.4 Unbolt fairing brackets from the cylinder head

7 Remove the radiator (see Chapter 3).

8 On models with an oil cooler, disconnect the hoses from the sump and remove the oil cooler and its sub-frame (see Section 21).

9 On Thunderbird models, disconnect the horn wires and remove it from the cylinder head **(see illustration)**. Also on Thunderbirds, mark a line across the gearshift shaft end and gear pedal as an aid to installation, then remove the pinch bolt and withdraw the gear pedal **(see illustration)**. Unscrew the sidestand switch from the stand bracket, then remove the three bolts to free the stand bracket from the engine.

10 Detach the link rod from the gearshift shaft lever by slackening its locknuts and rotating the rod via its knurled centre section so that it unscrews from lever and pedal at the same time **(see illustration)**. On models with a dog-leg link rod, slacken off the locknut and unscrew the threaded sleeve to separate the link rod from the shaft lever. Disconnect the sidestand switch wiring connector, then remove the sidestand bracket bolt and the engine left rear lower bolt **(see illustrations)**. Remove the sidestand with its bracket. Mark a line across the gearshift shaft end and shaft lever as an aid to installation, then remove the pinch bolt and withdraw the shaft lever **(see illustration)**.

11 Remove the exhaust system (Chapter 4).

12 Remove the airbox and carburettors (see Chapter 4). Plug the intake manifold joints with clean rags to prevent engine contamination.

13 Remove the alternator and starter motor (see Chapter 9).

14 Pull the spark plug caps off the spark

5.9a Remove horn from cylinder head on Thunderbird models

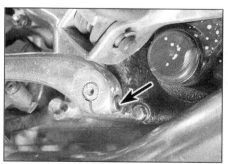

5.9b Remove the pinch bolt (arrowed) and pull the gear pedal off its shaft (Thunderbird model)

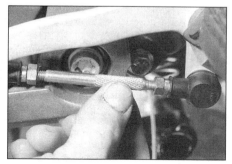

5.10a Rotate the link rod via its knurled section to unscrew it from the shaft lever and pedal

5.10b Remove the side stand bracket retaining bolt (all models except Thunderbird) . . .

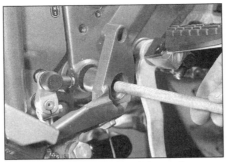

5.10c . . . then remove left rear lower mounting bolt to free the sidestand bracket

5.10d Remove the pinch bolt and pull the lever off the gearshift shaft

5.15 Remove its two bolts and free the water pump hose cover (later models)

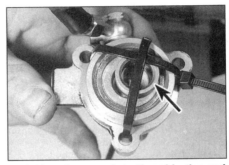

5.16 Note the use of plastic cable-ties and spacer (arrowed) to retain the piston in the clutch release cylinder

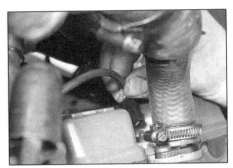

5.19 Pull the wire off the coolant temperature sender on the cylinder head

plugs. On all models except the Thunderbird, remove the two plastic valve cover cowls to access the plug caps.

15 Unbolt the water pump hose cover from the left side of the engine (later models only) **(see illustration)**. Slacken the clamp at the bottom of the hose and the two bolts retaining the union at the top of hose and withdraw it from the engine.

16 Remove the three clutch release cylinder bolts and lift off the release cylinder. Use plastic cable-ties to prevent the piston creeping out of the release cylinder body and loop the hose over the frame so it is clear of the engine **(see illustration)**.

17 Remove the sprocket cover and detach the final drive chain and sprocket from the engine (see Chapter 6).

18 Unhook one end of the rear brake pedal return spring. Extract the R-pin from the rear brake pedal-to-master cylinder pushrod clevis. Recover the washer and withdraw the clevis pin. Separate the pushrod from the pedal, allowing the pedal to drop away from the engine's lower rear mounting bolt.

19 Disconnect the wire from the temperature sender on the cylinder head **(see illustration)**.

20 Disconnect the wires from the alternator and side stand switch at their block connectors **(see illustrations)**. It was found that the water pump had to be removed because the side stand connector would not pass down behind the pump (see Chapter 3 for water pump removal details).

21 Disconnect the wires from the ignition

pick-up coil at the block connector **(see illustration)**. Similarly, disconnect the wire connector which contains the wires from the neutral and oil pressure switch sub-harness. If

desired, the sub-harness can be freed by disconnecting the wire from the neutral switch **(see illustration 5.29)** and oil pressure switch **(see illustration)**.

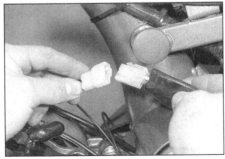

5.20a Trace the alternator wiring to the 2-pin connector and disconnect it

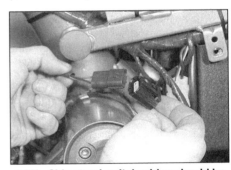

5.20b Side stand switch wiring should be disconnected at the 3-pin connector

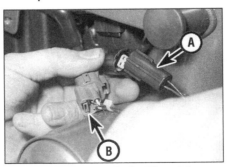

5.21a Disconnect the ignition pick-up coil (A) and neutral/oil pressure switch (B)

5.21b Oil pressure switch wire can also be disconnected at the switch

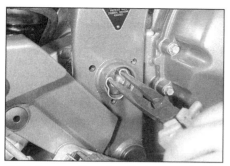

5.22 Remove the wire clip from each side of the swingarm

5.23 Support the engine on a jack prior to removing its mounting bolts

22 Remove the plug from the frame for access to the engine's rear lower mounting bolt. Remove the plug (early models) or end plate (later models) for access to the swingarm pivot. Pry out the wire clips on both sides and slacken the swingarm pivot bolt on the right side of the frame **(see illustration)**.
23 At this point, position an hydraulic jack under the engine with a block of wood between the jack head and sump **(see illustration)**. Take the weight of the engine on the jack. Also place a block of wood under the rear wheel to prevent it dropping when the engine mountings are withdrawn.
24 Slacken the engine mounting bolt nuts and withdraw the mounting bolts from all three locations on each side of the engine **(see illustrations)**. On all models except the Thunderbird, the side stand bracket bolt must be removed before the engine left rear lower bolt can be withdrawn. Retrieve all washers

from the mountings and slip them back on the bolts for safekeeping. Early models may have a spacer fitted between each linkage carrier and rear upper mounting bolt nut.
25 Have an assistant steady the engine as it is lowered on the jack until it is clear of the frame lugs, then move it to one side. Lift the engine off the jack and on to the work surface.

 Warning: The engine is heavy and may cause injury if it falls.

Installation

26 With the aid of an assistant place the engine on top of the jack and block of wood and carefully raise it into position in the frame. Check the alignment of the linkage carriers with the frame lugs and ensure that the rear wheel is supported.
27 Triumph advise the use of **new** engine

mounting bolts. Install the washers on the mounting bolts then install them in the frame. Install any spacers previously fitted and the mounting bolt nuts. Don't forget to install the radiator mounting brackets on the front mountings. Counterhold the nuts and tighten each mounting bolt to the specified torque setting.
28 Tighten the swingarm pivot bolt to the specified torque setting and install the wire clips. Install the end plate or plug (as applicable) over the swingarm pivot. Install the plug in the engine's rear lower bolt location in the frame.
29 The remainder of the installation procedure is a direct reversal of the removal sequence, noting the following points.
 a) *Tighten all nuts and bolts to the specified torque settings (where given).*
 b) *Align the previously made mark on the gearshift lever (or pedal) with that on the gearshift shaft end. Where a linkage rod is fitted adjust it to a comfortable riding position and secure with the locknuts.*
 c) *Make sure all wiring is correctly routed. In particular, check that the oil pressure switch wire does not become trapped between the crankcase and frame, and remember to route the neutral and side stand switch wiring behind the water pump (see illustration).*
 d) *Adjust the drive chain as described in Chapter 1.*
 e) *Fill the engine oil and cooling systems as described in Chapter 1.*

5.24a The engine rear upper mounting is formed by a bolt . . .

5.24b . . . and nut (arrowed) on each side of the crankcase lugs

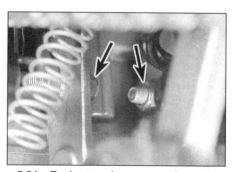

5.24c Engine rear lower mounting nuts (arrowed) are inside the linkage carriers

5.24d Right rear lower mounting bolt is accessed after removal of plastic plug

5.24e Remove engine-to-frame mounting bolt on the right . . .

5.24f . . . and left side

5.29 Side stand and neutral switch wiring must be installed before the water pump

6 Engine disassembly and reassembly - general information

Note: *Refer to the "Maintenance techniques, tools and working facilities" in the Reference section of this manual for further information.*

Disassembly

1 Before disassembling the engine, the external surfaces of the unit should be thoroughly cleaned and degreased. This will prevent contamination of the engine internals, and will also make working a lot easier and cleaner. A high flash-point solvent, such as paraffin can be used, or better still, a proprietary engine degreaser. Use old paintbrushes and toothbrushes to work the solvent into the various recesses of the engine casings. Take care to exclude solvent or water from the electrical components and intake and exhaust ports.

 Warning: The use of petrol as a cleaning agent should be avoided due to the risk of fire.

2 When clean and dry, arrange the unit on the workbench, leaving suitable clear area for working. Gather a selection of small containers and plastic bags so that parts can be grouped together in an easily identifiable manner. Some paper and a pen should be on hand to permit notes to be made and labels attached where necessary. A supply of clean rag is also required.
3 Before commencing work, read through the appropriate section so that some idea of the necessary procedure can be gained. When removing various engine components it should be noted that great force is seldom required, unless specified. In many cases, a component's reluctance to be removed is indicative of an incorrect approach or removal method. If in any doubt, re-check with the text.
4 When disassembling the engine, keep "mated" parts together (including gears, liners, pistons, valves, etc. that have been in contact with each other during engine operation). These "mated" parts must be reused or replaced as an assembly.
5 Engine/transmission disassembly should

be done in the following general order with reference to the appropriate Sections.
Remove the camshafts
Remove the cam chain/tensioner blade
Remove the cylinder head and cam chain guide blade
Remove the cylinder liners and pistons
Remove the clutch
Remove the alternator (see Chapter 9)
Remove the starter motor (see Chapter 9)
Remove the water pump (see Chapter 3)
Remove the sump
Remove the balancer(s)
Separate the crankcase halves
Remove the crankshaft/connecting rods
Remove the transmission shafts/gears
Remove the gearshift components
Remove the oil pump
Remove the alternator/starter drive

Reassembly

6 Reassembly is accomplished by reversing the general disassembly sequence.

7 Valve cover - removal and installation

Note: *The valve cover can be removed with the engine in the frame. If the engine has been removed, ignore the steps which do not apply.*

Removal

1 Remove the seat and disconnect the battery negative lead.
2 Remove the fuel tank (see Chapter 4).

7.5 Valve cover is retained by eight bolts on the 3 cylinder engine

7.9a Apply sealant to the cylinder head surface . . .

3 Remove the valve cover cowls on all models except the Thunderbird; they are secured by two screws.
4 Pull the plug caps off the spark plugs and remove the ignition HT coils (see Chapter 5).
5 Remove the eight (3 cylinder) or ten (4 cylinder) bolts, together with their seals, to free the valve cover from the cylinder head **(see illustration)**.
6 Withdraw the valve cover from the right side of the frame and retrieve the main cover seal and the two (3 cylinder) or three (4 cylinder) separate plug hole seals.
7 Examine the seals for signs of damage or deterioration and replace them if necessary. Also check the cover bolt seals for signs of damage and replace if necessary.

Installation

8 Apply silicone sealant to the plug hole seals and stick them to the valve cover. Insert the main seal into the cover groove, using silicone sealant, particularly at the ends, to hold it in place **(see illustration)**.
9 Smear silicone sealant on the cylinder head gasket face in the camshaft end areas **(see illustrations)**.
10 Install the valve cover on the cylinder head, making sure the seals stay in place **(see illustration)**. Install the valve cover bolt seals and bolts; the two longer bolts are located at the cam chain end **(see illustration)**. Tighten the bolts evenly in a criss-cross pattern, starting at the centre and working outwards; tighten to the specified torque **(see illustration)**.
11 Install the ignition HT coils and plug caps (see Chapter 5).

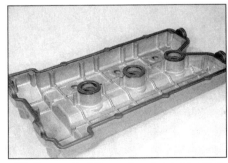

7.8 Ensure that the main valve cover seal and plug hole seals are stuck in place

7.9b . . . at each of the four corners

7.10a Ensure that all seals remain in place as the valve cover is installed

7.10b Install the bolt seals and the valve cover bolts . . .

7.10c . . . tightening them evenly to the specified torque setting

12 Install the valve cover cowls and secure with the two screws (where applicable).
13 Install the fuel tank (see Chapter 4). Refit the battery negative lead and install the seat.

8 Cam chain tensioner - removal, inspection and installation

Removal

1 Remove the valve cover (see Section 7).
2 Remove the screws to free the crankshaft right end cover; be prepared for oil loss as the cover is removed. Discard the cover gasket, a new one must be used on installation. Using a ring spanner on the engine turning hexagon, rotate the crankshaft clockwise so that the T 1 mark (3 cylinder) or T 1.4 mark (4 cylinder) on the ignition rotor is aligned with the centre of the pick-up coil **(see illustrations 9.1a and 9.1b)**. In this position, the arrow marks on the cam sprockets should face inwards towards each other **(see illustration 9.1c)**.
3 When the tensioner is withdrawn from the cylinder block, the cam chain will be untensioned, and may jump a tooth on the intake cam sprocket. To prevent this, Triumph recommend that a wood wedge be inserted between the tensioner blade and the crankcase (via the crankshaft end cover aperture) to hold the tensioner blade in firm contact with the cam chain whilst the tensioner is removed.
4 Undo the large end bolt from the tensioner

and withdraw the spring, noting that it will be under tension **(see illustration)**.
5 Remove the two bolts and withdraw the tensioner. Recover its gasket.

Inspection

6 Examine the tensioner components for signs of wear or damage. Check that the plunger moves smoothly in the tensioner body. **Note:** *Very early Trophy and Trident models had a cap over the tensioner plunger's tip. This was not fitted to all subsequent models, and Triumph advise that it be discarded where found on early machines.*
7 If the spring has sagged, the spring will not be able to take up chain play effectively. Measure the free length of the spring and compare to the specification. If the spring length has reduced significantly, the tensioner must be replaced.

8.4 Be careful unscrewing the tensioner end cap - it will be under spring tension

Installation

Method A

8 Lift the catch on the tensioner body and push the plunger inwards **(see illustration)**. Release the catch to lock the tensioner in the retracted position **(see illustration)**.
9 Install the spring in the tensioner. Fit a new sealing washer to the end bolt and install the end bolt in the end of the spring **(see illustration)**. Hold the tensioner body against the palm of your hand and compress the spring into the body so that the brass threaded ring on the end bolt contacts the body surface; turn the end bolt anti-clockwise to thread the brass ring into the end of the body **(see illustration)**. This will hold the spring compressed whilst the tensioner is installed in the engine. **Note:** *It may take several attempts to achieve this.*

8.8a Hold back the catch and press the plunger inwards . . .

8.8b . . . so that it is fully retracted

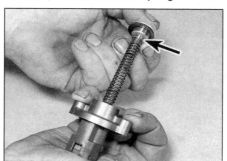

8.9a Hold the tensioner body as shown and compress the spring until the brass ring (arrowed) can be screwed into the body - note that it has a left-hand thread

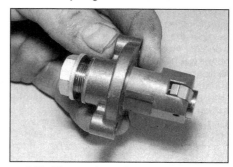

8.9b The tensioner is now held in the retracted position and ready for installation

2

8.10a Install the tensioner on the engine using a new gasket . . .

8.10b . . . and retain with the two bolts

9.2a Using a ring spanner on the hexagon, rotate the crankshaft clockwise . . .

10 Slip a new gasket over the tensioner body and install the tensioner in the cylinder block **(see illustration)**. Secure it with the two bolts, tightening them to the specified torque setting **(see illustration)**.

11 Remove the wood wedge from the tensioner blade. Screw the tensioner end bolt into the tensioner body; the tensioner ratchet will be heard to release and the plunger shoot out into contact with the tensioner blade as the brass ring releases the spring. Tighten the end bolt to the specified torque setting.

12 Check that the valve timing marks are correct (see Step 2). Rotate the engine several times and recheck the timing marks - if the cam chain has jumped whilst the tensioner was removed, reposition it as described in Section 9. Install the valve cover (see Section 7).

13 Install the crankshaft right end cover using a new gasket and tighten its bolts to the specified torque setting.

14 Check the engine oil level and top-up if necessary (see Chapter 1).

Method B

15 Lift the catch on the tensioner body and push the plunger fully inwards **(see illustration 8.8a)**. Release the catch to lock the plunger in the retracted position **(see illustration 8.8b)**.

16 Slip a new gasket over the tensioner body and install the tensioner on the cylinder block. Secure it with the two bolts, tightening them to the specified torque setting.

17 Remove the wood wedge from the tensioner blade. Using a slim rod inserted into the tensioner body, use finger pressure only to push the tensioner plunger into contact with the tensioner blade; the ratchet and catch will hold it in this position. Fit a new sealing washer to the end bolt and install the spring and end bolt into the tensioner body. Tighten the end bolt to the specified torque setting.

18 Check that the valve timing marks are correct (see Step 2). Rotate the engine several times and recheck the timing marks - if the cam chain has jumped whilst the tensioner was removed, reposition it as described in Section 9. Install the valve cover (see Section 7).

19 Install the crankshaft right end cover using

a new gasket and tighten its bolts to the specified torque setting.

20 Check the engine oil level and top-up if necessary (see Chapter 1).

9 Camshafts and tappets - removal, inspection and installation

Note: *This procedure can be carried out with the engine in the frame.*

Removal

1 Remove the valve cover (see Section 7).

2 Remove its retaining screws to free the crankshaft right end cover; be prepared for oil loss as the cover is removed. Discard the cover gasket, a new one must be used on installation. Using a ring spanner on the

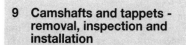

9.2b . . . until cylinder No. 1 is at TDC (T 1 mark on ignition rotor aligned with centre of pick-up coil) - 3 cylinder engine shown

9.4 Cam chain upper guide is retained by four screws (arrowed)

engine turning hexagon, rotate the crankshaft so that the T 1 mark (3 cylinder) or T 1.4 mark (4 cylinder) on the ignition rotor is aligned with the centre of the pick-up coil **(see illustrations)**. In this position, the arrow marks on the cam sprockets should face inwards towards each other **(see illustration)**.

3 Remove the cam chain tensioner (see Section 8).

4 Remove its four screws and lift off the cam chain upper guide **(see illustration)**.

5 Before disturbing the camshaft caps, check for identification markings scribed on their top surfaces. These markings ensure that the caps can be matched up to their original journals on installation. The caps are numbered 1 to 6 on 3 cylinder engines, and 1 to 8 on 4 cylinder engines; the two outrigger caps on the cam chain end are denoted A and B **(see illustrations)**.

9.2c The arrow markings on the camshaft sprockets should face each other and lie parallel with the gasket surface

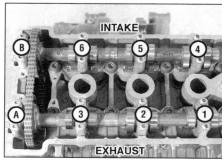

9.5a Camshaft cap markings - 3 cylinder engine

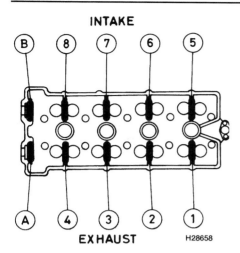

**9.5b Camshaft cap markings -
4 cylinder engine**

6 Working on one camshaft at a time, slacken all eight (3 cylinder) or ten (4 cylinder) cap bolts evenly in a criss-cross sequence, then remove the caps. Retrieve the dowels on each cap if they are loose.

7 Slip the cam chain off the sprocket and withdraw the camshaft.

8 Repeat the procedure for the other camshaft.

9 Obtain a container which is divided into twelve (3 cylinder) or sixteen (4 cylinder) compartments, and label each compartment with the number of its corresponding valve in the cylinder head. Pick each shim and tappet out of the cylinder head and store it in the corresponding compartment in the container.

Inspection

Note: *Before replacing the camshafts or the cylinder head and camshaft caps because of damage, check with local machine shops specialising in motorcycle engineering work. In the case of the camshafts, it may be possible for cam lobes to be welded, reground and hardened, at a cost far lower than that of a new camshaft. If the bearing surfaces in the cylinder head are damaged, it may be possible for them to be bored out to accept bearing inserts. Due to the cost of a new cylinder head, it is recommended that all options are explored.*

10 Inspect the cam bearing surfaces of the head and the caps. Look for score marks, deep scratches and evidence of spalling (a pitted appearance). Check the camshaft lobes for heat discoloration (blue appearance), score marks, chipped areas, flat spots and spalling **(see illustration)**.

11 Camshaft runout can be checked by supporting each end of the camshaft on V-blocks, and measuring any runout using a dial gauge. If the runout exceeds the specified limit the camshaft must be replaced.

12 The camshaft bearing oil clearance should then be checked using a product known as Plastigauge.

13 Clean the camshafts, the bearing surfaces

**9.10 Check the cam lobes for wear -
damage like this requires attention**

in the cylinder head and the caps with a clean, lint-free cloth, then lay the camshafts in place in the cylinder head. The intake camshaft can be identified by its grooved centre section and the exhaust by its plain section **(see illustration)**.

14 Cut strips of Plastigauge and lay one piece on each bearing journal, parallel with the camshaft centreline. Make sure the camshaft cap dowels are installed and fit the caps in their proper positions **(see illustration 9.5a or b)**. Ensuring that the camshafts are not rotated at all, tighten all eight (3 cylinder) or ten (4 cylinder) cap bolts evenly, a little at a time, in a criss-cross sequence, until the specified torque setting is reached. Repeat for the other camshaft.

15 Now unscrew the bolts evenly, a little at a time, in a criss-cross sequence and carefully lift off the caps, again making sure the camshaft is not rotated. Repeat on the other camshaft.

16 To determine the oil clearance, compare the crushed Plastigauge (at its widest point) on each journal to the scale printed on the Plastigauge container.

17 Compare the results to this Chapter's Specifications. If the oil clearance is greater than specified, the camshaft and/or cylinder head and camshaft cap bearing surfaces are worn. Remove all traces of Plastigauge from the components when the check is complete. **Note:** *You can measure the camshaft journal diameter and the head/cap bearing inside diameter to determine which component is worn.*

**9.20a Lubricate each tappet with engine
oil and install in the cylinder head**

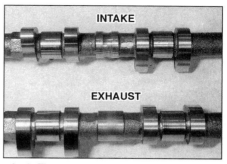

**9.13 The camshafts can be identified by
their grooved (intake) or plain (exhaust)
centre section**

18 Check the sprockets for wear, cracks and other damage, replacing them if necessary. If the sprockets are worn, the cam chain is also worn, and also the sprocket on the crankshaft. If wear this severe is apparent, the cam chain and all sprockets should be replaced (see Section 10).

19 The same design sprocket is used for each camshaft, but different hole positions are provided for fitting to the intake or exhaust camshaft. When fitted to the intake camshaft the holes next to the IN marking should be used, and those next to the EX marking for the exhaust camshaft. The sprocket bolts must have a drop of non-permanent thread locking compound applied to their threads and be tightened to the specified torque setting.

Installation

20 Lubricate each tappet with engine oil and install with its shim in the cylinder head **(see illustrations)**. **Note:** *It is most important that the tappets and shims are returned to their original valves otherwise the valve clearances will be inaccurate.*

21 Position the crankshaft as described in Step 2.

22 Apply a smear of clean engine oil to the cylinder head camshaft bearing surfaces **(see illustration)**.

23 Hook the cam chain up from its tunnel so that it is engaged around the lower sprocket teeth on the crankshaft. Check that the crankshaft is positioned as described in Step 2. Keeping the front run of the chain taut, lay the exhaust camshaft in position so that

**9.20b Insert the corresponding shim in the
top of the tappet**

2

9.22 Apply engine oil to the camshaft bearing surfaces in the cylinder head

9.23 Keeping the front run of the chain taut, install the exhaust camshaft in the cylinder head . . .

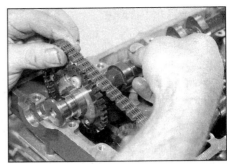

9.24 . . . then install the intake camshaft

9.25a Apply engine oil to the camshaft journals

9.25b Check that the two dowels are in place . . .

9.25c . . . and install the camshaft caps

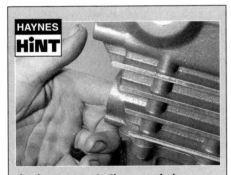

HAYNES HiNT

Apply pressure to the cam chain tensioner blade by pressing on it with a finger through the tensioner hole to prevent the chain jumping a tooth on the intake sprocket

9.27 Install the cam chain upper guide on the cylinder head

9.30 Use a new gasket on the crankshaft right cover

the arrow mark on its sprocket points rearwards, then engage the chain on the sprocket teeth **(see illustration)**.

24 Slip the intake camshaft through the cam chain so that the arrow mark on its sprocket points forwards **(see illustration)**. Engage the chain fully on the sprocket teeth. Before proceeding, check that everything aligns as described in Step 2. If it doesn't, the valve timing is inaccurate, and the valve will contact the pistons when the engine is turned over.

25 Oil the camshaft journals **(see illustration)**. Ensure that the camshaft cap dowels are installed **(see illustration)** and fit the caps in their proper positions **(see illustration 9.5a or b)**. Oil the threads of the cap bolts and

tighten all eight (3 cylinder) or ten (4 cylinder) cap bolts evenly, a little at a time, in a criss-cross sequence, until the specified torque setting is reached **(see illustration)**. Repeat for the other camshaft. **Note:** *Be careful that the cam chain doesn't jump a tooth as the intake camshaft is tightened down* **(see Haynes Hint)**.

26 With all caps tightened down, check that the valve timing marks still align (see Step 2). If the chain has jumped a tooth, the camshafts must be released and the chain repositioned. Check that each camshaft is not pinched by turning it a few degrees in each direction with a spanner on the camshafts' cast hexagon.

27 Install the cam chain upper guide and tighten its screws to the specified torque setting **(see illustration)**.

28 Install the cam chain tensioner (Section 8).

29 If any of the valve components have been replaced, check the valve clearances (see Chapter 1).

30 Install the crankshaft right end cover using a new gasket and tighten its bolts to the specified torque setting **(see illustration)**.

31 Install the valve cover (see Section 7).

32 Check the engine oil level and top-up if necessary (see Chapter 1).

10 Cam chain and tensioner/guide blades - removal and installation

Note: *The cam chain and blades can be removed with the engine in the frame.*

Cam chain tensioner blade (rear)

Removal

1 Remove the intake camshaft as described in Section 9.

2 Undo the tensioner blade pivot bolt from

10.2a Remove the cam chain tensioner blade pivot bolt . . .

the crankcase right cover aperture **(see illustration)**. Retrieve the washer, collar and bolt and lift the blade out of the cam chain tunnel **(see illustration)**.

3 Check the tensioner blade for cracking and other damage, replacing it if necessary.

Installation

4 Install the tensioner blade down through the chain tunnel. Install the collar on the pivot bolt with its shoulder against the bolt flange, slip the bolt through the blade, then install the washer and thread the bolt into the crankcase. Tighten the bolt to the specified torque setting.

5 Install the intake camshaft (see Section 9).

Cam chain guide blade (front)

6 The blade can only be accessed once the cylinder head has been removed. Refer to Section 11 for details.

Cam chain

Removal

7 Remove the camshafts (see Section 9).

8 Remove the tensioner blade pivot bolt and withdraw it from the engine **(see illustration 10.2a)**.

9 Counterhold the engine turning hexagon with a ring spanner and unscrew the Allen bolt from the end of the crankshaft **(see illustration)**. Withdraw the hexagon and ignition rotor from the crankshaft **(see illustrations)**.

10 Slip the chain off the crankshaft sprocket and lift it out of the head **(see illustrations)**.

11 The crankshaft sprocket can be slipped off the crankshaft; it is located by a square-section key.

10.9c . . . and the ignition rotor

10.2b . . . and lift the blade out of the cylinder head

Inspection

12 Check the cam chain for binding and obvious damage and replace it if necessary. Inspect the sprocket for chipped or missing teeth. If the chain and sprocket show signs of extensive wear replace them as a set (including the camshaft sprockets).

Installation

13 Installation is a reverse of the removal procedure, noting the following:

 a) Locate the sprocket, ignition rotor and hexagon on the crankshaft with the square-section key.

 b) Install the ignition rotor with its marked side facing outwards.

 c) Apply a drop of non-permanent thread locking compound to the Allen bolt threads and tighten it to the specified torque setting.

10.9a Counterhold the engine turning hexagon with a ring spanner and undo the bolt from the end of the crankshaft

10.10a Loop the cam chain off the crankshaft sprocket . . .

11 Cylinder head - removal and installation

Caution: *The engine must be completely cool before beginning this procedure or the cylinder head may become warped.*

Note: *This procedure can be performed with the engine in the frame. If the engine has already been removed, ignore the preliminary steps which don't apply. It will be necessary to support the engine under the sump during this procedure, therefore position the bike on its centre stand or, where only a side stand is fitted, support the bike using an auxiliary motorcycle stand.*

Removal

1 Remove the exhaust system as described in Chapter 4.

2 On Thunderbird models detach the two wires from the horn and remove its mounting nut to free the horn from the cylinder head.

3 On models so equipped, it is advisable to detach the fairing mounting brackets from the side of the cylinder head. If left in place they may become distorted when the cylinder head is being manoeuvred or valve service work is being carried out.

4 Remove the carburettors as described in Chapter 4.

5 Remove the valve cover (see Section 7).

6 Disconnect the wire from the coolant temperature sender unit. Drain the cooling system (see Chapter 1), then slacken its

2

10.9b Lift off the hexagon . . .

10.10b . . . and out of the cam chain tunnel

11.8a The external oil pipe is secured to the cylinder head . . .

11.8b . . . and crankcase by banjo union bolts

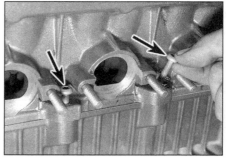

11.9a The cylinder head front edge is retained by two (3 cylinder) or three (4 cylinder) screws (arrowed)

11.9b Three screws retain the right side of the cylinder head . . .

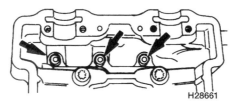

11.9c . . . although on Thunderbird models these are accessed from inside the cam chain tunnel (arrowed)

11.14 The cam chain guide blade can be removed once the cylinder head is off

clamp and pull the coolant hose off the cylinder head top surface.

7 Remove the camshafts and tappets (see Section 9).

8 Remove the two banjo bolts which retain the external oil pipe to the cylinder head and crankcase **(see illustrations)**. Withdraw the oil pipe and discard the sealing washers - new washers must be fitted on installation.

9 Remove the two (3 cylinder) or three (4 cylinder) screws from the front of the cylinder head-to-crankcase joint and the three screws from the right side **(see illustrations)**. Note that on Thunderbird models, the three side screws are hidden inside the cam chain tunnel **(see illustration)**.

10 Make sure the wood block and jack are positioned under the sump, and remove the cylinder head-to-frame bolts on each side. As they are withdrawn, take the weight of the

engine on the jack so that no additional strain is placed on the rear engine mountings.

11 Slacken the eight (3 cylinder) or ten (4 cylinder) head bolts by half a turn at a time in a **reverse** of the specified sequence **(see illustration 11.22b or 11.22c)**.

12 Tap around the joint faces of the cylinder head with a soft-faced mallet to free the head. Don't attempt to free the head by inserting a screwdriver between the head and cylinder block - you'll damage the sealing surfaces.

13 Lift the head off the block, and remove it from the engine. Remove the old gasket and the horseshoe-shaped pieces from the front of the gasket. Recover the two dowels if they are loose.

14 Lift the cam chain guide blade from the front of the cylinder block **(see illustration)**.

15 Whenever the cylinder head is disturbed the seal between the liners and crankcase will

be broken. It is essential that this procedure is not overlooked, otherwise coolant from the cylinder block water jacket will seep into the crankcase. Refer to Section 14 for liner removal and installation details.

Installation

16 Fit and seal the liners in the cylinder block (see Section 14).

17 Install the cam chain guide blade into the cylinder block. Its lower end locates in a cast recess in the cam chain tunnel and the two lugs near its upper end locate in the cutouts in the cylinder head surface **(see illustrations)**.

18 Ensure both cylinder head and block mating surfaces are clean. Fit the dowels to the block (if removed). Check that the cylinder head bolt holes in the block are clean and dry.

19 Fit the new head gasket over the dowels **(see illustration)**.

11.17a The cam chain guide blade lower end locates in the recess . . .

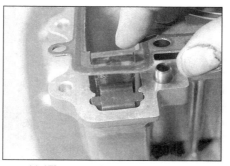

11.17b . . . and its upper end lugs locate in the cast slots

11.19 Always use a new cylinder head gasket

11.20a Install the cylinder head . . .

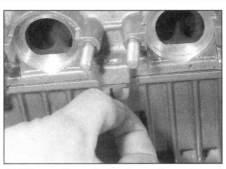

11.20b . . . then slip the horseshoe-shaped pieces in the front screw mountings

11.21 Ensure that the cylinder head bolt threads are clean and dry before inserting them in the head

11.22a Tighten the cylinder head bolts . . .

during tightening, remove the head for investigation. If the head is detached, the liners must be resealed.

23 Tighten the screws at the front and right side (inside on Thunderbird) of the cylinder head to the specified torque setting.

24 Realign the engine mounting lugs with the frame, using pressure from the jack if necessary, and install the mounting bolts, washers and nuts, including the radiator mounting brackets. Tighten the bolts to the specified torque setting. Remove the jack.

25 Using new sealing washers on each side of the external oil pipe banjo unions, install the pipe on the engine and tighten the banjo union bolts to the specified torque setting **(see illustration)**.

26 Push the coolant pipe onto its union on the cylinder head, tightening the clamp securely. Reconnect the coolant temperature sensor wire.

27 Install the tappets and camshafts (see Section 9).

28 Install the valve cover (see Section 7).

29 Fill the cooling system (see Chapter 1).

12 Valves/valve seats/valve guides - overhaul

1 Owing to the complexity of this job and the special tools and equipment needed, most owners leave this work to a professional.

2 The home mechanic can, however, remove the valves from the cylinder head, check the components for wear and grind in the valves

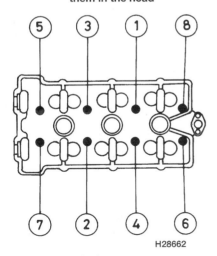

11.22b . . . in the correct sequence (3 cylinder engine) . . .

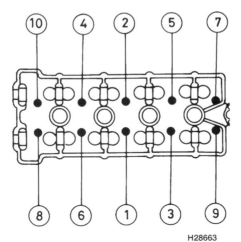

11.22c . . . (or 4 cylinder engine) . . .

11.22d . . . noting that final tightening is expressed in terms of degrees

20 Carefully lower the cylinder head onto the block **(see illustration)**. Slip the two (3 cylinder) or three (4 cylinder) horseshoe-shaped pieces between the head and block protrusions at the front of the engine **(see illustration)**. **Note:** *If was found that the new gaskets required cutting in half to create the required shape.* If the cam chain is still in the engine, pass it up through the tunnel and slip a piece of wire through the chain to prevent it falling back into the engine.

21 Install the cylinder head bolts and tighten only finger-tight at this stage **(see illustration)**.

22 Tighten the cylinder head bolts in the correct sequence to the stage 1 torque setting **(see illustrations)**. Repeat to the stage 2 torque setting, noting that the torque differs on early and late models; the cylinder head bolts were modified at the same time as the detachable cover for alternator/starter clutch access was deleted from the upper crankcase top surface. Finally, attached a degree disc to the torque wrench and angle-tighten each bolt 90° following the sequence **(see illustration)**. **Note:** *The cylinder head may not seat fully when placed on the block due to the liners being slightly proud - if it does not pull down*

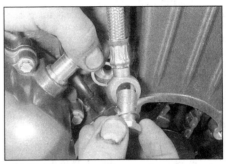

11.25 Use new sealing washers on each side of the oil pipe banjo union

2

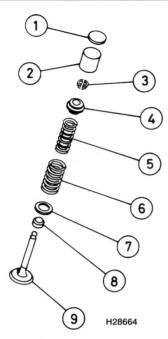

13.6a Valve components

1 Shim   6 Outer spring
2 Tappet   7 Spring seat
3 Collets   8 Seal
4 Spring retainer   9 Valve
5 Inner spring

(Section 13). Tasks like valve seat recutting should be entrusted to a Triumph dealer.
3 After the valve overhaul has been performed, the head will be in like-new condition. When the head is returned, be sure to clean it again very thoroughly before installation on the engine to remove any metal particles or abrasive grit that may still be present from the valve service operations. Use compressed air, if available, to blow out all the holes and passages.

13 Cylinder head and valves - disassembly, inspection and reassembly

1 As mentioned in the previous section, valve seat recutting should be left to a Triumph dealer. However, disassembly, cleaning and inspection of the valves and related components can be done (if the necessary special tools are available) by the home mechanic. This way no expense is incurred if the inspection reveals that overhaul is not required at this time.
2 To disassemble the valve components without the risk of damaging them, a valve spring compressor is absolutely necessary.

Disassembly

3 Remove the tappets and their shims if you haven't already done so (see Section 9). Store the components in such a way that they can

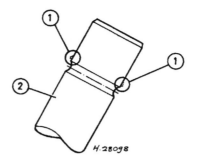

13.6b Remove burrs (1) if valve stem (2) won't pull through the guide

be returned to their original locations without getting mixed up.
4 Carefully scrape all carbon deposits out of the combustion chamber area. A hand held wire brush or a piece of fine emery cloth can be used once the majority of deposits have been scraped away. Do not use a wire brush mounted in a drill motor, or one with extremely stiff bristles, as the head material is soft and may be eroded away or scratched by the wire brush.
5 Arrange to label and store the valves along with their related components so they can be kept separate and reinstalled in the same valve guides they are removed from (labelled plastic bags work well for this).
6 Compress the valve spring on the first valve with a spring compressor, then remove the collets and the retainer from the valve assembly. **Note:** *Take great care not to mark the tappet bore with the spring compressor.* Do not compress the springs any more than is necessary. Carefully release the valve spring compressor and remove the springs and the valve from the head **(see illustration)**. If the valve binds in the guide (won't pull through), push it back into the head and deburr the area around the collet groove with a very fine file or whetstone **(see illustration)**.
7 Repeat the procedure for the other valves. Keep the parts for each valve together so they can be reinstalled in the same location.
8 Once the valves have been removed and labelled, pull off the valve stem seals with pliers and discard them (the old seals should not be reused), then remove the spring seats.

13.14a Insert a small hole gauge in the valve guide and expand it so there's a slight drag . . .

13.13 Measuring the valve seat width

9 Next, clean the cylinder head with solvent and dry it thoroughly. Compressed air will speed the drying process and ensure that all holes and recessed areas are clean.
10 Clean all of the valve springs, collets, retainers and spring seats with solvent and dry them thoroughly. Do the parts from one valve at a time so that no mixing of parts between valves occurs.
11 Scrape off any deposits that may have formed on the valve, then use a motorised wire brush to remove deposits from the valve heads and stems. Again, make sure the valves do not get mixed up.

Inspection

12 Inspect the head very carefully for cracks and other damage. If cracks are found, a new head will be required. Check the cam bearing surfaces for wear and evidence of seizure. Check the camshafts and tappets for wear as well (see Section 9).
13 Examine the valve seats in each of the combustion chambers. If they are pitted, cracked or burned, the head will require work beyond the scope of the home mechanic. Measure the valve seat width and compare it to the Specifications **(see illustration)**. If it exceeds the service limit, or if it varies around its circumference, valve overhaul is required.
14 Clean the valve guides to remove any carbon build-up, then measure the inside diameters of the guides (at both ends and the centre of the guide) with a small hole gauge and micrometer **(see illustrations)**. Record the measurements for future reference. These

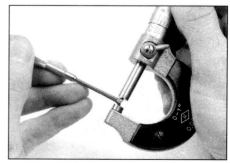

13.14b . . . then measure the small hole gauge with a micrometer

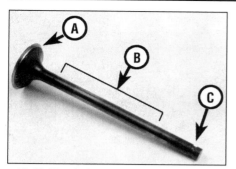

13.15 Check the valve face (A), stem (B) and collet groove (C) for signs of wear

13.16 Measure the valve stem diameter with a micrometer

13.20 Apply grinding compound very sparingly, in small dabs to the valve face

measurements, along with the valve stem diameter measurements, will enable you to compute the valve stem-to-guide clearance. This clearance, when compared to the Specifications, will be one factor that will determine the extent of the valve service work required. The guides are measured at the ends and at the centre to determine if they are worn in a bell-mouth pattern (more wear at the ends). If the guides are worn they must be replaced - check the availability of replacement guides with a Triumph dealer.

15 Carefully inspect each valve face for cracks, pits and burned spots. Check the valve stem and the collet groove area for cracks **(see illustration)**. Rotate the valve and check for any obvious indication that it is bent. Check the end of the stem for pitting and excessive wear. Measure the valve seat width and compare to the Specifications. The presence of any of the above conditions indicates the need for valve overhaul.

16 Measure the valve stem diameter **(see illustration)**. By subtracting the stem diameter from the valve guide diameter, the valve stem-to-guide clearance is obtained. If any valve stem is worn the valve must be replaced.

17 Check the spring retainers and collets for obvious wear and cracks. Any questionable parts should not be reused, as extensive damage will occur in the event of failure during engine operation.

18 If the inspection indicates that no overhaul work is required, the valve components can be reinstalled in the head.

Reassembly

19 Before installing the valves in the head, they should be ground in to ensure a positive seal between the valves and seats. This procedure requires coarse and fine valve grinding compound and a valve grinding tool. If a grinding tool is not available, a piece of rubber or plastic hose can be slipped over the valve stem (after the valve has been installed in the guide) and used to turn the valve.

20 Apply a small amount of coarse grinding compound to the valve face, then slip the valve into the guide **(see illustration)**. **Note:** *Make sure the valve is installed in the correct guide and be careful not to get any grinding compound on the valve stem.*

21 Attach the grinding tool (or hose) to the valve and rotate the tool between the palms of your hands. Use a back-and-forth motion rather than a circular motion. Lift the valve off the seat and turn it at regular intervals to distribute the grinding compound properly. Continue grinding until the valve face and seat contact area is of uniform width and unbroken around the entire circumference of the valve face and seat **(see illustrations)**.

22 Carefully remove the valve from the guide and wipe off all traces of grinding compound. Use solvent to clean the valve. Wipe the seat area thoroughly with a solvent soaked cloth.

23 Repeat the procedure with fine valve grinding compound, then repeat the entire procedure for the remaining valves.

24 Lay the spring seats in place in the cylinder head, then install new valve stem

13.21a After grinding, the valve face should exhibit a uniform unbroken appearance . . .

13.21b . . . and the seat should be the specified width (arrowed) with a smooth unbroken appearance

13.25a Install the valve springs with their closer-wound coils downwards, towards the valve head

seals on each of the guides. Use a deep socket to push the seals over the end of the valve guide until they are felt to clip into place. Don't twist or cock them, or they will not seal properly against the valve stems. Also, don't remove them again or they will be damaged.

25 Coat the valve stems with clean engine oil, then install one of them into its guide. Next, install the springs and retainer, compress the springs and install the collets. **Note:** *Install the springs with the closely-wound coils at the bottom, towards the valve head (see illustration)*. When compressing the springs with the valve spring compressor, depress them only as far as is absolutely necessary to slip the collets into place. Apply a small amount of grease to the collets to help hold them in place as the pressure is released from the springs **(see illustration)**. Make

13.25b A small dab of grease will help hold the collets in place as they are installed

2

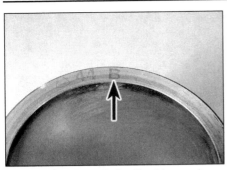

14.2 Liner for cylinder No. 2 has a size marking (arrowed) on its top face

14.5 Prise the circlip from one side of the piston - make sure it's the inner side if working on either of the outer pistons

14.9 Compression rings can be removed with a ring removal and installation tool

certain that the collets are securely locked in their retaining grooves.

26 Support the cylinder head on blocks so the valves can't contact the workbench top, then very gently tap each of the valve stems with a soft-faced hammer. This will help seat the collets in their grooves.

You can check for proper sealing of the valves by pouring a small amount of solvent into each of the valve ports. If the solvent leaks past any valve into the combustion chamber area the valve grinding operation on that valve should be repeated.

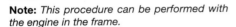

14 Cylinder liners and pistons - removal, inspection and installation

Note: *This procedure can be performed with the engine in the frame.*

Removal

1 Remove the cylinder head (see Section 11).
2 Before removing the liners, mark the top edge of each liner with a felt marker pen or similar, which will not damage the gasket surfaces. Indicate the cylinder number and front face of each liner. **Note:** *Cylinder No. 2 is a selective fit during manufacture; it will be denoted by a green dot on early engines and by the letter "B" on later engines - other markings are for manufacturing use and should be ignored* **(see illustration)**.
3 Gently pull each liner out of the cylinder block using hand force only. Do not resort to the use of metal levers because the gasket surfaces will be damaged.
4 As each liner is removed, stuff the crankcase aperture with clean rag to cushion the piston and prevent anything falling into the crankcase.
5 Before removing the pistons, use a felt marker pen to write the cylinder number on the crown of each piston. Pry out the circlip on one side and push the piston pin out from the other side **(see illustration)**. On the outer

pistons, the piston pins will have to be extracted inwards. Rotate the crankshaft so that the best access is obtained and remember the importance of the rag in preventing dropped circlips from falling into the crankcase. **Note:** *If a piston pin is a tight fit in the piston bosses, soak a rag in boiling water then wring it out and wrap it around the piston - this will expand the alloy piston sufficiently to release its grip of the pin.*

Inspection

Liners

6 Check the cylinder walls carefully for scratches and score marks.
7 Using the appropriate precision measuring tools, check each bore's diameter. Measure near the top, centre and bottom of the bore, parallel to the crankshaft axis. Next, measure each bore's diameter at the same three locations across the crankshaft axis. Compare the results to this Chapter's Specifications. If any cylinder bore is tapered, out-of-round, worn beyond the service limit, or badly scuffed or scored, it should be replaced together with its piston.

Pistons

8 Before the inspection process can be carried out, the pistons must be cleaned and the old piston rings removed.
9 Using the thumbs or a piston ring removal and installation tool, carefully remove the rings from the pistons **(see illustration)**. Do not nick or gouge the pistons in the process.
10 Scrape all traces of carbon from the tops of the pistons. A hand-held wire brush or a piece of fine emery cloth can be used once most of the deposits have been scraped away. Do not, under any circumstances, use a wire brush mounted in a drill motor to remove deposits from the pistons; the piston material is soft and will be eroded away by the wire brush.
11 Use a piston ring groove cleaning tool to remove any carbon deposits from the ring grooves. If a tool is not available, a piece broken off an old ring will do the job. Be very careful to remove only the carbon deposits. Do not remove any metal and do not nick or gouge the sides of the ring grooves.

12 Once the deposits have been removed, clean the pistons with solvent and dry them thoroughly. Make sure the oil return holes below the oil ring groove are clear.
13 Carefully inspect each piston for cracks around the skirt, at the pin bosses and at the ring lands. Normal piston wear appears as even, vertical wear on the thrust surfaces of the piston and slight looseness of the top ring in its groove. If the skirt is scored or scuffed, the engine may have been suffering from overheating and/or abnormal combustion, which caused excessively high operating temperatures. The oil pump and cooling systems should be checked thoroughly.
14 A hole in the piston crown, an extreme to be sure, is an indication that abnormal combustion (pre-ignition) was occurring. Burned areas at the edge of the piston crown are usually evidence of spark knock (detonation). If any of the above problems exist, the causes must be corrected or the damage will occur again.
15 Measure the piston ring-to-groove clearance by laying a new piston ring in the ring groove and slipping a feeler blade in beside it **(see illustration)**. Check the clearance at three or four locations around the groove. If the clearance is greater than that specified, the piston is worn. Confirm this by measuring the piston ring groove width and comparing with the specification. **Note:** *Make sure you have the correct ring for the groove - the two compression rings can be identified by their profile* **(see illustration 14.28)**.

14.15 Measuring the ring-to-groove clearance

14.16 Measuring the piston diameter

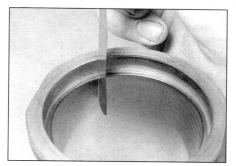

14.20 Measuring piston ring end gap

14.22 Ring end gap can be enlarged by clamping a file in a vice and filing

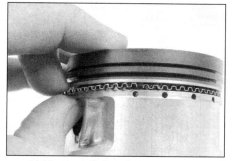
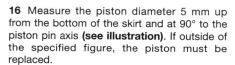

14.26a Install the oil ring expander in its groove . . .

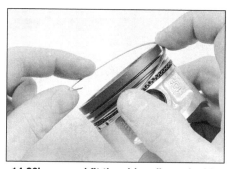

14.26b . . . and fit the side rails each side of it - the oil ring must be installed by hand

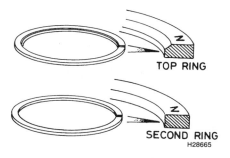

14.28 The compression rings differ in profile - the N mark indicates top surface

16 Measure the piston diameter 5 mm up from the bottom of the skirt and at 90° to the piston pin axis **(see illustration)**. If outside of the specified figure, the piston must be replaced.

17 If the necessary measuring equipment is available, measure the connecting rod small-end bore diameter, the piston pin outside diameter and the inside diameter of the piston bosses. Replace any component which is outside of the specification.

Piston rings

18 It is good practice to replace the piston rings when an engine is being overhauled. Before installing the new piston rings, the ring end gaps must be checked.

19 Lay out the pistons and the new ring sets so the rings will be matched with the same piston and cylinder during the end gap measurement procedure and engine assembly.

20 Insert the top ring into the top of the first liner and square it up with the cylinder walls by pushing it in with the top of the piston. The ring should be about 20 mm below the top edge of the liner. To measure the end gap, slip a feeler blade between the ends of the ring and compare the measurement to the Specification **(see illustration)**.

21 If the gap is larger or smaller than specified, double check to make sure that you have the correct rings before proceeding.

22 If the gap is too small, it must be enlarged or the ring ends may come in contact with each other during engine operation, which can cause serious damage. The end gap can

be increased by filing the ring ends very carefully with a fine file. When performing this operation, file only from the outside in **(see illustration)**.

23 Excess end gap is not critical unless it is greater than 1 mm. Again, double check to make sure you have the correct rings for your engine and check that the bore is not worn.

24 Repeat the procedure for each ring that will be installed in the first cylinder and for each ring in the remaining cylinders. Remember to keep the rings, pistons and cylinders matched up.

25 Once the ring end gaps have been checked/corrected, the rings can be installed on the pistons.

26 The oil control ring (lowest on the piston) is installed first. It is composed of three separate components. Slip the expander into the groove, then install the upper side rail. Do not use a piston ring installation tool on the oil ring side rails as they may be damaged. Instead, place one end of the side rail into the groove between the expander and the ring land. Hold it firmly in place and slide a finger around the piston while pushing the rail into the groove. Next, install the lower side rail in the same manner **(see illustrations)**.

27 After the three oil ring components have been installed, check to make sure that both the upper and lower side rails can be turned smoothly in the ring groove.

28 Install the second (middle) ring next. **Note:** *The second ring and top rings are slightly different in profile.* To avoid breaking the ring, use a piston ring installation tool and

make sure that the letter N near the end gap is facing up **(see illustration)**. Fit the ring into the middle groove on the piston. Do not expand the ring any more than is necessary to slide it into place.

29 Finally, install the top ring in the same manner. The top ring can be distinguished from the second ring by its chamfer and chromed finish **(see illustration 14.28)**. Make sure the letter N near the end gap is facing up.

30 Correct positioning of the ring end gaps is important **(see illustration)**.

2

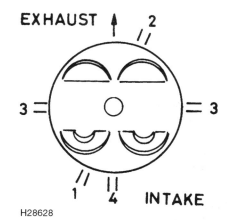

H28628

14.30 Position the ring end gaps correctly

1 Top ring end gap
2 Second (middle) ring end gap
3 Oil ring side rail end gaps
4 Oil ring expander end gap

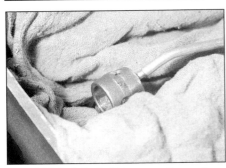

14.31 Lubricate the connecting rod small-end with engine oil

14.32a Install the piston so the arrow mark is opposite the con-rod oilway (arrowed)

14.32b Install the piston pin . . .

14.32c . . . and secure with a new circlip

14.34a Apply a continuous bead of Blue Hylomar sealant to the liner seating . . .

14.34b . . . smooth it off and wait for it to cure

14.36 Install the cylinder liners in their original locations

Installation

31 Remove all traces of old sealant from around the cylinder liners and their sealing surface in the crankcase. Stuff clean rag into the crankcase mouth to prevent any dropped circlips falling in. Lubricate the small-end bore with engine oil **(see illustration)**.

32 Insert a new circlip in one side of the piston bore and install the piston on its rod so that the arrow marking on its crown is facing forwards, and opposite to the oilway in the connecting rod **(see illustration)**. Push the piston pin fully into the piston and secure with a second new circlip - make sure the circlip is fully seated in its groove **(see illustrations)**.

33 Install the other pistons in the same way, rotating the crankshaft to gain the best access.

34 Remove any rag from the crankcase and make sure the liner seating area is clean, oil-free and dry. Do the same with the seating on the liners. Apply a continuous bead of Blue

14.38 Make sure the liner top surfaces are level with the cylinder block surface

Hylomar sealant, 3 to 4 mm wide, to the liner seating **(see illustrations)**. Wait 15 minutes for the sealant to cure.

35 Check that the piston rings are correctly positioned in relation to the front of the engine **(see illustration 14.30)**.

36 Lubricate the bore surface of the liner with engine oil. Make sure that the piston is at TDC and slip the liner for that piston over the rings; make sure the liner is the correct way round **(see illustration)**. Compress each ring with your fingers as it enters the liner and use a gentle rocking motion as the liner is pushed downwards. The liner has a chamfered lead-in to enable the pistons to be installed without the use of ring compressors.

37 Install the other liners in the same way. As the piston is rotated to position the other pistons at TDC make sure that the installed liners do not lift off their seating. If this happens, the liners must be removed, cleaned and fresh sealant applied.

38 When all liners are in position with their top surfaces level with the cylinder block, install the cylinder head (see Section 11) **(see illustration)**.

15 Clutch - removal, inspection and installation

Note: *This procedure can be performed with the engine in the frame. If the engine has already been removed, ignore the preliminary steps which don't apply.*

Removal

1 On Trophy and Daytona models, remove the fairing right lower panel (see Chapter 8).

2 Drain the engine oil (Chapter 1).

3 On 3 cylinder models except the Thunderbird and early 4 cylinder models (up to VIN 2970), detach the breather hose from its union on the clutch cover.

4 Working in a criss-cross pattern, evenly slacken the clutch cover retaining bolts **(see illustration)**. Lift the cover away from the engine, being prepared to catch any residual oil which may be released as the cover is removed.

5 Remove the gasket and discard it. Note the two locating dowels fitted to the crankcase and remove these for safe-keeping if they are loose.

6 Remove the crankshaft right end cover with its gasket.

7 Working in a criss-cross pattern, gradually

15.4 The clutch cover is retained by twelve bolts on 3 cylinder engines (arrowed)

15.7 Remove the five bolts to free the pressure plate

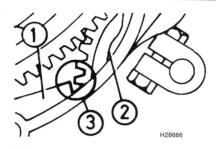

15.10 Balancer timing - 4 cylinder engine

1 *Crankcase index mark*
2 *Balancer gear*
3 *Gear tooth and index mark alignment*

slacken the clutch spring retaining bolts until spring pressure is released **(see illustration)**. Remove the bolts, washers and springs, then lift out the clutch pressure plate complete with bearing and pushrod end piece. Withdraw the long pushrod.

8 Grasp the complete set of clutch plates and remove them as a pack. Unless the plates are being replaced with new ones, keep them in their original order.

9 The mainshaft must be locked to enable the clutch nut to be slackened. This can be done in several ways. If the engine is in the frame, engage 1st gear and have an assistant hold the rear brake on hard with the rear tyre in firm contact with the ground. Alternatively, the Triumph service tool (Pt. No. 3880025) can be located between the clutch centre and outer drum, and the engine positioned at TDC for cylinder No. 1 (T 1 mark aligned on 3 cylinder, T 1.4 mark aligned on 4 cylinder) and the transmission in gear as described above. If the engine is out of the frame, the tool shown in the reassembly sequence **(see illustration 15.27d)** can be used to grip the clutch centre whilst the nut is slackened. Unscrew the nut and washer from the mainshaft.

10 On 4 cylinder models, it is important to make a reference mark on the rear balancer drive gear at this stage. This will ensure correct timing of the balancers on reassembly. Position the engine at TDC for cylinders 1 and 4 (ie the T 1.4 mark on the ignition rotor in alignment with the centre of the pickup coil). Using white paint, or a

permanent marker pen, mark the gear tooth of the balancer drive gear which is in alignment with the crankcase index mark in this position **(see illustration)**.

11 On all models, slide the clutch centre off the mainshaft, followed by the large thrustwasher and shim.

12 Pick the needle roller bearing and splined sleeve out of the middle of the clutch boss. Wiggle the outer drum gently back and forth to assist their removal. The outer drum can then be manoeuvred out of the crankcase.

13 Disengage the large auxiliary drive gear from the oil pump drive gear and alternator driveshaft gear. Slip the bush off the mainshaft.

Inspection

14 After an extended period of service the clutch friction plates will wear and promote clutch slip. Measure the thickness of each friction plate using a vernier caliper **(see illustration)**. If any plate has worn to or beyond the service limit given in the Specifications, the friction plates must be replaced as a set.

15 The plain plates should not show any signs of excess heating (bluing). Check for warpage using a flat surface and feeler blades **(see illustration)**. If any plate exceeds the maximum permissible amount of warpage, or shows signs of bluing, all plain plates must be replaced as a set. Check that there is no obvious sign of wear to the anti-judder plain plate in the middle of the clutch pack.

16 Inspect the clutch assembly for burrs and indentations on the edges of the protruding tangs of the friction plates and/or slots in the edge of the outer drum with which they engage. Similarly check for wear between the inner tongues of the plain plates and the slots in the clutch centre. Wear of this nature will cause clutch drag and slow disengagement during gear changes, as the plates will snag when the pressure plate is lifted. With care a small amount of wear can be corrected by dressing with a fine file, but if this is excessive the worn components should be replaced.

17 Inspect the mainshaft, bush and splined sleeve bearing surfaces for signs of wear and damage. Similarly, check the condition of the needle roller bearing.

18 Check the pressure plate bearing for wear. Ensure that the inner race of the bearing spins freely without any sign of notchiness. Push the bearing out of the pressure plate if replacement is required **(see illustration)**.

19 The clutch cover incorporates a noise damper on all models, and on 3 cylinder models except the Thunderbird and early 4-cylinder models, also a breather. Where applicable, remove the retaining screws to free the breather plate, then remove the rubber seal **(see illustrations)**. Remove the retaining screws to free the noise damper plate, then lift out the damping foam pad **(see illustrations)**.

Installation

20 Remove all traces of gasket from the crankcase and clutch cover surfaces.

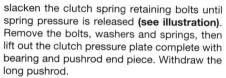

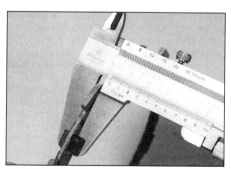

15.14 Measuring friction plate thickness

15.15 Measuring plain plate warpage

15.18 Bearing can be pressed out of pressure plate with hand pressure

2

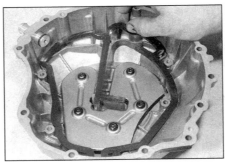

15.19a Where fitted, remove six screws (arrowed) to release breather plate

15.19b Seal resides between breather plate and clutch cover

15.19c All models incorporate a noise damper in the clutch cover . . .

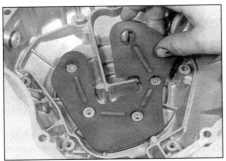

15.19d . . . which consists of a foam pad

15.21 Install bush on mainshaft - shouldered side faces the crankcase

15.22 Auxiliary gear meshes with alternator driveshaft gear at the top and oil pump drive gear at the bottom

21 Lubricate the bush with engine oil and slide it on the mainshaft so that its shouldered side faces the crankcase (**see illustration**).

22 Install the auxiliary gear so that its dished side faces that the crankcase, meshing it with the oil pump drive gear and alternator

driveshaft gear (**see illustration**). **Note:** *If necessary, rotate the two-piece alternator driveshaft gear until its teeth align, permitting engagement with the auxiliary gear.* Make sure the auxiliary gear is central about the mainshaft.

23 On 3 cylinder engines, guide the outer drum over the mainshaft and into engagement with the primary drive gear on the crankshaft (**see illustration**).

24 On 4 cylinder engines, check that the balancer shaft mark is aligned exactly with the index mark on the crankcase (see Step 10). Guide the outer drum over the mainshaft and into engagement with the primary drive gear on the crankshaft and the balancer drive gear - check that the marks still align.

25 On all models, hold the outer drum central to the mainshaft and insert the splined sleeve, ensuring that it passes through the auxiliary drive gear (**see illustrations**). Lubricate the needle roller bearing and insert it between the sleeve and bush (**see illustration**). Recheck the balancer shaft markings on 4 cylinder models.

26 Install the shim and large thrustwasher over the mainshaft (**see illustrations**).

27 Insert the clutch centre over the mainshaft splines and install the washer, with its OUT marking facing outwards, followed by the clutch nut (**see illustrations**). Using the method employed on dismantling to lock the mainshaft, secure the nut to the specified torque setting (**see illustration**). **Note:** *Check that the clutch centre rotates freely after tightening.*

15.23 Manoeuvre clutch outer drum into the crankcase

15.25a Install the splined sleeve in the outer drum . . .

15.25b . . . and push it through into the auxiliary gear so that it lies flush with the outer drum boss

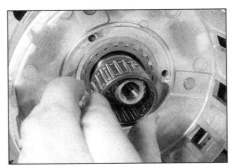

15.25c Slip the needle roller bearing between the outer drum and mainshaft bush

15.26a Install the shim on the mainshaft . . .

15.26b . . . followed by the large thrustwasher

15.27a Install the clutch centre over the mainshaft splines

15.27b OUT marked face of washer must face outwards

15.27c Install the clutch nut . . .

15.27d . . . and tighten to the specified torque, holding the clutch centre stationary

15.28a Start off with a friction plate . . .

15.28b . . . followed by a plain plate

15.28c Install the special plain plate in the middle of the clutch pack

2

15.29a Slide the pushrod into the mainshaft

15.29b Pushrod end piece locates in the pressure plate bearing as shown

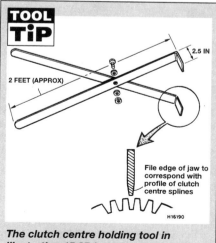

2.5 IN

2 FEET (APPROX)

File edge of jaw to correspond with profile of clutch centre splines

H16190

The clutch centre holding tool in illustration 15.27d can be made from steel strips

28 Build up the clutch plates in the outer drum, starting with a friction plate, then a plain plate and alternating friction and plain plates until all are installed **(see illustrations)**. The special plain plate (incorporating the anti-judder device) is installed in the middle of the clutch pack, as the 4th or 5th plain plate.

Note: *If new plates are being fitted, coat their surfaces with engine oil to prevent seizure.*
29 Slip the pushrod into the mainshaft and install the end piece in the pressure plate bearing **(see illustrations)**.
30 Insert the pressure plate in the clutch, engaging the pushrod end piece with the

15.30a Install the pressure plate . . .

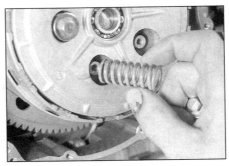

15.30b . . . the springs . . .

15.30c . . . bolts and washers

15.30d Tighten the bolts to the specified torque

15.31a A dowel (arrowed) is fitted at the bottom . . .

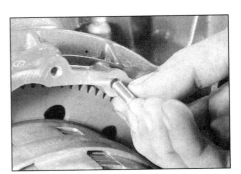

15.31b . . . and top of the crankcase

15.31c Install a new gasket (hold it in place with a dab of sealant if necessary) . . .

15.31d . . . and fit the clutch cover

pushrod **(see illustration)**. Install the springs, washers and bolts and tighten them evenly in a criss-cross sequence to the specified torque setting **(see illustrations)**.

31 Insert the dowels in the crankcase **(see illustrations)**. Place a new gasket on the crankcase and install the cover **(see illustrations)**. Tighten the cover bolts evenly in a criss-cross sequence to the specified torque setting. On all 3 cylinder models except the Thunderbird and early 4 cylinder models (up to VIN 2970), reconnect the breather hose.

32 Install the crankshaft right end cover using a new gasket and tighten its bolts to the specified torque setting.

33 Refill the engine with oil (see Chapter 1).

34 Where applicable, install the fairing sections (see Chapter 8).

16 Clutch master cylinder - removal, overhaul and installation

1 If the master cylinder is leaking fluid, or if the clutch does not function when the lever is applied, and bleeding the clutch does not help, master cylinder overhaul is advised.

Removal

2 Remove the two screws holding the reservoir cap in place. Lift off the cap and diaphragm.

3 Pull the dust cap off the bleed valve on the release cylinder. Attach a length of clear tubing to the valve and direct its other end into a container. Pump the clutch lever until all fluid has drained from the reservoir. Tighten the bleed valve.

4 Remove the clutch lever pivot bolt, locknut and collar and withdraw the lever. On Tiger models this will also release the hand guard.

5 Disconnect the wire connectors from the clutch switch **(see illustration)**.

6 Pull back the rubber boot, loosen the banjo union bolt, and separate the clutch hose from the master cylinder. Wrap the hose end in a clean rag, then suspend it in an upright position or bend it down carefully and place the open end in a clean container. The objective is to prevent excessive loss of fluid, fluid spills and system contamination.

7 Remove the two master cylinder clamp bolts and remove the unit from the handlebar.

Overhaul

8 Remove the dust boot from the end of the master cylinder piston. Using circlip pliers, release the circlip and withdraw the pushrod, washer, piston and spring **(see illustration)**.

16.5 Pull back the dust boot and pull the wires off the clutch switch

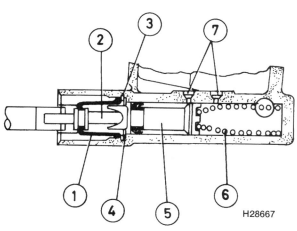

16.8 Master cylinder piston components

1 Dust boot
2 Pushrod
3 Circlip
4 Washer
5 Piston
6 Spring
7 Fluid ports

H28667

Lay the parts out in order on a clean surface.

9 Remove the screw to release the clutch switch from the base of the master cylinder.

10 Clean the piston and master cylinder bore with clean hydraulic fluid or brake system cleaner. *Caution: Do not, under any circumstances, use a petroleum-based solvent to clean hydraulic parts.*

11 Inspect the piston and master cylinder bore for signs of corrosion, nicks and burrs and loss of plating. If surface defects are found, the piston and cylinder should be replaced. If the master cylinder is in poor condition the release cylinder should also be overhauled. Check that the fluid inlet and outlet ports in the master cylinder are clear.

12 Note the fitted position of the piston seal,

then pry it off the piston and replace it with a new seal, installed in the same direction.

13 Install the spring in the master cylinder so that its tapered end faces the piston. Lubricate the piston seal with clean hydraulic fluid and slip the piston into the master cylinder, followed by the washer and pushrod. Retain these components with the circlip, making sure that it locates in the master cylinder groove. Locate the dust boot in the bore and engage its outer end in the pushrod groove.

Installation

14 Position the master cylinder and its clamp on the handlebar with clamp arrow pointing upwards and the top edge of the clamp

aligned with the punched dot on the handlebar **(see illustrations)**. Install the two clamp bolts, fully tighten the upper bolt first to the specified torque setting, then do the same with the lower.

15 Reconnect the wires to the clutch switch **(see illustration 16.5)**.

16 Using a new sealing washer on each side of the banjo union, bolt it into place on the master cylinder. Tighten the banjo bolt to the specified torque setting so that it abuts the lug on the master cylinder **(see illustration)**.

17 Install the clutch lever (and hand guard on Tiger models), locate the collar in the base of the pivot and secure with the bolt and locknut.

18 Fill the reservoir with new hydraulic fluid and bleed the clutch (see Section 18).

---

17 Clutch release cylinder - removal, overhaul and installation

Removal

1 On Trophy and Daytona models, remove the left lower fairing panel as described in Chapter 8.

2 Remove the clutch hose banjo union bolt and separate the hose from the release cylinder. Plug the hose end or wrap a plastic bag around it to minimise fluid loss and prevent dirt entering the system. Discard the sealing washers; new ones must be used on installation. **Note:** *If you're planning to overhaul the release cylinder and don't have a source of compressed air to blow out the piston, just loosen the banjo bolt at this stage and retighten it lightly. The bike's hydraulic system can then be used to force the piston out of the body once the cylinder has been unbolted. Disconnect the hose once the piston has been sufficiently displaced.*

3 Remove the three bolts and withdraw the release cylinder from the sprocket cover **(see illustration)**. If the release cylinder is not being disassembled, the piston can be prevented from creeping out of the release cylinder by restraining it with a couple of cable-ties **(see illustration 5.16)**. **Note:** *The hydraulic hose is routed behind the large coolant hose from the water pump to the cylinder block. The coolant must be drained and the coolant hose removed before the hydraulic hose can be freed.*

Overhaul

4 The release cylinder has a slot on its underside which allows the escape of hydraulic fluid in the event of the piston seal failing **(see illustration)**. Hydraulic fluid might otherwise be forced under pressure past the single-lipped pushrod seal and into the transmission.

5 Have a supply of clean rags on hand, then pump the clutch lever to expel the piston under hydraulic pressure. If the hose has already been detached, use a jet of

2

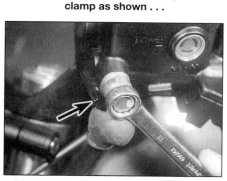

16.14a Install clutch master cylinder clamp as shown . . .

16.14b . . . and align joint with dot on handlebar (arrowed)

16.16 Hydraulic hose banjo union must abut lug (arrowed) on master cylinder

17.3 Clutch release cylinder is retained by three bolts (arrowed)

17.4 Fluid escape slot (arrowed) on underside of release cylinder

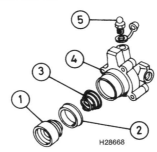

17.10 Release cylinder components

1 Piston
2 Piston seal
3 Spring
4 Release cylinder body
5 Bleed valve

compressed air directed into the fluid inlet to expel the piston.

 Warning: Use only low air pressure, otherwise the piston may be forcibly expelled causing injury.

6 Recover the spring from the piston.

7 Using a plastic or wood tool, remove the piston seal from the piston groove.

8 Clean the piston and release cylinder bore with clean hydraulic fluid or brake system cleaner. *Caution: Do not, under any circumstances, use a petroleum-based solvent to clean hydraulic parts.*

9 Inspect the piston and release cylinder bore for signs of corrosion, nicks and burrs and loss of plating. If surface defects are found, the piston and cylinder should be replaced. If the release cylinder is in poor condition the master cylinder should also be overhauled.

10 Lubricate the new piston seal with clean hydraulic fluid and install it on the piston; make sure it is fitted the correct way round. Install the spring in the release cylinder so that its tapered end faces the piston **(see illustration)**. Lubricate the piston and seal with clean hydraulic fluid and insert the piston in the release cylinder. Use the thumbs to press it fully into the cylinder.

11 The pushrod can be withdrawn from the sprocket cover if required. If the pushrod oil seal requires renewal, remove the sprocket cover (see Chapter 6), slide out the pushrod, and prise the old seal out with a flat-bladed screwdriver **(see illustration)**. Press the new seal in using thumb pressure.

Installation

12 If the pushrod was removed smear it with engine oil and slide it back into the sprocket

cover. Apply a dab of grease to its end and install the release cylinder **(see illustration)**.

13 Install the two long retaining bolts in the left holes and the short bolt in the right hole; tighten them to the specified torque setting **(see illustration)**.

14 If the hydraulic hose was disconnected, use a new sealing washer on each side of the banjo union. Position the union so that its tab abuts the lug on the release cylinder and tighten the banjo bolt to the specified torque setting **(see illustration)**.

15 Remove the two screws and lift off the master cylinder reservoir cap and diaphragm. Fill the reservoir with new fluid and bleed the system as described in the next section.

18 Clutch - bleeding

1 Bleeding the clutch is simply the process of removing all the air bubbles from the clutch fluid reservoir, the hydraulic hose and the release cylinder. Bleeding is necessary whenever a clutch system hydraulic connection is loosened, when a component or hose is replaced, or when the master cylinder or release cylinder is overhauled. Leaks in the system may also allow air to enter, but leaking clutch fluid will reveal their presence and warn you of the need for repair.

2 To bleed the clutch, you will need some new, clean fluid of the recommended type (see Chapter 1), a length of clear vinyl or plastic tubing, a small container partially filled with clean fluid, a supply of clean rags and a spanner to fit the bleed valve.

3 Cover the fuel tank and other painted components to prevent damage in the event that fluid is spilled.

4 On Trophy and Daytona models, remove the left lower fairing panel (see Chapter 8). On models so equipped, rotate the clutch lever span adjuster to position No. 1.

5 Position the bike on its centre stand, or where only a side stand is fitted, have an assistant hold it upright so that the master cylinder is level. Remove the two screws retaining the master cylinder reservoir cap, then lift off the cap and diaphragm. Slowly pump the clutch lever a few times until no air bubbles can be seen floating up from the bottom of the reservoir. Doing this bleeds air from the master cylinder end of the hose.

6 Pull the dust cap off the bleed valve on the release cylinder and attach one end of the clear tubing to the valve **(see illustration)**. Submerge the other end in the fluid in the container. Check the fluid level in the reservoir. Do not allow it to drop below the lower mark during the bleeding process.

7 Pump the clutch lever three or four times and hold it in against the handlebar whilst opening the bleed valve. When the valve is opened, fluid will flow out of the release cylinder into the clear tubing.

17.11 Pushrod oil seal can be prised out of the crankcase

17.12 Grease the end of the pushrod and install the release cylinder

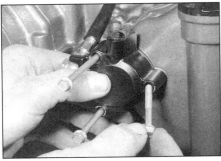

17.13 The shorter of the three retaining screws locates in the right-hand hole

17.14 Ensure that the tab on the banjo union abuts the lug on the release cylinder

8 Tighten the bleed valve, then release the lever gradually. Repeat the process until no air bubbles are visible in the fluid leaving the release cylinder and the clutch action feels smooth and progressive.

9 Ensure that the reservoir is topped up above the lower level mark on the sightglass, install the diaphragm and cap and secure with the two screws. Wipe up any spilled fluid and check that there are no leaks from the system. Refit the dust cap over the bleed valve.

10 Install the fairing panel (where applicable). Where applicable, return the front brake lever span adjuster to its original position.

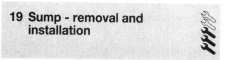

19 Sump - removal and installation

Note: *The sump can be removed with the engine in the frame. If work is being carried out with the engine removed ignore the steps which don't apply.*

Removal

1 On Trophy and Daytona models, remove the fairing lower panels (see Chapter 8). On Tiger models, remove the sump guard (see Chapter 8).
2 Where equipped, remove the oil cooler (see Section 21).
3 Remove the exhaust system (Chapter 4).
4 Drain the engine oil and remove the oil filter (see Chapter 1).
5 Disconnect the wires from the oil pressure switch.

18.6 Locate the spanner and tubing over the bleed valve on the release cylinder

6 Remove all seventeen (3 cylinder) or twenty (4 cylinder) bolts, slackening them evenly in a criss-cross sequence to prevent distortion **(see illustration)**. Withdraw the sump and its gasket. **Note:** *On 3 cylinder engines, the internal oil pipes may stick in the sump - carefully ease them free with a long flat-bladed screwdriver rather than risk distorting them by pulling the sump off.*

7 Recover the large O-ring from the oil filter housing.

8 The internal oil pipe can be unbolted from the base of the crankcase if desired **(see illustration)**. Take note of the exact position of the bolts on 4 cylinder models - their hole diameters differ. Recover the O-rings from the oil pipe.

9 A gauze strainer is located in the sump. Clean the strainer whenever the sump is removed. Remove its five bolts to free the retaining plate and lift out the gauze **(see**

19.6 Sump is retained by seventeen bolts on 3 cylinder engine

illustration). Wash the gauze in solvent. Four cylinder models have a second gauze strainer for the oil cooler; this can be removed after releasing its three bolts.

Installation

10 Remove all traces of gasket from the sump and crankcase mating surfaces.
11 Installed the cleaned oil strainer(s) and tighten the bolts securely **(see illustrations)**.
12 Fit new O-rings to the internal oil pipe(s) and to the oil filter housing **(see illustration)**. Install the oil pipe using new sealing washers on each side of the banjo unions, and tighten the banjo bolts to the specified torque setting **(see illustration)**. On 4 cylinder engines, ensure that the bolts with the larger holes are fitted in their original locations **(see illustration)**.
13 Place a new gasket on the crankcase and install the sump; if the engine is in the frame,

---

19.8 Internal oil pipe is retained by two bolts (arrowed) on 3 cylinder engine

19.9 Oil strainer is retained by five bolts

19.11a Clean the strainer gauze and locate it back in the sump

---

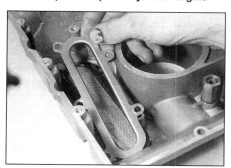

19.11b Secure the strainer with the retaining plate

19.12a Use a new O-ring on the oil filter housing . . .

19.12b . . . and new sealing washers on the oil pipe banjo unions

2

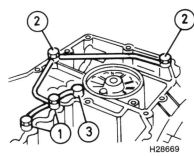

19.12c Use new O-rings (arrowed) on the small oil pipe (3 cylinder only)

use a smear of grease on the gasket to hold it in place as the sump is installed (see illustrations). Check that the bolts are returned to their original locations and tighten them evenly in a criss-cross sequence to the specified torque setting.

14 Reconnect the oil pressure switch wires.

15 Install the oil cooler (see Section 21).

16 Install the exhaust system as described in Chapter 4.

17 Install a new oil filter, then fill the engine with the correct type and quantity of oil as described in Chapter 1. Start the engine and check for leaks.

18 If all is well, fit the fairing lower panels (Trophy and Daytona models) or sump guard (Tiger) (see Chapter 8).

19.12d Ensure that the banjo bolts are fitted in the correct holes when installing the internal oil pipe on 4 cylinder engines

   1 Banjo bolts with 1.5 mm holes
   2 Banjo bolts with 3.0 mm holes
   3 O-ring location

20 Oil pressure relief valve - removal, inspection and installation

Removal

1 Remove the sump (see Section 19). Use a socket to unscrew the relief valve from inside of the sump (see illustration).

Inspection

2 Push the plunger into the relief valve body and check for free movement. If the valve operation is sticky it must be replaced (individual parts are not available).

19.13a Always use a new sump gasket

19.13b Install the sump on the crankcase

20.1 Pressure relief valve is located in sump

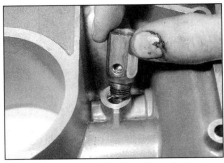

20.3 Apply thread lock to the relief valve threads on installation

Installation

3 Apply a drop of non-permanent thread locking compound to the pressure relief valve threads and tighten the valve to the specified torque setting (see illustration).

4 Install the sump (see Section 19).

21 Oil cooler - removal and installation (where fitted)

Note: *The oil cooler can be removed with the engine in the frame. If work is being carried out with the engine removed ignore the preliminary steps.*

Removal

1 Remove the fairing lower panels (see Chapter 8).

2 Drain the engine oil (see Chapter 1).

3 On 3 cylinder engines, remove the two banjo union bolts and free the oil pipes from their connections on the sump. On 4 cylinder engines the oil feed pipe is retained by a banjo union bolt, and the oil return pipe by a gland nut on the union at the front of the sump; hold the union with an open-ended spanner whilst the gland nut is unscrewed (see illustration).

4 Remove the three bolts, with their collars which retain the oil cooler to its sub-frame.

5 The oil pipes can be released from the oil cooler by removing their banjo union bolts.

Caution: Always counterhold the hexagonal union of the oil cooler when slackening or tightening the banjo bolts. The oil cooler front stone guard is secured by four bolts.

6 Remove the bolts to free the sub-frame from its mounting brackets on the engine.

Installation

7 Installation is a reverse of the removal procedure, noting the following:

  a) Use new sealing washers on each side of the banjo unions.

  b) Tighten the banjo union bolts to the specified torque settings.

  c) On 4 cylinder models, counterhold the return pipe union on the sump whilst the gland nut is tightened.

  d) Refill the engine with oil (see Chapter 1) and check that there are no leaks from the oil cooler pipe connections when the engine is run.

22 Balancer - removal, inspection and installation

3 cylinder models

Note: *The balancer can be removed with the engine in the frame.*

Removal

1 On Trophy and Daytona models, remove the fairing lower panels (see Chapter 8).

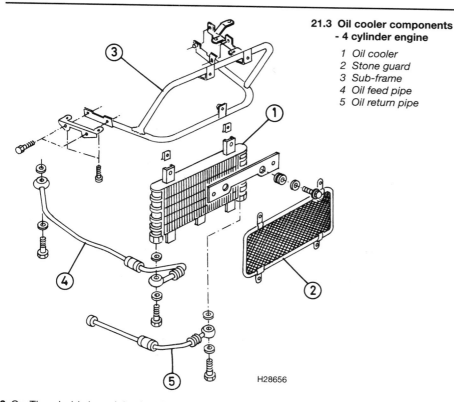

21.3 Oil cooler components - 4 cylinder engine

1 Oil cooler
2 Stone guard
3 Sub-frame
4 Oil feed pipe
5 Oil return pipe

H28656

the balancer gears on the left side of the engine. It will be seen that the drive gear on the crankshaft has two dots on consecutive teeth which will be in the 10 o'clock position. There is a similar dot on the balancer shaft outer gear, which when aligned between the two dots on the drive gear will permit access to the balancer shaft retaining plate screws through the holes in the gear.

6 The balancer shaft gear is a two-piece assembly, the main gear and the outer gear described above. Designed to prevent gear chatter, the outer gear has a different number of teeth to the main gear. Therefore, it is likely that when first inspected, the outer gear dot will not be in alignment with those on the drive gear. To correct this, rotate the crankshaft as necessary until its dot lies between the dots on the drive gear teeth, remembering at every stage to align the No. 1 T mark on the ignition rotor with the pick-up coil. Alternatively, remove the large circlip, convex washer and plain washer from the end of the balancer shaft and withdraw the outer gear **(see illustration)**.

7 With access to the balancer shaft retaining plate bolts, pass a Torx bit through the holes in the balancer gear and slacken the retaining plate bolts. Note that the screws will not withdraw through the gear - the objective is to slacken them just enough for the plate to drop down via its elongated holes.

8 When the retaining plate is heard to drop down out of engagement with the balancer shaft, withdraw the shaft from the crankcase.

2 On Thunderbird models, free its clip and pull the breather hose off the union on the crankcase left cover **(see illustration)**. All early models (up to VIN 4338) have an external oil pipe to the crankcase left cover - remove the banjo union bolts and washers to free the pipe from the left cover.

3 On all models remove the ten bolts to free the crankcase left cover and gasket **(see illustration)**. On Thunderbird models, retrieve the cover dowels if they are loose. **Note:** *Have a drain tray ready to catch any escaping oil, particularly if the bike is on its side stand.*

4 Moving to the other side of the engine, remove the balancer shaft end cover (three bolts) **(see illustration)** and the crankcase right end cover (seven bolts). On Thunderbird models, a combined cover is fitted to the crankcase right side, retained by eight bolts **(see illustration)**.

5 Using a wrench on the large hexagon, rotate the crankshaft until the T mark for cylinder No. 1 aligns with the centre of the pick-up coil **(see illustration 9.2b)**. Observe

22.2 Release its clip and pull the breather hose off its union (arrowed) - Thunderbird model

22.3 Remove the ten bolts to free the crankshaft left end cover

2

22.4a All models except the Thunderbird have a separate balancer end cover on the right side of the engine

22.4b A combined cover is fitted to Thunderbird models

22.6 Balancer shaft gear can be disassembled after removal of the circlip

22.10a Needle roller bearing inner race is retained to balancer shaft by a circlip . . .

22.10b . . . and the bearing itself is located in the crankcase

22.10c The needle roller bearing can only be removed once the peg (arrowed) in the crankcase surface has been withdrawn

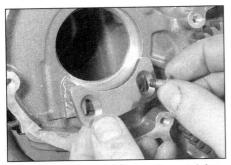

22.11a Apply thread lock to the retaining plate screws . . .

22.11b . . . and install them so that the plate is in the lowest position - leave the screws loose at this stage

22.12a Install the balancer shaft . . .

22.12b . . . guiding it into the needle roller bearing

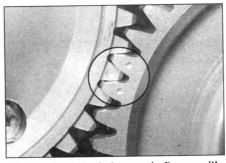

22.12c Mesh the balancer shaft gear with the drive gear so that the teeth dots align

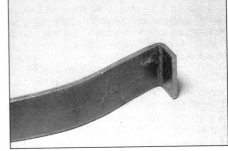

22.13a Make up a tool to access the retaining plate . . .

Inspection

9 Inspect the teeth of all gears for signs of wear or damage. Early models (up to VIN 6957) were fitted with anti-backlash springs in the balancer shaft outer gear.

10 Check the ball bearing on the shaft left end, noting that if worn, the complete balancer shaft must be replaced. The bearing on the right end of the shaft is of the caged needle roller type; its inner race is secured by a circlip and its outer race by peg which can only be accessed after the crankcases have been separated **(see illustrations)**.

Installation

11 Clean the threads of the retaining plate screws and apply a drop of non-permanent thread locking compound to their them **(see illustration)**. Secure the retaining plate to the

crankcase so that it is at its lowest setting, but leave the screws fairly loose **(see illustration)**.
12 Check that the crankshaft is positioned so that the No. 1 cylinder T mark on the ignition rotor aligns with centre of the pick-up coil. Install the balancer shaft in the crankcase, guiding its left end into the needle bearing **(see illustrations)**. Mesh the balancer shaft gear with the drive gear so that their dots align (see Step 5) **(see illustration)**. **Note:** *If the balancer outer gear is in place on the balancer shaft, use finger pressure only to hold the main gear and outer gear teeth in alignment while they are meshed with the drive gear teeth.*
13 Some means must now be devised to lift the retaining plate into engagement with the balancer shaft whilst the screws are tightened. We found a length of steel strip with the end bent over at a right angle, to be ideal **(see**

illustration). With the tool holding the retaining plate in position, tighten the screws to the specified torque **(see illustration)**.

22.13b . . . and lift the retaining plate into position whilst the screws are tightened through the access holes in the gear

22.14a If removed, install the outer gear . . .

22.14b . . . followed by the washer . . .

22.14c . . . and convex washer

22.14d Secure the outer gear components with the circlip

22.16a Crankshaft left end cover noise damper is retained by six screws

22.16b Use a new gasket when installing the crankshaft left end cover

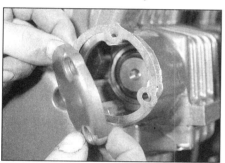

22.17 Fit a new gasket and install the balancer shaft end cover - all models except Thunderbird

14 If previously removed, install the outer gear, plain washer and convex washer (dished side facing inwards), then retain them with the large circlip **(see illustrations)**.

15 On Thunderbird models, the oil seal set in the crankshaft left end cover must be replaced whenever the cover is disturbed - failure to do so will prevent the engine breather from operating properly. Prise the old seal out with a flat-bladed screwdriver. The new seal is supplied complete with a shaped mandrel; press the seal into the cover so that it lies just below the face of the cover recess. Remove the mandrel from the seal immediately before the cover is fitted to the engine. *Caution: It is important that the seal is allowed 15 minutes to form on the breather tube before the crankshaft is rotated from its present position - the breather will not operate correctly if this*

precaution is not observed.

16 All models have sound absorbing material housed inside the crankcase cover; if required, this can be accessed by removing the retaining screws **(see illustration)**. Install a new gasket on the crankcase and on Thunderbird models only, install the two dowels **(see illustration)**. Install the cover and tighten its bolts evenly in a criss-cross sequence to the specified torque setting. On early models, reconnect the external oil pipe using new sealing washers. On Thunderbird models, reconnect the breather hose. *Caution: On Thunderbird models, make sure to observe the time requirement in Step 15.*

17 Using new gaskets, install the crankcase right cover and balancer end cover (one-piece cover on Thunderbird), tightening the bolts securely **(see illustration)**.

18 Check the oil level and top-up if any was lost whilst the covers were removed.

19 Install the fairing lower panels on Trophy and Daytona models.

4 cylinder models

Note: *It should be possible to remove the balancer shafts with the engine in the frame. However, working will be awkward and aligning the marks on the shafts may prove difficult due to limited access. Removal of the engine is advised.*

Removal

20 Remove the sump (see Section 19). Where fitted, remove the oil cooler (see Section 21).

21 Remove the crankcase right cover and using a spanner on the engine turning hexagon, rotate the engine in the direction of the arrow on the ignition rotor so that the T 1.4 mark aligns with the centre of the ignition pick-up coil. Inspect both balancer weights for alignment marks **(see illustration 22.27)**. If they are indistinct or none are found, mark your own with white paint or a marker pen.

22 Slacken off the balancer shaft pinch bolts, and the two clamp retaining bolts, then pull the clamp off the shaft ends **(see illustration 22.24)**.

23 Hold the balancer weight from inside the sump area and withdraw the shaft from the side of the crankcase. Retrieve the thrustwashers from each end of the weight assembly. Label the shafts front and rear to ensure that they are returned to their original locations.

Inspection

24 Separate the balancer gear from the weight and inspect the rubber damping blocks. If damaged or deteriorated, these must be replaced **(see illustration)**.

25 Check the needle roller bearings in the weight. If damaged or worn they must be extracted and new ones pressed into place.

Installation

26 Install new O-rings on the end of each balancer shaft.

27 With the engine positioned as described in Step 21, install the first weight in the crankcase, complete with thrustwashers, so that its alignment mark corresponds with that

2

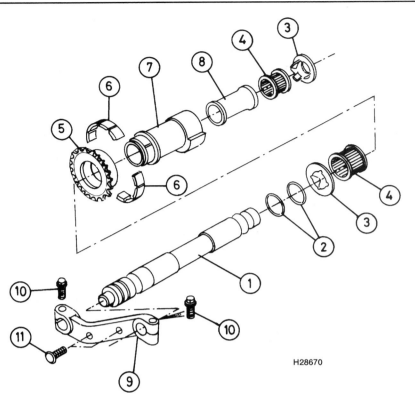

H28670

22.24 Balancer shaft components - 4 cylinder models

1 *Balancer shaft*	5 *Drive gear*	9 *Clamp*
2 *Shaft O-rings*	6 *Rubber damping blocks*	10 *Shaft pinch bolts*
3 *Thrustwashers*	7 *Balancer weight*	11 *Clamp retaining bolts*
4 *Needle roller bearings*	8 *Spacer*	

on the casing **(see illustration)**. Holding the weight in this position, slide the balancer shaft into the crankcase so that the dot on its end is facing downwards (toward to the sump). Install the second weight and balancer shaft in the same way, making sure that the drive gears mesh correctly.

28 Install the balancer clamp over the shaft ends and secure with its retaining screws. Using a flat-bladed screwdriver in the front balancer shaft, turn it clockwise until it will turn no further, then back it off a fraction; hold this position and tighten the shaft pinch bolt **(see illustration)**.

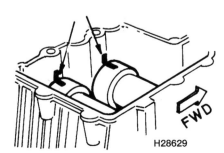

H28629

22.27 Balancer shaft weight and crankcase alignment marks (arrowed)

29 Using a flat-bladed screwdriver in the rear balancer shaft, turn it anti-clockwise until it will turn no further, then back it off a fraction; hold it here, and tighten the shaft pinch bolt.

30 Install the crankcase right cover using a new gasket. Install the sump (see Section 19), oil cooler (see Section 21) and refill the engine with oil (see Chapter 1).

31 Start the engine and whilst allowing it to idle, listen for any noise from the balancers. A rattle indicates that the balancer gears are too

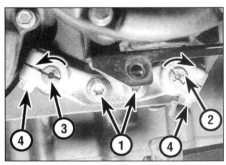

22.28 Balancer shaft adjustment

1 *Clamp retaining bolts*
2 *Front balancer shaft*
3 *Rear balancer shaft*
4 *Shaft pinch bolts*

loosely meshed, whereas a whine indicates they are too tightly meshed. Make adjustment whilst the engine is idling, noting that only one balancer pinch bolt should be slackened and adjustment made at a time.

23 Crankcase - separation and reassembly

Separation

1 To gain access to the crankshaft and connecting rods, bearings, alternator/ starter drive, oil pump and transmission components, the crankcase must be split into two parts. **Note:** *Early models have a detachable cover on the upper crankcase which permits removal of the alternator driveshaft and starter clutch (see Section 32). Later models do not have the detachable cover. Note that the crankcase bolt locations differ accordingly.*

2 To enable the crankcases to be separated, the engine must be removed from the frame (see Section 5) and the following components first removed with reference to the relevant Sections.

  a) *Camshafts and tappets*
  b) *Cam chain and tensioner blade*
  c) *Cylinder head and cam chain guide blade**
  d) *Cylinder liners and pistons**
  e) *Clutch*
  f) *Engine left cover*
  g) *Sump*
  h) *Ignition pick-up coil (see Chapter 5)*
  i) *Alternator and starter motor (Chapter 9)*

*If the crankcase halves are being separated just to examine the transmission components, crankshaft, oil pump or alternator/starter clutch drive, then there is no need to remove the cylinder head.

3 If a complete engine overhaul is planned, also remove the balancer(s) (see Section 22), the oil galley plug, the water pump (see Chapter 3), and the neutral switch (see Chapter 9).

4 On early engines (with an alternator driveshaft/starter clutch access cover), remove the nine bolts from the top of the crankcase, then withdraw the cover and gasket.

5 With the crankcase the right way up, slacken and remove all bolts from the top of the crankcase following the numbered sequence **(see illustrations)**. **Note:** *As each bolt is removed, store it in its relative position in a cardboard template of the crankcase halves. This will ensure that all bolts are installed in the correct location on reassembly.*

6 Turn the crankcase upside down. Again, following the numbered sequence, slacken and remove all bolts from the bottom of the crankcase **(see illustrations)**. **Note:** *As each bolt is removed, store it in its relative position in a cardboard template of the crankcase halves. This will ensure that all bolts are*

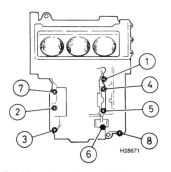

**23.5a Upper crankcase bolt sequence -
early engines with access cover (see text)**
Bolt locations same for 4 cylinder engines

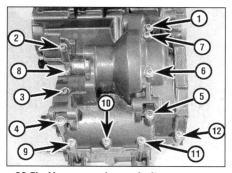

**23.5b Upper crankcase bolt sequence -
later engines (see text)**
Bolt locations same for 4 cylinder engines

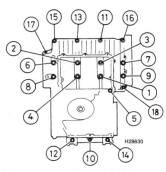

**23.6a Lower crankcase bolt sequence -
early 3 cylinder engines (see text)**

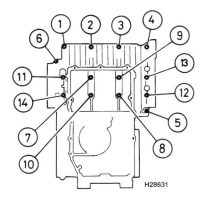

**23.6b Lower crankcase bolt sequence -
later 3 cylinder engines (see text)**

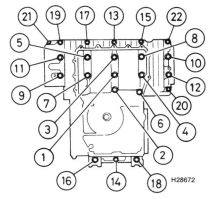

**23.6c Lower crankcase bolt sequence -
early 4 cylinder engines (see text)**

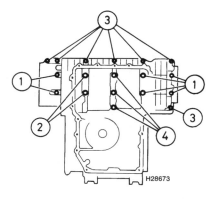

**23.6d Lower crankcase bolt sequence -
later 4 cylinder engines (see text)**

*installed in the correct location on reassembly.
Also, take note of any mounting brackets on
the bolts and store them with the bolts to
ensure correct reassembly.*
7 Carefully lift off the lower crankcase half,
leaving the crankshaft and transmission shafts
in the upper half of the crankcase. As the
lower half is lifted away take care not to
dislodge or lose any main bearing inserts.
Note: *If it won't come easily away, make sure
all fasteners have been removed. Don't pry
against the crankcase mating surfaces or they
will leak; initial separation can be achieved by
tapping gently with a soft-faced mallet.*
8 Remove the three locating dowels from the
upper crankcase half **(see illustration)**.

Discard the clutch pushrod oil seal; it must be
replaced with a new one on reassembly.
Retrieve the O-ring from the oil pump outlet
and obtain a new one for reassembly.

Reassembly

9 Remove all traces of sealant from the
crankcase mating surfaces.
10 Ensure that all components are in place in
the upper and lower crankcase halves. Note
the instructions in Section 28 concerning
applying thread lock to the transmission shaft
bearing outer races.
11 Lubricate the transmission shafts and
crankshaft with clean engine oil, then use a
rag soaked in high flash-point solvent to wipe

over the gasket surfaces of both halves to
remove all traces of oil.
12 Install the three locating dowels in the
upper crankcase half **(see illustration 23.8)**.
13 Apply a small amount of suitable sealant
to the mating surface of the upper crankcase
half **(see illustration)**. **Caution: Take care
not to apply an excessive amount of
sealant, as it will ooze out when the case
halves are assembled and may obstruct oil
passages and prevent the bearings from
seating.**
14 Install a new O-ring to the oil pump outlet
(see illustration).
15 Check the position of the gearshift cam,
gearshift forks and transmission shafts - make

2

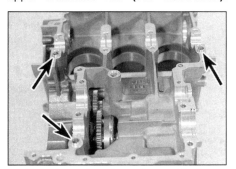

**23.8 Three dowels are located in the
crankcase mating surface (arrowed)**

**23.13 Smear sealant on the crankcase
mating surfaces**

**23.14 Use a new O-ring on the oil pump
outlet**

23.16 Ensure that the gearshift forks engage the gear grooves correctly as the cases are joined (arrowed)

23.18 Check that any brackets are returned to their original locations

23.25 Press a new clutch pushrod oil seal into the crankcase joint

sure they're in the neutral position (ie the mainshaft and countershaft rotate independently of each other).

16 Make sure that the main bearing shells are in position and carefully guide the lower crankcase half onto the upper half. The gearshift forks must engage with their respective slots in the transmission gears as the halves are joined **(see illustration)**.

17 Check that the lower crankcase half is correctly seated and that all shafts are free to rotate. **Note:** *If the casings are not correctly seated, remove the lower crankcase half and investigate the problem. Do not attempt to pull them together using the crankcase bolts as the casing will crack and be ruined.*

18 Clean the threads of the lower crankcase bolts and insert them in their original locations, including any brackets **(see illustration)**. Secure all bolts hand-tight at this stage.

19 Turn the crankcase over so that it is upright. Clean the threads of the upper crankcase bolts and install them in their original locations. Secure all bolts hand-tight at this stage.

20 Turn the crankcase over and tighten the lower bolts to 12 Nm, working in the numbered sequence **(see illustrations 23.6a, b, c or d)**.

21 Turn the crankcase over and tighten all upper crankcase bolts to 12 Nm, working in the numbered sequence **(see illustrations 23.5a or 5b)**.

22 Turn the crankcase over and tighten the 8 mm lower crankcase bolts to 28 Nm in the numerical sequence.

23 Turn the crankcase over and tighten the 8 mm upper crankcase bolts to 28 Nm in the numerical sequence.

24 With all crankcase fasteners tightened, check that the crankshaft and transmission shafts rotate smoothly and easily. If there are any signs of undue stiffness or of any other problem, the fault must be rectified before proceeding further.

25 Using thumb pressure, push a new clutch pushrod oil seal in the left side of the crankcase **(see illustration)**.

26 Install all other removed assemblies in the reverse of the sequence in Steps 3 and 2.

27 When installing the crankshaft left end cover on the Thunderbird model and all later 4 cylinder engined models (from VIN 2971 on), the oil seal set in the cover must be replaced with a new one. Failure to do so will prevent the crankcase breather from operating properly. Prise the old seal out with a flat-bladed screwdriver. The new seal is supplied complete with a shaped mandrel; leaving the mandrel in place, press the seal squarely into the cover so that it lies just below the face of the cover recess. Remove the mandrel from the seal immediately before the cover is fitted to the engine. *Caution: It is important that the seal is allowed 15 minutes to form on the breather tube before the crankshaft is rotated from its present position - the breather will not operate correctly is this precaution is not observed. If care is not taken with replacement and installation, engine oil may leak past the seal and into the crankcase breather system.*

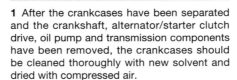

24 Crankcase - inspection

1 After the crankcases have been separated and the crankshaft, alternator/starter clutch drive, oil pump and transmission components have been removed, the crankcases should be cleaned thoroughly with new solvent and dried with compressed air.

2 Remove any oil gallery plugs that haven't already been removed. All oil passages should be blown out with compressed air.

3 All traces of old gasket sealant should be removed from the mating surfaces. Minor damage to the surfaces can be cleaned up with a fine sharpening stone or grindstone. *Caution: Be very careful not to nick or gouge the crankcase mating surfaces or leaks will result. Check both crankcase halves very carefully for cracks and other damage.*

4 Small cracks or holes in aluminium castings may be repaired with an epoxy resin adhesive as a temporary measure. Permanent repairs can only be effected by argon-arc welding, and only a specialist in this process is in a

position to advise on the economy or practical aspect of such a repair. If any damage is found that can't be repaired, replace the crankcase halves as a set.

5 Damaged threads can be economically reclaimed by using a diamond section wire insert, of the Helicoil type, which is easily fitted after drilling and re-tapping the affected thread. Most motorcycle dealers and small engineering firms offer a service of this kind.

6 Sheared studs or screws can usually be removed with screw extractors, which consist of a tapered, left thread screws of very hard steel. These are inserted into a pre-drilled hole in the stud, and usually succeed in dislodging the most stubborn stud or screw. If a problem arises which seems beyond your scope, it is worth consulting a professional engineering firm before condemning an otherwise sound casing. Many of these firms advertise regularly in the motorcycle press.

25 Main and connecting rod bearings - general information

1 Even though main and connecting rod bearings are generally replaced with new ones during the engine overhaul, the old bearings should be retained for close examination as they may reveal valuable information about the condition of the engine.

2 Bearing failure occurs mainly because of lack of lubrication, the presence of dirt or other foreign particles, overloading the engine and/or corrosion. Regardless of the cause of bearing failure, it must be corrected before the engine is reassembled to prevent it from happening again.

3 When examining the bearings, remove the main bearings from the crankcase halves and the rod bearings from the connecting rods and caps and lay them out on a clean surface in the same general position as their location on the crankshaft journals. This will make it possible for you to match any noted bearing problems with the corresponding crankshaft journal.

4 Dirt and other foreign particles get into the engine in a variety of ways. It may be left in

26.2 Measuring connecting rod side clearance

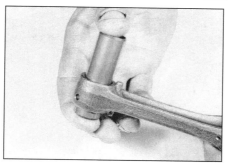

26.5 Slip the piston pin into the connecting rod small-end and feel for freeplay

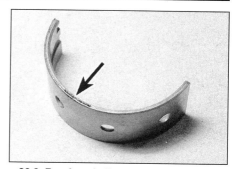

26.8 Bearing shells carry a colour code size marking (arrowed)

the engine during assembly or it may pass through filters or breathers. It may get into the oil and from there into the bearings. Metal chips from machining operations and normal engine wear are often present. Abrasives are sometimes left in engine components after reconditioning operations, especially when parts are not thoroughly cleaned using the proper cleaning methods. Whatever the source, these foreign objects often end up imbedded in the soft bearing material and are easily recognised. Large particles will not imbed in the bearing and will score or gouge the bearing and journal. The best prevention for this cause of bearing failure is to clean all parts thoroughly and keep everything spotlessly clean during engine reassembly. Frequent and regular oil and filter changes are also recommended.

5 Lack of lubrication or lubrication breakdown has a number of interrelated causes. Excessive heat (which thins the oil), overloading (which squeezes the oil from the bearing face) and oil leakage or throw off from excessive bearing clearances, worn oil pump or high engine speeds all contribute to lubrication breakdown. Blocked oil passages will also starve a bearing and destroy it. When lack of lubrication is the cause of bearing failure, the bearing material is wiped or extruded from the steel backing of the bearing. Temperatures may increase to the point where the steel backing and the journal turn blue from overheating.

6 Riding habits can have a definite effect on bearing life. Full throttle low speed operation, or labouring the engine, puts very high loads on bearings, which tend to squeeze out the oil film. These loads cause the bearings to flex, which produces fine cracks in the bearing face (fatigue failure). Eventually the bearing material will loosen in pieces and tear away from the steel backing. Short trip riding leads to corrosion of bearings, as insufficient engine heat is produced to drive off the condensed water and corrosive gases produced. These products collect in the engine oil, forming acid and sludge. As the oil is carried to the engine bearings, the acid attacks and corrodes the bearing material.

7 Incorrect bearing installation during engine assembly will lead to bearing failure as well.

Tight fitting bearings which leave insufficient bearing oil clearances result in oil starvation. Dirt or foreign particles trapped behind a bearing insert result in high spots on the bearing which lead to failure.

8 To avoid bearing problems, clean all parts thoroughly before reassembly, double check all bearing clearance measurements and lubricate the new bearings with clean engine oil during installation.

26 Connecting rods - removal, inspection and installation

Removal

1 Separate the crankcase halves as described in Section 23. Note that the pistons must be removed (see Section 14) because they will not pass through the upper crankcase half with the connecting rods. Lift the crankshaft out of the upper crankcase.

2 Before removing the rods from the crankshaft, measure the side clearance on each rod with a feeler blade (see illustration). If the clearance on any rod is greater than the service limit listed in this Chapter's Specifications, that rod will have to be replaced with a new one.

3 Using paint or a felt marker pen, mark the relevant cylinder number on each connecting rod and bearing cap (No. 1 cylinder on left end of crankshaft). Mark across the cap-to-connecting rod join to ensure that the cap is fitted the correct way around on reassembly.

4 Unscrew the big-end cap nuts and separate the connecting rod, cap and both bearing shells from the crankpin. Keep the cap, nuts and (if they are to be reused) the bearing shells together in their correct sequence.

Inspection

Connecting rods

5 Check the connecting rods for cracks and other obvious damage Lubricate the piston pin for each rod, install it in its original rod and check for play (see illustration). If it wobbles, replace the connecting rod and/or the pin. If the necessary measuring equipment is available measure the pin diameter and

connecting rod bore and check the readings obtained do not exceed the limits given in this Chapter's Specifications. Replace components that are worn beyond the specified limit.

6 Refer to Section 25 and examine the connecting rod bearing shells. If they are scored, badly scuffed or appear to have seized, new shells must be installed. Always replace the shells in the connecting rods as a set. If they are badly damaged, check the corresponding crankpin. Evidence of extreme heat, such as discoloration, indicates that lubrication failure has occurred. Be sure to thoroughly check the oil pump and pressure relief valve as well as all oil holes and passages before reassembling the engine.

7 Have the rods checked for twist and bending by a Triumph dealer if you are in doubt about their straightness.

Bearing shell selection

8 The connecting rod bearing running clearance is controlled in production by selecting one of three grades of bearing shell. The grades are indicated by a colour-coding marked on the edge of each shell (see illustration). In order, from the thickest to the thinnest, the insert grades are: blue, red, white. New bearing inserts are selected as follows using the crankpin journal diameter and connecting rod size marking.

9 Use a micrometer to determine the crankpin journal diameter. Inspect the connecting rod for its size marking, either the letter A or B (see illustration).

2

26.9 Connecting rod size marking is located on rod cap (arrowed)

26.14 Tighten the connecting rod nuts to the specified torque

26.15 Place the Plastigauge scale next to the flattened Plastigauge to measure the bearing clearance

10 Match the journal diameter with the rod marking and select a new set of bearing shells using the following table.

Con-rod marking	Crankpin journal diameter	Shell colour
A	40.954 to 40.960 mm	White
A	40.946 to 40.953 mm	Red
B	40.954 to 40.960 mm	Red
B	40.946 to 40.953 mm	Blue

Oil clearance check

11 Whether new bearing shells are being fitted or the original ones are being re-used, the connecting rod bearing oil clearance should be checked prior to reassembly.

12 Clean the backs of the bearing shells and the bearing locations in both the connecting rod and cap.

13 Press the bearing shells into their locations, ensuring that the tab on each shell engages the notch in the connecting rod/cap. Make sure the bearings are fitted in the correct locations and take care not to touch any shell's bearing surface with your fingers.

14 Cut several lengths of the appropriate size Plastigauge (they should be slightly shorter than the width of the crankpin). Place a strand of Plastigauge on each (cleaned) crankpin journal and fit the (clean) connecting rod assemblies, shells and caps. Make sure the cap is fitted the correct way around so the previously made markings align and tighten the bearing cap nuts to the specified torque wrench setting whilst ensuring that the connecting rod does not rotate **(see illustration)**. Take care not to disturb the Plastigauge. Slacken the cap nuts and remove the connecting rod assemblies, again taking great care not to rotate the crankshaft.

15 Compare the width of the crushed Plastigauge on each crankpin to the scale printed on the Plastigauge envelope to obtain the connecting rod bearing oil clearance **(see illustration)**.

16 If the clearance is not within the specified limits, the bearing shells may be the wrong grade (or excessively worn if the original shells are being reused). Before deciding that different grade shells are needed, make sure that no dirt or oil was trapped between the bearing shells and the connecting rod or cap when the clearance was measured. If the clearance is excessive, even with new shells (of the correct size), the crankpin is worn and the crankshaft should be replaced.

17 On completion carefully scrape away all traces of the Plastigauge material from the crankpin and bearing shells using a fingernail or other object which is unlikely to score the shells.

Installation

Note: *New connecting rod bolts and nuts must be used whenever the rods have been disassembled.*

18 Install the bearing shells in the connecting rods and caps. Lubricate the shells with new engine oil and assemble the components on the crankpin. **Note:** *The oilway in the rod must face to the rear of the engine when installed on the crankshaft (see illustration 14.32a).* Install the new connecting rod bolts and nuts, having applied a smear of molybdenum disulphide grease to the bolt threads and nut face; tighten them finger-tight at this stage. Check to make sure that all components have been returned to their original locations using the marks made on disassembly.

19 The connecting rod nuts must be tightened in the three stages specified (see Specifications) - do not tighten to the full setting in the first stage. Torque both nuts to the first setting, then both to the second and finally both to the third setting.

20 Check that the rod rotates freely on the crankpin, then install those for the other cylinders.

21 Install the crankshaft and assemble the crankcase halves (see Section 23).

27 Crankshaft and main bearings - removal, inspection and installation

Removal

1 Separate the crankcase halves as described in Section 23.

2 The crankshaft can be removed with the connecting rods attached if the pistons have previously been removed (see Section 14). Alternatively, the connecting rod caps can be removed, leaving the rods and pistons in the upper crankcase.

3 On all later 4 cylinder engined models (VIN 2971 on) and the Thunderbird model, unscrew the breather disc from the left end of the crankshaft and, where fitted, remove the locating dowel.

4 Lift the crankshaft out of the upper crankcase half, taking care not to dislodge the bearing shells **(see illustration)**.

5 The main bearing shells can be removed from the crankcase halves by pushing their centres to the side, then lifting them out **(see illustration)**. Keep the bearing shells in order. All shells are of the grooved type except for later 4 cylinder models, which have plain shells fitted to journals 1, 3 and 5.

Inspection

6 Clean the crankshaft with solvent, using a rifle-cleaning brush to scrub out the oil passages. If available, blow the crank dry with compressed air.

7 Refer to Section 25 and examine the main bearing shells. If they are scored, badly scuffed or appear to have been seized, new bearings must be installed. Always replace the main bearings as a set. If they are badly damaged, check the corresponding crankshaft journal. Evidence of extreme heat,

27.4 Lift the crankshaft out of the upper crankcase

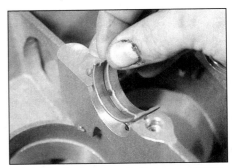

27.5 Slip the bearing shells to one side to remove them from their saddles

such as discoloration, indicates that lubrication failure has occurred. Be sure to thoroughly check the oil pump and pressure relief valve as well as all oil holes and passages before reassembling the engine.

8 The crankshaft journals should be given a close visual examination, paying particular attention where damaged bearing shells have been discovered. If the journals are scored or pitted in any way a new crankshaft will be required. Note that undersizes are not available, precluding the option of re-grinding the crankshaft.

Bearing shell selection

9 The main bearing running clearance is controlled in production by selecting one of four grades of bearing shell. The grades are indicated by a colour-coding marked on the edge of each shell **(see illustration 26.8)**. In order, from the thickest to the thinnest, the insert grades are: Green, Blue, Red, White. New bearing inserts are selected with reference to the following chart, having measured the crankshaft journal diameter and the crankcase bore diameter.

10 Measure the crankshaft journal diameter with a micrometer **(see illustration)**. The crankcase bore diameter is measured with the shells removed and the crankcase halves bolted together - the bore diameters are then measured with a hole gauge and micrometer.

Crankcase bore diameter	Crankshaft journal dia.	Shell colour
41.118 to 41.126 mm	37.969 to 37.976 mm	White
41.118 to 41.126 mm	37.960 to 37.968 mm	Red
41.127 to 41.135 mm	37.969 to 37.976 mm	Red
41.127 to 41.135 mm	37.960 to 37.968 mm	Blue
41.136 to 41.144 mm	37.969 to 37.976 mm	Blue
41.136 to 41.144 mm	37.960 to 37.968 mm	Green

27.10 Measuring the crankshaft journal diameter

Oil clearance check

11 Whether new bearing shells are being fitted or the original ones are being re-used, the main bearing oil clearance should be checked prior to reassembly.

12 Clean the backs of the bearing shells and the bearing locations in both crankcase halves.

13 Press the bearing shells into their locations, ensuring that the tab on each shell engages in the notch in the crankcase. Make sure the bearings are fitted in the correct locations and take care not to touch any shell's bearing surface with your fingers.

14 Ensure that the shells and crankshaft are clean and dry. Lay the crankshaft in position in the upper crankcase.

15 Cut several lengths of the appropriate size Plastigauge (they should be slightly shorter than the width of the crankshaft journal). Place a strand of Plastigauge on each (cleaned) crankshaft journal.

16 Carefully install the lower crankcase half on to the upper half. Make sure that the gearshift forks (if fitted) engage with their respective slots in the transmission gears as the halves are joined. Check that the lower crankcase half is correctly seated. **Note:** *Do not tighten the crankcase bolts if the casing is not correctly seated.* Install the eight (3 cylinder) or ten (4 cylinder) 8 mm lower crankcase bolts in their original locations and, starting from the centre and working outwards in a criss-cross pattern, tighten them to the specified torque setting. Make sure that the crankshaft is not rotated as the bolts are tightened.

17 Slacken and remove the crankcase bolts, working in a criss-cross pattern from the outside in, then carefully lift off the lower crankcase half, making sure the Plastigauge is not disturbed.

18 Compare the width of the crushed Plastigauge on each crankshaft journal to the scale printed on the Plastigauge envelope to obtain the main bearing oil clearance **(see illustration 26.15)**.

19 If the clearance is not within the specified limits, the bearing shells may be the wrong grade (or excessively worn if the original inserts are being reused). Before deciding that different grade shells are needed, make sure that no dirt or oil was trapped between the bearing shells and the crankcase halves when the clearance was measured. If the clearance is excessive, even with new shells (of the correct size), the crankshaft journal is worn and the crankshaft should be replaced.

20 On completion carefully scrape away all traces of the Plastigauge material from the crankshaft journal and bearing shells; use a fingernail or other object which is unlikely to score them.

Installation

21 Clean the backs of the bearing shells and the bearing recesses in both crankcase

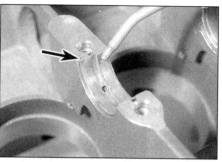

27.22 Engage the tab on the shell with the notch in the casing (arrowed). Lubricate the shells with engine oil

halves. If new shells are being fitted, ensure that all traces of the protective grease are cleaned off using paraffin. Wipe dry the shells and crankcase halves with a lint-free cloth.

22 Press the bearing shells into their locations. Make sure the tab on each shell engages in the notch in the casing and lubricate the shell with clean engine oil **(see illustration)**. Make sure the bearings are fitted in the correct locations and take care not to touch any shell's bearing surface with your fingers.

23 Lower the crankshaft into position in the upper crankcase.

24 Fit the connecting rod caps to the crankshaft as described in Section 26 if they were disconnected.

25 On all later 4 cylinder engined models (VIN 2971 on) and the Thunderbird model, install the breather disc (and its dowel, where fitted) to the left end of the crankshaft. Tighten the breather discs screws to the specified torque setting.

26 Reassemble the crankcase halves as described in Section 23.

28 Transmission shafts - removal and installation

Removal

1 Separate the crankcase halves as described in Section 23.

2 Lift the countershaft out of the lower crankcase half. Retrieve the bearing dowel pin from the needle bearing outer race location. The ball bearing on the left end of the shaft is located by a complete ring which remains on the shaft.

3 Lift the mainshaft out of the lower crankcase half. Recover the mainshaft bearing half ring from the right (clutch) end and the dowel pin from the left end. If the clutch outer drum was not removed prior to crankcase separation, it can be withdrawn at this stage.

4 If necessary, the transmission shafts can be disassembled and inspected for wear or damage as described in Section 29.

28.5a Check that the needle roller bearing outer race dowels (arrowed) are in position in the upper crankcase

28.5b Smear locking compound on the bearing locations in the upper crankcase

28.6a Install the mainshaft so that the hole in the needle roller bearing outer race engages the dowel . . .

28.6b . . . and locate the ball bearing with the half ring

28.7a Install the countershaft so that the hole in the needle roller bearing outer race engages the dowel . . .

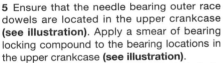

28.7b . . . and locate the bearing locating ring and oil seal lip with the grooves in the casing (arrowed)

Installation

5 Ensure that the needle bearing outer race dowels are located in the upper crankcase **(see illustration)**. Apply a smear of bearing locking compound to the bearing locations in the upper crankcase **(see illustration)**.

6 Install the mainshaft, locating the hole in its needle bearing outer race with the dowel **(see illustration)**. Locate the bearing half ring in the ball bearing groove so that it bridges both casing halves when reassembled **(see illustration)**. The clutch can be installed on the mainshaft prior to crankcase reassembly or afterwards (see Section 15).

7 If not already done, slip the old oil seal off the countershaft left end and replace it with a new seal **(see illustration 29.37d)**. Install the countershaft in the upper crankcase so that the hole in the needle bearing outer race locates over the dowel, and so that the bearing ring and oil seal lip both locate in their grooves **(see illustrations)**.

8 Ensure that the gears of both shafts mesh correct and position them so that they're in the neutral position (mainshaft can be turned whilst countershaft is held stationary).

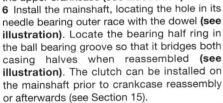

29 Transmission shafts - disassembly, inspection and reassembly

1 Remove the shafts from the casing as described in Section 28.

Mainshaft

Disassembly

2 Slide off the needle roller bearing outer race from the left end of the shaft **(see illustration)**.

3 Remove the circlip from the shaft end and withdraw the needle roller bearing inner race and thrustwasher. Slide the second gear off the shaft.

4 On Speed Triple and Thunderbird models (5-speed transmission), slide the sleeve off

> **HAYNES HINT**
> When disassembling the transmission shafts, place the parts on a long rod or thread a wire through them to keep them in order and facing the proper direction.

the shaft. On all other models (6-speed transmission), slide the 6th gear and its bush off the shaft.

5 Slide the thrustwasher off the shaft and

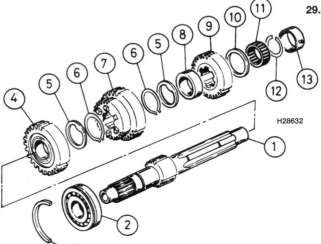

29.2 Mainshaft components

1 Mainshaft
2 Ball bearing
3 Locating ring
4 5th gear
5 Splined thrustwasher
6 Circlip
7 3rd/4th gear
8 Sleeve (Speed Triple and Thunderbird), 6th gear (other models)
9 2nd gear
10 Plain thrustwasher
11 Needle roller bearing
12 Circlip
13 Bearing outer race

H28632

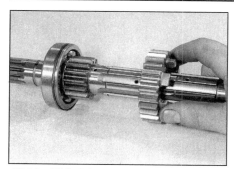

29.14a Slide 5th gear on the mainshaft so its dogs face away from integral 1st gear

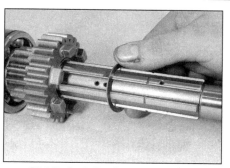

29.14b Install a thrustwasher . . .

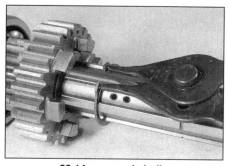

29.14c . . . and circlip

29.14d Ensure that the circlip locates in its groove

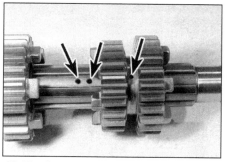

29.15a Combined 3rd/4th gear is installed with the smaller (3rd) gear facing 5th gear. Align the oil holes (arrowed)

29.15b Install a circlip in the shaft groove . . .

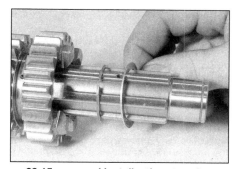

29.15c . . . and install a thrustwasher against the circlip

29.16a Slip the 6th gear bush on the mainshaft so that their oil holes align (arrowed) . . .

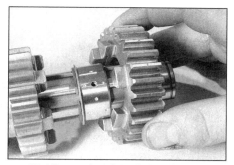

29.16b . . . then install the 6th gear

remove the circlip to free the combined 3rd/4th gear.

6 Remove the circlip, followed by the thrustwasher and 5th gear.

Inspection

7 Wash all of the components in clean solvent and dry them off.

8 Check the gear teeth for cracking and other obvious damage. Check the 6th gear bush and the surface in the inner diameter of the gear for scoring or heat discoloration. If the gear or bush is damaged, replace it.

9 Inspect the dogs and the dog holes in the gears for excessive wear. Replace the paired gears as a set if necessary.

10 Measure the gearshift fork groove width in the 3rd/4th gear as described in Section 30.

11 The shaft is unlikely to sustain damage unless the engine has seized, placing an unusually high loading on the transmission, or the machine has covered a very high mileage. Check the surface of the shaft, especially where a pinion turns on it, and replace the shaft if it has scored or picked up. Damage of any kind can only be cured by replacement.

12 If the ball bearing requires replacement, a bearing puller will be required to extract the bearing from its shaft. Note the position of the locating groove in the outer race of the bearing prior to removing it and ensure that the new bearing is fitted with the groove in the same position. Pull the bearing off the shaft and install the new bearing using a press.

Reassembly

13 During reassembly, always use new circlips. Lubricate the components with the correct grade of engine oil before assembling them.

14 Slide on the 5th gear with its dogs facing away from the integral 1st gear **(see illustration)**. Install a thrustwasher and circlip, making sure that the circlip locates in the shaft groove **(see illustrations)**.

15 Install the combined 3rd/4th gear so that the smaller (3rd) gear faces the 5th gear and so that the oilway in the gearshift fork groove aligns with the two oilways in the shaft **(see illustration)**. Locate a circlip in the shaft groove and slide a thrustwasher on the shaft so that it abuts the circlip **(see illustrations)**.

16 On Speed Triple and Thunderbird models (which have a 5-speed transmission), install the sleeve. On all other models, install the 6th gear bush so that its oilway aligns with the shaft oilway, then slide on the 6th gear with its dogs facing the 4th gear **(see illustrations)**.

17 Install 2nd gear with its stepped side

2

29.17a Install the 2nd gear with its stepped side facing away from 6th gear

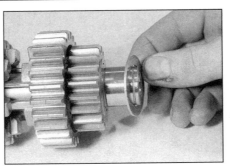

29.17b Slip a thrustwasher over the shaft . . .

29.17c . . . followed by the needle roller bearing

29.17d Secure the bearing with a circlip (arrowed)

29.17e Finally, install the outer race over the bearing

facing away from 6th gear (or sleeve) **(see illustration)**. Slide on a thrustwasher and the needle roller bearing, then secure them with the circlip **(see illustrations)**. Install the bearing outer race on the shaft **(see illustration)**.

Countershaft

Disassembly

18 Remove the needle roller bearing outer race, inner race and thrustwasher from the shaft right end **(see illustration)**.

19 Make a paint mark on the outer face of the 1st gear, then slide it off the shaft, followed by the 5th gear.

20 Remove the circlip, then slide off the thrustwasher, 3rd gear, bush, 4th gear, bush and thrustwasher.

21 Remove the circlip and slide off 6th gear.

22 Remove the circlip, then slide off the thrustwasher and 2nd gear.

23 Moving to the left end of the shaft, remove the oil seal and discard it; a new seal must be installed on reassembly. Withdraw the sleeve and locating ring from the shaft. Slip the thick washer off the shaft, followed by the bearing. **Note:** *The bearing inner race is a press fit on the shaft and must not be disturbed unless replacement is required.*

Inspection

24 Wash all of the components in clean solvent and dry them off.

25 Check the gear teeth for cracking and other obvious damage. Check the 3rd and 4th gear bushes and the surface in the inner diameter of each gear for scoring or heat discoloration. If the gear or bush is damaged, replace it.

26 Inspect the dogs and the dog holes in the gears for excessive wear. Replace the paired gears as a set if necessary.

27 Measure the gearshift fork groove width in the 5th and 6th gears (see Section 30).

28 The shaft is unlikely to sustain damage unless the engine has seized, placing an unusually high loading on the transmission, or the machine has covered a very high mileage. Check the surface of the shaft, especially where a pinion turns on it, and replace the shaft if it has scored or picked up. Damage of any kind can only be cured by replacement.

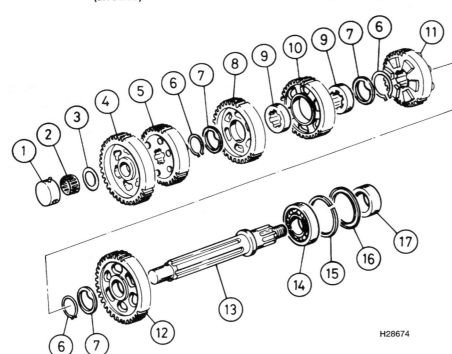

H28674

29.18 Countershaft components

1 Bearing outer race	7 Splined thrustwasher	13 Countershaft
2 Needle roller bearing	8 3rd gear	14 Bearing
3 Plain thrustwasher	9 Bush	15 Locating ring
4 1st gear	10 4th gear	16 Oil seal
5 5th gear	11 6th gear	17 Sleeve
6 Circlip	12 2nd gear	

29.31a Fit 2nd gear on countershaft with dished side facing away from ball bearing

29.31b Install a thrustwasher . . .

29.31c . . . and secure the gear with the circlip (arrowed)

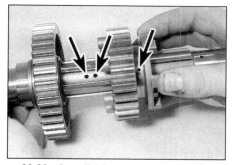

29.32a Install 6th gear so that its fork groove faces away from the 2nd gear and so that the oil holes align (arrowed)

29.32b Insert a circlip into the countershaft groove

29.33a Slip a thrustwasher on the shaft . . .

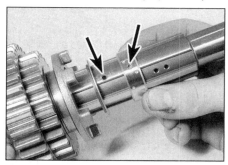

29.33b . . . followed by the 4th gear bush, aligning the oil holes (arrowed)

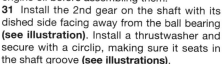

29.33c Install 4th gear so that its stepped centre faces away from the 6th gear

29.34a Align the 3rd gear bush oil hole with the shaft oil hole (arrowed) . . .

29.34b . . . then install the 3rd gear so that its stepped centre faces the 4th gear

29 The bearing inner race at the left end of the shaft is a press fit. Replacement necessitates splitting the inner race and pressing a new race on to the shaft; it is advised that this task be performed by a Triumph dealer.

Reassembly

30 During reassembly, always use new circlips. Lubricate the components with engine oil before assembling them.

31 Install the 2nd gear on the shaft with its dished side facing away from the ball bearing **(see illustration)**. Install a thrustwasher and secure with a circlip, making sure it seats in the shaft groove **(see illustrations)**.

32 Slide 6th gear on the shaft with its gearshift fork groove facing away from the 2nd gear, and so that the oilway in the fork groove aligns with the two oilways in the shaft **(see illustration)**. Secure the gear with the circlip, making sure it locates in the shaft groove **(see illustration)**.

33 Install a thrustwasher on the shaft, followed by the 4th gear bush; align the bush oilway with the shaft oilway **(see illustrations)**. Slide 4th gear on the shaft so

that its stepped side faces away from the 6th gear **(see illustration)**.

34 Install the 3rd gear bush so that its oilway aligns with the shaft oilway **(see illustration)**. Slide on the 3rd gear so that its stepped side faces the 4th gear **(see illustration)**. Install a thrustwasher and retain with a circlip, making sure it locates in the shaft groove **(see illustrations)**.

35 Slide 5th gear on the shaft so that its gearshift fork groove faces the 3rd gear and so that the oilway in the groove aligns with the two oilways in the shaft **(see illustration)**.

36 Install 1st gear on the shaft as noted on removal **(see illustration)**. Install the thrustwasher, needle roller bearing and outer race **(see illustrations)**.

37 At the left end of the shaft, fit the bearing over its inner race on the shaft **(see illustration)**. Slide the thick washer up against

2

29.34c Slip a thrustwasher on the shaft . . .

29.34d . . . and secure the gear with the circlip

29.35 Install 5th gear with fork groove facing 3rd gear and oil holes aligned (arrowed)

29.36a Install the 1st gear in the direction noted on disassembly . . .

29.36b . . . install the thrustwasher . . .

29.36c . . . needle roller bearing and bearing outer race

29.37a Slip on the bearing . . .

29.37b . . . followed by the thick washer . . .

29.37c . . . and sleeve (chamfered side out)

29.37d Install the bearing locating ring over the shaft

29.37e Always use a new oil seal and install with its marked side outwards

the bearing **(see illustration)**. Install the sleeve with its chamfered edge facing outwards then fit the bearing locating ring (the ring will float on the shaft until the countershaft is installed in the crankcase) **(see illustrations)**. Install a new oil seal over the sleeve **(see illustration)**.

30 Gearshift mechanism - removal, inspection and installation

Note: *Access can be gained to the detent cam and detent arms with the engine in the frame and the clutch outer drum removed (see*

Section 15). All other operations require the crankcases to be separated.

Removal

1 Separate the crankcase halves (Section 23).
2 Remove the screw and retaining plate from the left side of the crankcase to free the gearshift fork rod. Slide the rod out of the crankcase and lift each fork out as it clears the rod. Install the forks back on the rod as a guide to reassembly **(see illustration)**.
3 Remove the circlip and washer from the outer end of the gearshift shaft, then remove the circlip, spring guide and return spring from the inner end of the shaft **(see illustration)**. Unscrew the quadrant stopper bolt from the crankcase and remove the two screws which retain the stopper plate to the crankcase. Rotate the stopper plate to allow the gearshift shaft quadrant to be disengaged from the pawl carrier teeth and withdrawn from the crankcase.
4 Remove the oil pump and its drive gear (see Section 31).

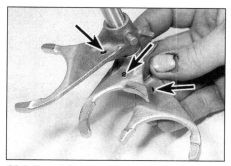

30.2 Install the gearshift forks back on the rod as a guide to reassembly. Note the identification numbers (arrowed)

5 Working from the right side of the crankcase half. Remove the nuts securing the neutral and gear detent arm assemblies. Keep the components of each assembly separate to avoid their parts being interchanged.

6 Remove the screw from the end of the drum to free the detent cam **(see illustration)**.

7 Remove the screw and washer which retain the ball bearing in the right side of the crankcase. Push the bearing out from inside of the crankcase and lift out the gearshift drum.

8 If the pawl carrier requires removal from the gearshift drum, remove the circlip and lift off the neutral disc. Slip the stopper plate off the pawl assembly and drive out the roll pin in the shaft. Carefully withdraw the pawl carrier from the drum, taking care not to lose the spring-loaded pawls.

Inspection

9 The gearshift forks and rod should be closely inspected to ensure that they are not badly damaged or worn.

10 Locate each gearshift fork with its corresponding gear groove and measure the gearshift fork-to-groove clearance using feeler blades **(see illustration)**. If outside of the maximum clearance (see Specifications) either the gearshift fork or gear groove is worn. Using a vernier caliper measure the gearshift fork end widths and the gear groove **(see illustrations)**. Replace any component which is worn beyond the service limit (see Specifications).

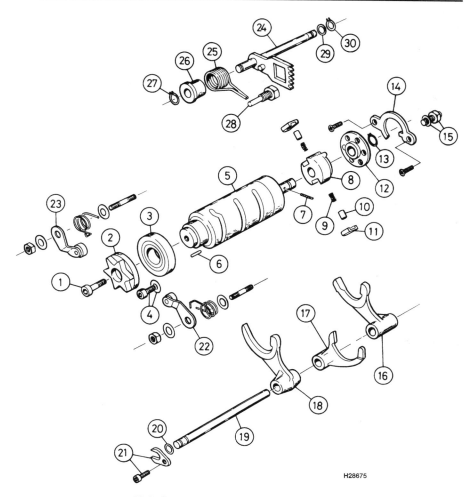

30.3 Gearshift mechanism components

1 Detent cam screw	11 Pawls
2 Detent cam	12 Neutral disc
3 Bearing	13 Circlip
4 Bearing retaining washer and screw	14 Stopper plate
5 Gearshift drum	15 Neutral switch and O-ring
6 Peg	16 Gearshift fork No. 1
7 Roll pin	17 Gearshift fork No. 2
8 Pawl carrier	18 Gearshift fork No. 3
9 Springs	19 Fork rod
10 Plungers	20 O-ring

21 Retaining plate and screw
22 Gear detent cam
23 Neutral detent cam
24 Gearshift shaft
25 Return spring
26 Spring guide
27 Circlip
28 Stopper bolt
29 Washer
30 Circlip

H28675

2

30.6 Detent cam is retained by a single screw (arrowed)

30.10a Measuring gearshift fork-to-groove clearance

30.10b Measuring gearshift fork end thickness

30.10c Measuring gear groove width

30.14a Retain the pawl carrier with the roll pin (arrowed)

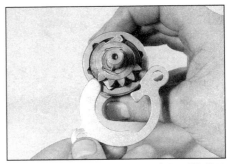

30.14b Engage the stopper plate with the pawl carrier . . .

30.14c . . . then install the neutral disc and retain it with the circlip

30.15a Install the gearshift drum in the lower crankcase . . .

30.15b . . . and install the ball bearing over its right end

30.15c Retain the bearing with the screw and washer

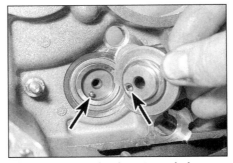

30.16a Engage the detent cam hole over the peg in the end of the drum (arrowed)

30.16b Secure the cam with the retaining screw

11 The gearshift fork rod can be checked for trueness by rolling it along a flat surface. A bent rod will cause difficulty in selecting gears and make the gearshift action heavy.

12 Inspect the gearshift drum grooves and selector fork guide pins for signs of wear or damage. If either component shows signs of wear or damage the gearshift fork(s) and drum must be replaced.

13 Check that the gearshift drum bearing rotates freely and has no sign of freeplay between its inner and outer race. Replace the bearing if necessary.

Installation

14 If the pawl assembly was disturbed, install the pawls, plungers and springs on the carrier and hold them compressed whilst the carrier is inserted in the end of the gearshift drum. Drift the roll pin into the hole in the shaft to retain the carrier (see illustration). Locate the

stopper plate in the carrier and slip the neutral disc over the drum end so that its cutout aligns with the roll pin (see illustrations). Secure the disc with the circlip.

15 Install the gearshift drum in the lower crankcase, locating its left end in the casing bore (see illustration). Install the ball bearing in the right side of the casing, noting that it must be installed from the outside (see illustration). Retain the bearing with the screw and washer; a drop of non-permanent thread locking compound should be applied to the screw threads (see illustration). Secure the screw to the specified torque

16 Locate the detent cam over the right end of the gearshift drum, aligning the hole in its rear face with the peg in the drum (see illustration). Secure the cam with the retaining screw, having applied a drop of non-permanent thread locking compound to its threads, and tighten the screw to the

specified torque setting (see illustration).

17 Build up the neutral detent arm assembly, taking care not to interchange components with the gear detent arm; the neutral arm return spring can be identified by its white paint marking (see illustrations). Tighten the retaining nut to the specified torque setting.

30.17a Install the washer . . .

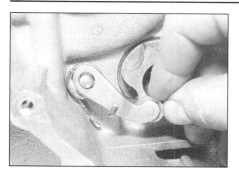

30.17b . . . spring and neutral detent arm

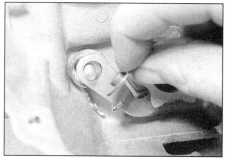

30.17c Fit the collar with its stepped side facing inwards

30.17d Secure the neutral detent arm pivot with the nut

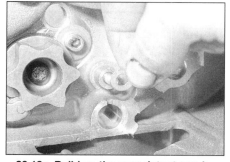

30.18a Build up the gear detent arm by installing the washer . . .

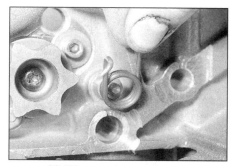

30.18b . . . return spring . . .

30.18c . . . gear detent arm and collar

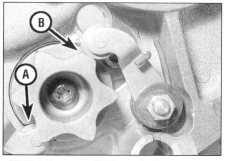

30.18d Secure with the nut. Detent cams are shown in neutral position

A Neutral detent
B Gear detent

30.19a Install the gearshift shaft in the lower crankcase . . .

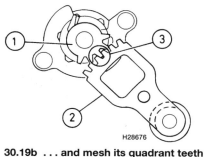

30.19b . . . and mesh its quadrant teeth with those of the pawl carrier

1 Pawl carrier   2 Quadrant
3 Centre tooth of pawl carrier meshed between 3rd and 4th teeth of quadrant

18 Similarly build up the gear detent arm assembly **(see illustrations)**.

19 Install the gearshift shaft in the crankcase and mesh its quadrant teeth with the pawl carrier teeth **(see illustration)**. Note that the stopper plate must be rotated out of the way to allow the teeth to engage. It is important that the centre tooth on the pawl carrier locates between the 3rd and 4th teeth of the quadrant **(see illustration)**. Align the stopper plate holes with those in the crankcase, apply a drop of non-permanent thread locking compound to the retaining screw threads and tighten them securely **(see illustration)**.

20 Install the quadrant stopper bolt in the crankcase and tighten it to the specified torque setting **(see illustration)**. Install the washer and circlip on the gearshift shaft to retain it in the crankcase **(see illustrations)**.

Slip the return spring over the gearshift shaft, noting that its ends must locate over the quadrant peg and stopper bolt, then install the spring guide and secure with the circlip **(see illustrations)**.

21 Temporarily install the gearshift lever on

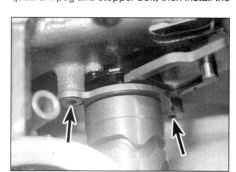

30.19c Secure the stopper plate with the two screws (arrowed)

30.20a Install the stopper bolt in the crankcase

30.20b Slip the thrustwasher on the gearshift shaft . . .

30.20c . . . and retain the shaft with the circlip

30.20d Install the return spring, engaging its ends with the quadrant peg and stopper bolt. Slip the spring guide into place . . .

30.20e . . . and secure all components with the circlip

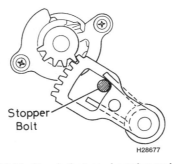

30.21 Check that pawl carrier and quadrant teeth still engage at the fullest extent of shifting

30.23a Slip the fork rod partway into the crankcase . . .

30.23b . . . and engage the left shift fork (No. 1) . . .

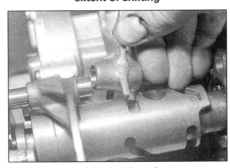

30.23c . . . then the centre shift fork (No. 2) . . .

30.23d . . . and finally the right shift fork (No. 3)

30.23e Secure the fork rod with the retaining plate and screw

the shaft end and rotate the gearshift drum fully in both directions. Check that when fully extended with the quadrant contacting the stopper bolt, the gear teeth engage as shown

(see illustration). If the teeth do not engage correctly, check the pawl carrier and quadrant teeth for accurate alignment as described in Step 19.

22 Install the oil pump and its drive gear (see Section 31).

23 Slip the gearshift rod into its bore in the crankcase and engage the forks on the rod so that their guide pins locate in the drum tracks **(see illustrations)**. Note that the forks are marked 1, 2 and 3 to correspond with the cylinder numbers. Lock the rod in position with the retaining plate and screw, tightening it to the specified torque **(see illustration)**.

24 Position the gearshift drum in the neutral position, and assemble the crankcase halves (see Section 23).

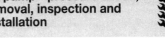

31 Oil pump - pressure check, removal, inspection and installation

Pressure check

1 To check the oil pressure, a suitable gauge and the Triumph adapter (Pt. No. 3880095) will be needed.

2 Warm the engine up to normal operating temperature then stop it. Remove the right lower fairing panel on Trophy and Daytona models (see Chapter 8).

3 Swiftly unscrew the banjo bolt from the external oil pipe on the cylinder block and screw the adapter in its place **(see illustration 11.25)**. The Triumph adapter is drilled to

31.11 Release four screws (arrowed) to free the oil pump from the lower crankcase

31.12a Free the circlip . . .

31.12b . . . and washer from the outside of the crankcase . . .

31.12c . . . then withdraw the driven gear from inside the crankcase

31.12d Remove the screw and washer . . .

31.12e . . . to free the drive gear from the outside of the crankcase

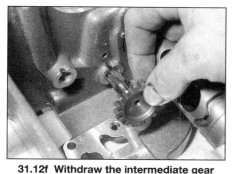

31.12f Withdraw the intermediate gear from inside the crankcase

31.14 Remove the four screws to remove the pump cover

12 Release the circlip and washer and withdraw the driven gear from inside the crankcase **(see illustrations)**. Remove the oil pump drive gear retaining screw and washer, and withdraw the drive gear from its shaft **(see illustrations)**. The intermediate gear can be withdrawn from inside the crankcase **(see illustration)**.

Inspection

Note: *No replacement parts are available for the oil pump; if the checks described below indicate that the pump is worn, it must be replaced with a new unit.*

13 Wash the oil pump in solvent, then dry it off.

14 Remove the four screws to free the pump end cover **(see illustration)**. Recover the two dowels if they are loose.

15 Measure the clearance between the inner rotor tip and the outer rotor tip **(see illustration)**. Measure the clearance between the outer rotor and body with a feeler blade **(see illustration)**. Finally, lay a straightedge across the rotors and pump body and measure the rotor endfloat (gap between the rotors and pump body) with a feeler blade **(see illustration)**. If any of the results are outside the limits listed in this Chapter's Specifications, replace the pump.

16 Pick the inner and outer rotors out of the pump. Examine them for scoring and wear. Slip the inner rotor drive pin out of the shaft and withdraw the thrustwasher.

17 On 3 cylinder engines, the pump driveshaft can be withdrawn from the pump body. On 4 cylinder engines, another set of

accept the oil pipe banjo union and thus retain oil supply to the camshafts. Connect the gauge to the adapter.

4 Start the engine and increase the engine speed to 5000 rpm whilst watching the gauge reading. The oil pressure should be similar to that given in the Specifications at the start of this Chapter.

5 If the pressure is significantly lower than the standard, either the relief valve is stuck open, the oil pump is faulty, the oil pump pick-up strainer is blocked or there is other engine damage. Begin diagnosis by checking the oil pump pick-up strainer and relief valve (see Sections 19 and 20), then the oil pump. If those items check out okay, chances are the bearing oil clearances are excessive and the engine needs to be overhauled.

6 If the pressure is too high, the relief valve is stuck closed. To check it, see Section 20.

7 Stop the engine and unscrew the gauge

and adapter from the crankcase. Install the banjo bolt using a new sealing washer on each side of the union, and tighten it to the specified torque setting.

8 On Trophy and Daytona models install the fairing panel (see Chapter 8).

Removal

9 Separate the crankcase halves (see Section 23). If not already done, remove the water pump (see Chapter 3).

10 The oil pump is housed in the crankcase lower half. Remove the screw and retaining plate from the left side of the crankcase to free the gearshift fork rod. Slide the rod out of the crankcase and lift each fork out as it clears the rod. Install the forks back on the rod as a guide to reassembly.

11 Remove the four screws from the base of the crankcase to free the oil pump **(see illustration)**.

2

31.15a Measuring the rotor tip clearance

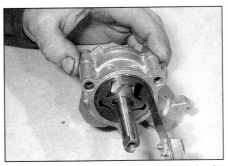

31.15b Measuring the outer rotor-to-body clearance

31.15c Measuring rotor endfloat

31.17 Remove three screws to remove the cover from the opposite end of the pump

31.18a Install the driveshaft in the pump body . . .

31.18b . . . followed by the thrustwasher

31.18c Insert the drive pin in the shaft . . .

31.18d . . . and locate the cutouts in the rear of the inner rotor over the pin

31.18e Install the outer rotor so that the side with the dot faces outwards (arrowed)

rotors is fitted to the back of the pump; remove the cover from the back of the pump and extract the other set of rotors (used to pump oil around the oil cooler) as described in Step 16 **(see illustration)**. **Note:** *Although largely of academic interest, the pump outlet has a cast number 3 or 4 to denote its engine application.*

18 Before reassembling the pump, make sure that all parts are clean. Have a supply of the correct grade of engine oil on hand to lubricate the rotors as they are installed. Insert the driveshaft into the body, followed by the thrustwasher **(see illustrations)**. Carefully install the drive pin and locate the cutouts in the back of the inner rotor over it **(see illustrations)**. Install the outer rotor so that the side with the dot faces outwards **(see illustration)**. If you are working on a 4 cylinder engine, build up the other set of rotors in the same way.

19 Secure the pump end cover(s) noting that the gold-coloured screws are located in the pump holes with dowels **(see illustrations)**.
20 Inspect the oil pump drive gear, intermediate gear and driven gear for signs of wear or damage.

31.19a Check that the two dowels are in position (arrowed)

Installation

21 Lubricate the shafts of the pump driven gear and intermediate gear and insert them in the crankcase **(see illustration)**. Position the drive slot in the driven gear vertically to allow engagement of the pump driveshaft tab.

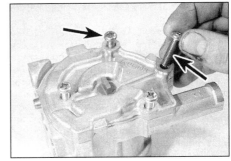

31.19b Install the gold-coloured screws in the holes with the dowels (arrowed)

31.21 Fit the intermediate shaft and driven gear in the crankcase. Position the driven gear so that its slot is vertical (arrowed)

31.22 Retain the driven gear with the washer and circlip

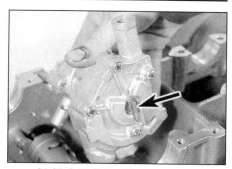

31.23 Install the oil pump in the crankcase, aligning its drive tab (arrowed) with the slot in the driven gear

22 Install the drive gear on the other end of the intermediate shaft and secure with its washer and screw, having applied a drop of non-permanent thread locking compound to its threads **(see illustration 31.12d)**. Tighten the screw to the specified torque setting. Secure the end of the pump driven gear with the washer and circlip **(see illustration)**.
23 Check that the pump driveshaft rotates freely and that the two dowels are in place in the pump mating flange. Install the oil pump in the crankcase so that its tab engages the driven gear slot **(see illustration)**. Apply a drop of non-permanent thread locking compound to the four retaining screws and tighten them to the specified torque setting.
24 Slip the gearshift rod into its bore in the crankcase and engage the forks on the rod. Note that the forks are marked 1, 2 and 3 to correspond with the cylinder numbers. Lock the rod in position with the retaining plate and screw, tightening it to the specified torque setting.
25 Reassemble the crankcase halves (see Section 23) and install the water pump (see Chapter 3).

32 Alternator/starter clutch drive - removal, inspection and installation

Note: *These components can be accessed on early models via a cover in the top of the crankcase. On later models, crankcase separation is necessary.*

Removal

Early models (with access cover on the upper crankcase)

Note: *Extreme care must be taken not to allow any components to fall into the crankcase when carrying out this procedure. The procedure can also be carried out in full as described below for later models.*

1 On early models, the alternator/starter clutch drive and starter idler gear can be removed with the engine in the frame. The clutch outer drum (Section 15), alternator and starter motor (Chapter 9), carburettors and airbox (Chapter 4) must first be removed to gain the necessary access.
2 Remove the nine bolts to free the access cover from the top of the crankcase; withdraw the cover and gasket.
3 Proceed as described in Step 5.

Later models

4 Separate the crankcase halves (Section 23) and remove the transmission shafts from the upper crankcase (see Section 28). The alternator/starter clutch drive is housed in the upper crankcase half.
5 Remove the bolt and washer securing the alternator drive gear on the clutch side of the crankcase **(see illustration)**. You may need to counterhold the shock absorber housing bolt on the opposite end of the shaft whilst the drive gear bolt is slackened. A service

tool (Pt. No. 3880040) is available which locates into one of the housing webs when the damping rubbers have been removed, although this was not found to be necessary on the machine featured.
6 Slide the alternator driveshaft complete with shock absorber housing out of the left side of the crankcase **(see illustration)**. Recover the splined sleeve from the right side of the crankcase **(see illustration)**.
7 Lift out the starter clutch and recover the small spacer from its left side **(see illustration)**.
8 Remove the bolt and washer from the right side of the crankcase which retains the starter idler gear shaft **(see illustration)**. Support the idler gear from inside the crankcase and fully withdraw the shaft **(see illustration)**.

32.5 Remove the bolt and washer to free the alternator driveshaft gear from the clutch side of the upper crankcase

32.6a Withdraw the driveshaft complete with shock absorber housing from the alternator side of the upper crankcase

32.6b Slip the splined sleeve from the driveshaft as it is withdrawn

32.7 Lift the starter clutch out of the crankcase

2

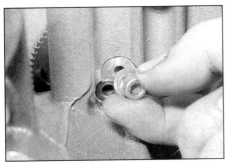

32.8a Remove the bolt and washer . . .

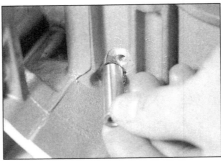

32.8b . . . and slip out the starter idler gear shaft

32.9a Remove the circlip (arrowed) . . .

32.9b . . . and thrustwasher from the starter clutch gear

32.11 Disassemble the starter clutch by removing the six screws

32.12a Install the roller assembly into the housing . . .

32.12b . . . and install the boss

32.12c Apply thread lock to the starter clutch screws

32.13a Install the thrustwasher over the centre boss . . .

Inspection

9 Remove the circlip and thrustwasher to free the gear from the starter clutch **(see illustrations)**. Withdraw the needle roller bearing and second thrustwasher from the boss.

10 Examine the bearing surface of the starter clutch gear and the condition of the rollers inside the clutch body. If the gear surface shows signs of excessive wear or the rollers are damaged, they should be replaced.

11 Extract the starter clutch caged roller assembly (termed a "sprag") by removing the six screws **(see illustration)**.

12 To reassemble, insert the roller assembly into its housing, noting that its shoulder abuts the inner face of the housing **(see illustration)**. Insert the centre boss through the assembly **(see illustration)**. Apply non-permanent thread locking compound to the

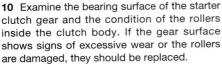

32.13b . . . followed by the needle roller bearing

threads of the six screws and tighten them to the specified torque setting **(see illustration)**.

13 Slip the thrustwasher over the centre boss, followed by the needle roller bearing. Install the gear in the starter clutch, taking

32.13c Install the starter clutch gear

care not to damage the rollers as it is manoeuvred into position **(see illustrations)**.

14 Examine the teeth of the starter idler gear and the corresponding teeth of the starter clutch gear and starter motor gear. Also

32.16a The ball bearing at the alternator end of the crankcase is retained by two screws and washers

32.16b The needle roller bearing at the clutch end of the crankcase has a screw and washer on each side of the casing

32.17 Starter idler gear is installed with the large gear against the crankcase

32.18 Tilt the starter clutch to one side to allow the spacer to be inserted

32.19 Tighten the drive gear bolt . . .

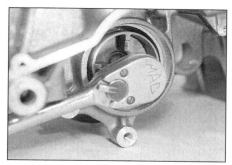

32.20 . . . and shock absorber housing bolt to the specified torque

examine the alternator drive gear teeth and those of the clutch auxiliary gear. Replace the gears as a set if worn or chipped teeth are discovered.

15 Inspect the shock absorber rubbers in the alternator driveshaft housing. If compacted or deteriorated they should be replaced. The housing can be withdrawn from the driveshaft after the retaining bolt and washer have been removed.

16 The driveshaft locates in a ball bearing at its left end and by a needle roller bearing at it right end. The ball bearing is secured by two bolts and washers **(see illustration)**. The needle roller bearing is secured by a screw and washer on each side of the crankcase **(see illustration)**.

Installation

17 Position the starter idler gear in the crankcase with its larger gear against the side of the crankcase **(see illustration)**. Lubricate the idler gear shaft and slide it fully into place from the outside of the crankcase **(see illustration 32.8b)**. Secure the shaft with the washer and bolt, having applied a drop of non-permanent thread locking compound to the bolt threads **(see illustration 32.8a)**. Tighten the bolt to the specified torque setting.

18 Insert the assembled starter clutch in the crankcase and angle it to one side to allow the small spacer to locate in its left side **(see illustration)**. **Note:** *If working on an early model via the upper crankcase aperture take*

great care not to drop the spacer into the crankcase. Holding the starter clutch steady, insert the driveshaft through the assembly from the left side of the crankcase **(see illustration 32.6a)**.

19 Slip the splined sleeve over the right end of the driveshaft **(see illustration 32.6b)**. Install the drive gear over the driveshaft and secure with the washer and bolt. Tighten the bolt to the specified torque setting whilst counterholding the shock absorber housing at the other end of the shaft **(see illustration)**.

20 Tighten the shock absorber housing bolt to the specified torque setting **(see illustration)**.

21 On early models, install a new gasket on the crankcase and fit the cover, tightening its bolts evenly in a criss-cross sequence to the specified torque setting. Install all components described in Step 1.

22 On later models, install the transmission shafts (see Section 28) and reassemble the crankcase halves (see Section 23).

33 Initial start-up after overhaul

1 Make sure the engine oil and coolant levels are correct (see Chapter 1).

2 Make sure there is fuel in the tank, then turn the fuel tap to the ON position and operate the choke.

3 Start the engine and let it run at a moderately fast idle until it reaches operating temperature.

 Warning: If the oil pressure indicator light doesn't go off, or it comes on while the engine is running, stop the engine immediately.

4 Check carefully for oil leaks and make sure the transmission and controls, especially the brakes, function properly before road testing the machine. Refer to Section 34 for the recommended running-in procedure.

5 Upon completion of the road test, and after the engine has cooled down completely, recheck the valve clearances and check the engine oil and coolant levels (see Chapter 1).

34 Recommended running-in procedure

1 Treat the machine gently for the first few miles to make sure oil has circulated throughout the engine and any new parts installed have started to seat.

2 Even greater care is necessary if new pistons and liners or a new crankshaft has been installed. In the case of new pistons and liners, the bike will have to be run in as when new. This means greater use of the transmission and a restraining hand on the throttle. There's no point in keeping to any set speed limit - the main idea is to keep from labouring the engine and to gradually increase performance. These recommendations can be lessened to an extent when only a new

2

crankshaft is installed. Experience is the best guide, since it's easy to tell when an engine is running freely. The table shows maximum engine speed limitations, which Triumph provide for new motorcycles, and this can be used as a guide.

3 If a lubrication failure is suspected, stop the engine immediately and try to find the cause. If an engine is run without oil, even for a short period of time, severe damage will occur.

Maximum engine speeds when running-in

Up to 100 miles (160 km):	3500 rpm max
100 to 300 miles (160 to 480 km):	5000 rpm max
300 to 600 miles (480 to 965 km):	6000 rpm max
600 to 800 miles (965 to 1287 km):	7000 rpm max
800 to 1000 miles (1287 to 1609 km):	8000 rpm max

Chapter 3
Cooling system

Contents

Degrees of difficulty

Easy, suitable for novice with little experience		Fairly easy, suitable for beginner with some experience		Fairly difficult, suitable for competent DIY mechanic		Difficult, suitable for experienced DIY mechanic		Very difficult, suitable for expert DIY or professional	

Specifications

Coolant
Mixture type and capacity . . . .   see Chapter 1

Radiator
Cap valve opening pressure . . . .   16 psi (1.1 Bar)

Thermostat
Opening temperature . . . .   83°C

Fan switch
Cooling fan cut-in temperature
   Thunderbird . . . .   100°C
   All other models . . . .   99°C

Temperature gauge sender unit
Resistance . . . .   255 to 310 ohms @ 60°C

Torque settings
Coolant drain plug	13 Nm
Coolant reservoir mounting bolts (Thunderbird only)	7 Nm
Coolant temperature sender unit	8 Nm
Radiator top mounting bolts	18 Nm
Radiator bottom bracket bolts	9 Nm
Radiator stone guard/electric fan mounting screws	2.5 Nm
Radiator end cover screws (Thunderbird only)	7 Nm
Thermostat housing bolts (Thunderbird only)	7 Nm
Water pump mounting bolts	10 Nm
Water pump inlet pipe bolt (at pump end)	8 Nm
Water pump inlet pipe bolt (at crankcase mounting)	10 Nm
Water pipe outlet union bolts (on cylinder head)	12 Nm
Water pipe inlet union bolts (on cylinder block)	12 Nm

3

1 General information

The cooling system uses a water/antifreeze coolant to carry away excess energy in the form of heat. The cylinders are surrounded by a water jacket from which the heated coolant is circulated by thermo-syphonic action in conjunction with a water pump, driven off the oil pump. The hot coolant passes upwards to the thermostat and through to the radiator. The coolant then flows across the radiator core, where it is cooled by the passing air, down to the water pump and back up to the engine where the cycle is repeated. On models fitted with fairings, air ducts direct the air flow to the radiator to ensure adequate cooling.

A thermostat is fitted in the system to prevent the coolant flowing through the radiator when the engine is cold, therefore accelerating the speed at which the engine reaches normal operating temperature. A thermostatically-controlled cooling fan is also fitted to aid cooling in extreme conditions.

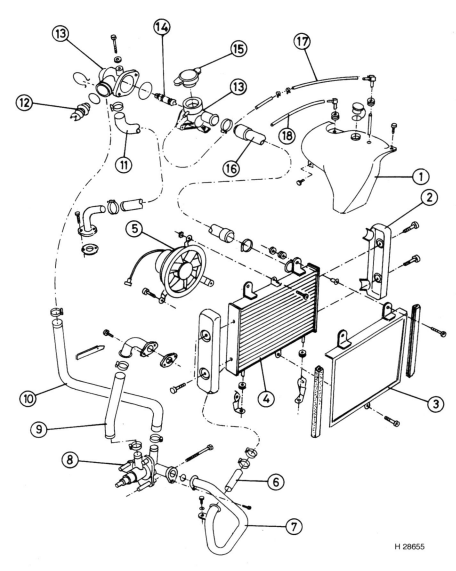

1.1a **Cooling system components - Thunderbird**

H 28655

1 Coolant reservoir	8 Water pump	14 Thermostat
2 Radiator end covers	9 Water pump outlet	15 Radiator pressure cap
3 Stone guard	(engine inlet) hose	16 Radiator top hose
4 Radiator	10 By-pass hose	17 Reservoir overflow hose
5 Fan assembly	11 Engine outlet hose	18 Reservoir breather hose
6 Radiator bottom hose	12 Fan switch	
7 Water pump inlet pipe	13 Thermostat housing	

The complete cooling system is partially sealed and pressurised, the pressure being controlled by a valve contained in the spring-loaded radiator cap. By pressurising the coolant the boiling point is raised, preventing premature boiling in adverse conditions. The overflow pipe from the system is connected to a reservoir into which excess coolant is expelled under pressure. The discharged coolant automatically returns to the radiator when the engine cools **(see illustrations)**.

⚠️ *Warning: Do not remove the pressure cap from the radiator when the engine is hot. Scalding hot coolant and steam may be blown out under pressure, which could cause serious injury. When the engine has cooled, place a thick rag, like a towel over the pressure cap; slowly rotate the cap anti-clockwise to the first stop. This procedure allows any residual pressure to escape. When the*

steam has stopped escaping, press down on the cap while turning it anti-clockwise and remove it.

⚠️ *Warning: Do not allow antifreeze to come in contact with your skin or painted surfaces of the motorcycle. Rinse off any spills immediately with plenty of water. Antifreeze is highly toxic if ingested. Never leave antifreeze lying around in an open container or in puddles on the floor; children and pets are attracted by its sweet smell and may drink it. Check with the local authorities about disposing of used antifreeze. Many communities will have collection centres which will see that antifreeze is disposed of safely.*

Caution: At all times use the specified type of antifreeze, and always mix it with distilled water in the correct proportion. The antifreeze contains corrosion inhibitors which are essential to avoid damage to the cooling system. A lack of these inhibitors could lead to a build-up of corrosion which would block the coolant passages, resulting in overheating and severe engine damage. Distilled water must be used as opposed to tap water to avoid a build-up of scale which would also block the passages.

2 Radiator pressure cap - check

If problems such as overheating or loss of coolant occur, check the entire system as described in Chapter 1. The radiator cap opening pressure should be checked by a Triumph dealer with the special tester required to do the job. If the cap is defective, replace it with a new one.

3 Coolant reservoir - removal and installation

Removal

1 On Thunderbird models, remove the fuel tank as described in Chapter 4. On all other models remove the seat as described in Chapter 8.
2 Disconnect the hoses from the reservoir, then unscrew the two reservoir mounting bolts **(see illustrations)**.
3 Lift the reservoir away from the bike, then remove the cap and drain the coolant into a suitable container **(see illustration)**.

Installation

4 Installation is the reverse of removal. On completion refill the reservoir as described in Chapter 1.

1.1b Cooling system components - all models except Thunderbird

1 Radiator pressure cap
2 Radiator
3 Radiator bottom hose
4 Stone guard
5 Water pump inlet pipe
6 Water pump
7 Water pump outlet (engine inlet) hose
8 Reservoir
9 Reservoir overflow hose
10 Reservoir breather hose
11 Fan assembly
12 Radiator top hose
13 Thermostat housing
14 Temperature gauge sender unit
15 Fan switch
16 Thermostat

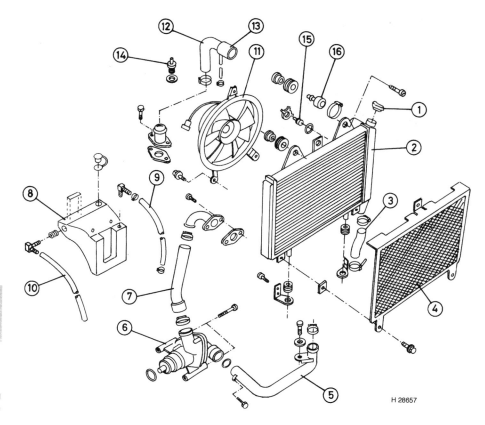

H 28657

4 Cooling fan and cooling fan switch - check and replacement

Cooling fan

Check

1 If the engine is overheating and the cooling fan isn't coming on, first check the cooling fan circuit fuse (see Chapter 9) and then the fan switch as described in Steps 8 to 12 below.

2 If the fan does not come on, (and the fan switch is good), the fault lies in either the cooling fan motor or the relevant wiring. Remove any fairing panels as necessary to gain access (requirements vary according to model and are described in Chapter 8), and test all the wiring and connections as described in Chapter 9.

3 To test the cooling fan motor, separate the two-pin fan wiring connector behind the radiator **(see illustration)**. Using a 12 volt battery and two jumper wires, connect the blue fan wire to the battery positive (+ve) lead and the black fan wire to the battery negative (-ve) lead. Once connected the fan should operate. If it does not, and the wiring is all good, then the fan is faulty. As no individual components are available for the fan assembly, if it is faulty it must be replaced as a unit.

Replacement

> ⚠️ **Warning: The engine must be completely cool before carrying out this procedure.**

4 Remove the radiator as described in Section 7.

5 Unscrew the three fan mounting bolts and separate the fan assembly from the radiator **(see illustration)**.

3.2a On Thunderbird models the reservoir is located under the fuel tank and is secured by two bolts (arrowed)

3.2b On all other models the reservoir is located under the seat and is secured by two bolts (arrowed)

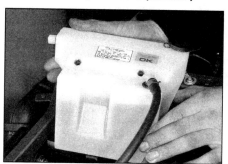

3.3 Lift the reservoir out of the frame to remove it

4.3 Trace the fan wiring to the connector behind the radiator and disconnect it

3

4.5 Remove the three bolts (arrowed) to separate the fan assembly from the radiator

6 Installation is the reverse of removal. Tighten the mounting bolts securely.
7 Install the radiator (refer to Section 7).

Cooling fan switch

Check

8 If the engine is overheating and the cooling fan isn't coming on, first check the cooling fan circuit fuse (see Chapter 9). If the fuse is blown, check the fan circuit for a short to earth (see the wiring diagrams at the end of this book).
9 If the fuse is good, disconnect the wires from the fan switch fitted to the thermostat housing (Thunderbird model), or to the left side of the radiator (all other models) **(see illustrations)**. Remove any fairing panels as necessary to gain access (requirements vary according to model - refer to Chapter 8). Using a jumper wire, connect between the two wires. The fan should come on. If it does, the fan switch is defective and must be replaced. If it does not come on, the fan should be tested as described in Step 3 above.
10 If the fan works but is suspected of cutting in at the wrong temperature, a more comprehensive test of the switch can be made as follows.
11 Remove the switch from the bike as described in Steps 13 to 16 or 19 to 22 below, according to model. Fill a small heatproof container with water and place it on a stove. Connect the probes of an ohmmeter to the terminals of the switch, and using some wire or other support suspend the switch in the water so that just the sensing portion and the threads are submerged. Also place a thermometer capable of reading temperatures up to 110°C in the water so that its bulb is close to the switch. The testing set-up is similar to that used for the temperature gauge sender unit **(see illustration 5.6)**. **Note:** *None of the components should be allowed to directly touch the container.*
12 Initially the ohmmeter reading should be very high indicating that the switch is open (OFF). Heat the water, stirring it gently.

> **Warning: This must be done very carefully to avoid the risk of personal injury.**

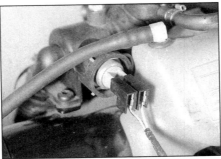

4.9a On Thunderbird models the fan switch is located in the thermostat housing under the tank

When the temperature reaches around 99°C (100°C for Thunderbird) the meter reading should drop to around zero ohms, indicating that the switch has closed (ON). Now turn the heat off. As the temperature falls below 99°C the meter reading should show infinite (very high) resistance, indicating that the switch has opened (OFF). If the meter readings obtained are different, or they are obtained at different temperatures, then the switch is faulty and must be replaced.

Replacement

Thunderbird

> **Warning: The engine must be completely cool before carrying out this procedure.**

13 Drain the cooling system (Chapter 1).
14 Remove the fuel tank (Chapter 4).
15 The fan switch is located in the thermostat housing underneath the fuel tank, and is secured in place by a clip **(see illustration 4.9a)**. Disconnect the wiring from the switch and pull off the clip using a pair of pliers.
16 Remove the switch by carefully pulling it out of the housing, and remove the rubber O-ring, which should be renewed.
17 Fit a new O-ring and install the switch in the housing, then fit the clip making sure it is properly secured. Reconnect the switch wiring.
18 Refill the cooling system (Chapter 1), and fit the fuel tank (Chapter 4).

All other models

> **Warning: The engine must be completely cool before carrying out this procedure.**

19 Remove any fairing panels necessary to gain access to the radiator (requirements vary according to the model - refer to Chapter 8).
20 Drain the cooling system (Chapter 1).
21 The fan switch is located in the left side of the radiator, and is secured by a locking ring **(see illustration 4.9b)**. Disconnect the wiring from the switch, then unscrew the locking ring.
22 Remove the switch by carefully pulling it out of the radiator, and remove the rubber O-ring, which should be renewed.

4.9b On all other models the fan switch is located on the left side of the radiator

23 Fit a new O-ring and install the switch in the radiator, then fit the locking ring and tighten it securely. Reconnect the switch wiring.
24 Refill the cooling system as described in Chapter 1, then fit any fairing panels that have been removed as described in Chapter 8.

5 Temperature gauge/warning light and sender unit - check and replacement

Temperature gauge/warning light

Check

1 The circuit consists of the sender unit mounted in the left end of the cylinder head and the gauge assembly mounted in the instrument panel; on Speed Triple and Thunderbird models, a warning light is fitted instead of the gauge. If the system malfunctions check first that the battery is fully charged and that the fuses are all good.
2 If the gauge is not working, first remove any fairing panels necessary to gain access to the temperature gauge sender unit (requirements vary according to model and are described in Chapter 8). Turn the ignition switch ON and disconnect the wire from the sender unit **(see illustration)**. The temperature gauge needle should be on the "C" on the gauge or the warning light should remain extinguished (as applicable). Now earth the sender unit wire on the engine. The needle should swing

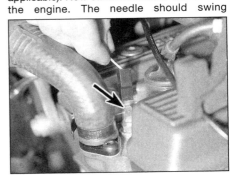

5.2 Disconnect the wire from the temperature gauge sender unit, located in the left side of the cylinder head

immediately over to the "H" on the gauge or the warning light should come on (as applicable). **Caution: Do not earth the wire for any longer than is necessary to take the reading, or the gauge may be damaged.**
If the needle moves as described above, the sender unit is proven defective and must be replaced.
3 If the needle movement is still faulty, or if it does not move at all, the fault lies in the wiring or the gauge/bulb itself. Remove the instrument cluster as described in Chapter 9 (if necessary), and check all the relevant wiring and wiring connectors. If all appears to be well, the gauge/bulb is defective and must be replaced.

Replacement

4 See Chapter 9.

Temperature gauge sender unit

Check

5 Remove the sender unit as described in Steps 8 to 10 below.
6 Fill a small heatproof container with water and place it on a stove. Using an ohmmeter, connect the positive (+ve) probe of the meter to the terminal on the sender unit, and the negative (-ve) probe to the body of the sender unit. Using some wire or other support suspend the sender unit in the water so that just the sensing portion and the threads are submerged. Also place a thermometer in the water so that its bulb is close to the sender unit **(see illustration)**. Note: *None of the components should be allowed to directly touch the container.*
7 Heat the water, stirring it gently.

 Warning: This must be done very carefully to avoid the risk of personal injury. When the temperature reaches around 60°C the meter should read between 255 and 310 ohms. If the meter readings obtained are different, or they are obtained at different temperatures, then the sender unit is faulty and must be replaced.

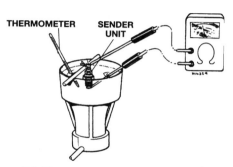

5.6 Temperature gauge sender unit testing set-up

Replacement

 Warning: The engine must be completely cool before carrying out this procedure.

8 Drain the cooling system as described in Chapter 1.
9 If not already done, remove any fairing panels necessary to gain access to the sender unit which is fitted to the cylinder head on the left side (requirements vary according to model and are described in Chapter 8) and disconnect the sender unit wiring.
10 Unscrew the sender unit and remove it from the cylinder head.
11 Apply a smear of sealant to the threads of the new sender unit, then install it into the cylinder head and tighten to the torque setting specified at the beginning of the Chapter.
12 Connect the wiring connector to the sender unit.
13 Refill the cooling system as described in Chapter 1, then install any fairing panels as described in Chapter 8.

---

6 Thermostat - removal, check and installation

Thunderbird model

Removal

 Warning: The engine must be completely cool before carrying out this procedure.

1 The thermostat is automatic in operation and should give many years service without requiring attention. In the event of a failure, the valve will probably jam open, in which case the engine will take much longer than normal to warm up. Conversely, if the valve jams shut, the coolant will be unable to circulate and the engine will overheat. Neither condition is acceptable, and the fault must be investigated promptly.
2 Remove the fuel tank as described in Chapter 4 and drain the cooling system as described in Chapter 1.
3 The thermostat is located in the thermostat housing just behind the radiator pressure cap **(see illustration)**. Disconnect the fan switch wiring connector from the housing, then slacken the clamps securing the hoses to the housing and detach the hoses. Note that the crimp type clamps fitted to some models cannot be re-used and must be replaced.
4 Unscrew the two bolts securing the thermostat housing to the frame and remove the housing.
5 The housing is in two halves secured together by two bolts. Unscrew the bolts and separate the halves to gain access to the thermostat, then withdraw the thermostat, noting how it fits. Discard the O-ring from the housing as a new one must be fitted.

6.3 On Thunderbird models the thermostat housing (arrowed) is under the fuel tank

Check

6 Examine the thermostat visually before carrying out the test. If it remains in the open position at room temperature, it should be replaced.
7 Suspend the thermostat by a piece of wire in a container of cold water. Place a thermometer in the water so that the bulb is close to the thermostat **(see illustration)**. Heat the water, noting the temperature when the thermostat opens, and compare the result with that given in the Specifications. If the reading obtained differs from that given, the thermostat is faulty and must be replaced.
8 In the event of thermostat failure, as an emergency measure only, it can be removed and the machine used without it. **Note:** *Take care when starting the engine from cold as it will take much longer than usual to warm up. Ensure that a new unit is installed as soon as possible.*

Installation

9 Fit the thermostat into the rear half of the housing, making sure that the base slots into the grooves in the housing.
10 Fit a new O-ring to the front half of the housing, then align the two halves, making sure that the point on the top of the thermostat fits into the recess in the front housing half.
11 Fit the halves together and install the two bolts, tightening them to the torque setting specified at the beginning of the Chapter.
12 Fit the housing to the frame and install the two mounting bolts, tightening them securely.

3

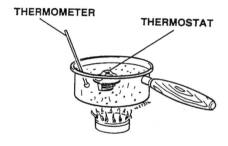

6.7 Thermostat opening check

6.18a Detach the top hose from the radiator to access the thermostat . . .

6.18b . . . and withdraw the thermostat from the hose

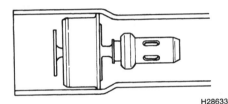

H28633

6.20 Make sure the thermostat fits correctly in the hose

13 Fit the hoses to the housing and tighten their clamps, using new ones if necessary. Connect the fan switch wiring connector.

14 Refill the cooling system (Chapter 1).

15 Fit the fuel tank as described in Chapter 4.

All other models

Removal

 Warning: The engine must be completely cool before carrying out this procedure.

16 The thermostat is automatic in operation and should give many years service without requiring attention. If it fails, the valve will probably jam open, in which case the engine will take much longer than normal to warm up. Conversely, if the valve jams shut, the coolant will be unable to circulate and the engine will overheat. Neither condition is acceptable, and the fault must be investigated promptly.

17 Remove any fairing panels necessary to gain access to the radiator (requirements vary according to model - refer to Chapter 8). Drain the cooling system as described in Chapter 1.

18 The thermostat is located inside the radiator top hose in the larger diameter portion which joins to the radiator. On Speed Triple and later Trident models, the radiator top hose cover screw can be accessed after removing the side cover from the radiator; peel off the reflector and remove the two screws to free the radiator side cover. Remove the clamp securing the hose to the radiator and detach the hose. Note that the crimp type clamps fitted to some models cannot be reused and must be replaced. Carefully withdraw the thermostat from inside the hose using a suitable pair of pliers, noting which way round it fits **(see illustrations)**.

Check

19 Refer to Steps 6, 7 and 8.

Installation

20 Install the thermostat in the radiator top hose, making sure it is the right way round and that it is inserted fully and squarely **(see illustration)**.

21 Fit the hose on the radiator and tighten the clamp, using a new one if necessary, to secure it in place. Install the top hose cover and radiator side cover on Speed Triple and

later Trident models; use a new strip of adhesive on the reflector if necessary.

22 Refill the cooling system (Chapter 1).

23 Fit any fairing panels that have been removed as described in Chapter 8.

7 Radiator - removal and installation

Removal

 Warning: The engine must be completely cool before carrying out this procedure.

1 Remove any fairing panels necessary to gain access to the radiator (requirements vary according to model - refer to Chapter 8).

2 Drain the cooling system (Chapter 1).

3 On Speed Triple and later Trident models,

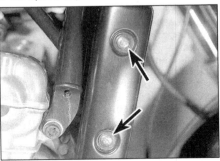

7.3 Thunderbird radiator end cover mounting screws (arrowed)

7.4b Release the clamp and detach the radiator top hose . . .

pull off the adhesive reflector strips fitted to the radiator end covers to access to the end cover retaining screws. On these models and also on Thunderbird, unscrew the screws and remove the end covers **(see illustration)**. Discard the adhesive strips as they will have to be replaced. On Speed Triple and later Trident models, release its retaining screw and clip, then remove the top hose cover.

4 On all models except the Thunderbird, detach the reservoir hose from the radiator neck. On all models remove the clamps securing the top and bottom hoses to the radiator, and detach the hoses. The crimp type clamps fitted to some models cannot be re-used and must be replaced **(see illustrations)**.

5 Disconnect the cooling fan wiring at the connector, and on all models except Thunderbird also disconnect the fan switch wiring from the switch on the left side of the radiator **(see illustrations 4.3 and 4.9b)**.

7.4a Detach the reservoir hose (arrowed) from the radiator filler neck

7.4c . . . and bottom hose

7.6a Unscrew the radiator bottom mounting bolts (arrowed) . . .

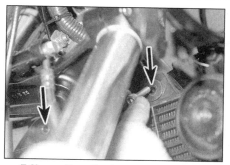

7.6b . . . then the top mounting bolts (arrowed)

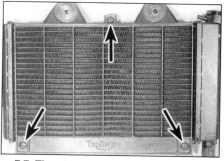

7.7 The stone guard is secured to the radiator by three screws (arrowed)

6 Unscrew the two bolts securing the bottom mounting to the bracket on each side of the radiator. Make sure the radiator is supported, then remove the two top mounting bolts and withdraw the radiator assembly carefully from the side **(see illustrations)**.

7 If necessary, unscrew the three screws to free the stone guard from the radiator **(see illustration)**. Note that the stone guard top mounting screw on all models except the Thunderbird also secures the cooling fan top mounting. Take care not to lose the sleeves on the Thunderbird stone guard top mounting bolts, noting how they fit.

8 Check the stone guard and the radiator for signs of damage and clear any dirt or debris that might obstruct air flow and inhibit cooling. If the radiator fins are badly damaged or broken the radiator must be replaced. Also check the rubber mounting grommets, and replace if necessary.

Installation

9 Installation is the reverse of removal, noting the following.
  a) *Install the radiator top mounting bolts first, but do not fully tighten. Install the bottom bolts then tighten all the bolts to the specified torque setting.*
  b) *Ensure the fan wiring is reconnected.*
  c) *Ensure the coolant hoses are securely retained by their clamps, and use new ones if necessary.*
  d) *On Speed Triple and later Trident models, do not forget to install the top hose cover and replace the adhesive reflector strips on the radiator end covers.*
  e) *On completion refill the cooling system as described in Chapter 1.*

---

8 Water pump - check, removal and installation

Check

1 The water pump is located on the lower left side of the engine. Visually check the area around the pump for signs of leakage. On Trophy and Daytona models, the fairing left lower panel will need to be removed for access (see Chapter 8).

2 To prevent leakage of water from the cooling system to the lubrication system and vice versa, two seals are fitted on the pump shaft. On the underside of the pump body there is also a drainage hole **(see Chapter 1, Section 14)**. If either seal fails, this hole should allow the coolant or oil to escape and prevent the oil and coolant mixing.

3 The seal on the water pump side is of the mechanical type which bears on the rear face of the impeller. The second seal, which is mounted behind the mechanical seal is of the normal feathered lip type. However, neither seal is available as a separate item as the pump is sold as an assembly. Therefore, if on inspection the drainage hole shows signs of leakage, the pump must be removed and replaced.

Removal

4 On Trophy and Daytona models, remove

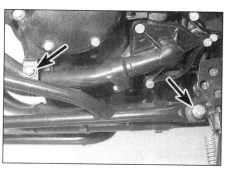

8.6 The sump guard (Tiger model) is secured by two bolts on each side (arrowed)

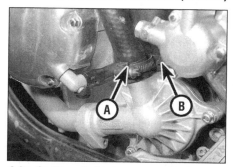

8.8a On Thunderbirds, remove the bypass hose (A) then the outlet hose behind it (B)

the fairing lower panels to gain access to the pump (see Chapter 8).

5 Drain the cooling system (Chapter 1).

6 On models fitted with lower fairing panels it is necessary to detach and support the oil cooler and its sub-frame and mounting brackets as an assembly (see Chapter 2). On Tiger models, unscrew the sump guard mounting bolts and remove the sump guard **(see illustration)**. On Thunderbird remove the horn assembly (see Chapter 9).

7 On later models, unscrew the water pump hose cover retaining bolts and remove the cover **(see illustration)**.

8 On Thunderbird models only, remove the clamp securing the bypass hose to the pump and detach the hose, then do the same for the outlet hose behind it **(see illustration)**. On all other models, remove the clamp securing the outlet hose to the water pump and detach the hose from the pump **(see illustration)**. Some

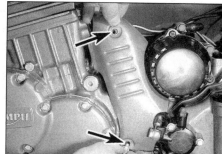

8.7 The water pump hose cover is secured by two bolts (arrowed)

8.8b Release the clamp (arrowed) and detach the outlet hose from the pump

3

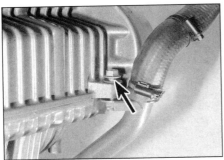

8.9a Unscrew the bolt securing the inlet pipe to the front of the crankcase (arrowed) . . .

8.9b . . . and the bolt securing the inlet pipe to the pump

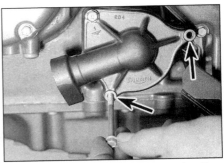

8.10 Unscrew the two bolts securing the water pump to the crankcase (arrowed) - third bolt secures the cover to the pump and also serves as the coolant drain plug

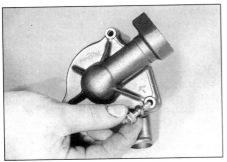

8.11a Unscrew the bolt securing the cover to the pump . . .

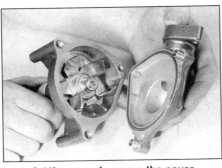

8.11b . . . and remove the cover

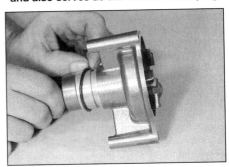

8.13a Fit a new O-ring to the rear of the pump body

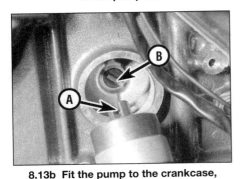

8.13b Fit the pump to the crankcase, aligning the slot in the water pump shaft (A) with the tab on the oil pump shaft (B)

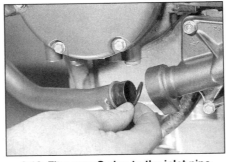

8.16 Fit a new O-ring to the inlet pipe before installing it in the pump

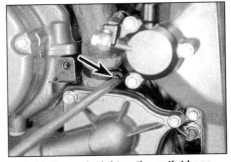

8.17 Securely tighten the outlet hose clamp

models use crimp type clamps which cannot be reused and must be replaced.

9 Unscrew and remove the bolt securing the inlet pipe to the front of the crankcase, taking care not to lose or damage the fibre washer **(see illustration)**. Unscrew and remove the bolt securing the inlet pipe to the water pump and detach the pipe from the pump **(see illustration)**. Remove the rubber O-ring and discard it as a new one should be used.

10 Unscrew the two water pump mounting bolts and remove the pump from the crankcase **(see illustration)**. Remove the O-ring from the rear of the pump body and discard it as a new one must be used.

11 Unscrew the remaining bolt securing the pump cover to the body and remove the cover **(see illustrations)**.

12 Wiggle the water pump impeller back-and-forth and in-and-out. If there is excessive movement the pump must be replaced. Also check for corrosion or a build-up of scale in the pump body and clean or replace the pump as necessary.

Installation

13 Fit a new O-ring to the rear of the pump body and install the pump, aligning the slot in the impeller shaft with the tab on the oil pump shaft **(see illustrations)**.

14 Fit a new O-ring to the pump body and fit the cover.

15 Install the cover retaining bolt (using a new sealing washer) and the pump mounting bolts, and tighten them to the torque setting specified at the beginning of the Chapter.

16 Fit a new O-ring to the inlet pipe and install it into the pump **(see illustration)**. Tighten both pipe mounting bolts to the specified torque setting.

17 Fit the outlet hose to the pump and secure with its clamp; use a new clamp if necessary **(see illustration)**. On Thunderbird models also fit the bypass hose.

18 Install the hose cover (where fitted). On Thunderbird models install the horn assembly (see Chapter 9). On Tiger models fit the sump guard.

19 Install the oil cooler and sub-frame assembly (where fitted).

20 Refill the cooling system as described in Chapter 1.

21 Install the lower fairing panels (where applicable) as described in Chapter 8.

9 Coolant hoses - removal and installation

Removal

1 Before removing a hose, drain the coolant as described in Chapter 1.

2 Use a screwdriver to slacken the hose clamps, then slide them back along the hose and clear of the union spigot. Many of the smaller-bore hoses are secured by spring clamps which can be expanded by squeezing their ears together with pliers. Note that some models use crimp type clamps which cannot be reused and must be replaced. ***Caution: The radiator unions are fragile. Do not use excessive force when attempting to remove the hoses.***

3 If a hose proves stubborn, release it by rotating it on its union before working it off. If all else fails, cut the hose with a sharp knife then slit it at each union so that it can be peeled off in two pieces. Whilst this is expensive it is preferable to buying a new radiator.

4 The water pipe inlet union to the cylinder

9.7a Fit a new gasket to the inlet union . . .

block and the outlet union from the cylinder head can be removed by unscrewing the two retaining bolts. If they are removed, the gasket behind each must be renewed.

Installation

5 Slide the clips onto the hose and then work it on to its respective union.

6 Rotate the hose on its unions to settle it in position before sliding the clamps into place and tightening them securely.

7 If either the inlet union to the cylinder block or the outlet union from the cylinder head has

9.7b . . . and to the outlet union if they are removed

been removed, fit a new gasket, then install the union and tighten the mounting bolts to the torque setting specified at the beginning of the Chapter **(see illustrations)**.

HAYNES HINT *If the hose is difficult to push on its union, it can be softened by soaking it in very hot water, or alternatively a little soapy water can be used as a lubricant.*

3

Chapter 4
Fuel and exhaust systems

Contents

Degrees of difficulty

Easy, suitable for novice with little experience		Fairly easy, suitable for beginner with some experience		Fairly difficult, suitable for competent DIY mechanic		Difficult, suitable for experienced DIY mechanic		Very difficult, suitable for expert DIY or professional	

Specifications

Fuel

Grade
   UK models . . . . Unleaded, minimum 95 RON (Research Octane Number)
   US models . . . . Unleaded, minimum 89 octane CLC and AKI
Fuel tank capacity
   Thunderbird . . . . 15 litres
   All other models . . . . 25 litres
Fuel tank reserve capacity
   Thunderbird . . . . 4 litres
   All other models . . . . 5 litres
Low fuel level warning light cut-in (not Thunderbird) . . . . 7 litres

Carburettors

Type (all models) . . . . Mikuni BST 36 mm flat slide CV

Carburettor adjustments

Pilot screw - initial setting (turns out)
   Trophy, Daytona and Speed Triple models 2
   Trident, Sprint, Thunderbird and Tiger models
      Cylinders 1 and 3 2
      Cylinder 2 . . . . 2.25
Float height (all models) . . . . 14.5 mm
Fuel level (above joint face) - see text . . . . 1.5 mm
Idle speed . . . . see Chapter 1

Torque settings

Fuel tank mounting bolts
   Tiger and Thunderbird . . . . 9 Nm
   All other models . . . . 12 Nm
Exhaust system
   Cylinder head clamps (see text)
      Stage one . . . . 8 Nm
      Stage two . . . . 20 Nm
   Silencer mounting bolt
      Tiger . . . . 27 Nm
      Thunderbird . . . . Not available
      All other models . . . . 15 Nm

4

1 General information and precautions

General information

The fuel system consists of the fuel tank, the fuel tap and filter, the carburettors, fuel hoses and control cables.

The fuel tap is of the gravity-fed type on Thunderbird and Tiger models, with one fuel delivery hose to the carburettors. On all other models, a vacuum tap is fitted, which has two fuel delivery hoses to the carburettors.

The carburettors used on all models are Mikuni BST 36 mm flat slide CV types. Whilst the carburettor body is the same on all models, differences in requirements of the various engines are catered for by using different jet sizes. On all models there is a carburettor for each cylinder. For cold starting, a choke lever mounted on the left handlebar and connected by a cable controls an enrichment circuit in the carburettor.

Air is drawn into the carburettors via air ducts and an airbox.

The exhaust system is either a four-into-two or a three-into-two design, depending on the engine. Certain California market models have a catalytic converter fitted in the exhaust downpipes, near the joint with the silencer.

Many of the fuel system service procedures are considered routine maintenance items and for that reason are included in Chapter 1.

Precautions

Warning: Petrol is extremely flammable, so take extra precautions when you work on any part of the fuel system.
Don't smoke or allow open flames or bare light bulbs near the work area, and don't work in a garage where a natural gas-type appliance is present. If you spill any fuel on your skin, rinse it off with soap and water. When you perform any work on the fuel system, wear safety glasses and have a fire extinguisher suitable for a class B type fire (flammable liquids) on hand.

Always carry out any servicing work in a well-ventilated area to prevent a build-up of fumes.

Never work in a building containing a gas appliance with a pilot light, or any other form of naked flame. Ensure that there are no naked light bulbs or any sources of flame or sparks nearby.

Do not smoke (or allow anyone else to smoke) while in the vicinity of petrol or of components containing it. Remember the possible presence of vapour from these sources and move well clear before smoking.

Check all electrical equipment belonging to the house, garage or workshop where work is being undertaken (see the Safety first! section of this manual). Remember that certain electrical appliances such as drill, cutters etc create sparks in the normal course of operation and must not be used near petrol or any component containing it. Again, remember the possible presence of fumes before using electrical equipment.

Always mop up any spilt fuel and safely dispose of the rag used.

Any stored fuel that is drained off during servicing work, must be kept in sealed containers suitable for holding petrol, and clearly marked as such; the containers themselves should be kept in a safe place. This last point applies equally to the fuel tank, if it is removed from the machine; also remember to keep its cap closed at all times.

Note that the fuel system consists of the fuel tank and tap, with its cap and related hoses. On California models, this includes the evaporative loss system components.

Read the Safety first! section of this manual carefully before starting work.

Owners of machines used in the US, particularly California, should note that their machines must comply at all times with Federal or State legislation governing the permissible levels of noise and of pollutants such as unburnt hydrocarbons, carbon monoxide etc that can be emitted by those machines. All vehicles offered for sale must comply with legislation in force at the date of manufacture and must not subsequently be altered in any way which will affect their emission of noise or of pollutants.

In practice, this means that adjustments may not be made to any part of the fuel, ignition or exhaust systems by anyone who is not authorised or mechanically qualified to do so, or who does not have the tools, equipment and data necessary to properly carry out the task. Also if any part of these systems is to be replaced it must be replaced with only genuine Triumph components or by components which are approved under the relevant legislation. The machine must never be used with any part of these systems removed, modified or damaged.

2 Fuel tank and tap - removal and installation

Fuel tank

Warning: Refer to the precautions given in Section 1 before starting work.

Removal

Tiger
1 Make sure the fuel tap is turned to the OFF position and the fuel cap is secure.
2 Remove the seat as described in Chapter 8, then disconnect the battery, negative (-ve) terminal first.
3 Unscrew and remove the fasteners securing the fairing panels to the tank; don't lose the rubber washers **(see illustration)**.
4 Remove the screws securing the airbox end covers to the airbox and remove the covers.
5 Unscrew and remove the fuel tank front mounting bolt together with its sleeve and rubber, noting their order **(see illustration)**. Unscrew and remove the rear bolts together with their washers, noting their order. Don't lose the sleeve which houses the bolt and fits into the tank rubber mounting pad.
6 Partially raise the rear of the tank, supporting it if necessary, and disconnect the low fuel level sensor wires at the tank. Also release the fuel hose and the tank breather hose clamps and detach the hoses, having taken note of their routing and locations **(see illustration)**.

2.3 Remove the fasteners securing the fairing panels to the tank (arrowed)

2.5 Unscrew the tank front mounting bolt (arrowed) and remove it with its sleeve and rubber

2.6 The fuel delivery pipe is secured to the fuel tap by a clamp (arrowed). Release the clamp and detach the pipe

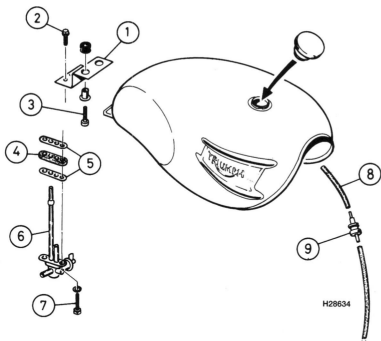

2.11 Fuel tank components - Thunderbird model

1 Mounting bracket	4 Spacer	7 Tap mounting bolt
2 Bracket-to-frame bolt	5 Gaskets	8 Breather hose
3 Bracket-to-tank bolt	6 Fuel tap	9 Roll-over valve

7 Remove the tank by carefully drawing it back and away from the bike. Take care not to displace the front mounting rubbers from the lugs on the frame and note how they fit into the grooves in the tank.

8 Inspect the tank mounting rubbers for signs of damage or deterioration and replace if necessary.

Thunderbird

9 Make sure the fuel tap is turned to the OFF position and the fuel cap is secure.

10 Remove the seat (refer to Chapter 8), then disconnect the battery, removing the negative (-ve) terminal first.

11 Unscrew and remove the two bolts at the rear of the tank which secure the tank mounting bracket to the frame **(see illustration)**.

12 Partially raise the rear of the tank, supporting it if necessary, and release the fuel hose and the tank breather hose clamps and detach the hoses, noting their routing and location.

13 Remove the tank by carefully drawing it back and away from the bike. Also take care not to displace the front mounting rubbers from the lugs on the frame and note how they fit into the grooves in the tank.

14 If necessary, unscrew the two bolts securing the tank mounting bracket to the underside of the tank and remove the bracket, taking care not to lose the sleeve or the rubber grommets and noting how they fit. Inspect the rubber grommets for damage or deterioration and replace if necessary.

All other models

15 Make sure the fuel tap is turned to either the ON or RES position and the fuel cap is secure.

16 Remove the seat (refer to Chapter 8), then disconnect the battery, removing the negative (-ve) terminal first.

17 Remove the side panels (see Chapter 8).

18 Unscrew and remove the two bolts from each side of the tank which secure the tank mounting bracket to the frame **(see illustration)**.

19 Partially raise the rear of the tank, supporting it if necessary, and disconnect the low fuel level sensor wires at the connector **(see illustration)**. Also release the fuel drain hose, vacuum hose and fuel delivery hose clamps and detach the hoses, noting their routing and where they fit.

20 Remove the ... back and away fr... not to displace th... from the lugs on the... fit into the grooves in...

21 If necessary, u... securing the tank m... underside of the tank a... ...ket, taking care not to lo... ...eve or the rubber grommets and ...oting how they fit. Inspect the rubber grommets for signs of damage or deterioration and replace if necessary.

Installation

Tiger

22 Carefully lower the fuel tank into position, making sure the mounting rubbers remain in place. Partially raise the rear of the tank, supporting it if necessary, and reconnect the breather hose to its union and the fuel hose to the tap, making sure they are correctly fitted and routed. Secure them with their clamps. Also connect the low fuel level sensor wires to the tank.

23 Ensure that the sleeves are correctly positioned in the mounting rubbers, then install the mounting bolts and washers (where fitted), tightening them to the torque setting specified at the beginning of the Chapter.

24 Fit the airbox end covers and install the fasteners securing the fairing panels to the tank.

25 Connect the battery, fitting the negative (-ve) terminal last, then install the seat as described in Chapter 8.

26 Turn the fuel tap to the ON position and check that there is no sign of fuel leakage, then turn the tap back to the OFF position.

Thunderbird

27 If removed, fit the tank mounting bracket to the tank, making sure the sleeves and rubber grommets are correctly fitted.

28 Carefully lower the fuel tank into position, making sure the front mounting rubbers remain in place. Partially raise the rear of the tank, supporting it if necessary, and reconnect the breather hose to its union and the fuel hose to the tap, making sure they are correctly fitted and routed. Secure them in place with their clamps.

29 Install the mounting bolts and tighten them to the specified torque setting.

2.18 Unscrew the two tank bracket mounting bolts (arrowed)

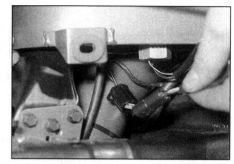

2.19 Disconnect the low fuel level sensor wires at the connector

4

nect the battery, fitting the negative (-
terminal last, then install the seat as
described in Chapter 8.

31 Turn the fuel tap to the ON position and
check that there is no sign of fuel leakage,
then turn the tap back to the OFF position.

All other models

32 If removed, fit the tank mounting bracket
to the tank, making sure the sleeves and
rubber grommets are correctly fitted.

33 Carefully lower the fuel tank into position,
making sure the front mounting rubbers
remain in place. Partially raise the rear of the
tank, supporting it if necessary, and
reconnect the breather hose, the vacuum
hose and the fuel delivery hoses, making sure
they are correctly fitted and routed. Secure
them in place with their clamps. Also connect
the low fuel level sensor wires at the
connector.

34 Install the four tank bracket mounting
bolts and tighten them to the torque setting
specified at the beginning of the Chapter.

35 Connect the battery, fitting the negative (-
ve) terminal last, then install the seat as
described in Chapter 8.

36 Start the engine and check that there is no
sign of fuel leakage, then shut if off.

Fuel tap

Removal

37 Remove the fuel tank as described above.
Connect a drain hose to the fuel tap stub and
insert its end in a container suitable for storing
petrol. Turn the fuel tap to the RES position on
Tiger and Thunderbird models, or the PRI
position on all other models, and allow the
tank to fully drain.

38 Unscrew the two bolts securing the tap to
the tank and withdraw the tap assembly,
taking care not to lose or damage any of the
seals or the gauze filter **(see illustration)**.

39 Clean the gauze filter to remove all traces
of dirt and fuel sediment.

40 Note that individual components are not
available for the tap, including the rubber
seals and the gauze filter. The tap should not
be removed unnecessarily from the bike to
prevent the possibility of damaging the seal or
the filter, and the tap should not be

**2.38 Withdraw the tap assembly carefully
from the tank to avoid damaging
the gauze filter**

dismantled - if it fails, or if the gauze filter is
holed or torn, a new tap must be fitted.

Installation

41 Installation is the reverse of removal.

3 Fuel tank - cleaning and repair

1 All repairs to the fuel tank should be carried
out by a professional who has experience in
this critical and potentially dangerous work.
Even after cleaning and flushing of the fuel
system, explosive fumes can remain and
ignite during repair of the tank.

2 If the fuel tank is removed from the bike, it
should not be placed in an area where sparks
or open flames could ignite the fumes coming
out of the tank. Be especially careful inside
garages where a natural gas-type appliance is
located, because the pilot light could cause
an explosion.

4 Idle fuel/air mixture adjustment - general information

1 Due to the increased emphasis on
controlling motorcycle exhaust emissions,
certain governmental regulations have been
formulated which directly affect the
carburation of this machine. In order to
comply with the regulations, the carburettors
on US models are sealed so they can't be
tampered with. The pilot screws on other
models are accessible, but the use of an
exhaust gas analyser capable of taking
readings from the exhaust downpipes rather
than from the silencer is the only accurate way
to adjust the idle fuel/air mixture and be sure
the machine doesn't exceed the emissions
regulations.

2 The pilot screws are set to their correct
position by the manufacturer and should not
be adjusted unless it is necessary to do so for
a carburettor overhaul. If the screws are
adjusted they should be reset to the settings
specified at the beginning of the Chapter.

 HAYNES HiNT *A special adjusting tool
(Part no 3880015) is available
to aid adjustment of the
screws whilst the
carburettors are in situ.*

3 If the engine runs extremely rough at idle or
continually stalls, and if a carburettor overhaul
does not cure the problem, take the
motorcycle to a Triumph dealer equipped with
an exhaust gas analyser. They will be able to
properly adjust the idle fuel/air mixture to
achieve a smooth idle and restore low speed
performance.

5 Carburettor overhaul - general information

1 Poor performance, hesitation, hard starting,
stalling, flooding and backfiring are all signs
that major carburettor work may be required.

2 Keep in mind that many so-called
carburettor problems are really not
carburettor problems at all, but mechanical
problems within the engine or ignition system
malfunctions. Try to establish for certain that
the carburettors are in need of maintenance
before beginning a major overhaul.

3 Check the fuel filters, the fuel hoses, the
tank breather hose (except California models),
the intake manifold joint clamps, the airbox,
the ignition system, the spark plugs and
carburettor synchronisation before assuming
that a carburettor overhaul is required.

4 Most carburettor problems are caused by
dirt particles, varnish and other deposits
which build up in and block the fuel and air
passages. Also, in time, gaskets and O-rings
shrink or deteriorate and cause fuel and air
leaks which lead to poor performance.

5 When the carburettor is overhauled, it is
generally disassembled completely and the
parts are cleaned thoroughly with a
carburettor cleaning solvent and dried with
filtered, unlubricated compressed air. The fuel
and air passages are also blown through with
compressed air to force out any dirt that may
have been loosened but not removed by the
solvent. Once the cleaning process is
complete, the carburettor is reassembled
using new gaskets and O-rings.

6 Before disassembling the carburettors,
make sure you have a carburettor rebuild kit
(which will include all necessary O-rings and
other parts), some carburettor cleaner, a
supply of clean rags, some means of blowing
out the carburettor passages and a clean
place to work. It is recommended that only
one carburettor be overhauled at a time to
avoid mixing up parts.

6 Carburettors - removal and installation

⚠️ *Warning: Refer to the
precautions given in Section 1
before starting work.*

Removal

1 Referring to Chapter 8, remove the fairing
on Sprint models, the fairing side panels on
Tiger models, and the fairing lower panels on
Trophy and Daytona models. On Thunderbird
models, remove the horn (see Chapter 9).

2 On all models, remove the seat, side panels
and fuel tank, referring to Chapter 8 and
Section 2 of this Chapter.

3 Remove the air chambers (Section 12).

6.4 Pull the airbox as far back as possible to allow room to remove the carburettors

6.7 Ease the carburettors off the cylinder head with the rubber manifolds attached

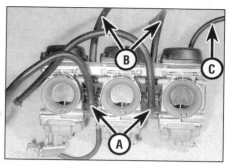

6.8 Fuel hoses (A), vent hoses (B), and vacuum hose (C)

4 Release the clamps securing the airbox to the carburettors and carefully detach the airbox. Pull the airbox as far back as possible against the frame to make room for the carburettors to be removed **(see illustration)**.
5 Detach the choke cable from the linkage on the carburettors as described in Section 11.
6 Release the clamps securing the rubber inlet manifolds to the cylinder head, leaving them attached to the carburettors.
7 Ease the carburettors off the cylinder head stubs and support them in a position that gives access to the throttle cam **(see illustration)**. Release the throttle cable from the carburettors as described in Section 10. **Note:** *Keep the carburettors upright to prevent fuel spillage from the float chambers and the possibility of the piston diaphragms being damaged.*
8 Note the routing of the fuel hoses, the vacuum hose (and on California the evaporative loss system hoses) and the vent hoses, then withdraw the carburettors with the hoses attached **(see illustration)**. Place a suitable container below the float chambers then slacken the drain screws and drain the fuel from

the carburettors. Once all the fuel has been drained, tighten all the drain screws securely.

Installation

9 Installation is the reverse of removal. Check for cracks or splits in the rubber inlet manifolds. Make sure they are fully engaged with the cylinder head and their retaining clamps are securely tightened. Position the vent hoses in between the outer and inner carburettors. Prior to installing the airbox, adjust the throttle and choke cables as described in Chapter 1.

---

7 Carburettors - disassembly, cleaning and inspection

> ⚠ **Warning: Refer to the precautions given in Section 1 before starting work.**

Disassembly

1 Remove the carburettors from the machine as described in the previous Section. **Note:** *Do not separate the carburettors unless absolutely necessary; each carburettor can be dismantled sufficiently for all cleaning and adjustments while in place on the mounting brackets. Dismantle the carburettors separately to avoid interchanging parts* **(see illustration)**.
2 Unscrew and remove the top cover retaining screws. Lift off the cover and remove the spring from inside the piston **(see illustration)**.

4

7.1 Carburettor detail

1 Top cover
2 Spring
3 Vacuum take-off stub O-ring
4 Diaphragm
5 Piston
6 Needle
7 Spring spacer
8 Needle spacer
9 Float chamber
10 Rubber seal
11 Float assembly
12 Main jet
13 Needle jet
14 Piston guide
15 Pilot jet
16 Pilot screw and spring
17 Choke plunger

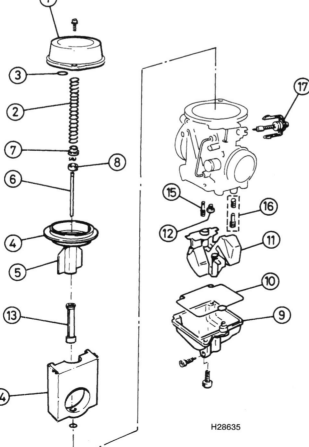

H28635

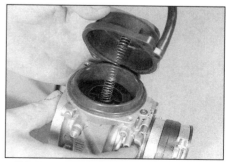

7.2 Unscrew the top cover screws and remove the top cover and spring

7.3 Remove the vacuum take-off stub O-ring (arrowed)

7.4 Withdraw the diaphragm and piston assembly from the carburettor

7.5 Withdraw the needle from the piston, noting how the spacers fit

7.6a Unscrew the float chamber retaining screws . . .

7.6b . . . and remove the float chamber

5 Push the needle from the bottom of the piston and remove it from the top. Don't lose any spacers - note how they fit **(see illustration)**.

6 Undo the screws and remove the float chamber from the base of the carburettor. Remove the rubber seal and discard it as a new one must be fitted **(see illustrations)**.

7 Carefully ease the float assembly out of the carburettor body **(see illustration)**. Remove the O-rings and discard them as new ones must be fitted on reassembly. Do not attempt to separate the needle valve from the float. If the needle valve is damaged or worn the float assembly must be replaced as a unit.

8 Unscrew the main jet **(see illustration)**.

9 With the main jet removed the needle jet can now be withdrawn from the body **(see illustration)**. Note the flat on the threaded end of the needle jet which has to align with the pin in the jet housing. Withdraw the piston guide from the carburettor **(see illustration)**.

10 Unscrew and remove the pilot jet, located next to the needle jet bore **(see illustration)**.

11 The pilot screw can be removed from the carburettor, but note that its setting will be disturbed. Remove the pilot screw along with its spring and O-ring.

7.7 Carefully ease the float assembly out of the carburettor

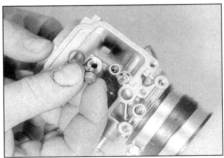

7.8 Unscrew and remove the main jet

3 Remove the vacuum take-off stub O-ring and discard it as a new one must be fitted **(see illustration)**.

4 Carefully peel the diaphragm away from its sealing groove in the carburettor. Carefully

withdraw the diaphragm and piston assembly **(see illustration)**. *Caution: Do not use any sharp instruments to displace the diaphragm as it is delicate and easily damaged.*

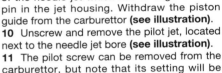

> **HAYNES HINT**
> *To record the pilot screw's current setting, turn the screw in until it seats lightly, counting the number of turns necessary to achieve this, then fully unscrew it. On installation, the screw is simply backed out the number of turns you've recorded.*

7.9a Withdraw the needle jet (noting its flat (arrowed)) . . .

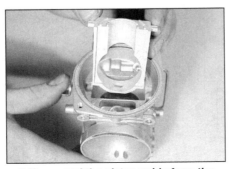

7.9b . . . and the piston guide from the carburettor body

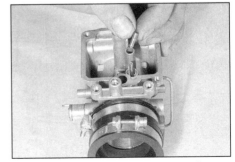

7.10 Unscrew the pilot jet from the carburettor

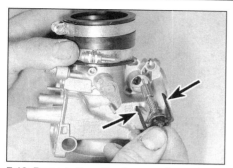

7.13 Press in the clips (arrowed) to release the choke plunger from the carburettor

7.17 Check the choke plunger assembly for signs of wear or damage

12 If the carburettors have not been separated, ease the choke shaft sliders out of their retainers to release the choke shaft, then remove the choke shaft from the plungers **(see illustrations 8.3a and 8.3b)**.

13 Release the clips securing the choke plunger to the carburettor body and remove the plunger and spring **(see illustration)**.

Cleaning

Caution: Use only a petroleum-based solvent for carburettor cleaning. Don't use caustic cleaners.

14 Submerge the metal components in the solvent for approximately thirty minutes (or longer, if the directions recommend it).

15 After the carburettor has soaked long enough for the cleaner to loosen and dissolve most of the varnish and other deposits, use a brush to remove the stubborn deposits. Rinse it again, then dry it with compressed air.

16 Use a jet of compressed air to blow out all of the fuel and air passages in the main and upper body. *Caution: Never clean the jets or passages with a piece of wire or a drill bit, as they will be enlarged, causing the fuel and air metering rates to be upset.*

Inspection

17 Check the operation of the choke plunger. If it doesn't move smoothly, inspect the needle on the end of the choke plunger and the choke shaft. Replace either component if worn or bent **(see illustration)**.

18 Check the tapered portion of the pilot screw and the spring for wear or damage. Replace them if necessary.

19 Check the carburettor body, float chamber and top cover for cracks, distorted sealing surfaces and other damage. If any defects are found, replace the faulty component, although replacement of the entire carburettor will probably be necessary (check with a Triumph dealer on the availability of separate components).

20 Check the diaphragm for splits, holes and general deterioration. Holding it up to a light will help to reveal problems of this nature.

21 Insert the piston guide and piston in the carburettor body and check that the piston moves up-and-down smoothly. Check the surface of the piston for wear. If it's worn

excessively or doesn't move smoothly in the guide, replace the components as necessary.

22 Check the needle for straightness by rolling it on a flat surface (such as a piece of glass). Replace it if it's bent or if the tip is worn.

23 Check the tip of the float needle valve. If it has grooves or scratches in it, the float assembly must be replaced. If the needle valve seat is damaged the carburettor assembly must be replaced as it is not possible to replace the seat individually.

24 Operate the throttle shaft to make sure that the throttle butterfly valve opens and closes smoothly. If it doesn't, replace the carburettor.

25 Check the floats for damage. This will usually be apparent by the presence of fuel inside one of the floats. If the floats are damaged, they must be replaced.

26 Clean the fuel filters set in the fuel hose T-pieces (see Chapter 1).

8 Carburettors - separation and joining

⚠️ *Warning: Refer to the precautions given in Section 1 before starting work.*

Separation

1 The carburettors do not need to be separated for normal overhaul. If you need to separate them (to replace a carburettor body, for example), refer to the following procedure **(see illustration)**.

2 Remove the carburettors from the machine as described in Section 6. Mark the body of each carburettor with its cylinder number to ensure that it is positioned correctly on reassembly.

8.1 Carburettor linkage detail

1 Choke shaft
2 Choke shaft retainers
3 Throttle return spring and linkage assembly
4 Throttle synchronisation assembly
5 Upper mounting bracket
6 Lower mounting bracket
7 Fuel hoses
8 Vacuum take-off cap
9 Vent hoses
10 Vacuum hose
11 Idle speed adjuster

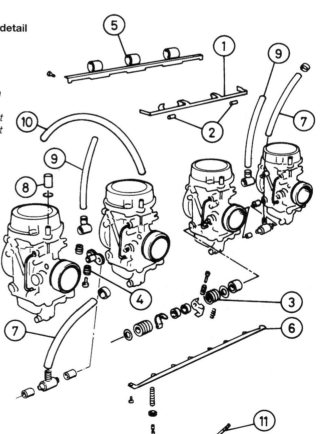

H28639

4

8.3b . . . then remove the shaft from the choke plungers (arrowed)

8.4 Note the arrangement of the linkage and synchronisation assembly springs before dismantling

8.5a Unscrew the screws securing the carburettors to both the top . . .

8.5b . . . and the bottom mounting brackets

8.6 Separate the carburettors, noting how fuel and vent hose T-pieces fit (arrowed)

3 Ease the choke shaft sliders out of their retainers to release the shaft, then remove the choke shaft from the plungers **(see illustrations)**.

4 Make a note of how the throttle return springs, linkage assembly and carburettor synchronisation springs are arranged to ensure that they are fitted correctly on reassembly **(see illustration)**.

5 Remove the screws securing the carburettors to the two mounting brackets and remove the brackets. If it is not essential to separate all the carburettors, only release those necessary and leave the others attached to the brackets **(see illustrations)**.

6 Carefully separate the carburettors. Retrieve the synchronisation springs and note the fitting of the fuel and vent hose T-pieces as they are separated **(see illustration)**.

Joining

7 Assembly is the reverse of the disassembly procedure, noting the following.

a) Make sure the fuel and vent hose T-pieces are correctly and securely inserted into the carburettors **(see illustration)**.

b) Install the synchronisation springs after the carburettors are joined together. Make sure they are correctly and squarely seated **(see illustration)**.

c) Check the operation of both the choke and throttle linkages ensuring that both operate smoothly and return quickly under spring pressure before installing the carburettors on the machine.

d) Install the carburettors (see Section 6) and check carburettor synchronisation (see Chapter 1).

8.7a Make sure the hose T-pieces (arrowed) are securely fitted in the carburettors

8.7b Make sure the synchronisation springs (arrowed) sit squarely in the throttle linkage

9 Carburettors - reassembly, float height check and fuel level check

Warning: Refer to the precautions given in Section 1 before starting work.

Reassembly and float height check

Note: When reassembling the carburettors, be sure to use the new O-rings, seals and other parts supplied in the rebuild kit. Do not overtighten the carburettor jets and screws as they are easily damaged.

1 Install the choke plunger assembly in its bore. Make sure the plunger retaining clips are securely in place **(see illustration 7.13)**.

2 Install the pilot screw (if removed) along with its spring and O-ring, turning it in until it seats lightly. Now, turn the screw out the number of turns previously recorded.

3 Fit a new O-ring to the base of the piston guide **(see illustration)**. Install the piston guide into the carburettor body, making sure it is the right way round **(see illustration 7.9b)**.

4 Install the needle jet through the piston guide and into the carburettor **(see illustration 7.9a)**. Align the flat in the needle jet with the pin in the jet housing **(see illustration)**. Hold the needle jet in place and screw the main jet into the end of the needle jet **(see illustration 7.8)**.

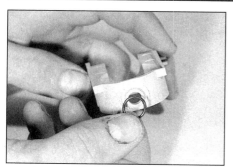

9.3 Fit a new O-ring to the base of the piston guide

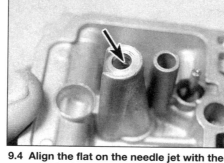

9.4 Align the flat on the needle jet with the pin in the jet housing (arrowed)

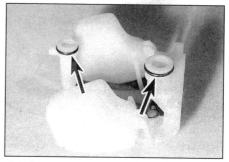

9.6 Fit new O-rings to the float assembly, making sure they are correctly seated in their grooves (arrowed)

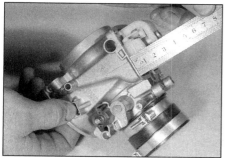

9.7 Check the float heights on all carburettors

9.8 Fit a new rubber seal to the float chamber, ensuring it seats in the groove

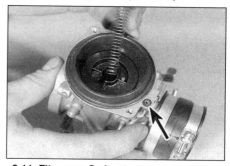

9.11 Fit a new O-ring to vacuum take-off stub (arrowed), then fit spring into piston

5 Screw the pilot jet into position next to the main jet.

6 Make sure the float assembly O-rings are seated properly in their grooves **(see illustration)**. Carefully press the assembly into position in the carburettor **(see illustration 7.7)**.

7 To check the float height, hold the carburettor so the float hangs down, then tilt it back until the needle valve is just seated, but not so far that the needle's spring-loaded tip is compressed. Measure the distance between the gasket face and the bottom of the float with an accurate ruler **(see illustration)**. The correct setting should be as given in the Specifications Section. If it is incorrect, adjust the float height by carefully bending the tab a little at a time until the correct height is obtained. Repeat the procedure for all carburettors.

8 With the float height checked, fit a new rubber seal to the float chamber and install the chamber on the carburettor **(see illustration)**.

9 Fit the spacers to the needle and insert the needle into the piston **(see illustration 7.5)**.

10 Insert the piston assembly into the carburettor body and lightly push it down, ensuring that the needle is correctly aligned with the needle jet. Press the diaphragm outer edge into its groove, making sure it is correctly seated. Check the diaphragm is not creased, and that the piston moves smoothly up and down in its guide.

11 Fit a new O-ring to the vacuum take-off stub, then insert the spring into the piston

(see illustration). Fit the top cover to the carburettor and tighten the screws securely.

12 If removed, fit the inlet manifold rubber to the carburettor. Note that the widest portion of the rubber must fit at the top and the narrowest at the bottom.

Fuel level check

13 A check can be made of the fuel level in the carburettors without the need to remove and dismantle the carburettors to measure the float height. To perform the check, two special tools are needed, an adapter (Pt. No. 3880120) and a gauge (Pt. No. 3880125), together with a short length of fuel hose.

14 Make sure the bike is on level ground and place it on its centre stand. If no centre stand is fitted, use an auxiliary stand and make sure that the bike is upright and level.

15 On Thunderbird and Tiger models, turn the fuel tap OFF. On all other models turn the fuel tap ON.

16 Unscrew the drain screw on the bottom of the float chamber and drain the fuel from the carburettor into a suitable container.

17 Thread the adapter into the float chamber in place of the drain screw, then attach the fuel hose to the adapter and plug the gauge into the other end of the hose.

18 Hold the gauge against the side of the carburettor body so that the bottom mark on its scale aligns with the joining faces of the float chamber and the carburettor, and so that it is vertical. Hold the gauge in this position whilst the fuel tap is turned ON (Thunderbird and Tiger) or to the PRI position (all other

models) - fuel will flow into the gauge **(see illustration)**.

19 The fuel level should be the specified distance above the joint face of the carburettor (see Specifications at the beginning of this Chapter).

20 On completion, turn the fuel tap OFF (Thunderbird and Tiger) or ON (all other models). Invert the gauge and drain the fuel into a suitable container, then remove the adapter and install the drain screw, tightening it securely. Check the other carburettors in the same way.

21 If the fuel level in any carburettor is incorrect, remove the float chambers (see Section 7) and adjust the float height as described in Step 7 above.

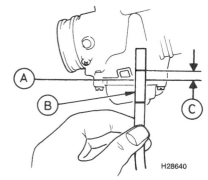

9.18 Fuel level measurement
A Joint face of carburettor
B Gauge
C Fuel level measurement

10 Throttle cable - removal and installation

Warning: Refer to the precautions given in Section 1 before starting work.

Removal

1 Detach the carburettors from the cylinder head as described in Section 6 and support them in a position that gives access to the throttle cable cam. **Note:** *Take care to keep the carburettors upright, to prevent fuel spillage from the float chambers and the possibility of the piston diaphragms being damaged.*

2 Back off the adjuster upper locknut and move the adjuster down in its housing to release the bottom locknut from the housing; where fitted, release the spring clip from the adjuster. Fully unscrew the lower locknut so that it comes off the adjuster **(see illustration)**.

3 Pull the adjuster up and out of the housing, then guide the cable through the slot to free it from the housing. If necessary, hold the throttle linkage open with a finger to aid removal of the adjuster from its housing.

4 Release the cable end from the throttle cam.

5 Unscrew the two right side handlebar switch/throttle pulley housing screws and separate the two halves. Remove the cable elbow from the housing, noting how it fits and hook the throttle cable end out of the pulley **(see illustration)**.

6 Remove the cable from the machine noting its routing.

Installation

7 Install the cable making sure it is correctly routed. The cable must not interfere with any other component and should not be kinked or bent sharply.

8 Lubricate the upper end of the cable with multi-purpose grease and install it into the throttle pulley. Install the cable elbow into the switch/throttle pulley housing **(see illustrations)**. Fit the two halves of the housing onto the handlebar and install the screws, tightening them securely.

9 Lubricate the lower end of the cable with multi-purpose grease and attach it to the carburettor throttle cam.

10 Make sure the cable is correctly connected, then lift the cable adjuster, slot the cable into the adjuster housing and allow the adjuster to be drawn into the housing by the pull of the throttle return spring.

11 Screw the bottom adjuster locknut onto the adjuster. Tighten the top adjuster locknut to secure the adjuster in place. Where fitted, install the spring clip. Operate the throttle to check that it opens and closes freely.

12 Check and adjust the throttle cable as

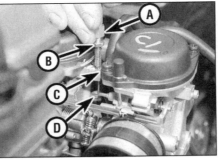

10.2 Throttle cable adjuster (A), upper locknut (B), adjuster housing (C), and lower locknut (D)

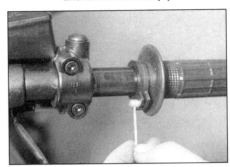

10.8a Fit the cable end into the throttle pulley . . .

described in Chapter 1. Turn the handlebars back and forth to make sure the cable doesn't cause the steering to bind.

13 Fit the carburettors to the cylinder head as described in Section 6.

14 Start the engine and check that the idle speed does not rise as the handlebars are turned. If it does, correct the problem before riding the motorcycle.

11 Choke cable - removal and installation

Removal

1 Unscrew the two left side handlebar switch/choke lever housing screws and

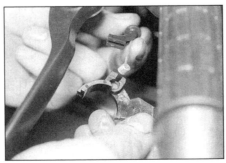

11.1 Remove the elbow from the housing and unhook the cable end from the lever

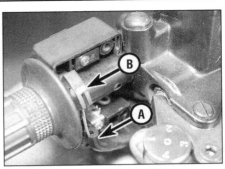

10.5 Remove the elbow (A) from the housing and unhook the cable end (B) from the pulley

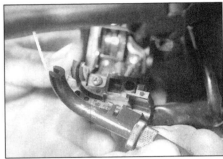

10.8b . . . and the cable elbow into the housing

separate the two halves. Remove the cable elbow from the housing, noting how it fits. Hook the choke cable end out of the lever **(see illustration)**.

2 Free the choke outer cable from its housing on the carburettor and detach the inner cable from the choke linkage **(see illustration)**.

3 Remove the cable from the machine noting its correct routing.

Installation

4 Install the cable, ensuring it is correctly routed. The cable must not interfere with any other components and should not be kinked or bent sharply.

5 Lubricate the lower cable end with multi-purpose grease and attach it to the choke shaft on the carburettor. Fit the outer cable into its housing.

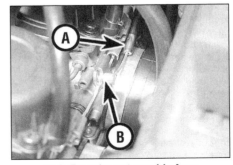

11.2 Free the outer cable from its housing (A) and the cable end from the choke shaft (B)

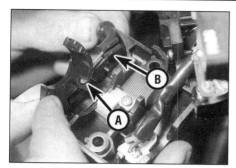

11.6 Fit the choke lever (A) and cable elbow (B) into the housing

6 Lubricate the upper cable end with multi-purpose grease and attach it to the choke lever. Install the choke lever and cable elbow into the left side handlebar switch/choke lever housing **(see illustration)**. Fit the two halves of the housing onto the handlebar and install the screws, tightening them securely.

7 Adjust the choke cable (see Chapter 1).

---

12 Auxiliary air chambers and airbox - removal and installation

Auxiliary air chambers

Removal

1 Remove the seat and the side panels (see Chapter 8), and the battery (Chapter 1). On Thunderbird and Tiger models, remove the airbox end covers **(see illustration)**.

2 On Thunderbird models, release the clamp securing the air chamber and air intake duct to the airbox, then unscrew the screw securing the air chamber to the frame and remove the chamber with the duct attached.

3 On all other models, prise the air intake ducts off the auxiliary air chambers (Tiger has one duct only, on the left side), then unscrew the air chamber mounting bolts. Note that the rear mounting bolts also secure the battery box to the frame and are held by nuts which locate on the inside of the battery box; the front mounting bolts screw directly into captive nuts on the frame. Remove the chamber from the bike **(see illustration)**.

4 Remove the rubber gaiter from the airbox **(see illustration)**.

Installation

5 Installation is the reverse of removal. Ensure that the rubber gaiter seals the joint between the air chamber and airbox.

Airbox

Removal

6 Remove both auxiliary air chambers as described above.

7 Remove the carburettors (see Section 6).

8 Release the clip securing the breather hose to the front of the airbox and detach the hose **(see illustration)**. The breather hose is routed off the clutch cover on early 4 cylinder engines and all 3 cylinder engines except the Thunderbird. On later 4 cylinder engines and the Thunderbird it is routed off the crankshaft left cover.

9 Remove the airbox from the bike with its drain hose attached, noting its routing **(see illustration)**. Note the expansion rings fitted to the airbox/carburettor venturi and take care not to lose them.

10 Note that the airbox is sold as an assembly, it is not possible to purchase the element separately. There is however nothing to be lost by removing the element and cleaning it, but the airbox must be replaced with a new one at the interval specified in Chapter 1. Unscrew the screws securing the two halves of the airbox, then separate them to access the element **(see illustrations)**.

Installation

11 Installation is the reverse of removal. Make sure the expansion rings are installed correctly in the venturi, and that the drain pipe is correctly routed. Attach the breather pipe to the front of the airbox before installing the carburettors.

12.1 On Thunderbird models the airbox end covers have two screws (arrowed)

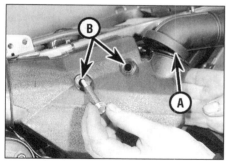

12.3 Prise off the air intake duct (A), then unscrew the chamber mounting bolts (B)

12.4 Remove the rubber gaiter from the airbox intake

12.8 Detach the breather hose (arrowed) from the front of the airbox

12.9 Remove the airbox from the frame

12.10a Remove the screws securing the airbox halves . . .

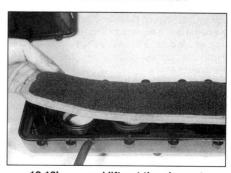

12.10b . . . and lift out the element

4

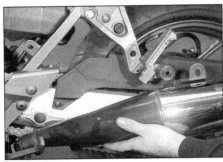

13.2 Release the silencer from the rest of the system using a twisting and pulling motion

13.3 Note how the sleeves fit into the bushes and how they both fit into the carrier

13.4a On the Thunderbird, the silencer fits to the inside of the carrier and is secured by the footpeg bracket bolt

13.4b On all models except Thunderbird, the silencer fits outside of the carrier

13.10a Unscrew the downpipe clamp nuts . . .

13.10b . . . then remove the downpipe assembly from the bike

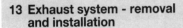

13 Exhaust system - removal and installation

Warning: If the engine has just been running, the exhaust system will be very hot. Allow the system to cool before carrying out any work. This applies particularly to California market models due to the high operating temperature of the catalytic converter.

Silencer

Removal

1 On Tiger models, remove the side panels as described in Chapter 8.

2 Unscrew and remove the silencer mounting nut and bolt (nut only on Thunderbird) and loosen the silencer clamp bolt, then release the silencer from the exhaust downpipe assembly using a twisting motion **(see illustration)**.

3 Recover the sleeves and rubber bushes, noting how they fit together **(see illustration)**. Inspect the bushes for signs of damage and replace if necessary. On Thunderbird models, note that the silencer mounts to the footrest bracket bolt, and that there is only one sleeve and bush for each silencer.

Installation

4 Install the silencer into the downpipe assembly. On Thunderbird models, the silencer mounting bracket fits to the inside of the carrier **(see illustration)**. On all other models the silencer bracket fits to the outside of the carrier. Ensure that the sleeves and bushes are in place, then install the bolt (not Thunderbird), washers and nut **(see illustrations)**. Tighten the clamp bolt securely, and the mounting bolt (nut on Thunderbird) to the torque setting specified at the beginning of the Chapter.

Complete system

Removal

5 On Daytona and Trophy models remove the lower fairing panels, on Tiger models remove the fairing side panels, and on Sprint models remove the fairing. All procedures are described in Chapter 8.

6 On Daytona and Trophy models, detach and support the oil cooler and its sub-frame as an assembly, referring to Chapter 2 for details.

7 On Tiger models, unscrew the sump guard mounting bolts and remove the sump guard **(see illustration 8.6 in Chapter 3)**.

8 Remove the silencers as described in Steps 1 to 3 above.

9 If fitted, unscrew the mounting bolt securing the balancer pipe to the rear of the engine and recover the bush.

10 Support the downpipe assembly, then unscrew the downpipe retaining nuts from the cylinder head studs and remove the assembly. Remove the gaskets from the

cylinder head, noting how they fit, and discard them as new ones must be fitted **(see illustrations)**.

11 If necessary, the downpipe assembly can be split into its various parts by releasing the relevant clamp bolts and separating the components. The downpipe assemblies vary according to model **(see illustration)**.

Installation

12 If dismantled, reassemble the downpipe assembly, tightening all clamp bolts securely.

13 If fitted, inspect the balancer pipe rubber bush for signs of damage and replace if necessary.

14 Fit a new gasket into each of the cylinder head ports with the flanged side inwards. Apply a smear of grease to the gaskets to keep them in place whilst fitting the downpipe assembly **(see illustration)**.

15 Install the exhaust downpipe assembly, aligning the pipes with the cylinder head ports. Support the assembly from underneath and slide the clamps on the cylinder head studs and fit the nuts. Tighten the downpipe nuts evenly and in two stages, first to the stage one torque setting and then to the stage two torque setting, as specified at the beginning of the Chapter.

16 If fitted, install the bush and the mounting bolt to secure the balancer pipe to the rear of the engine and tighten it securely.

17 Fit the silencers as described in Step 4 above.

18 On Daytona and Trophy models, install the oil cooler assembly as described in

Chapter 2. On Tiger models, install the sump guard.
19 Install the fairing sections (where applicable) and side panels (Tiger only) as described in Chapter 8.

14 Evaporative loss system and catalytic converter (California only) - general information

Evaporative loss system

1 On all California models, an evaporative loss system is fitted to prevent the escape of fuel vapours into the atmosphere **(see illustration)**. The system functions as follows:
2 When the engine is stopped, fuel vapour from the tank and the carburettor float chambers is directed into a charcoal canister where it is absorbed and stored whilst the motorcycle is standing. When the engine is started, inlet manifold depression opens a vacuum switch in the canister and the vapours which are stored are drawn into the engine to be burned during the normal combustion process.
3 The fuel tank incorporates a special vapour chamber. When the pressure in the chamber rises above 0.75 psi (0.05 Bar) a pressure control valve in the vent pipe opens and allows the tank vapour to pass into the canister. The tank vent pipe also incorporates a roll-over valve which closes and prevents any fuel from escaping through it in the event of the bike falling over. The tank filler cap has a one way valve which allows air into the tank as the volume of fuel decreases, but prevents any fuel vapour from escaping.
4 A solenoid operated valve in the float chamber vent pipes allows air to flow into the float chamber whilst the engine is running. The fuel vapour cannot escape as it is being constantly drawn into the combustion chamber and burnt. When the engine is stopped the solenoid closes the vent to the air and any fuel vapour then passes down the vent pipe to the canister.
5 The system is not adjustable and can be tested only by a Triumph dealer. Checks which can be performed by the owner are given in Chapter 1.

13.14 Fit a new gasket into each cylinder head port, with the flanged side inwards

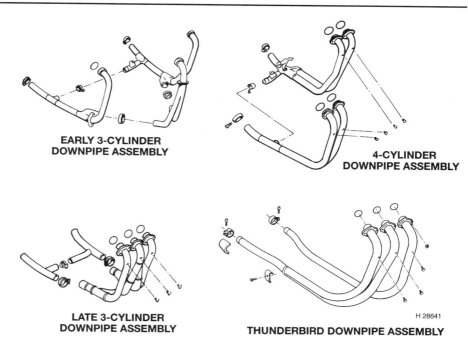

EARLY 3-CYLINDER DOWNPIPE ASSEMBLY

4-CYLINDER DOWNPIPE ASSEMBLY

LATE 3-CYLINDER DOWNPIPE ASSEMBLY

THUNDERBIRD DOWNPIPE ASSEMBLY

H 28641

13.11 Downpipe assembly detail

14.1 Evaporative loss system - US California models only

1 Fuel tank vapour chamber
2 Solenoids
3 Control valve
4 Canister

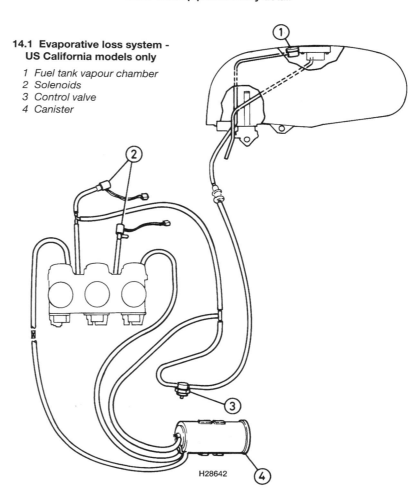

H28642

4

Catalytic converter

6 Certain California market models have a catalytic converter located in the exhaust downpipes to minimise the amount of pollutants which escape into the atmosphere. It is an open-loop system, which has no link with the fuel and ignition system.

7 The catalytic converter is a simple device in operation and one which requires no routine maintenance.

8 Note the following points:

a) *Always use unleaded fuel - the use of leaded fuel will destroy the converter.*

b) *Do not use any fuel or oil additives.*

c) *Keep the fuel and ignition systems in good order - if the fuel/air mixture is suspected of being incorrect have it checked on an exhaust gas analyser.*

d) *If the catalytic converter is ever removed from the downpipes, handle it carefully and do not drop it.*

Chapter 5
Ignition system

Contents

Degrees of difficulty

Easy, suitable for novice with little experience		**Fairly easy,** suitable for beginner with some experience		**Fairly difficult,** suitable for competent DIY mechanic	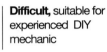	**Difficult,** suitable for experienced DIY mechanic		**Very difficult,** suitable for expert DIY or professional	

Specifications

General information

Firing order
  3 cylinder engines 1-2-3
  4 cylinder engines 1-2-4-3
Cylinder identification
  3 cylinder engines . . . . 1-2-3 left to right
  4 cylinder engines . . . . 1-2-3-4 left to right
Spark plugs . . . . See Chapter 1

Ignition timing

At idle . . . . 5° BTDC @ 1000 rpm
Full advance
  1200 Trophy and Tiger . . . . 29° BTDC @ 6500 rpm
  1000 Daytona . . . . 38° BTDC @ 6500 rpm
  750 Daytona and 750 Trident . . . . 35° BTDC @ 6500 rpm
  Thunderbird . . . . 30° BTDC @ 6500 rpm
  All other models . . . . 26° BTDC @ 6500 rpm
Electronic rev-limiter
  750/1000 Daytona and 750 Trident . . . . 11000 rpm
  Tiger and Thunderbird . . . . 8750 rpm
  All other models . . . . 9700 rpm

Pick-up coil

Resistance . . . . 530 ohms ± 10%
Air gap . . . . 0.6 to 0.8 mm

Ignition HT coils

Primary winding resistance . . . . 0.63 ohms ± 10%
Secondary winding resistance . . . . 10.5 K ohms ± 10%

Torque settings

Crankshaft right end cover retaining bolts . . . . 9 Nm
Ignition coil mounting bolts . . . . 5 Nm
Pick-up coil mounting bolts . . . . 10 Nm

1 General information

All models are fitted with an inductive tran-sistorised digital electronic ignition system, which due to its lack of mechanical parts is totally maintenance free. The system comprises a rotor, pick-up coil, igniter and ignition HT coils (refer to the wiring diagrams at the end of Chapter 9 for details).

The triggers on the rotor, which is fitted to the right end of the crankshaft, magnetically operate the pick-up coil as the crankshaft rotates. The pick-up coil sends a signal to the igniter which then supplies the ignition HT coils with the power necessary to produce a spark at the plugs.

Three cylinder engines have one coil for each cylinder, whilst four cylinder engines have only two coils, with cylinders 1 and 4 operating off one coil and cylinders 2 and 3 off the other. Under the 4 cylinder arrangement each plug is fired twice for every engine cycle, but one of the sparks occurs during the exhaust stroke and therefore performs no useful function. This arrangement is usually known as a "spare spark" or "wasted spark" system.

Because of their nature, the individual ignition system components can be checked but not repaired. If ignition system troubles occur, and the faulty component can be isolated, the only cure for the problem is to replace the part with a new one. Keep in mind that most electrical parts, once purchased, cannot be returned. To avoid unnecessary expense, make very sure the faulty component has been positively identified before buying a replacement part.

2 Ignition system - check

Caution: The energy levels in electronic systems can be very high. On no account should the ignition be switched on whilst the plugs or plug caps are being held. Shocks from the HT circuit can be most unpleasant. Secondly, it is vital that the plugs are soundly earthed when the system is checked for sparking. The ignition system components can be seriously damaged if the HT circuit becomes isolated.

1 As no means of adjustment is available, any failure of the system can be traced to failure of a system component or a simple wiring fault. Of the two possibilities, the latter is far more likely. In the event of failure, check the system in a logical fashion, as described below.
2 On four cylinder engines disconnect the HT leads from No. 1 and No. 2 cylinder spark plugs, on three cylinder engines disconnect the HT leads from all three spark plugs. Connect each lead to a spare spark plug and lay each plug on the engine with the threads contacting the engine. If necessary, hold each spark plug with an insulated tool.

⚠️ **Warning: Do not remove any of the spark plugs from the engine to perform this check - atomised fuel being pumped out of the open spark plug hole could ignite, causing severe injury!**

3 Having observed the above precautions, check that the kill switch is in the RUN position, turn the ignition switch ON and turn the engine over on the starter motor. If the system is in good condition a regular, fat blue spark should be evident at each plug electrode. If the spark appears thin or yellowish, or is non-existent, further investigation will be necessary. Before proceeding further, turn the ignition off and remove the key as a safety measure.
4 Ignition faults can be divided into two categories, namely those where the ignition system has failed completely, and those which are due to a partial failure. The likely faults are listed below, starting with the most

probable source of failure. Work through the list systematically, referring to the subsequent sections for full details of the necessary checks and tests. **Note:** *Before checking the following items, ensure the battery is fully charged and all fuses are in good condition.*

a) *Loose, corroded or damaged wiring connections, broken or shorted wiring between any of the component parts of the ignition system (see Chapter 9).*
b) *Faulty HT lead or spark plug cap, faulty spark plug, dirty, worn or corroded plug electrodes, or incorrect gap between electrodes.*
c) *Faulty ignition switch or engine kill switch (see Chapter 9).*
d) *Faulty side stand switch/relay (see Chapter 9).*
e) *Faulty pick-up coil or damaged rotor.*
f) *Faulty ignition HT coil(s).*
g) *Faulty igniter.*

5 If the above checks don't reveal the cause of the problem, have the ignition system tested by a Triumph dealer. Triumph produce a tester which can perform a complete diagnostic analysis of the ignition system.

3 Ignition HT coils - check, removal and installation

Check

1 In order to determine conclusively that the ignition coils are defective, they should be

tested by a Triumph dealer equipped with the special diagnostic tester.
2 However, the coils can be checked visually (for cracks and other damage) and the primary and secondary coil resistance can be measured with an ohmmeter. If the coils are undamaged, and if the resistance readings are as specified at the beginning of the Chapter, they are probably capable of proper operation.
3 To gain access to the coils, remove the seat and disconnect the battery negative (-ve) lead, then remove the fuel tank as described in Chapter 4. The coils are mounted on each side of the main frame tube **(see illustration)**.
4 Disconnect the primary circuit electrical connectors and the HT lead(s) from the coil being tested **(see illustration)**. Mark the locations of all wires and leads before disconnecting them.
5 Set the meter to the ohms x 1 scale and measure the resistance between the primary circuit terminals **(see illustration)**. This will give a resistance reading of the primary windings and should be consistent with the value given in the Specifications at the beginning of the Chapter.
6 To check the condition of the secondary windings, set the meter to the K ohm scale. On four cylinder engines, connect one meter probe to each HT lead socket. On three cylinder engines, connect one probe to one of the primary circuit terminals and the other probe to the HT lead socket **(see illustration)**. If the reading obtained is not within the range shown in the Specifications, it is likely that the coil is defective.

3.3 Ignition HT coils are mounted each side of the main frame tube

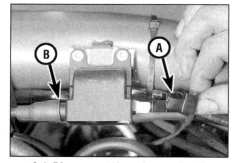

3.4 Disconnect the primary circuit connections (A) and HT lead (B) from coil

3.5 Measuring ignition HT coil primary winding resistance

3.6 Measuring ignition HT coil secondary winding resistance (3 cylinder models)

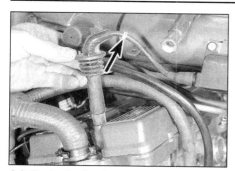

3.9 Each plug lead should be labelled with its cylinder number (arrowed)

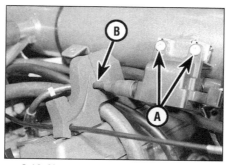

3.10 Unscrew the two coil mounting bolts (A). Note the routing of the HT leads through the separator (B)

7 Should any of the above checks not produce the expected result, have your findings confirmed on the diagnostic tester (see Step 1). If the coil is confirmed to be faulty, it must be replaced; the coil is a sealed unit and cannot therefore be repaired. Note that the HT leads can be unscrewed from the coils and replaced separately.

Removal

8 Remove the seat and disconnect the battery negative (-ve) lead, then remove the fuel tank as described in Chapter 4. On all models except the Thunderbird, remove the valve cover cowls from each side of the frame; they are secured by two screws.
9 Disconnect the primary circuit electrical connectors from the coil(s) and disconnect the HT lead(s) from the plug(s) that are connected to the coil being removed. Mark the locations of all wires and leads before disconnecting them. **(see illustration)**.
10 Unscrew the two bolts securing each coil to the frame and remove the coil. Note the routing of the HT leads through the separator **(see illustration)**.

Installation

11 Installation is the reverse of removal. Make sure the wiring connectors and HT leads are securely connected. Tighten the coil mounting bolts to the torque setting specified at the beginning of the Chapter.

---

4 Pick-up coil - check, removal and installation

Check

1 Remove the seat as described in Chapter 8 and disconnect the battery negative (-ve) lead. On Trophy and Daytona models, remove the right side lower fairing panel (see Chapter 8).
2 Trace the pick-up coil wiring from the right side crankshaft end cover to the two-pin connector. Disconnect the connector and using a multimeter set to the ohms x 100 scale, measure the resistance between the black and red wires on the pick-up coil side of the connector.

HAYNES HINT *On certain models it may be impossible to access the pick-up coil connector without first removing the left air chamber.*

3 Compare the reading obtained with that given in the Specifications at the beginning of this Chapter. The pick-up coil must be replaced if the reading obtained differs greatly from that given, particularly if the meter indicates a short circuit (no measurable resistance) or an open circuit (infinite, or very high resistance).
4 If the pick-up coil is thought to be faulty, first check that this is not due to a damaged or broken wire from the coil to the connector; pinched or broken wires can usually be repaired.

Removal

5 Remove the seat as described in Chapter 8 and disconnect the battery negative (-ve) lead. On Trophy and Daytona models, remove the right side lower fairing panel (see Chapter 8).
6 Trace the pick-up coil wiring from the right side crankshaft end cover to the two-pin connector (see Haynes Hint). Disconnect the connector and free the wiring from any relevant ties or clips.
7 Place a suitable container under the cover to catch any residual oil, then unscrew the retaining bolts and remove the cover squarely from the engine. Discard the gasket as a new one must be used.

4.8 Pick-up coil is secured by two bolts (arrowed)

8 Remove the two bolts which secure the pick-up coil to the crankcase and remove the coil, noting how it fits **(see illustration)**.
9 Examine the rotor triggers for signs of damage such as chipped or missing teeth and replace if necessary (See Chapter 2).

Installation

10 Fit the pick-up coil to the crankcase and install the mounting bolts, but do not yet fully tighten them.
11 Rotate the crankshaft so that one of the triggers on the rotor is opposite the pick-up on the coil. Using feeler blades, measure the gap between the trigger and the pick-up coil and adjust as necessary until the gap is as specified at the beginning of the Chapter **(see illustration)**. When the gap is set, tighten the bolts to the specified torque setting.
12 Remove all traces of old gasket from the crankcase and cover mating surfaces and fit a new gasket to the crankcase.
13 Apply a smear of sealant to the end cover wiring grommet and fit the grommet in its recess in the crankcase.
14 Fit the cover to the engine and tighten the cover bolts to the specified torque setting.
15 Route the wiring up to the wire harness and reconnect the two-pin connector. Secure the wiring in position with all the necessary clips and ties. Install the air chamber, where necessary.
16 Check the engine oil level as described in Chapter 1 and top-up if necessary.
17 Reconnect the battery negative (-ve) lead, then fit the seat and lower fairing panel as described in Chapter 8.

---

5 Igniter - removal, check and installation

Removal

1 Remove the seat as described in Chapter 8 and disconnect the battery negative (-ve) lead. On Tiger models, remove the fairing left side panel to gain access to the igniter. On all other models remove the seat, and on Thunderbird models also remove the right side cover. For details, refer to Chapter 8.

4.11 Measure the air gap between pick-up coil and rotor trigger using feeler blades

5

5.2 Disconnect the igniter at its wiring connector rather than at the igniter itself

2 Disconnect the igniter wiring at the connector **(see illustration)**.

3 Free the igniter from its mounting bracket and remove it from the bike **(see illustration)**.

Check

4 If the tests shown in the preceding Sections have failed to isolate the cause of an ignition fault, it is likely that the igniter itself is faulty. No test details are available with which the unit can be tested on home workshop equipment. Take the machine to a Triumph dealer for testing on the diagnostic tester.

Installation

5 Installation is the reverse of removal ensuring that the wiring connector is securely connected.

---

6 Ignition timing - general information and check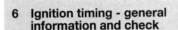

General information

1 Since no provision exists for adjusting the ignition timing and since no component is

5.3 Free the igniter with its strap from the mounting bracket

subject to mechanical wear, there is no need for regular checks; only if investigating a fault such as a loss of power or a misfire, should the ignition timing be checked.

2 The ignition timing is checked dynamically (engine running). Triumph produce a special tool which is basically a replacement crankshaft right end cover with an inspection hole to enable the timing marks to be viewed with the cover in place. Note that checking the timing without this cover is not possible due to the presence of engine oil in the casing.

3 Check the timing using a stroboscopic lamp. The inexpensive neon lamps should be adequate in theory, but in practice may produce a pulse of such low intensity that the timing mark remains indistinct. If possible, one of the more precise xenon tube lamps should be used, powered by an external source of the appropriate voltage. **Note:** *Do not use the machine's own battery as an incorrect reading may result from stray impulses within the machine's electrical system.*

Check

4 Warm the engine up to normal operating temperature then stop it.

5 On Daytona and Trophy models, remove the right side fairing lower panel as described in Chapter 8.

6 Place a suitable container under the rotor cover to catch any residual oil, then unscrew the retaining bolts and remove the cover squarely from the engine. Install the timing check cover in its place.

7 Identify the timing mark (the F next to the No. 1 (3 cylinder) or No. 1.4 (4 cylinder)) stamped on the rotor.

> **HAYNES HiNT**
> *The rotor timing mark can be highlighted with white paint to make it more visible under the stroboscopic light.*

8 Connect the timing light to the No. 1 cylinder HT lead as described in the manufacturer's instructions.

9 Start the engine and aim the light through the inspection hole.

10 With the machine idling at the specified speed, the timing mark should align with the pick-up coil centre.

11 Slowly increase the engine speed whilst observing the timing mark. The timing mark should move anti-clockwise, increasing in relation to the engine speed.

12 As already stated, there is no means of adjustment of the ignition timing on these machines. If the ignition timing is incorrect, or suspected of being incorrect, one of the ignition system components is at fault, and the system must be tested as described in the preceding Sections of this Chapter.

13 When the check is complete, fit the original rotor cover and top-up the engine oil if necessary (see Chapter 1).

14 Where applicable, install the fairing panel as described in Chapter 8.

Chapter 6
Frame, suspension and final drive

Contents

Degrees of difficulty

Easy, suitable for novice with little experience	Fairly easy, suitable for beginner with some experience	Fairly difficult, suitable for competent DIY mechanic	Difficult, suitable for experienced DIY mechanic	Very difficult, suitable for expert DIY or professional

Specifications

Front forks

Oil level*
900 Trophy to VIN 4901**	84 mm
1200 Trophy to VIN 4901**	103 mm
900/1200 Trophy from VIN 4902	117 mm (102 mm max)
750 Daytona	139 mm
900/1000/1200 Daytona to VIN 9082	132 mm
900/1200 Daytona from VIN 9083	139 mm (132 mm max)
Sprint to VIN 7491	109 mm (97 mm max)
Sprint from VIN 7492	117 mm (102 mm max)
Trident to VIN 4901**	94 mm
Trident from VIN 4902	109 mm (97 mm max)
Speed Triple	141 mm
Thunderbird	109 mm
Tiger	130 mm

Fork oil type
900/1200 Trophy to VIN 9082	SAE 10W fork oil
900/1200 Trophy from VIN 9083	SAE 15W fork oil
750 Daytona	SAE 10W fork oil
All other Daytona models	SAE 5W fork oil
Sprint to VIN 11541	SAE 10W fork oil
Sprint from VIN 11542	SAE 15W fork oil
Trident, Tiger and Speed Triple	SAE 10W fork oil
Thunderbird	SAE 15W fork oil

*Oil level is measured from the top of the tube with the fork spring removed and the leg fully compressed.
**On Trophy and Trident models to VIN 4901, if Triumph fork modification kits have been fitted then VIN 4902-on oil levels apply.

6

Torque settings

Handlebar clamp bolts	
Tiger and Thunderbird	18 Nm
All other models	22 Nm
Yoke pinch bolts	
Top yoke	
Tiger	18 Nm
All other models	20 Nm
Bottom yoke	
Tiger	22 Nm
All other models	20 Nm
Bottom yoke brake hose union assembly bolts	9 Nm
Front forks	
Top bolt	23 Nm
Adjuster (Daytona and Speed Triple only)	15 Nm
Damper rod/cartridge bolt	
Daytona, Speed Triple and Thunderbird	43 Nm
All other models	60 Nm
Steering stem nut	65 Nm
Steering head bearing adjuster ring pinch bolt (early models)	7 Nm
Steering head bearing adjuster locknut (later models)	40 Nm
Rear shock absorber and linkage	
Thunderbird and Tiger	
Shock absorber top mounting bolt.	95 Nm
Shock absorber lower mounting bolt	55 Nm
Linkage connecting rod to swingarm mount	100 Nm
Linkage connecting rod to linkage arm mount	100 Nm
Linkage arm to frame mount	100 Nm
All other models	
Shock absorber top mounting bolt	95 Nm
Linkage spindle bolt	85 Nm
Linkage spindle clamp bolts	10 Nm
Linkage connecting rod to swingarm mount	55 Nm
Linkage arm to frame mount	100 Nm
Swingarm pivot shaft bolt	85 Nm
Front sprocket nut	132 Nm
Rear sprocket nuts	85 Nm
Centre stand pivot bolts (where applicable)	40 Nm
Sidestand pivot bolt	20 Nm
Sidestand pivot bolt locknut	25 Nm

1 General information

All models use a spine type frame made of micro alloyed high tensile steel, which uses the engine as a stressed member.

Front suspension is by a pair of conventional oil-damped telescopic forks with 43 mm stanchions. Daytona and Speed Triple models have cartridge forks, adjustable for preload, compression and rebound damping.

At the rear, an aluminium alloy swingarm acts on a single shock absorber via a two-piece linkage which provides a rising rate system. On all models the shock absorber is adjustable for preload, and on Trophy, Daytona, later 900 Trident, Sprint, Speed Triple and Tiger models for rebound damping; the shock on Tiger models is also adjustable for compression damping.

The final drive uses an "endless" chain (it doesn't have a joining link). A rubber damper (often called a "cush drive") is fitted between the rear wheel coupling and the wheel.

2 Frame - inspection and repair

1 The frame should not require attention unless accident damage has occurred. In most cases, frame replacement is the only satisfactory remedy for such damage. A few frame specialists have the jigs and other equipment necessary for straightening the frame to the required standard of accuracy, but even then there is no simple way of assessing to what extent the frame may have been over stressed.

2 After the machine has accumulated a lot of miles, the frame should be examined closely for signs of cracking or splitting at the welded joints. Loose engine mount bolts can cause ovaling or fracturing of the mounting tabs. Minor damage can often be repaired by welding, depending on the extent and nature of the damage.

3 Remember that a frame which is out of alignment will cause handling problems. If misalignment is suspected as the result of an accident, it will be necessary to strip the machine completely so the frame can be thoroughly checked. On Thunderbird models, the rear sub-frame is bolted to the main frame, whereas on all other models it is welded.

3 Footrests and brackets - removal and installation

Rider's footrests

Removal

1 Remove the circlip from the end of the pivot pin, then slide out the pivot pin and remove the footrest from the footrest bracket along with its return spring. On all models except the Thunderbird, the footrest rubber can be separated from the footrest by removing its retaining screws.

Installation

2 Installation is the reverse of removal.

3.3 The left footrest bracket is secured to the frame by two bolts (arrowed)

3.11 Remove the cap from the upper bolt, then unscrew both bolts (arrowed) and remove the carrier

3.12 Unscrew the footrest bracket bolt from behind the carrier

Rider's left footrest bracket

Removal

Thunderbird

3 Unscrew the two bracket-to-frame bolts, and remove the bracket **(see illustration)**.

Tiger

4 On Tiger models the left footrest and the sidestand are mounted on the same bracket. To remove the bracket it is necessary to support the bike using an auxiliary stand. Make sure the bike is securely supported.

5 Detach the link rod from the gearshift pedal by slackening its locknuts and rotating the rod via its knurled centre section so that it unscrews from the lever and pedal at the same time.

6 Unscrew the two bolts securing the sidestand switch to the bracket and remove the switch.

7 Unhook the sidestand return spring, then unscrew the sidestand pivot bolt and remove the stand.

8 Unscrew the gearshift pedal-to-bracket pivot bolt, and remove the pedal.

9 Unscrew the two bolts securing the bracket to the frame and remove the bracket.

All other models

10 Detach the link rod from the gearshift shaft lever and pedal by slackening its locknuts and rotating the rod via its knurled centre section so that it unscrews from the lever and pedal at the same time. On models with a dog-leg link rod, slacken off the locknut

and unscrew the threaded sleeve to separate the link rod from the shaft lever.

11 Remove the cap from the upper carrier mounting bolt, then unscrew both mounting bolts and remove the carrier, gearshift pedal and footrest assembly **(see illustration)**.

12 Unscrew the bolt located on the back of the carrier and separate the gearshift pedal, pivot bracket and footrest from the carrier **(see illustration)**.

Installation

13 Installation is the reverse of removal. On Tiger models, apply a smear of grease to the sidestand pivot bolt and the gearshift pedal pivot bolt. Tighten the bracket mounting bolts securely.

14 On all models except the Thunderbird and Tiger, apply a smear of grease to the bearing surface of the gearshift pedal pivot and a drop of non-permanent thread locking compound to the threads of the bolt.

Rider's right footrest bracket

Removal

Thunderbird

15 Remove the split pin and the clevis pin from the clevis joining the rear brake pedal to the rear brake master cylinder pushrod.

16 Unhook the brake pedal return spring. Remove the cap, then unscrew the brake pedal pivot bolt and remove the pedal from the bracket **(see illustration)**.

17 Unscrew the two footrest bracket

mounting bolts and remove the bracket **(see illustration 3.16)**.

Tiger

18 Remove the split pin and the clevis pin from the clevis joining the rear brake pedal to the rear brake master cylinder pushrod **(see illustration)**.

19 Unhook the brake pedal return spring. Unscrew the pivot bolt securing the brake pedal to the bracket and remove the pedal.

20 Unscrew the sump guard-to-bracket bolt, and the two bolts securing the bracket to the frame, and remove the bracket.

All other models

21 Remove the split pin and the clevis pin from the clevis joining the rear brake pedal to the rear brake master cylinder pushrod.

22 Remove the cap from the upper footrest carrier mounting bolt, then unscrew both carrier mounting bolts and remove the carrier, brake pedal and footrest assembly.

23 Unhook the brake pedal return spring, then unscrew the pivot bolt on the back of the carrier and separate the rear brake pedal, pivot bracket and footrest from the carrier.

Installation

24 Installation is the reverse of removal. Apply a smear of grease to the bearing surface of the brake pedal pivot bolt and a drop of non-permanent thread locking compound to the threads of the bolt. Fit a new split pin to the brake pushrod clevis pin, and do not forget to hook up the brake pedal return spring **(see illustration)**.

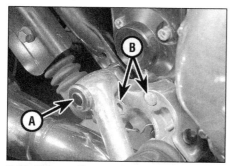

3.16 Remove the cap from the brake pedal pivot bolt (A), then unscrew the bolt and remove the pedal. Footrest bracket is secured by two bolts (B)

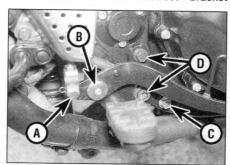

3.18 Release pushrod (A) from brake pedal, then unscrew pedal bolt (B). Sump guard is secured to bracket by bolt (C), and bracket to frame by two bolts (D)

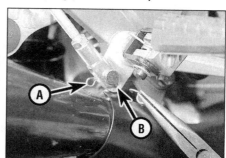

3.24 Fit a new split pin to the pushrod (A) and hook the return spring into the hole in the pedal (B)

6

3.27a Unscrew the nut at the back of the carrier and remove the footrest pivot bracket

3.27b On Thunderbird models note that the footrest bracket bolt also secures the silencer (arrowed)

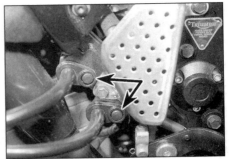

3.27c On Tiger models the footrest carrier is secured to the frame by two bolts (arrowed)

Passenger footrests

Removal

25 Remove the circlip from the end of the pivot pin, then slide out the pivot pin and remove the footrest from the pivot bracket. As the footrest is removed, recover the detent ball and spring, noting how they fit. On all models except the Thunderbird and Tiger, the footrest rubber can be separated from the footrest by unscrewing the retaining screws.

Installation

26 Installation is the reverse of removal using a new circlip.

Passenger footrest brackets

Removal

27 Remove the nut securing the footrest pivot bracket to the carrier and remove the bracket **(see illustration)**. On Thunderbird models the silencer mounts on the footrest bracket bolt at the back of the carrier **(see illustration)**. Support or tie the silencer to avoid putting too much strain on the rest of the system. On Tiger models the carrier can be removed if necessary by unscrewing the two mounting bolts, having first prised out their caps **(see illustration)**.

Installation

28 Installation is the reverse of removal.

4 Stands - removal and installation

Centre stand - 750/1000 Daytona, Trophy, Trident and Sprint only

1 The centre stand is attached to the frame and linkage carriers by two countersunk bolts passing through sleeves in the stand pivots. Support the bike on its sidestand and free one end of the centre stand return spring. Counterhold the pivot bolt nut and unscrew the pivot bolt from each side **(see illustration)**. Remove the stand and withdraw the sleeves from its pivot.

2 Inspect the stand, sleeves and bolts for signs of wear and replace if necessary. Apply a smear of grease to the sleeves and bolts and fit the stand back on the bike, tightening the bolts to the torque setting specified at the beginning of the Chapter. Reconnect the return spring.

3 Make sure the return spring is in good condition and is capable of holding the stand up when not in use. A broken or weak spring is an obvious safety hazard.

Sidestand - all models

4 The sidestand is attached to a bracket on the frame. An extension spring anchored to the bracket ensures that the stand is held in the retracted position. The side stand incorporates a switch which is part of the ignition cut-out circuit. Trophy and Trident models have a warning light on the instrument panel which illuminates when the ignition is ON and the sidestand is down.

5 Support the bike on its centre stand. Where no centre stand is fitted, use an auxiliary stand to support the bike.

6 Free the stand spring and unscrew the locknut from the pivot bolt. Unscrew the pivot bolt to free the stand from its bracket. On installation apply grease to the pivot bolt shank and tighten the pivot bolt, followed by the locknut, to their specified torque settings. Reconnect the sidestand spring and check that it holds the stand securely up when not in use - an accident is almost certain to occur if

the stand extends while the bike is in motion.

7 For check and replacement of the side stand switch see Chapter 9.

5 Handlebars - removal and installation

Thunderbird and Tiger models

Removal

1 Remove the left and right side handlebar switches as described in Chapter 9.

2 Detach the clutch and front brake master cylinders from the handlebar (see Chapters 2 and 7 respectively).

3 Unscrew the handlebar clamp bolts and remove the handlebars **(see illustration)**. If necessary, unscrew the handlebar weight retaining screws, then remove the weight from the end of the handlebar. The throttle grip can be slid off the handlebar end, whereas the left side grip must be slit with a knife and peeled off the handlebar if replacement is required.

4 If necessary, remove the split pin from the bottom of the handlebar clamp base mounting bolt, then unscrew the nut securing the clamp base to the top yoke and remove the base **(see illustration)**. Note the fitting of the rubber dampers. Inspect the dampers for signs of wear or damage and replace if necessary.

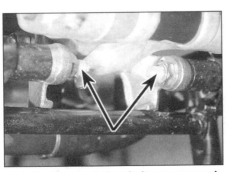

4.1 Centre stand pivot bolts are secured by nuts on inside of linkage carriers (arrowed)

5.3 Tiger handlebar clamp bolts (arrowed)

5.4 Remove the split pin from the clamp base mounting bolt (arrowed), then unscrew the nut and remove the base

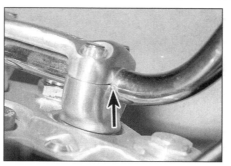

5.5 Align the punch mark on the handlebar (arrowed) with the clamp mating surfaces (Thunderbird shown)

Installation

5 Installation is the reverse of removal, noting the following.

a) If the left side grip is being replaced, degrease the end of the handlebar and use adhesive to bond the new grip in place.

b) If removed, fit a new split pin to the bottom of the clamp base mounting bolt.

c) Align the punch mark(s) on the handlebar with the mating surfaces of the handlebar clamps **(see illustration)**.

d) Tighten the clamp bolts to the torque setting specified at the beginning of the Chapter.

Trophy, Trident and Sprint models

Right handlebar

Removal

6 Remove the right side handlebar switch as described in Chapter 9.

7 Remove the front brake master cylinder assembly as described in Chapter 7.

8 Prise out the caps, then unscrew the bolts securing the handlebar to the top yoke and remove the handlebar. If necessary, unscrew the handlebar weight retaining screw, then remove the weight from the end of the handlebar and slide off the throttle twistgrip.

Installation

9 Installation is the reverse of removal. If removed, apply a smear of grease to the throttle twistgrip. Tighten the handlebar clamp bolts to the torque setting specified at the beginning of the Chapter.

Left handlebar

Removal

10 Remove the left side handlebar switch as described in Chapter 9.

11 Remove the clutch master cylinder assembly as described in Chapter 2.

12 Prise out the caps, then unscrew the bolts securing the handlebar to the top yoke and remove the handlebar **(see illustrations)**. If necessary, unscrew the handlebar weight retaining screw, then remove the weight from the end of the handlebar. If replacement of the handlebar grip is necessary, slit the grip with a knife and peel it off the handlebar.

Installation

13 Installation is the reverse of removal, noting that if the grip is being replaced, the handlebar end must be degreased and an adhesive applied to bond the grip in place. Tighten the handlebar clamp bolts to the torque setting specified at the beginning of the Chapter.

Daytona and Speed Triple models

Right handlebar

Removal

14 Remove the right side handlebar switch as described in Chapter 9.

15 Remove the front brake master cylinder assembly as described in Chapter 7.

16 If necessary, unscrew the handlebar weight retaining screw, then remove the weight from the end of the handlebar and slide off the throttle twistgrip.

17 As it is not possible to remove the top

yoke with the front forks in place, the right side fork must be lowered or removed to allow removal of the handlebar. See Section 6 for fork removal.

Installation

18 Install the handlebar and front fork as described in Section 6.

19 If removed, apply a smear of grease to the throttle twistgrip and slide the grip on the handlebar, then install the weight and securely tighten the screw.

20 Install the front brake master cylinder assembly as described in Chapter 7.

21 Install the handlebar switch (Chapter 9).

Left handlebar

Removal

22 Remove the left side handlebar switch as described in Chapter 9.

23 Remove the clutch master cylinder assembly as described in Chapter 2.

24 If necessary, unscrew the handlebar weight retaining screw, then remove the weight from the end of the handlebar. If replacement of the handlebar grip is necessary, slit the grip with a knife and peel it off the handlebar.

25 As it is not possible to remove the top yoke with the front forks in place, the left side fork must be lowered or removed to allow removal of the handlebar. See Section 6 for fork removal.

Installation

26 Install the handlebar and front fork as described in Section 6.

27 If the grip is being replaced, the handlebar end must be degreased and an adhesive applied to bond the grip in place. Install the weight and securely tighten the screw.

28 Install the clutch master cylinder assembly as described in Chapter 2.

29 Install the handlebar switch (Chapter 9).

6 Forks - removal and installation

Removal

Caution: Although not strictly necessary, before removing the forks it is recommended that any fairing panels (where fitted) are

5.12a Prise out the caps . . .

5.12b . . . then unscrew the two handlebar clamp bolts . . .

5.12c . . . and lift the handlebar off the fork

6.6 Slacken the top yoke pinch bolts

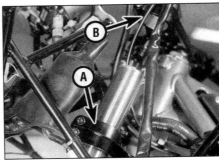

6.7 Slide each fork up through the bottom yoke (A) and the top yoke (B)

6.8a Set the height of the forks in the top yoke in accordance with the text

6.8b Tighten the bottom and top yoke pinch bolts to the specified torque setting

removed. This should prevent any accidental damage to their finish (see Chapter 8).

Note: *If the fork legs are to be dismantled it is preferable to adjust the preload setting to minimum as described in Section 12, then slacken the top bolts whilst the forks are still held in the yokes.*

1 Remove the front wheel as described in Chapter 7.

2 Remove the front mudguard as described in Chapter 8.

3 Slacken, but do not remove, the bottom yoke pinch bolts.

4 On Daytona and Speed Triple models, slacken but do not remove both left and right handlebar clamp bolts.

5 On Trophy, Trident and Sprint models, unscrew the handlebar mounting bolts and move the handlebars aside, making sure they are supported so that the master cylinder reservoirs are upright and no strain is placed on the hoses.

6 Slacken but do not remove the top yoke pinch bolts, and remove the forks by twisting them and pulling them downwards **(see illustration)**. On Daytona and Speed Triple models, once the forks are removed, make sure the handlebars are supported so that the master cylinder reservoirs are upright and no strain is placed on their hoses. On Thunderbird, Speed Triple and later Trident models, the forks pass through the headlight mounting tubes. When removing the forks make sure the headlight is supported. Take care not to lose the mounting tube rubber grommets.

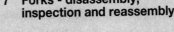

HAYNES HINT *If the fork legs are seized in the yokes, spray the area with penetrating oil and allow time for it to soak in before trying again.*

Installation

7 Remove all traces of corrosion from the fork tubes and the yokes and slide the forks back into place **(see illustration)**. On Thunderbird, Speed Triple and later Trident models make sure the forks pass through the headlight mounting tubes and that the tube rubber grommets remain correctly in place. On Daytona and Speed Triple models make sure the forks pass through the handlebar clamps.

8 Position each leg in the top yoke as follows. On Thunderbird and Tiger models, the top edge of each fork tube must align with the top surface of the top yoke. On Trophy, Trident and Sprint models, the top edge of each fork tube must be 25 mm above the top surface of the top yoke. On Daytona and Speed Triple models, the top edge of each fork tube must be 28 mm above the top surface of the top yoke. Note that the measurement is to the top of the fork tube, not to the top of the fork tube top bolt **(see illustration)**. Tighten the top and bottom yoke pinch bolts to the specified torque settings **(see illustration)**.

9 On Daytona and Speed Triple models, align each handlebar so that it abuts the lug on the underside of the top yoke, then tighten their clamp bolts to the specified torque setting.

10 On Trophy, Trident and Sprint, mount the

handlebars on the top yoke and tighten their bolts to the specified torque setting. Insert the caps into the bolt heads.

11 If the fork legs have been dismantled, the fork tube top bolts should now be tightened to the specified torque setting.

12 Install the front mudguard as described in Chapter 8.

13 Install the front wheel as described in Chapter 7.

14 Adjust the fork settings as described in Section 12. Check the operation of the front forks and brake before taking the machine out on the road.

7 Forks - disassembly, inspection and reassembly

Trophy, Trident, Sprint, Thunderbird and Tiger models

Disassembly

1 Always dismantle the fork legs separately to avoid mixing parts and causing accelerated wear. Store all components in separate, clearly marked containers **(see illustration)**.

2 Before dismantling the fork give some thought to the means of slackening the damper rod bolt. If the special tool or a home-made equivalent is not available (see Step 7), it is advised that the damper rod bolt be slackened at this stage. Compress the fork tube in the slider so that the spring exerts maximum pressure on the damper rod head, then have an assistant unscrew the damper rod bolt from the base of the fork slider. On Tiger models, free the gaiter clamps and slip the gaiter off the fork tube.

3 If the fork top bolt was not slackened with the fork in situ, carefully clamp the fork tube in a vice, taking care not to overtighten or score its surface, then slacken the fork top bolt.

4 Unscrew the fork top bolt from the top of the fork tube.

 Warning: The fork spring is pressing on the fork top bolt with considerable pressure. Unscrew the bolt very carefully, keeping a downward pressure on it and release it slowly as it is likely to spring clear. It is advisable to wear eye and face protection when carrying out this task.

5 Remove the spacer, then slide the fork tube down into the slider and withdraw the spring seat and the spring from the tube, noting which way up they fit.

6 Invert the fork leg over a suitable container and pump the fork vigorously to expel as much fork oil as possible.

7 Prise out the end cap (where fitted) from the base of the fork slider. If the damper rod bolt was not slackened before dismantling the fork, a special tool (Pt. No. 3880090) or home-made equivalent, will be needed to stop the damper rod from rotating inside the fork tube

7.1 Front fork detail - Trophy, Trident, Sprint, Thunderbird and Tiger models

1 Top bolt and O-ring
2 Spacer
3 Spring seat
4 Spring
5 Dust seal
6 Retaining clip
7 Oil seal
8 Washer
9 Top bush
10 Piston ring
11 Damper rod
12 Rebound spring
13 Fork tube
14 Bottom bush
15 Damper rod seat
16 Fork slider
17 Sealing washer
18 Damper rod bolt

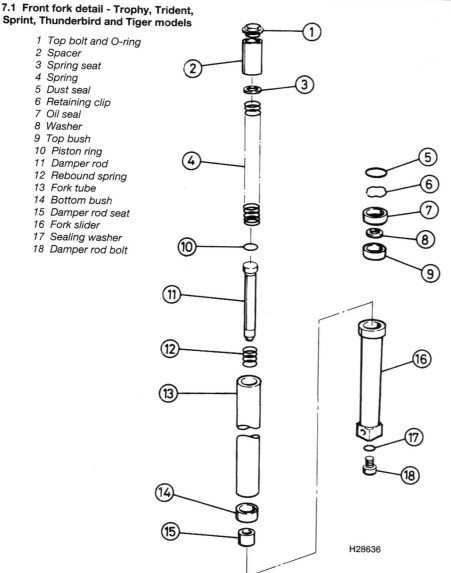

H28636

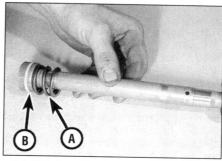

7.8 Withdraw the damper rod assembly, and remove the rebound spring (A) and the piston ring (B)

7.9 Use a flat-bladed screwdriver to prise out the dust seal . . .

7.10 . . . and the retaining clip from the top of the fork slider

when the damper rod bolt is unscrewed. With the tool engaged in the head of the damper rod, remove the bolt and its copper sealing washer from the bottom of the slider **(see Tool Tip)**. Discard the sealing washer as a new one must be used on reassembly.

8 Withdraw the damper rod from the fork tube **(see illustration)**. Remove the rebound spring, and remove the piston ring from the groove in the damper rod. Discard the piston ring - a new one must be used on reassembly.

9 Carefully prise out the dust seal from the top of the slider to gain access to the oil seal retaining clip **(see illustration)**. Discard the dust seal as a new one must be used.

10 Carefully remove the clip whilst taking care not to scratch the surface of the tube **(see illustration)**.

TOOL TiP

A damper rod holding tool can be made quite easily by threading or pinning a 30 mm nut on the end of a steel bar about 14 inches long, then sawing or filing flats on the other end of the bar so that it can be held with an adjustable spanner.

6

11 To separate the tube from the slider it will be necessary to displace the top bush and oil seal. The bottom bush should not pass through the top bush, and this can be used to good effect. Push the tube gently inwards until it stops against the damper rod seat. Take care not to do this forcibly or the seat may be damaged. Then pull the tube sharply outwards until the bottom bush strikes the top bush. Repeat this operation until the top bush and seal are tapped out of the slider.

12 With the tube removed, slide off the oil seal and washer, noting which way up they fit. Discard the oil seal as a new one must be used. The top bush can then also be slid off its upper end. *Caution: Do not remove the bottom bush from the tube unless it is to be replaced.*

13 Tip the damper rod seat out of the slider, noting which way up it fits.

Inspection

14 Clean all parts in solvent and blow them dry with compressed air, if available. Check the fork tube for score marks, scratches, flaking of the chrome finish and excessive or abnormal wear. Look for dents in the tube and replace the tube in both forks if any are found. Check the fork seal seat for nicks, gouges and scratches. If damage is evident, leaks will occur.

15 Have the fork tube checked for runout at a dealer service department or other repair shop. *Caution: If it is bent, the tube should not be straightened; replace it with a new one.*

16 Check the spring for cracks and other damage. If it is defective or sagged, replace both fork springs with new ones. Never replace only one spring.

17 Examine the working surfaces of the two bushes; if worn they must be replaced. To remove the bush from the fork tube, prise it apart at the slit and slide it off. Make sure the new one seats properly **(see illustration)**.

Reassembly

18 Install a new piston ring into the groove in the damper rod head, and slide the rebound spring over the bottom of the assembly **(see illustrations)**.

19 Insert the damper rod into the fork tube and slide it into place so that it projects fully from the bottom of the tube. Install the seat on the bottom of the damper rod so that the lipped end of the seat faces the damper rod **(see illustration)**.

20 Oil the fork tube and bottom bush and insert the assembly into the slider. Fit a new copper sealing washer to the damper rod bolt and install the bolt into the bottom of the slider. Tighten the bolt to the specified torque setting **(see illustrations)**. Use the method employed on dismantling (see Step 7) to prevent the damper rod rotating inside the fork tube when the bolt is tightened. Alternatively, temporarily install the fork spring, spacer and top bolt (see Steps 26 and 27) to hold the damper rod.

7.17 Prise the ends of the bottom bush apart with a flat-bladed screwdriver to remove it from the fork tube

7.18b ... and slide the rebound spring over the bottom of the assembly

21 Push the fork tube fully into the slider, then oil the top bush and slide it down over the tube. Press the bush squarely into its recess in the slider as far as possible, then

7.20a Fit a new sealing washer to the damper assembly bolt ...

7.21a Slide the top bush down the fork tube and into the top of the slider ...

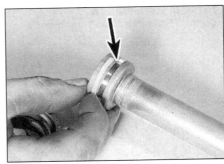

7.18a Fit a new piston ring into the groove in the damper assembly head (arrowed) ...

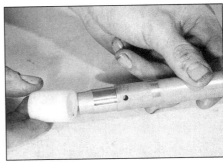

7.19 Slide damper assembly into the fork tube so that it protrudes, then fit the seat to the bottom of the damper assembly

install the washer **(see illustrations)**. Either use the service tool (Pt. No. 3880080) or a suitable piece of tubing to tap the bush fully into place; the tubing must be slightly larger in

7.20b ... then install the bolt and tighten it to the specified torque setting

7.21b ... followed by the washer

7.21c Use a piece of tubing as a drift to drive the top bush squarely into the slider

7.22 Remove the washer to check that the top bush is seated, then install the oil seal, with its spring side facing down

7.25 Check the oil level with the fork held vertical

diameter than the fork tube and slightly smaller in diameter than the bush recess in the slider **(see illustration)**. Take care not to scratch the fork tube during this operation; it is best to make sure that the fork tube is pushed fully into the slider so that any accidental scratching is confined to the area above the oil seal.

22 When the bush is seated fully and squarely in its recess in the slider, (remove the washer to check, wipe the recess clean, then reinstall the washer), install the new oil seal. Smear the seal's lips with fork oil and slide it over the tube so that its spring side faces downwards, towards the slider **(see illustration)**.

23 Place a large plain washer against the oil seal (to protect its surface) and drive the seal into place as described in Step 21 until the retaining clip groove is visible above the seal. Once the seal is correctly seated, remove the washer and fit the retaining clip, making sure it is correctly located in its groove **(see illustration 7.10)**.

24 Lubricate the lips of the new dust seal then slide it down the fork tube and press it into position **(see illustration 7.9)**.

25 Slowly pour in small quantities of the specified grade of fork oil at a time, and pump the fork to distribute the oil evenly. Note that specific oil quantities are not available; the oil level must be measured and adjustment made by adding or subtracting oil. Fully compress the fork tube into the slider and measure the fork oil level **(see illustration)**. Add or remove

fork oil until the oil is at the level specified in the Specifications Section of this Chapter.

26 Clamp the slider in a vice via the brake caliper mounting lugs, taking care not to overtighten and damage them. Pull the fork tube out of the slider as far as possible then install the spring, with its closer-wound coils at the top, followed by the spring seat, with its shoulder inserted into the spring, and the spacer **(see illustrations)**.

27 Fit a new O-ring to the fork top bolt and thread the bolt into the top of the fork tube **(see illustration)**.

⚠️ *Warning: It will be necessary to compress the spring by pressing it down using the top bolt to engage the threads of the top bolt with the fork tube. This is a potentially dangerous operation and*

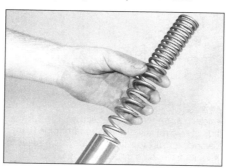

7.26a Install the fork spring making sure its closer-wound coils are at the top

7.26b Install the spring seat, with its shoulder fitting into the spring

should be performed with care, using an assistant if necessary.

Wipe off any excess oil before starting to prevent the possibility of slipping. Keep the fork tube fully extended whilst pressing on the spring. Screw the top bolt carefully into the fork tube making sure it is not cross-threaded. **Note:** *The top bolt can be tightened to the specified torque setting at this stage if the tube is held between the padded jaws of a vice, but do not risk distorting the tube by doing so. A better method is to tighten the top bolt when the fork has been installed in the bike and is securely held in the yokes.*

28 Fit the end cap (where fitted) into the bottom of the fork slider **(see illustration)**.

29 On Tiger models, install the gaiter.

30 Install the forks as described in Section 6.

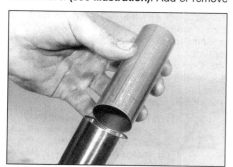

7.26c Fit the spacer into the fork tube

7.27 Fit a new O-ring to the top bolt, then install the bolt into the fork tube

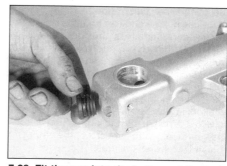

7.28 Fit the cap into the bottom of the fork

6

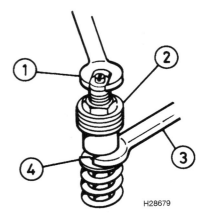

7.31 Front fork detail - Daytona and Speed Triple models

1 Top bolt and adjuster	11 Washer
2 O-ring	12 Top bush
3 Spring seat	13 Fork tube
4 Spring	14 Bottom bush
5 Locknut	15 Damper cartridge seat
6 Damper cartridge rod	16 Fork slider
7 Damper cartridge	17 Sealing washer
8 Dust seal	18 Damper cartridge bolt
9 Retaining clip	19 Cap
10 Oil seal	

H28637

H28679

7.34 Releasing the top bolt from the damper cartridge rod

1 Open-ended spanner on preload adjuster flats
2 Top bolt
3 Open-ended spanner on locknut
4 Spring seat

36 Remove the damper cartridge bolt with its copper washer from the end of the slider and withdraw the cartridge from the tube. Discard the copper washer as a new one must be used on reassembly.

37 Refer to Steps 9 to 13 above.

Inspection

38 Refer to Steps 14 to 17 above.

Reassembly

39 Insert the damper cartridge seat into the slider so that its larger diameter is downwards. Apply fork oil to the damper cartridge and insert it into the fork tube.

40 Oil the fork tube and bottom bush and insert the fork tube into the slider. Fit a new copper sealing washer to the damper cartridge bolt and install the bolt in the bottom of the slider so that it screws into the base of the damper cartridge. *Caution: Do not attempt to hold the cartridge rod in order to tighten the bolt, temporarily refit the fork spring, spring seat and top bolt (see Steps 43 to 45) and compress the fork to hold the cartridge.*

41 Refer to Steps 21 to 25 above.

42 Withdraw the damper cartridge rod as far as possible and install the spring, with its closer-wound coils at the top, followed by the spring seat, with its shoulder inserted into the spring.

43 Compress the spring and thread the locknut onto the damper cartridge rod until there is 11 mm of thread above the locknut (see illustration).

 Warning: This is a potentially dangerous operation and should be performed with care, using an assistant if necessary. Wipe any excess oil off the spring **before starting to prevent the possibility of slipping.**

Daytona and Speed Triple models

Disassembly

31 Always dismantle the fork legs separately to avoid interchanging parts and thus causing an accelerated rate of wear. Store all components in separate, clearly marked containers (see illustration).

32 Prise out the end cap from the base of the fork slider. Compress the fork tube in the slider so that the spring exerts maximum pressure on the damper cartridge, then have an assistant unscrew the damper cartridge bolt from the base of the fork slider.

33 If the fork top bolt was not slackened with the fork in situ, carefully clamp the fork tube in a vice, taking care not to overtighten or score its surface, then unscrew the fork top bolt/adjuster from the tube.

34 Hold the fork vertical and slide the fork tube down into the slider. Counterhold the locknut just below the top bolt/adjuster with an open-

ended spanner and unscrew the preload adjuster to release the top bolt from the damper cartridge rod (see illustration). Unscrew the locknut from the damper cartridge rod.

 Warning: The fork spring may be exerting considerable pressure on the spring seat, making this a potentially dangerous operation. Restrain the fork spring to prevent the locknut and spring seat from being sprung clear, and slowly release the spring once the locknut has been removed. Wipe off as much oil as possible to minimise the risk of your hands slipping on oily components and enlist the help of an assistant. Withdraw the spring seat and the spring from the tube, noting which way up they fit.

35 Invert the fork leg over a suitable container and pump the fork vigorously to expel as much fork oil as possible.

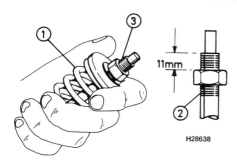

7.43 Screw the locknut onto the damper cartridge rod so that there is 11 mm of thread above the locknut

1 Fork spring
2 Damper cartridge rod
3 Locknut

44 Fit a new O-ring to the fork top bolt and lubricate it with a smear of fork oil. Screw the top bolt/adjuster onto the damper cartridge rod; counterhold the locknut with an open-ended spanner and tighten the adjuster. Watch carefully that the locknut and damper cartridge rod do not rotate as the adjuster is tightened - if they do, reposition the locknut on the rod as described in Step 43.

45 Carefully screw the top bolt into the fork tube making sure it is not cross-threaded. **Note:** *The top bolt can be tightened to the specified torque setting at this stage if the tube is held between the padded jaws of a vice, but do not risk distorting the tube by doing so. A better method is to tighten the top bolt when the fork leg has been installed and is securely held in the yokes.*

46 Fit the end cap (where fitted) into the bottom of the fork.

47 Install the forks as described in Section 6.

8 Steering stem - removal and installation

Caution: *Although not strictly necessary, before removing the steering stem it is recommended that the fuel tank and fairing panels (if fitted) be removed. This will prevent accidental damage to the paintwork.*

Removal

1 Remove the forks as described in Section 6 of this Chapter.

2 Unscrew the bolts securing the brake hose union assembly to the bottom yoke (not Thunderbird) **(see illustration)**. Do not disconnect the hoses from the union assembly.

3 On Trident and Speed Triple models, disconnect the horn wires, then unscrew the horn mounting bolts and remove the horns from the bottom yoke.

4 On all models except the Daytona and Speed Triple, detach the handlebars from the

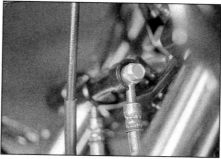

8.2 Remove the brake hose union from the bottom yoke with the hoses still connected

top yoke (see Section 5 of this Chapter). If required, also remove, or detach and move aside, the instrument panel (see Chapter 9). This enables the top yoke to be moved further aside than would otherwise be allowed. If the top yoke is to be removed from the bike altogether, it is also necessary to disconnect the ignition switch wiring at its connector, and on Tiger models to remove the cable-ties from underneath the clamp.

5 Remove the steering stem nut and washer **(see illustration)**.

6 On early models, slacken off the pinch bolt in the side of the bearing adjuster ring **(see illustration 5.8 in Chapter 1)** and whilst supporting the bottom yoke, unscrew

8.5 Unscrew the steering stem nut and remove the washer

and remove the adjuster ring from the steering stem.

7 On later models unscrew the locknut and whilst supporting the bottom yoke, unscrew and remove the adjuster nut from the steering stem **(see illustration)**. These nuts are very narrow and whilst removal can be accomplished with normal DIY tools, subsequent tightening and bearing freeplay adjustment is made easier with the use of the Triumph service tools (Pt. No. 3880140)

8 Gently lower the bottom yoke and steering stem out of the frame. Move the top yoke forwards to disengage the ignition main switch from the steering lock bracket welded to the frame.

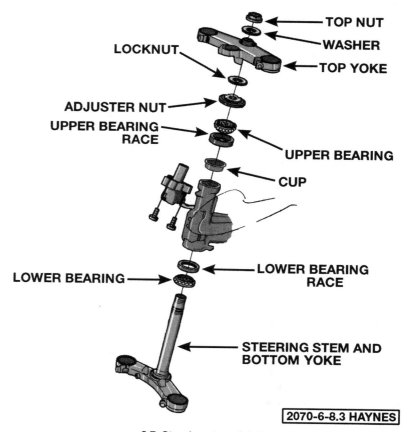

TOP NUT
WASHER
TOP YOKE
LOCKNUT
ADJUSTER NUT
UPPER BEARING RACE
UPPER BEARING
CUP
LOWER BEARING
LOWER BEARING RACE
STEERING STEM AND BOTTOM YOKE

2070-6-8.3 HAYNES

8.7 Steering stem detail

9 Remove the upper bearing from the top of the steering head. Remove all traces of old grease from the bearings and races and check them for wear or damage as described in Section 9. **Note:** *Do not attempt to remove the races from the frame or the lower bearing from the steering stem unless they are to be replaced.*

Installation

10 Smear a liberal quantity of grease on the bearing races in the frame. Work the grease well into both the upper and lower bearings. Install the upper bearing in the top of the steering head.

11 Install the top yoke on the steering head, engaging the ignition main switch with the steering lock bracket.

12 Carefully lift the steering stem/bottom yoke up through the frame. Thread the adjuster ring (early models) or adjuster nut (later models) on the steering stem before the stem passes up through the top yoke. Tighten the adjuster to preload the bearings, then turn the steering stem from lock to lock approximately 5 times to settle the bearings and races in position. After preloading the bearings, slacken the adjuster until pressure is just released, then turn it slowly clockwise until resistance is just evident. The object is to set the adjuster so that the bearings are under a very light loading, just enough to remove any freeplay. **Caution: Take great care not to apply excessive pressure because this will cause premature failure of the bearings.**

13 On early models, when the setting is correct, tighten the pinch bolt to the specified torque setting to lock the adjuster ring's position.

14 On later models, when the setting is correct, hold the adjuster nut with one spanner and tighten the locknut against it with another spanner. **Note:** *The torque setting for the locknut can be applied if using the service tool (see Step 7); the torque wrench locates in the square machined in the tool* **(see illustrations 5.17a and b in Chapter 1).**

15 Install the steering stem washer and nut to secure the top yoke, tightening the nut to the specified torque setting **(see illustration)**. If removed, fit the handlebars and instrument

8.15 Tighten the steering stem nut to the specified torque setting

panel, connect the speedometer cable and the ignition switch wiring, and fit any cable-ties as necessary.

16 On Trident and Speed Triple models, install the horns on the bottom yoke and tighten their retaining bolts securely, then fit the horn wires.

17 Fit the brake hose union assembly to the bottom yoke and tighten the retaining bolts to the specified torque setting.

18 Install the fork legs as described in Section 6 of this Chapter.

19 Carry out a check of the steering head bearing freeplay as described in Chapter 1, and if necessary re-adjust.

9 Steering head bearings - inspection and replacement

Inspection

1 Remove the steering stem as described in Section 8.

2 Remove all traces of old grease from the bearings and races and check them for wear or damage.

3 The races should be polished and free from indentations. Inspect the bearing rollers for signs of wear, damage or discoloration, and examine the bearing roller retainer cage for signs of cracks or splits. If there are signs of wear on any of the above components both upper and lower bearing assemblies must be replaced as a set.

Replacement

4 The races are an interference fit in the steering head and can be tapped from position with a suitable drift. Tap firmly and evenly around each race to ensure that it is driven out squarely. It may prove advantageous to curve the end of the drift slightly to improve access.

5 Alternatively, the races can be removed using a slide-hammer type bearing extractor; these can often be hired from tool shops.

6 The new races can be pressed into the head using a drawbolt arrangement **(see illustration)**, or by using a large diameter tubular drift which bears only on the outer edge of the race. Ensure that the drawbolt washer or drift (as applicable) bears only on the outer edge of the race and does not contact the working surface. Alternatively, have the races installed by a Triumph dealer equipped with the bearing race installing tools. Note that the cup must be in place in the frame before installing the upper bearing race.

7 To remove the lower bearing from the steering stem, use two screwdrivers placed on opposite sides of the race to work it free. If the bearing is firmly in place it will be necessary to use a bearing puller, or in extreme circumstances to split the bearing's inner section.

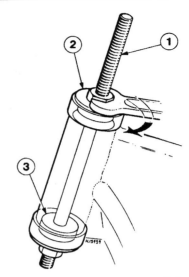
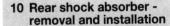

9.6 Drawbolt arrangement for fitting steering stem bearing races

1 Long bolt or threaded bar
2 Thick washer
3 Guide for lower race

8 Fit the new lower bearing onto the steering stem. A length of tubing with an internal diameter slightly larger than the steering stem will be needed to tap the new bearing into position. Ensure that the drift bears only on the inner edge of the bearing and does not contact the rollers.

9 Install the steering stem as described in Section 8.

10 Rear shock absorber - removal and installation

Removal

1 In order to remove the shock absorber, it is necessary to support the bike securely in an upright position using an auxiliary stand or hoist. On Thunderbird and Tiger models the bike must be supported so that the rear wheel is just resting on the ground (ie so that the bike's weight is off the rear suspension) but also so that the rear suspension will not drop, with the possible risk of personal injury, when the shock absorber mounting bolts are removed. On all other models the bike must be supported so that the rear wheel is off the ground. This is to give room for the wheel to be lowered when the top shock absorber mounting bolt is removed so that the suspension linkage clears the exhaust system to enable the linkage spindle to be removed; it is advisable to place a block of wood or other support under the wheel to avoid having to manually support the wheel and so that the rear suspension will not drop, with the possible risk of personal injury, when the top

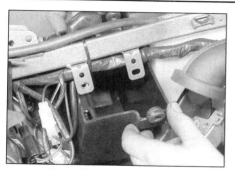

10.4a Move the battery box
out to one side . . .

10.4b . . . then pull the inner end up and
out from the top

10.5 Release the reservoir from its
retaining clamps (arrowed)

shock absorber mounting bolt is removed. After the bolt is removed, take the weight of the wheel, remove the support and gently lower the wheel to the ground.

2 Remove the seat and the side panels as described in Chapter 8.

3 Remove the battery as described in Chapter 1 and the auxiliary air chambers (one only on the Thunderbird model) as described in Chapter 4.

4 Remove the remaining battery box mounting bolt from the bottom of the box. The battery box comes out from the top, but first has to be twisted on its end by moving out to one side and then pulling the end up and out **(see illustrations)**.

5 On Tiger models, remove the fuel tank as described in Chapter 4, then unscrew the four bolts securing the fuel tank bracket to the frame and remove the bracket. Unscrew the retaining clamps securing the shock absorber reservoir to the left side of the cylinder head and remove the reservoir **(see illustration)**.
Caution: Do not attempt to separate the reservoir from the shock absorber.

6 On all models except the Thunderbird, Tiger, 750 Trident and early 900 Trident (to VIN 9082), unscrew the bolts securing the preload adjuster to the top of the frame, and the screws securing the damping adjuster to the right side of the frame **(see illustrations)**.

7 If fitted, remove the bolts securing the bottom of the mudflap to the swingarm.

8 On Thunderbird and Tiger models, unscrew the nut on the shock absorber lower mounting bolt but do not remove the bolt.

9 On all other models, slacken but do not

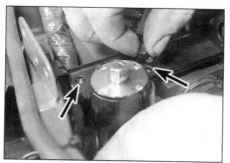

10.6a Unscrew the bolts securing the
pre-load adjuster to the top
of the frame (arrowed) . . .

remove the suspension linkage spindle clamp bolts and unscrew the spindle bolt, but do not remove the spindle **(see illustration)**.

10 Unscrew and remove the shock absorber top mounting nut and bolt, making sure the rear wheel is adequately supported **(see illustration)**.

11 On Thunderbird and Tiger models, remove the shock absorber lower mounting bolt, then raise the wheel and manoeuvre the shock absorber carefully out of the frame, noting how and which way around it fits. On Tiger models, take care not to snag the reservoir.

12 On all other models, carefully remove the support from under the wheel and gently lower the wheel to the ground. Withdraw linkage spindle **(see illustration)**, then raise the rear wheel and manoeuvre the shock absorber carefully out of the frame, noting how and which way around it fits and taking

10.6b . . . and the screws securing the
damping adjuster to the right side
of the frame (arrowed)

care not to snag either the preload or the damping adjuster mechanisms, if fitted.

13 Inspect the bushes and seals (where fitted) for wear and replace worn components as necessary. Prise the seals out using a flat-bladed screwdriver. The bushes can be drifted out using a suitable drift or punch, or a drawbolt assembly (see Section 11).

Installation

14 Check that the mounting bolt and spindle are unworn (replace them if necessary); apply molybdenum grease to their shanks.

15 Raise the wheel and manoeuvre the shock absorber into place, making sure the preload and damping adjusters (if fitted) are correctly positioned. On Tiger models, make sure the rebound damping adjuster is on the bottom of the shock absorber is on the right side of the bike and that the reservoir is correctly routed and positioned.

6

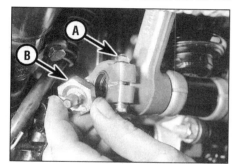

10.9 Slacken the spindle clamp bolts (A)
and remove the spindle bolt (B)

10.10 Remove the shock absorber top
mounting bolt (arrowed)

10.12 Withdraw linkage spindle to release
the shock absorber from the linkage

10.18 Install the shock absorber top mounting bolt

10.19 Tighten the spindle clamp bolts and the spindle bolt to the specified torque

16 On Thunderbird and Tiger models install the shock absorber lower mounting bolt, but do not yet fully tighten the nut.

17 On all other models install the linkage spindle through the linkage connecting rods and the shock absorber, but do not yet fully tighten the spindle bolt or the clamp bolts.

18 Raise the wheel if necessary and install the shock absorber top mounting bolt and nut and tighten to the torque setting specified at the beginning of the Chapter **(see illustration)**.

19 Tighten the shock absorber lower mounting bolt (Thunderbird and Tiger) or the linkage spindle bolt and spindle clamp bolts (all other models) to the specified torque setting **(see illustrations)**.

20 If fitted, secure the mudflap to the swingarm.

21 If fitted, mount the preload adjuster to the top of the frame and the damping adjuster to the right side of the frame.

22 Install the battery box, not forgetting its bottom mounting bolt, and the auxiliary air chambers (one only on Thunderbird) as described in Chapter 4.

23 On Tiger models, fit the reservoir to the left side of the cylinder head and tighten the retaining clamps securely. Fit the tank mounting bracket to the frame and install the tank as described in Chapter 4.

24 Install and connect the battery, negative lead last, as described in Chapter 1.

25 Install the side panels and seat as described in Chapter 8.

26 Check the operation of the rear

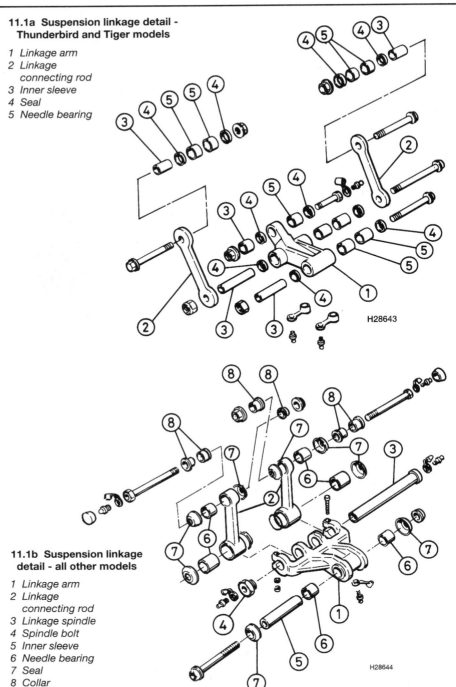

**11.1a Suspension linkage detail -
Thunderbird and Tiger models**

1 Linkage arm
2 Linkage
  connecting rod
3 Inner sleeve
4 Seal
5 Needle bearing

H28643

**11.1b Suspension linkage
detail - all other models**

1 Linkage arm
2 Linkage
  connecting rod
3 Linkage spindle
4 Spindle bolt
5 Inner sleeve
6 Needle bearing
7 Seal
8 Collar

H28644

suspension and adjust the suspension settings as described in Section 12 before taking the bike on the road.

11 Rear suspension linkage - removal, inspection and installation

Removal

1 In order to remove the rear suspension

linkage, it is necessary to support the bike securely in an upright position using an auxiliary stand or hoist. The bike must be supported so that the bike's weight is off the rear suspension, but also so that the rear suspension will not drop, with the possible risk of personal injury, when the rear suspension lower mounting bolt is removed **(see illustrations)**.

2 Remove the complete exhaust system as described in Chapter 4.

3 On Thunderbird and Tiger models, unscrew

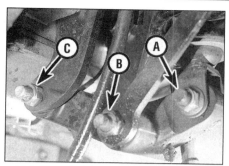

11.3 Thunderbird and Tiger suspension linkage: shock absorber lower mounting bolt (A), linkage connecting rod bolt (B), linkage arm to linkage carrier bolt (C)

11.5a Unscrew the nut and remove the bolt securing the linkage arm to the linkage carrier . . .

11.5b . . . then remove the linkage arm

and remove the shock absorber lower mounting nut and bolt (see illustration).

4 On all other models, slacken but do not remove the suspension linkage spindle clamp bolts, then unscrew the spindle bolt and withdraw the spindle (see illustrations 10.9 and 10.12).

5 Unscrew and remove the nut and pivot bolt securing the linkage arm to the linkage carriers. On all models except the Thunderbird and Tiger, the linkage arm can now be removed (see illustrations).

6 On Thunderbird and Tiger models, remove the nut and pivot bolt securing the linkage arm to the linkage connecting rods, and remove the arm (see illustration 11.3).

7 Remove the caps on the bolts securing the linkage connecting rods to the swingarm, then unscrew the bolts and remove the connecting rods (see illustrations). Note how the collars fit (except Thunderbird and Tiger models).

Inspection

8 Remove the collars (where fitted), and withdraw the dust seals and inner sleeves from the linkage pivots (see illustrations).

9 Thoroughly clean all components, removing all traces of dirt, corrosion and grease.

10 Inspect all components closely, looking for obvious signs of wear such as heavy scoring, or for damage such as cracks or distortion.

11 Carefully lever out the dust seals, using a flat-bladed screwdriver, and check them for signs of wear or damage; replace them if necessary (see illustration).

12 Worn bearings can be drifted out of their bores, but note that removal will destroy them; new bearings should be obtained before work commences. The new bearings should be pressed or drawn into their bores rather than driven into position. In the absence of a press, a suitable drawbolt arrangement can be made up as described below.

13 It will be necessary to obtain a long bolt or a length of threaded rod from a local engineering works or similar supplier. The bolt or rod should be about one inch longer than the combined length of either link, and one bearing. Also required are suitable nuts and two large and robust washers having a larger outside diameter than the bearing housing. In the case of the threaded rod, fit one nut to one end of the rod and stake it in place for convenience.

14 Fit one of the washers over the bolt or rod so that it rests against the head, then pass the assembly through the relevant bore. Over the projecting end place the bearing, which should be greased to ease installation, followed by the remaining washer and nut.

15 Holding the bearing to ensure that it is kept square, slowly tighten the nut so that the bearing is drawn into its bore.

16 Once it is fully home, remove the drawbolt arrangement and, if necessary, repeat the procedure to fit the other bearings. The dust seals can then be pressed into place.

17 Lubricate all the seals, needle roller

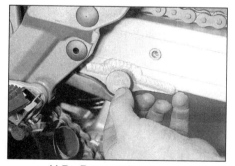

11.7a Remove the caps . . .

11.7b . . . and unscrew the bolts securing linkage connecting rods to the swingarm

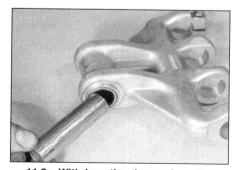

11.8a Withdraw the sleeves from the linkage arm . . .

11.8b . . . and from the connecting rod pivots (all models except Thunderbird and Tiger shown)

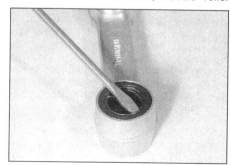

11.11 Lever out the dust seals using a flat-bladed screwdriver

6

11.19 Do not forget to fit the seals before installing the linkage arm

11.20c Fit connecting rod to swingarm, then install the bolt and collar (arrowed) (except Thunderbird and Tiger) . . .

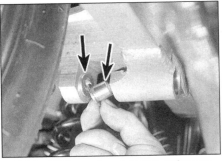

11.20a Fit the collars into the swingarm mounts (arrowed) . . .

11.20d . . . and fit the nut to the bolt, but do not yet fully tighten it

11.20b . . . and the seals onto connecting rods (except Thunderbird and Tiger)

bearings, inner sleeves and the pivot bolts with molybdenum disulphide grease. Insert the inner sleeves into the bearings (where applicable).

Installation

18 If not already done, lubricate the seals, needle roller bearings, inner sleeves and the pivot bolts with molybdenum disulphide grease.

19 Install the seals in the linkage arm, then fit the linkage arm to the linkage carriers, but do not yet fully tighten the bolt **(see illustration)**.

20 Install the seals in the linkage connecting rod ends, and the collars into the swingarm mounts and onto the bolt (except Thunderbird and Tiger models), then fit the connecting rods on the swingarm mounts, but do not yet fully tighten the bolts **(see illustrations)**.

21 On Thunderbird and Tiger models, fit the linkage arm to the shock absorber lower mount, then fit the linkage arm to the linkage connecting rods, but do not yet fully tighten the bolts. Make a final check of the suspension linkage to ensure that all components are correctly fitted, then tighten all the linkage bolts to the torque settings specified at the beginning of the Chapter **(see illustration 11.3)**.

22 On all other models, fit the linkage connecting rods and the shock absorber to the linkage arm and install the spindle and spindle bolt **(see illustrations 10.9 and 10.12)**. Make a final check of the suspension linkage to ensure that all components are correctly fitted, then tighten all the linkage

bolts to the torque settings as specified at the beginning of the Chapter.

23 Install the exhaust system as described in Chapter 4.

24 Check the operation of the rear suspension before taking the machine on the road.

---

12 Suspension - adjustments

Front forks - Daytona and Speed Triple only

Caution: Always ensure that both front fork settings are the same. Uneven settings will upset the handling of the machine and could cause it to become unstable.

12.1 Adjust spring preload using an open-ended spanner. Damping adjustment is made with a flat-bladed screwdriver

Spring preload

Note: *It is important to obtain the correct balance between suspension settings - refer to the suspension setting chart in your owners handbook or at the end of this Section.*

1 The front fork spring preload adjuster is located in the centre of each fork top bolt and is adjusted using an open-ended spanner **(see illustration)**.

2 The amount of preload is indicated by the number of grooves which are visible on the adjuster above the top surface of the top bolt hexagon. There are eight grooves on the adjuster. To set the preload to the standard amount, turn the adjuster until the fifth groove from the top aligns with the top surface of the hexagon **(see illustration)**.

3 To reduce the preload (ie soften the ride), rotate the adjuster anti-clockwise.

4 To increase the preload (ie stiffen the ride), rotate the adjuster clockwise.

5 Always ensure both adjusters are set to the same position.

Rebound damping

Note: *It is important to obtain the correct balance between suspension settings - refer to the suspension setting chart in your owners handbook or at the end of this Section.*

6 The rebound damping adjuster is situated in the centre of the preload adjuster and is adjusted using a flat-bladed screwdriver **(see illustration 12.1)**.

7 Damping positions are identified by counting the number of clicks emitted by the adjuster when it is turned. There are twelve damping positions.

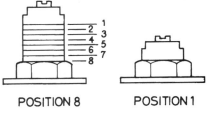

POSITION 8   POSITION 1

H28645

12.2 Front fork preload adjuster settings

12.13 The compression damping adjuster (arrowed) is situated in the bottom of the fork slider

12.21 Rear shock absorber spring preload adjuster (arrowed)

8 The standard setting recommended is six clicks anti-clockwise from the maximum damping setting. The maximum setting is when the adjuster is turned fully clockwise.

9 To establish the present setting, turn one of the adjusters fully clockwise whilst counting the number of clicks emitted, then rotate it back to its original position. Repeat the procedure on the other adjuster to ensure both are set to the same position.

10 To reduce the rebound damping, turn the adjuster anti-clockwise.

11 To increase the rebound damping, turn the adjuster clockwise.

12 Always ensure both adjusters are set to the same position.

Compression damping

Note: *It is important to obtain the correct balance between suspension settings - refer to the suspension setting chart in your owners handbook or at the end of this Section.*

13 The compression damping adjuster is situated at the bottom of each fork slider and is adjusted using a flat-bladed screwdriver **(see illustration)**.

14 Damping positions are indicated by counting the number of clicks emitted by the adjuster when it is turned. There are twelve damping positions.

15 The standard setting recommended is six clicks anti-clockwise from the maximum damping setting. The maximum setting is when the adjuster is turned fully clockwise.

16 To establish the present setting, rotate one of the adjusters fully clockwise whilst counting the number of clicks emitted, then rotate it back to its original position. Repeat the procedure on the other adjuster to ensure both are set in the same position.

17 To reduce the compression damping, turn the adjuster anti-clockwise.

18 To increase the compression damping, turn the adjuster clockwise.

19 Always ensure both adjusters are set to the same position.

Rear shock absorber

Spring preload

Thunderbird, Tiger, 750 Trident and early 900 Trident (to VIN 9082) models

20 The rear shock absorber spring preload adjuster is in the form of two locking rings threaded to the body of the shock absorber. A special tool is needed to adjust the preload on these models and it is recommended that adjustment is carried out only by a Triumph dealer.

Trophy, Daytona, later 900 Trident (VIN 9083 on), Sprint and Speed Triple models

Note: *It is important to obtain the correct balance between suspension settings - refer to the suspension setting chart in your owners handbook or at the end of this Section.*

21 The rear shock absorber spring preload adjuster is located on the frame under the seat, and is adjusted by rotating the hexagon on its top with a suitable spanner **(see illustration)**.

22 The preload adjuster has five positions marked on the window in the side of the adjuster; number 1 is the minimum (ie softest) setting and number five the maximum (hardest) setting. Triumph recommend position two as the standard setting for all models except the Daytona, which is set to position three as standard. A pointer indicates which position is set. To increase preload turn the adjuster clockwise. To reduce preload turn the adjuster anti-clockwise.

Rebound damping

Tiger models

Note: *It is important to obtain the correct balance between suspension settings - refer to the suspension setting chart in your owners handbook or at the end of this Section.*

23 The rear suspension rebound damping adjuster is situated at the base of the shock absorber on its right side and is adjusted using a flat-bladed screwdriver.

24 Damping positions are indicated by counting the number of clicks when it is turned. There are sixteen damping positions altogether.

25 The standard setting recommended is eight clicks anti-clockwise from the maximum

damping setting. The maximum setting is when the adjuster is turned fully clockwise.

26 To establish the present setting, rotate the adjuster fully clockwise whilst counting the number of clicks, then rotate it back to its original position.

27 To reduce the rebound damping, turn the adjuster anti-clockwise.

28 To increase the rebound damping, turn the adjuster clockwise.

Trophy, Daytona, later 900 Trident (VIN 9083 on), Sprint and Speed Triple models

Note: *It is important to obtain the correct balance between suspension settings - refer to the suspension setting chart in your owners handbook or at the end of this Section.*

29 The rear suspension rebound damping adjuster is situated on the right side of the bike and is adjusted by turning the dial anti-clockwise only. The dial must not be rotated clockwise **(see illustration 10.6b)**.

30 There are four positions, as numbered on the dial and identified by a click. The position selected must align with the triangular index mark on the adjuster bracket. Number one is the softest setting and number four the hardest. The dial must be set in one of the four click positions only, not between them.

Compression damping - Tiger model only

Note: *It is important to obtain the correct balance between suspension settings - refer to the suspension setting chart in your owners handbook or at the end of this Section.*

31 The rear suspension compression damping adjuster is situated on the shock absorber reservoir, mounted on the left side of the cylinder head, and is adjusted using a flat-bladed screwdriver **(see illustration)**.

32 Damping positions are indicated by counting the number of clicks when it is turned. There are twenty-four damping positions.

33 The standard setting recommended is six clicks anti-clockwise from the maximum damping setting. The maximum setting is when the adjuster is turned fully clockwise.

34 To establish the present setting, rotate the adjuster fully clockwise whilst counting the number of clicks, then rotate it back to its original position.

12.31 Compression damping adjuster on Tiger model (arrowed)

6

Suspension setting chart - Trophy, Daytona, later 900 Trident, Sprint and Speed Triple models

Front fork (Daytona and Speed Triple only)

	Preload	Rebound	Compression
Solo riding - standard	5	6	6
Solo riding - softer	6	9	8
Solo riding - firmer	4	4	3
With pillion	4 - 5	4 - 6	3 - 6
With pillion and luggage	1 - 4	1 - 4	1 - 3

Rear shock absorber

	Preload	Damping
Solo riding - standard	2 or 3 (see text)	2
Solo riding - softer	2	1
Solo riding - firmer	4	3
With pillion	3 - 4	2 - 3
With pillion and luggage	3 - 4	3 - 4

Rear shock absorber setting chart - Tiger models

	Compression damping	Rebound damping
Solo riding - standard	6	8
Solo riding - softer	8	10
Solo riding - firmer	4	6
With pillion	6	4
With pillion and luggage	6	4

35 To reduce the compression damping, turn the adjuster anti-clockwise.

36 To increase the compression damping, turn the adjuster clockwise.

13 Swingarm bearings - check

1 Remove the rear wheel as described in Chapter 7, then remove the rear shock absorber (see Section 10 of this Chapter).

2 Grasp the rear of the swingarm with one hand and place your other hand at the junction of the swingarm and the frame. Try to move the rear of the swingarm from side-to-side. Any wear (play) in the bearings should be felt as movement between the swingarm and the frame at the front. If there is any play the swingarm will be felt to move forward and backward at the front (not from side-to-side). If any play is noted, the bearings should be replaced (see Section 15).

3 Next, move the swingarm up and down through its full travel. It should move freely, without any binding or rough spots. If it does not move freely, remove the swingarm for inspection of its bearings (see Section 14).

14 Swingarm - removal and installation

Removal

1 On all models except the Thunderbird and Tiger, remove the side panels (Chapter 8).

2 Remove its mounting screws and lift off the chainguard on all models except the Speed Triple and early Daytona models (up to VIN 9082) and Super III (see illustration).

3 On Speed Triple, later Daytona models (from VIN 9083) and the Super III, remove the swingarm-mounted mudguard as described in Chapter 8.

14.2 The chainguard is secured to the swingarm by two screws (arrowed)

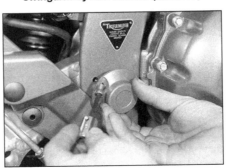

14.10 Remove the swingarm spindle end caps

4 On all models except the Tiger, remove the exhaust silencers as described in Chapter 4.

5 Remove the rear wheel as described in Chapter 7. Cover the drive chain with a rag to prevent it from resting directly on the ground or work surface and picking up any dirt.

6 Unscrew the bolt securing the brake torque arm to the swingarm and remove the sleeve. Discard the bolt as a new one must be used. Make sure the torque arm and brake caliper are adequately supported so that no strain is placed on the brake hose.

7 On Daytona and Speed Triple models remove the brake hose clamp from the right side of the swingarm.

8 If fitted, unscrew the bolts securing the bottom of the mudflap to the swingarm (see illustration).

9 Remove the caps on the bolts securing the suspension linkage connecting rods to the swingarm, then support the swingarm and remove the bolts (see illustrations 11.7a and 11.7b). On Thunderbird and Tiger models, remove the inner sleeves from the swingarm. On all other models, remove the collars, noting how they fit.

10 Remove the caps covering the swingarm pivot ends on both sides of the bike. On early models the caps are a press fit and can be prised off. On later models the caps are secured by three bolts (see illustration).

11 Slacken, but do not remove the upper rear engine mounting bolts.

12 Using a flat-bladed screwdriver or a pair of pliers, remove the retaining clips fitted to each end of the swingarm pivot, taking care not to scratch any surfaces (see illustration).

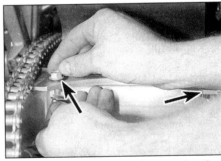

14.8 Unscrew the two bolts securing the mudflap to the swingarm

14.12 Remove the retaining clip from both ends of the swingarm spindle

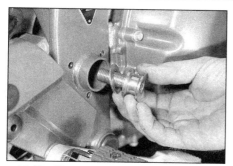

14.13a Unscrew the spindle bolt on the right side of the bike . . .

14.13b . . . and withdraw the spindle from the left side

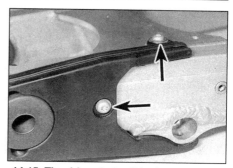

14.15 The drive chain slider is secured to the swingarm by two screws (arrowed)

13 Unscrew and remove the swingarm pivot bolt and washer from the right side of the bike, then support the swingarm and withdraw the pivot shaft from the left side of the bike **(see illustrations)**. It may be necessary to drift the pivot shaft out using a suitable drift applied from the right side of the bike. Remove the spacer from between the linkage carriers as the spindle is withdrawn, noting how it fits (where fitted on Thunderbird). Take care not to lose the dust seals and shims fitted to the swingarm lugs. Note which seals and shims fit on which lug as they must not be mixed up.
14 Note the positions of any breather and drain pipes and move them aside if necessary, then carefully remove the swingarm from the frame.
15 Remove the drive chain slider and slider block (Tiger only) from the swingarm if replacement is required **(see illustration)**.
16 Inspect all components for wear or damage as described in Section 15.

Installation

17 If removed, install the drive chain slider and slider block (Tiger only). Apply a drop of non-permanent locking compound to the threads of the chain slider mounting screws.
18 Remove the dust seals, shims and sleeves from the swingarm lugs, then lubricate the bearings, inner sleeves, centre spacer and the spindle with grease, and fit the inner sleeves back into the bearings. Fit the shims and dust seals, making sure they are each fitted in the same place from which they were removed **(see illustrations)**.

14.19a Breather and drain pipes fit inside the swingarm mounts so they are behind the swingarm spindle when it is installed

19 Loop the drive chain over the swingarm as it is offered up to the frame. Make sure the breather and drain pipes are correctly positioned behind and inside the front ends of the swingarm, and have an assistant hold the swingarm in place as the pivot shaft is fitted **(see illustration)**. Install the pivot shaft through the swingarm from the left side, not forgetting to install the centre spacer (where fitted on Thunderbird) in between the linkage carriers as the shaft passes through **(see illustration)**. If difficulty is experienced when installing the spacer between the linkage carriers, the left side upper engine mounting bolt should be tightened after installing the swingarm pivot shaft into the left side lug to locate the swingarm in place. Alternatively, a special tool (Pt. No. 3880060) is available to align the spacer; this tool consists of a tapered nose cone that fits into the pivot shaft

14.18a Fit the inner sleeve into the bearing . . .

14.19b Install the spacer (arrowed) inside the linkage carriers before installing the swingarm spindle

end to align the swingarm and spacer as the shaft passes through.
20 Install the swingarm pivot shaft bolt, but do not yet fully tighten it. Check the movement of the swingarm. Make sure any breather and drain pipes are correctly positioned.
21 Lubricate the suspension linkage seals, bearings and inner sleeves (where fitted) with grease. On Thunderbird and Tiger models the bearings are housed in the swingarm linkage mounts. On all other models they are housed in the connecting rod ends (see Section 11).
22 Fit the connecting rods to the swingarm, not forgetting the collars on all models except the Thunderbird and Tiger (see Section 11, Step 20, if necessary), and tighten the bolts to the torque setting specified at the beginning of the Chapter **(see illustration)**.
23 Tighten the pivot shaft bolt to the

6

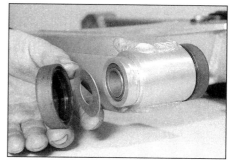

14.18b . . . and the shims and dust seals to the swingarm

14.22 Tighten the suspension linkage connecting rod bolts to the specified torque setting

14.23 Tighten the swingarm spindle bolt to the specified torque setting

14.26a Fit the sleeve into the torque arm mount . . .

14.26b . . . then fit the torque arm and tighten the bolt to the specified torque

specified torque setting **(see illustration)**. Check the movement of the swingarm, then fit the retaining clips and the caps covering the swingarm pivot ends **(see illustrations 14.12 and 14.10)**.

24 Tighten the upper rear engine mounting bolts to the torque setting specified at the beginning of Chapter 2.

25 If fitted, install the bolts securing the bottom of the mudflap to the swingarm.

26 Install the brake torque arm on the swingarm, not forgetting the sleeve, and, using a new bolt, tighten to the torque setting specified at the beginning of Chapter 7 **(see illustrations)**.

27 On Daytona and Speed Triple models fit

the brake hose clamp to the right side of the swingarm.

28 Install the rear wheel as described in Chapter 7.

29 Fit the exhaust silencers (not Tiger model).

30 On Daytona and Speed Triple models fit the swingarm-mounted mudguard as described In Chapter 8.

31 Fit the chainguard and tighten the screws securely.

32 On all models except the Thunderbird and Tiger, fit the side panels as described in Chapter 8.

33 Check the operation of the rear suspension before taking the machine on the road.

15 Swingarm - inspection and bearing replacement

Inspection

1 Thoroughly clean all components, removing all dirt, corrosion or grease **(see illustration)**.

2 Inspect all components closely, looking for obvious signs of wear such as heavy scoring, and cracks or distortion due to accident damage. Inspect the drive chain slider and slider block (Tiger only). If they are worn they must be replaced. Any damaged or worn component must be replaced.

Bearing replacement

3 Remove the dust seals, shims and the inner sleeves, noting where each one fits as they must be replaced in the same position. Inspect them for signs of wear or damage and replace them if necessary.

4 Worn bearings can be drifted out of their bores, but note that removal will destroy them; new bearings should be obtained before work commences. The new bearings should be pressed or drawn into their bores rather than driven into position. In the absence of a press, a suitable drawbolt arrangement can be made up (see Section 11 of this Chapter). Otherwise the bearings must be replaced by a Triumph dealer.

16 Drive chain - removal, cleaning and installation

Removal

Note: *The original equipment drive chain fitted to all models is an endless chain, which means it doesn't have a joining link and therefore cannot be split. Removal requires the removal of the swingarm as detailed below.*

> ⚠ **Warning: NEVER install a drive chain which uses a clip-type master (split) link.**

1 Remove the swingarm (see Section 14).

2 Remove the front sprocket cover as described in Section 17, Steps 1 to 8.

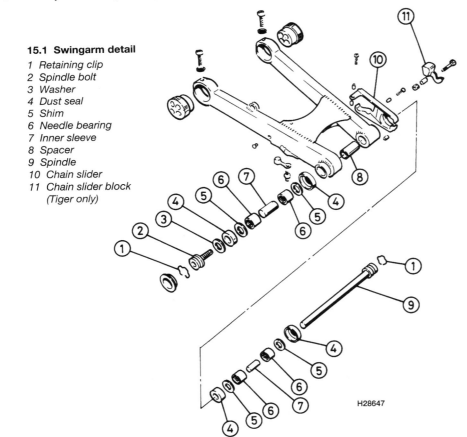

15.1 Swingarm detail

1 *Retaining clip*
2 *Spindle bolt*
3 *Washer*
4 *Dust seal*
5 *Shim*
6 *Needle bearing*
7 *Inner sleeve*
8 *Spacer*
9 *Spindle*
10 *Chain slider*
11 *Chain slider block (Tiger only)*

H28647

3 Slip the chain off the front sprocket and remove it from the bike.

Cleaning

4 Soak the chain in paraffin for approximately five or six minutes. *Caution: Don't use petrol, solvent or other cleaning fluids which might damage its internal sealing properties. Don't use high-pressure water. Remove the chain, wipe it off, then blow it dry with compressed air immediately. The entire process shouldn't take longer than ten minutes - if it does, the O-rings in the chain rollers could be damaged.*

Installation

5 Installation is the reverse of removal, as described in Section 17, Steps 14 and 15.

6 On completion, adjust and lubricate the chain following the procedures in Chapter 1. *Caution: Use only the recommended lubricant.*

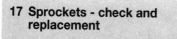

17 Sprockets - check and replacement

Check

1 Place the bike on its centre stand. On models without a centre stand, it is necessary to support the bike using an auxiliary stand or hoist as the sidestand must be removed in order to remove the sprocket cover (except Thunderbird models).

2 Drain the engine oil (refer to Chapter 1).

3 On Thunderbird models, unscrew the gearshift pedal pinch bolt and remove the pedal, then unscrew the footrest bracket mounting bolts and remove the footrest with its bracket **(see illustration)**.

4 On Tiger models, remove the rider's left footrest bracket (Section 3). Mark a line across the gearshift shaft end and shaft lever as an aid to installation, then remove the pinch bolt and withdraw the shaft lever.

5 On all other models detach the link rod from the gearshift shaft lever and pedal by slackening its locknuts and rotating the rod via its knurled centre section so that it unscrews from the lever and pedal at the same time. Where a dog-leg link rod is fitted, slacken off the locknut and unscrew the threaded sleeve to separate the link rod from the shaft lever. Disconnect the sidestand switch wiring connector, then remove the sidestand bracket bolt and the engine left rear lower bolt **(see illustrations 5.10b and 5.10c in Chapter 2)**. Remove the sidestand with its bracket. Mark a line across the gearshift shaft end and shaft lever as an aid to installation, then remove the pinch bolt and withdraw the shaft lever.

6 If fitted, unscrew the bolts securing the water pump hose cover and remove the cover.

7 Unscrew the bolts securing the clutch release cylinder to the sprocket cover, noting the location of the shorter bolt, and remove the cylinder **(see illustration and Haynes Hint)**. Take care not to pull in the clutch lever with the cylinder removed. Withdraw the clutch pushrod.

8 Unscrew the sprocket cover bolts and remove the cover **(see illustration)**. Take note of the bolt locations as they are of different lengths. Take care not to lose the locating dowels and note their positions. Discard the gasket as a new one must be used.

9 Check the wear pattern on both sprockets (see Chapter 1). If the sprocket teeth are worn excessively, replace the chain and both sprockets as a set. Whenever the drive chain is inspected, the sprockets should be inspected also. If you are replacing the chain, replace the sprockets as well.

Restrain the clutch release cylinder piston using cable-ties and a short spacer

Replacement

Front sprocket

10 Remove the sprocket cover as described in Steps 1 to 8 above.

11 Shift the transmission into gear and have an assistant sit on the seat and apply the rear brake hard. Bend the lock washer tabs away from the sprocket nut and unscrew the nut. Discard the lock washer as a new one must be used **(see illustration)**.

12 Slacken the drive chain adjusters if necessary (see Chapter 1), then pull the engine sprocket and chain off the shaft and separate the sprocket from the chain **(see illustration)**.

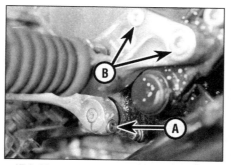

17.3 Unscrew the gearshift pedal pinch bolt (A) and the footrest bracket bolts (B)

17.7 Unscrew the three clutch release cylinder mounting bolts (arrowed) and remove the cylinder

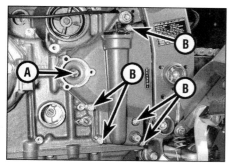

17.8 Remove the clutch pushrod (A), unscrew the remaining sprocket cover bolts (B) and remove the cover

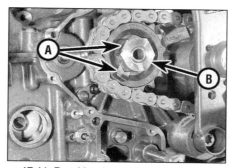

17.11 Bend back the tabs on the lock washer (A), then unscrew the nut (B)

17.12 Remove the sprocket from the shaft with the chain attached

6

17.13a Fit a new lock washer to the shaft, then install the nut . . .

17.13b . . . tighten it to the specified torque setting . . .

17.13c . . . and then bend up the tabs of the washer to lock the nut in place

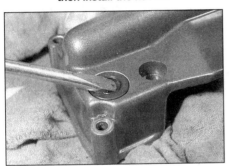

17.14a Lever the old gearshift shaft oil seal out of the cover . . .

17.14b . . . and press in a new seal

17.14c Make sure the two dowels are in position (arrowed), then fit a new gasket

17.17 The rear sprocket is held by five nuts

13 Engage the new sprocket with the chain and slide it on the shaft. Install the new lock washer and nut and tighten it to the specified torque setting whilst locking the transmission as described above. **Note:** *The nut should be installed with its recessed side towards the lock washer.* Bend the tabs on the lockwasher up against the nut **(see illustrations)**. Adjust the chain as necessary (see Chapter 1).

14 Install the engine sprocket cover and other components by reversing the removal procedure as described in Steps 1 to 8 above, noting the following:

a) *Fit a new oil seal to the gearshift shaft hole in the cover and a new gasket to the cover (**see illustrations**). It is advisable to cover the gearshift shaft threads with tape to avoid damaging the lips of the new seal when fitting the cover.*

b) *Make sure all locating dowels are in place when fitting the cover and use a new gasket (**see illustration**).*

c) *Smear the pushrod with engine oil and slide it back into the sprocket cover. Apply a dab of grease to its end before installing the release cylinder*

15 Fill the engine with oil (see Chapter 1).

Rear sprocket

16 To remove the rear sprocket, remove the rear wheel as described in Chapter 7. *Caution: Do not lay the wheel down on the disc as it could become warped. Lay the wheel on wooden blocks so that the disc is off the ground.*

17 Unscrew the nuts holding the sprocket to the wheel coupling and lift it off, noting which way around it fits **(see illustration)**. Check the condition of the rubber damper under the rear wheel coupling (see Section 18).

18 Fit the new sprocket with the recess and No. of teeth marking facing outwards. Install the sprocket retaining nuts and tighten them to the torque setting specified at the beginning of the Chapter.

18 Rear wheel coupling/rubber damper - check and replacement

1 Remove the rear wheel as described in Chapter 7. *Caution: Do not lay the wheel down on the disc as it could become warped. Lay the wheel on wooden blocks so that the disc is off the ground.*

2 If it has not already been removed, withdraw the spacer from the outside of the sprocket coupling.

3 Lift the sprocket coupling away from the wheel leaving the rubber dampers in position in the wheel. Take care not to lose the spacer from the inside of the coupling bearing.

4 Lift the rubber damper segments from the wheel and check them for cracks, hardening and general deterioration **(see illustration)**. Replace the rubber dampers as a set if necessary.

5 Checking and replacement procedures for the sprocket coupling bearing are described in Section 16 of Chapter 7.

6 Installation is the reverse of the removal procedure, making sure that the sprocket coupling spacers are correctly positioned.

7 Install the rear wheel as described in Chapter 7.

18.4 Remove the rubber dampers from the rear wheel and inspect them for wear and damage

Chapter 7
Brakes, wheels and tyres

Contents

Degrees of difficulty

Easy, suitable for novice with little experience	**Fairly easy,** suitable for beginner with some experience	**Fairly difficult,** suitable for competent DIY mechanic	**Difficult,** suitable for experienced DIY mechanic	**Very difficult,** suitable for expert DIY or professional

Specifications

Brakes

Brake fluid type	see Chapter 1
Brake pad minimum thickness	1.5 mm (see text)
Disc thickness:	
Front	
New	5.0 mm
Service limit	4.5 mm
Rear	
New	6.0 mm
Service limit	5.0 mm
Disc maximum runout (front and rear)	0.3 mm
Caliper piston dimensions - refer to Section 1 for caliper identification	
Front	
Type A	33.96 mm and 30.23 mm
Types B and D	27.0 mm
Type C	30.2 mm, 25.4 mm and 22.0 mm
Rear - all types	27.0 mm
Master cylinder piston dimensions - refer to Section 1 for master cylinder identification	
Front	
Types A and C	15.8 mm
Type B	14.0 mm
Type D	11.0 mm
Rear - all types	14.0 mm

Wheels

Maximum wheel runout (front and rear)	
Axial (side-to-side)	0.5 mm
Radial (out-of-round)	0.8 mm

7

Tyres

Tyre pressures . . . . see Chapter 1
Tyre sizes*
  Front
    Thunderbird . . . . 110/80 ZR or VR 18
    Tiger . . . . 110/80 R 19
    All other models . . . . 120/70 ZR 17
  Rear
    Trophy and Sprint . . . . 170/60 ZR 17
    Trident . . . . 160/60 ZR 18
    Daytona and Speed Triple . . . . 180/55 ZR 17
    Thunderbird . . . . 160/80 ZR 16 or 150/18 R 16
    Tiger . . . . 140/80 R 17
*Refer to the owner's handbook or the tyre information label on the drive chain guard for approved tyre brands.

Torque settings

Front brake caliper
  Mounting bolts
    Thunderbird . . . . 28 Nm
    All other models . . . . 40 Nm
  Pad retaining pin . . . . 18 Nm
  Pad pin plug (Thunderbird) . . . . 3 Nm
  Caliper body joining bolts (Type A) . . . . 25 Nm
Front brake disc retaining bolts . . . . 22 Nm
Front brake master cylinder clamp bolts . . . . 15 Nm
Front brake lever pivot bolt
  Thunderbird and Tiger . . . . 6 Nm
  All other models . . . . 1 Nm
Front brake lever pivot bolt locknut . . . . 6 Nm
Rear brake caliper
  Mounting bolt
    Thunderbird . . . . 28 Nm
    All other models . . . . 40 Nm
  Pad retaining pin . . . . 18 Nm
Rear brake disc retaining bolts . . . . 22 Nm
Rear brake master cylinder mounting bolts . . . . 27 Nm
Rear brake light switch . . . . 15 Nm
Rear brake torque arm mounting bolts . . . . 28 Nm
Brake caliper bleed valves . . . . 5 Nm
Brake hose banjo union bolts
  At rear master cylinder . . . . 28 Nm
  All other banjo union bolts . . . . 25 Nm
Front axle bolt
  Tiger . . . . 110 Nm
  All other models . . . . 60 Nm
Front axle clamp bolts (not Tiger) . . . . 20 Nm
Rear axle nut . . . . 85 Nm
Drive chain adjuster clamp bolts . . . . 35 Nm

1 General information

With the exception of the Thunderbird and Tiger, all models covered in this manual are fitted with cast alloy wheels designed for tubeless tyres. The Thunderbird and Tiger models are fitted with spoked wheels using alloy rims and tubed tyres. Both front and rear brakes are hydraulically operated disc brakes. Four different set-ups are used across the range of models on the front, as described in Table 1 opposite.

On the rear, all models have 2 piston sliding calipers with a single fixed disc. Three different mounting set-ups are used throughout the range, as described in Table 2 opposite.

Table 1 - Front brake set-ups

Type A	4 piston opposed caliper with twin floating discs	Daytona (not Super III), Speed Triple, Sprint and 900 Trophy from VIN 9083, 1200 Trophy from VIN 4902
Type B	2 piston sliding caliper, with twin fixed discs	Trident, Tiger, Sprint and 900 Trophy to VIN 9082, 1200 Trophy to VIN 4901
Type C	6 piston opposed caliper, with twin floating discs	Daytona Super III
Type D	2 piston sliding caliper, with single fixed disc	Thunderbird

Table 2 - Rear brake set-ups

Type A	Caliper mounted below disc	Daytona and Speed Triple
Type B	Caliper mounted above disc, with torque arm mounted on caliper	Trophy, Trident, Sprint and Tiger
Type C	Caliper mounted above disc, with torque arm mounted on caliper bracket	Thunderbird

2.1a Type A caliper - unscrew the pad retaining pin . . .

2.1b . . . remove the pad spring . . .

2.1c . . . and withdraw the brake pads

Caution: Disc brake components rarely require disassembly. Do not disassemble components unless absolutely necessary. If a hydraulic brake line is loosened, the entire system must be disassembled, drained, cleaned and then properly filled and bled upon reassembly. Do not use solvents on internal brake components. Solvents will cause the seals to swell and distort. Use only clean brake fluid or denatured alcohol for cleaning. Use care when working with brake fluid as it can injure your eyes and it will damage painted surfaces and plastic parts.

2 Front brake pads - replacement

Note: *For brake caliper type applications, see Section 1.*

⚠️ *Warning: When replacing the front brake pads always replace the pads in BOTH calipers - never just on one side (not Thunderbird). The dust created by the brake system may contain asbestos, which is harmful to your health. Never blow it out with compressed air and don't inhale any of it. An approved filtering mask should be worn when working on the brakes.*

1 On the Type A caliper, unscrew and remove the pad retaining pin from the caliper, then remove the pad spring, noting how it fits, and withdraw the pads from the caliper body **(see illustrations)**.

2 On the Type B caliper, slacken the pad retaining pins, then unscrew the caliper mounting bolts and remove the caliper from the disc. Support the caliper so that no strain is placed on its hose. Press down on the pads and remove the pad retaining pins. Withdraw the pads from the caliper body and remove the pad spring, noting how it fits.

3 On the Type C caliper, unscrew the caliper mounting bolts and remove the caliper from the disc **(see illustration)**. Support the caliper so no strain is placed on the hose. Drive the pad retaining pins out using a suitable drift. Remove the pad spring, noting how it fits, and withdraw the pads from the caliper body.

4 On the Type D caliper, unscrew the pad retaining pin plug, then unscrew and remove the pad retaining pin from the caliper **(see illustration)**. Withdraw the pads from the lower end of the caliper body and remove the pad spring, noting how it fits.

5 On all types, inspect the surface of each pad for contamination and check that the friction material has not worn beyond its service limit **(see illustration)**. If either pad is worn down to, or beyond, the service limit specification or wear grooves (ie the grooves are no longer visible), fouled with oil or grease, or heavily scored or damaged by dirt and debris, both pads must be replaced as a set. Note that it is not possible to degrease the friction material; if the pads are contaminated in any way they must be replaced.

6 If the pads are in good condition clean them carefully, using a fine wire brush which is completely free of oil and grease to remove all traces of road dirt and corrosion. Using a pointed instrument, clean out the grooves in the friction material and dig out any embedded particles of foreign matter. Any areas of glazing may be removed using emery cloth.

7 Check the condition of the brake discs (see Section 4).

8 Remove all traces of corrosion from the pad pin(s). Inspect the pin(s) for signs of damage and replace if necessary.

9 Push the pistons as far back into the caliper as possible using hand pressure only. Due to the increased friction material thickness of new pads, it may be necessary to remove the master cylinder reservoir cover and diaphragm and siphon out some fluid.

10 Smear the backs of the pads and the shanks of the pad pins with copper-based grease, making sure that none gets on the front or sides of the pads.

11 Installation of the pads, pad springs and retaining pins is the reverse of removal for each type. Insert the pads into the caliper so that the friction material of each pad is facing the disc. On the type D caliper, ensure the upper end of each pad engages the anti-rattle spring on the caliper mounting bracket. Make sure the pad spring(s) is correctly positioned and the pin(s) fits correctly through the holes in the pads **(see illustrations)**. Tighten the pad retaining pins and caliper mounting bolts (if removed) to the specified torque setting.

2.3 Caliper mounting bolts (arrows) - Type C caliper

2.4 Unscrew the pad retaining pin plug (arrowed) to reveal pad pin - Type D caliper

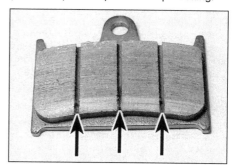

2.5 Brake pads must be replaced when the wear grooves (arrowed) are no longer visible (typical pad design shown)

7

2.11a Install the pads in the caliper . . .

2.11b . . . then fit the pad pin
and tighten it securely

3.2 Unscrew the caliper mounting bolts
and slide the caliper off the disc

12 Top-up the master cylinder reservoir if necessary (see Chapter 1), and replace the reservoir cover and diaphragm if removed.
13 Operate the brake lever several times to bring the pads into contact with the disc. Check the master cylinder fluid level (see Chapter 1) and the operation of the brake before riding the motorcycle.

3 Front brake caliper(s) - removal, overhaul and installation

⚠️ *Warning: If a caliper indicates the need for an overhaul (usually due to leaking fluid or sticky operation), all old brake fluid should be flushed from the system. Also, the dust created by the brake system may contain asbestos, which is harmful to your health. Never blow it out with compressed air and don't inhale any of it. An approved filtering mask should be worn when working on the brakes. Do not, under any circumstances, use petroleum-based solvents to clean brake parts. Use clean brake fluid, brake cleaner or denatured alcohol only.*

Note: *For brake caliper type applications, see Section 1.*

Removal

1 Remove the brake hose banjo bolt, noting its position on the caliper, and separate the hose from the caliper. Plug the hose end or wrap a plastic bag tightly around it to minimise fluid loss and prevent dirt entering the system. Discard the sealing washers as new ones must be used on installation. **Note:** *If you are planning to overhaul the caliper and don't have a source of compressed air to blow out the pistons, just loosen the banjo bolt at this stage and retighten it lightly. The bike's hydraulic system can then be used to force the pistons out of the body once the pads have been removed. Disconnect the hose once the pistons have been sufficiently displaced.*
2 Unscrew the caliper mounting bolts, noting the spacers (where fitted) on the Type B

caliper, and slide the caliper away from the disc **(see illustration)**. Remove the brake pads as described in Section 2. On the Type D caliper, unscrew the speedometer cable guide from the caliper.

Overhaul

3 Clean the exterior of the caliper with denatured alcohol or brake system cleaner **(see illustration)**.
4 Remove the pistons from the caliper body, either by pumping them out by operating the front brake lever until the pistons are displaced, or by forcing them out using compressed air. Mark each piston head and caliper body with a felt marker to ensure that the pistons can be matched to their original bores on reassembly. If the compressed air method is used, place a wad of rag between the opposed pistons (Types A and C) or

between the pistons and caliper body (Types B and D) to act as a cushion, then use compressed air directed into the fluid inlet to force the pistons out of the body. Use only low pressure to ease the pistons out and make sure both pistons are displaced at the same time. If the air pressure is too high and the pistons are forced out, the caliper and/or pistons may be damaged. On the Type C caliper, even though the caliper body is manufactured in two halves and is bolted together, the two halves must not be split. Because of this it is not possible to remove all six pistons from the caliper at the same time. It is necessary to use a special tool (Pt. No. 3880185) which prevents the pistons in one half of the caliper from moving so that the pistons in the other half can be removed. When one side has been overhauled, reverse the tool and do the other side.

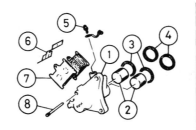

TYPE A

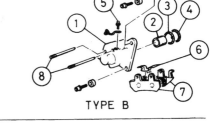

TYPE B

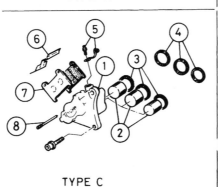

TYPE C

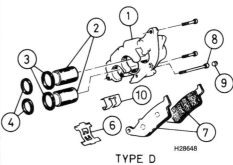

TYPE D

H28648

3.3 Front brake caliper detail

1 Caliper body	4 Dust seal	7 Brake pad	9 Pad pin plug
2 Piston	5 Bleed nipple	8 Pad pin	10 Anti-rattle spring
3 Piston seal	6 Pad spring		

3.17 Install the caliper on the disc

 Warning: Never place your fingers in front of the pistons in an attempt to catch or protect them when applying compressed air, as serious injury could result.

5 On the Type A caliper, unscrew the caliper body joining bolts and split the caliper body into its two halves, and withdraw the pistons. Recover the seals between the caliper halves.

6 Using a wooden or plastic tool, remove the dust seals from the caliper bores and discard them. New seals must be used on installation. If a metal tool is being used, take great care not to damage the caliper bores.

7 Remove and discard the piston seals in the same way.

8 Clean the pistons and bores with denatured alcohol, clean brake fluid or brake system cleaner. *Caution: Do not, under any circumstances, use a petroleum-based solvent to clean brake parts. If compressed air is available, use it to dry the parts thoroughly (make sure it's filtered and unlubricated).*

9 Inspect the caliper bores and pistons for signs of corrosion, nicks and burrs and loss of plating. If surface defects are present, the caliper assembly must be replaced. If the caliper is in bad shape the master cylinder should also be checked.

10 On Types B and D, check that the caliper body is able to slide on the mounting bracket pins. If seized due to corrosion, separate the two components and clean off all traces of corrosion and hardened grease. Apply a smear of copper-based grease to the mounting bracket pins and reassemble the two components. If the dust seals have deteriorated, they should be replaced with new ones; check first on their availability.

11 On Types A, B and D, lubricate the new piston seals with clean brake fluid and install them in their grooves in the caliper bores. Note that on the Type A caliper different sizes of bore and piston are used and care must therefore be taken when installing the new seals to ensure that they are fitted to the correct bores. The same care must be taken when fitting the new dust seals and the pistons.

3.18 Tighten the caliper mounting bolts to the specified torque setting

12 On the Type C caliper, there are two seals in each cylinder, an inner pressure seal and an outer wiper seal. The inner seal is thicker than the outer seal. The inner seal must either be soaked in brake fluid for at least 10 minutes, or be smeared with silicone grease. Do not use a mineral-based grease. The outer seal must be smeared with silicone grease. Do not soak the outer seal in brake fluid. Note that different sizes of bore and piston are used and care must therefore be taken when installing the new seals to ensure that the correct size seals are fitted to the correct bores. The same care must be taken when fitting the new dust seals and the pistons.

13 On all models, lubricate the new dust seals with clean brake fluid and install them in their grooves in the caliper bores.

14 Lubricate the pistons with clean brake fluid and install them closed-end first into the caliper bores. Using your thumbs, push the pistons all the way in, making sure they enter the bore squarely.

15 On the Type A caliper, lubricate the new caliper seals and install them into one half of the caliper body. Join the two halves of the caliper body together, making sure that the caliper seals are correctly seated in their recesses. Apply a drop of non-permanent locking compound to the threads of the caliper body joining bolts, then install them in the caliper body and tighten to the torque setting specified at the beginning of the Chapter.

Installation

16 Install the brake pads as described in Section 2.

17 Install the caliper on the brake disc making sure the pads sit squarely either side of the disc **(see illustration)**.

18 Install the caliper mounting bolts, not forgetting the spacers on the Type B caliper, and tighten them to the torque setting specified at the beginning of this Chapter **(see illustration)**. On the Type D caliper secure the speedometer cable guide to the caliper.

19 Connect the brake hose to the caliper, using new sealing washers on each side of the fitting. Tighten the banjo bolt to the torque setting specified at the beginning of the Chapter.

20 Fill the master cylinder with the recommended brake fluid (see Chapter 1) and bleed the hydraulic system as described in Section 11.

21 Check for leaks and thoroughly test the operation of the brake before riding the motorcycle.

4 Front brake disc(s) - inspection, removal and installation

Inspection

1 Visually inspect the surface of the disc(s) for score marks and other damage. Light scratches are normal after use and won't affect brake operation, but deep grooves and heavy score marks will reduce braking efficiency and accelerate pad wear. If a disc is badly grooved it must be machined or replaced.

2 To check disc runout, position the bike on its centre stand and support it so that the front wheel is raised off the ground. Where only a side stand is fitted, the front wheel must be raised off the ground using an auxiliary stand - always make sure that the bike is properly supported. Mount a dial indicator to a fork leg, with the plunger on the indicator touching the surface of the disc about 10 mm (1/2 inch) from the outer edge **(see illustration)**. Rotate the wheel and watch the indicator needle, comparing the reading with the limit listed in the Specifications at the beginning of the Chapter. If the runout is greater than the service limit, check the hub bearings for play. If the bearings are worn, replace them and repeat this check. If the disc runout is still excessive, it will have to be replaced, although machining by a competent engineering shop may be possible.

3 The disc must not be machined or allowed to wear down to a thickness less than the service limit as listed in this Chapter's Specifications and as stamped on the outside of the disc itself. The thickness of the disc can be checked with a micrometer **(see illustration)**. If the thickness of the disc is less than the service limit, it must be replaced.

4.2 Using a dial indicator to measure disc runout

7

4.3 Using a micrometer to measure disc thickness

Removal

4 Remove the wheel (refer to Section 14). *Caution: Do not lay the wheel down and allow it to rest on one of the discs - the disc could become warped. Set the wheel on wood blocks so the disc doesn't support the weight of the wheel.*

5 Mark the relationship of the disc to the wheel, so it can be installed in the same position. Remove the disc retaining bolt caps (if fitted), then unscrew the bolts and remove the disc from the wheel **(see illustration)**. Loosen the bolts a little at a time, in a criss-cross pattern, to avoid distorting the disc.

6 On all models except the Thunderbird, if both discs are to be removed mark them LEFT and RIGHT to ensure that they are correctly positioned on installation.

Installation

7 Install the disc on the wheel, aligning the previously applied matchmarks (if you're reinstalling the original disc).

8 Install the bolts and tighten them in a criss-cross pattern evenly and progressively to the torque setting specified at the beginning of the Chapter. Install the bolt caps, if fitted. Clean off all grease from the brake disc(s) using acetone or brake system cleaner. If a new brake disc has been installed, remove any protective coating from its working surfaces.

9 Install the wheel as described in Section 14.

10 Operate the brake lever several times to bring the pads into contact with the disc. Check the operation of the brakes carefully before riding the bike.

5 Front brake master cylinder - removal, overhaul and installation

1 If the master cylinder is leaking fluid, or if the lever does not produce a firm feel when the brake is applied, and bleeding the brakes does not help (see Section 11), and the hydraulic hoses are all in good condition, then master cylinder overhaul is recommended.

2 Before disassembling the master cylinder, read through the entire procedure and make sure that you have the correct rebuild kit.

4.5 Unscrew the disc bolts a little at a time and in a criss-cross pattern to avoid distorting the disc

Also, you will need some new, clean brake fluid of the recommended type, some clean rags and internal circlip pliers. **Note:** *To prevent damage to the paint from spilled brake fluid, always cover the fuel tank when working on the master cylinder.* **Caution:** *Disassembly, overhaul and reassembly of the brake master cylinder must be done in a spotlessly clean work area to avoid contamination and possible failure of the brake hydraulic system components.*

Removal

3 Loosen, but do not remove, the screws holding the reservoir cover in place **(see illustration)**.

4 Disconnect the electrical connectors from the brake light switch.

5 Remove the locknut from the underside of the brake lever pivot bolt, then unscrew the

5.3 Loosen the reservoir cover screws

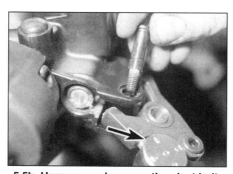

5.5b Unscrew and remove the pivot bolt, then remove the lever. Note the setting on the span adjuster (arrowed)

bolt (on Tiger remove the bolt cap first) and remove the brake lever **(see illustrations)**. On Tiger models, the plastic hand guard will be freed as the brake lever pivot bolt is withdrawn; retrieve the collar from the pivot bolt. If fitted, note the setting of the lever span adjuster.

6 Remove the rubber boot then unscrew the banjo bolt and separate the brake hose from the master cylinder. Note the alignment of the hose. Discard the two sealing washers as these must be replaced with new ones. Wrap the end of the hose in a clean rag and suspend the hose in an upright position or bend it down carefully and place the open end in a clean container. The objective is to prevent excessive loss of brake fluid, fluid spills and system contamination.

7 Remove the master cylinder mounting bolts to free the clamp, then lift the master cylinder and reservoir away from the handlebar **(see illustration)**. **Caution:** *Do not tip the master cylinder upside down or brake fluid will run out.*

Overhaul

8 Remove its retaining screws and lift off the reservoir cover and the rubber diaphragm **(see illustration)**. Drain the brake fluid from the reservoir into a suitable container. Wipe any remaining fluid out of the reservoir with a clean rag.

9 Undo the brake light switch retaining screw and remove the switch.

10 Carefully remove the dust boot from the end of the piston.

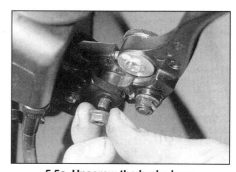

5.5a Unscrew the brake lever pivot bolt locknut

5.7 Remove the clamp bolts (arrowed) to free the master cylinder

5.8 Front brake master cylinder detail

1 Reservoir cover
2 Rubber diaphragm
3 Reservoir
4 Dust boot
5 Circlip
6 Piston assembly
7 Spring
8 Brake light switch
9 Sealing washers
10 Banjo bolt
11 Brake hose

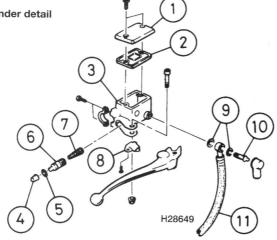

H28649

collar. On all models, install the pivot bolt locknut and tighten it to the specified torque setting. Install the pivot bolt cap on Tiger models. The front brake lever has an adjuster mechanism which alters the span of the lever from the handlebar according to the rider's requirements. Adjust this as necessary by turning the adjuster either clockwise or anti-clockwise until the desired position is achieved (see Chapter 1).
23 Connect the brake light switch wiring.
24 Fill the fluid reservoir with the specified brake fluid as described in Chapter 1. Refer to Section 11 of this Chapter and bleed the air from the system.
25 Carefully fit the rubber diaphragm, making sure that it is correctly seated, and the cover on the master cylinder reservoir (see illustration).

11 Using circlip pliers, remove the circlip and slide out the piston assembly and the spring, noting how they fit. Lay the parts out in the proper order to prevent confusion during reassembly. Triumph advise that the piston, seals and circlip assembly be replaced when disturbed.
12 Clean all parts with clean brake fluid or denatured alcohol. *Caution: Do not, under any circumstances, use a petroleum-based solvent to clean brake parts. If compressed air is available, use it to dry the parts thoroughly (make sure it's filtered and unlubricated).*
13 Check the master cylinder bore for corrosion, scratches, nicks and score marks. If damage is evident, the master cylinder must be replaced with a new one. If the master cylinder is in poor condition, then the caliper(s) should be checked as well. Check that the fluid inlet and outlet ports in the master cylinder are clear
14 The dust boot, piston assembly and spring are included in the rebuild kit. Use all of the new parts, regardless of the apparent condition of the old ones.
15 Install the spring in the master cylinder so that its tapered end faces the piston.
16 Lubricate the piston seal with clean

hydraulic fluid and slip the piston into the master cylinder. Depress the piston and install the new circlip, making sure that it locates in the master cylinder groove.
17 Locate the dust boot in the bore and engage its outer end in the piston groove.
18 Install the brake light switch and securely tighten its retaining screw.
19 Inspect the reservoir cover rubber diaphragm and replace if damaged or deteriorated.

Installation

20 Attach the master cylinder to the handlebar and fit the clamp making sure the "UP" mark is facing upwards (see illustration). Align the upper mating surfaces of the clamp with the punch mark on the handlebar, then tighten the upper clamp bolt first followed by the lower one (see illustration).
21 Connect the brake hose to the master cylinder, using new sealing washers on each side of the union. Tighten the banjo bolt to the torque setting specified at the beginning of this Chapter.
22 Install the brake lever and pivot bolt and tighten the bolt to the specified torque setting. On Tiger models also fit the hand guard and

6 Rear brake pads - replacement

Warning: The dust created by the brake system may contain asbestos, which is harmful to your health. Never blow it out with compressed air and don't inhale any of it. An approved filtering mask should be worn when working on the brakes.

Note: *For brake caliper type applications, see Section 1.*
1 With the exception of Tiger models, on the Type B caliper remove the right side exhaust silencer to improve access to the brake caliper (see Chapter 4).
2 On Type A and B calipers, slacken the pad retaining pins, then unscrew the caliper mounting bolts and remove the caliper from the disc (see illustrations). Support the calipers so that no strain is placed on the hose. Press down on the pads and remove the pad retaining pins. Withdraw the pads from the caliper body and remove the pad spring, if necessary, noting how it fits (see illustrations).
3 On the Type C caliper, unscrew the pad retaining pin plug, then unscrew and remove

5.20a Fit the master cylinder and clamp to the handlebar making sure they are correctly aligned

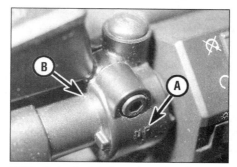

5.20b Note the "UP" mark on the clamp (A) and the punch mark on the handlebar (B)

5.25 Make sure the diaphragm is properly seated, then fit the reservoir cover

7

6.2a Type A caliper - Pad retaining pins (A), caliper mounting bolts (B)

6.2b Type B caliper - Pad retaining pins (A), caliper mounting bolts (B)

6.2c Slacken the pad retaining pins . . .

6.2d . . . unscrew the caliper mounting bolts . . .

6.2e . . . and remove the caliper from the disc

6.2f Unscrew the pad retaining pins . . .

6.2g . . . and remove the pads, noting how they fit against the lug (arrowed)

6.2h Note the fitting of the pad spring (arrowed)

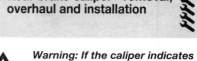

6.3 Type C caliper - Pad retaining pin plug and pin (A), caliper mounting bolts (B)

the pad retaining pin from the caliper **(see illustration)**. Withdraw the pads from the lower end of the caliper body and remove the pad spring, noting how it fits.

4 Inspect the brake pads and associated components as described in Steps 5 through 8 of Section 2.

5 Push the pistons as far back into the caliper as possible using hand pressure only. Due to tne increased friction material thickness of new pads, it may be necessary to remove the master cylinder reservoir cover and diaphragm and siphon out some fluid.

6 Smear the backs of the pads and the shanks of the pad pins with copper-based grease, making sure that none gets on the front or sides of the pads.

7 Installation of the pads, pad springs and retaining pins is the reverse of removal for each type. Insert the pads into the caliper so

that the friction material of each pad is facing the disc. On the Type C caliper, ensure that the upper end of each pad engages the anti-rattle spring on the caliper slider bracket. Make sure the pad spring is correctly positioned and the pins fit correctly through the holes in the pads. Tighten the pad retaining pins and caliper mounting bolts (if removed) to the specified torque setting.

8 Top-up the master cylinder reservoir if necessary (see Chapter 1), and replace the reservoir cap and diaphragm if removed.

9 Operate the brake pedal several times to bring the pads into contact with the disc. Check the master cylinder fluid level (see Chapter 1) and the operation of the brake before riding the motorcycle.

10 Check that the brake hose is located in the retaining clamp on the swingarm.

11 If removed, fit the exhaust silencer.

7 Rear brake caliper - removal, overhaul and installation

⚠️ *Warning: If the caliper indicates the need for an overhaul (usually due to leaking fluid or sticky operation), all old brake fluid should be flushed from the system. Also, the dust created by the brake system may contain asbestos, which is harmful to your health. Never blow it out with compressed air and don't inhale any of it. An approved filtering mask should be worn when working on the brakes. Do not, under any circumstances, use petroleum-based solvents to clean brake parts. Use clean brake fluid or denatured alcohol only.*

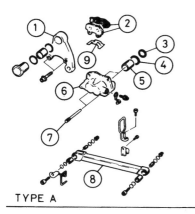

TYPE A

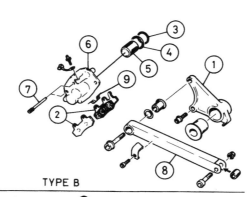

TYPE B

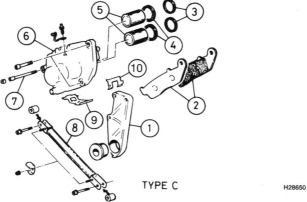

TYPE C

H28650

7.5 Rear brake caliper detail

1 Caliper bracket
2 Brake pads
3 Dust seal
4 Piston seal
5 Piston
6 Caliper body
7 Pad pin
8 Torque arm
9 Pad spring
10 Anti-rattle spring

Note: For brake caliper type applications, see Section 1.

Removal

1 With the exception of Tiger models, on the Type B caliper remove the right side exhaust silencer to improve access to the brake caliper (see Chapter 4).

2 Remove the brake hose banjo bolt and separate the hose from the caliper. Plug the hose end or wrap a plastic bag tightly around it to minimise fluid loss and prevent dirt entering the system. Discard the sealing washers; new ones must be used on installation. **Note:** If you are planning to overhaul the caliper and don't have a source of compressed air to blow out the pistons, just loosen the banjo bolt at this stage and retighten it lightly. The bike's hydraulic system can then be used to force the pistons out of the body once the pads have been removed. Disconnect the hose once the pistons have been sufficiently displaced.

3 Remove the caliper mounting bolts and slip the caliper off the disc **(see illustrations 6.2a, 6.2b and 6.3)**.

4 Remove the brake pads as described in Section 6.

Overhaul

5 Clean the exterior of the caliper with clean brake fluid or denatured alcohol **(see illustration)**.

6 If the pistons weren't forced out using the bike's hydraulic system, place a wad of rag between the piston and caliper body to act as a cushion, then use compressed air directed into the fluid inlet to force the piston out of the body. Use only low pressure to ease the piston out. If the air pressure is too high and the piston is forced out, the caliper and/or piston may be damaged.

 Warning: Never place your fingers in front of the piston in an attempt to catch or protect it when applying compressed air, as serious injury could result. Label the piston heads and caliper bores with a felt marker pen so that each piston can be returned to its original bore on reassembly.

7 Using a wooden or plastic tool, remove the dust seal from each caliper bore. If a metal tool is being used, take great care not to damage the caliper bore.

8 Remove the piston seals in the same way.

9 Clean the piston and bore with clean brake fluid or denatured alcohol. **Caution: Do not, under any circumstances, use a petroleum-based solvent to clean brake parts. If compressed air is available, use it to dry the parts thoroughly (make sure it's filtered and unlubricated).**

10 Inspect the caliper bore and piston for signs of corrosion, nicks and burrs and loss of plating. If surface defects are present, the caliper assembly must be replaced. If the caliper is in bad shape the master cylinder should also be checked.

11 Check that the caliper body is able to slide on the slider bracket pins. If seized due to corrosion, separate the slider bracket from the caliper body and clean off all traces of corrosion and hardened grease. Apply a smear of copper-based grease to the slider bracket pins and reassemble the two components. If the dust seals have deteriorated, they should be replaced with new ones; check first on their availability.

12 Lubricate the new piston seals with clean brake fluid and install them in the grooves in the caliper bores.

13 Lubricate the new dust seals with clean brake fluid and install them in the grooves in the caliper bores.

14 Lubricate the pistons with clean brake fluid and install them, closed-end first, in their original bores in the caliper. Using your thumbs, push the pistons all the way in, making sure they enter the bores squarely.

Installation

15 Install the brake pads as described in Section 6.

16 Slide the caliper into position on the mounting bracket. Fit the caliper mounting bolts and tighten them to the torque setting specified at the beginning of the Chapter **(see illustrations 6.2a, 6.2b and 6.3)**.

17 Connect the brake hose to the caliper, using new sealing washers on each side of the union. Tighten the banjo bolt to the specified torque setting. Check that the brake hose is located in the retaining clamp on the swingarm.

18 Fill the master cylinder with the recommended brake fluid (see Chapter 1) and bleed the hydraulic system as described in Section 11.

19 Check that there are no leaks and thoroughly test the operation of the brake before riding the motorcycle.

---

8 Rear brake disc - inspection, removal and installation

Inspection

1 Refer to Section 4 of this Chapter, noting that the dial indicator should be attached to the swingarm.

7

Removal

2 Remove the wheel (see Section 15).

3 Mark the relationship of the disc to the wheel so it can be installed in the same position. Remove the disc retaining bolt caps (if fitted), then unscrew the bolts and remove the disc **(see illustration)**. Loosen the bolts a little at a time, in a criss-cross pattern, to avoid distorting the disc.

Installation

4 Position the disc on the wheel, aligning the previously applied matchmarks (if you're reinstalling the original disc).

5 Install the bolts and tighten them in a criss-cross pattern evenly and progressively to the torque setting specified at the beginning of this Chapter. Install the bolt caps, if fitted. Clean off all grease from the brake disc using acetone or brake system cleaner. If a new brake disc has been installed, remove any protective coating from its working surfaces.

6 Install the wheel as described in Section 15.

7 Operate the brake pedal several times to bring the pads into contact with the disc. Check the operation of the brake carefully before riding the motorcycle.

9 Rear brake master cylinder - removal, overhaul and installation

1 If the master cylinder is leaking fluid, or if the pedal does not produce a firm feel when the brake is applied, and bleeding the brakes does not help (see Section 11), and the hydraulic hoses are all in good condition, then master cylinder overhaul is recommended.

2 Before disassembling the master cylinder, read through the entire procedure and make sure that you have the correct rebuild kit. Also, you will need some new, clean brake fluid of the recommended type, some clean rags and internal circlip pliers. *Caution: Disassembly, overhaul and reassembly of the brake master cylinder must be done in a spotlessly clean work area to avoid contamination and possible failure of the brake hydraulic system components.*

Removal

3 On all models except the Thunderbird and Tiger, remove the seat and right side panel as described in Chapter 8.

4 On Tiger models, unscrew the bolts securing the master cylinder cover to the frame and remove the cover **(see illustration)**.

5 Peel back the rubber cover and disconnect the brake light switch wiring from the switch on top of the master cylinder **(see illustration)**. Unscrew the brake light switch and, on all models except the Thunderbird and Tiger, the brake hose banjo bolt, noting the alignment of the hose union, and remove from the cylinder. Discard the sealing washers as new ones must be fitted. Wrap the end of the hose in a clean rag to prevent fluid spills and system contamination.

6 Remove the split pin or clip and withdraw the clevis pin which secures the master cylinder pushrod to the brake pedal **(see illustration)**.

7 Remove the screw securing the master cylinder fluid reservoir, then unscrew the reservoir cap and pour the fluid into a container **(see illustration)**.

8 Remove the bolts securing the master cylinder and cover (not Tiger model) to the frame, and remove the master cylinder assembly **(see illustration)**.

9 Separate the fluid reservoir hose from the elbow on the master cylinder by releasing the hose clamp.

Overhaul

10 Dislodge the rubber dust boot from the base of the master cylinder to reveal the pushrod retaining circlip **(see illustration)**.

11 Depress the pushrod and, using circlip pliers, remove the circlip. Slide out the piston assembly and spring. Lay the parts out in the proper order to prevent confusion during reassembly. Triumph advise that the circlip and piston seals be replaced with new ones when disturbed.

12 Clean all of the parts with clean brake fluid or denatured alcohol. *Caution: Do not, under any circumstances, use a petroleum-based solvent to clean brake parts. If compressed air is available, use it to dry the parts thoroughly (make sure it's filtered and unlubricated).*

13 Check the master cylinder bore for corrosion, scratches, nicks and score marks. If damage is evident, the master cylinder must be replaced with a new one. If the master

8.3 Rear brake disc mounting bolts

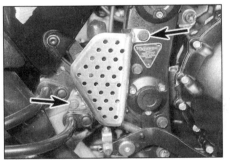

9.4 Remove two retaining bolts (arrowed) and remove the master cylinder cover

9.5 Remove the brake light switch cover and disconnect the wiring

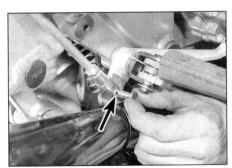

9.6 Remove the clevis pin (arrowed) to release the pushrod from the brake pedal

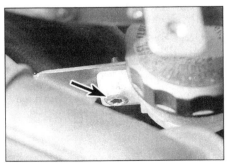

9.7 The reservoir is located behind the left side air duct and is secured to the frame by a screw (arrowed)

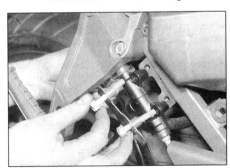

9.8 Remove the two bolts to release the master cylinder from the frame

9.10 Rear brake master cylinder detail (all models except Thunderbird and Tiger)

1 Split pin
2 Clevis pin
3 Reservoir hose
4 Pushrod
5 Rubber boot
6 Circlip
7 Piston assembly
8 Spring
9 Master cylinder
10 Brake light switch
11 Reservoir

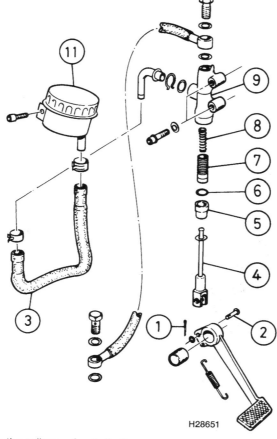

H28651

cylinder is in poor condition, then the caliper should be checked as well.

14 If required, the fluid reservoir hose elbow can be detached from the master cylinder once the circlip has been removed. Discard the O-ring as a new one must be fitted on installation. Inspect the reservoir hose for cracks or splits and replace if necessary.

15 Before reassembling the master cylinder, soak the piston and its new seals in clean brake fluid for 10 or 15 minutes. Lubricate the master cylinder bore with clean brake fluid, then carefully insert the parts in the reverse order of disassembly, ensuring the tapered end of the spring is facing the piston. Make sure the lips on the cup seals do not turn inside out when they are slipped into the bore.

16 Install and depress the pushrod, then install a new circlip, making sure it is properly seated in the groove.

17 Install the rubber dust boot, making sure the lip is seated properly in the groove.

18 If removed, fit a new O-ring to the fluid reservoir hose elbow and retain the elbow to the master cylinder with the circlip. Reconnect the fluid reservoir hose and secure with its clip.

Installation

19 Install the mounting bolts through the cover (not Tiger model) and master cylinder and attach the assembly to the frame, tightening the bolts to the specified torque setting **(see illustration 9.8)**.

20 Secure the fluid reservoir to the frame with its screw. Ensure the hose between the master cylinder and reservoir is correctly routed and secured by clamps at each end. If the clamps have weakened, use new ones.

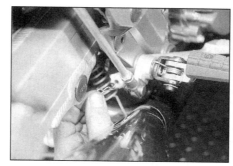

9.23 Fit a new split pin to secure the clevis pin

21 On all models except the Thunderbird and Tiger, connect the brake hose banjo bolt to the top of the master cylinder, using a new sealing washer on each side of the banjo union. Ensure that the hose is positioned at the correct angle and tighten the banjo bolt to the specified torque setting. Using a new sealing washer, screw the brake light switch into the banjo bolt and tighten to the specified torque setting. Reconnect the brake light switch wires and slip the rubber cover into place.

22 On Thunderbird and Tiger models, position the brake hose banjo union on the top of the master cylinder, using a new sealing washer on each side of it. Ensure that the hose is positioned at the correct angle and screw the brake light switch into place, tightening it to the specified torque setting. Reconnect the brake light switch wires and slip the rubber cover into place.

23 On all models, align the brake pedal with the master cylinder pushrod clevis and slide in the clevis pin. Secure the clevis pin with a new split pin **(see illustration)**.

24 If the clevis position on the pushrod was disturbed during overhaul, the brake pedal height should be reset. On Thunderbird and Tiger models, adjustment is made via the locknut and adjusting nut on the clevis; peel up the gaiter (Thunderbird only) on the threaded pushrod to access the adjuster nut and tighten the locknut when adjustment is complete **(see illustration)**. On all other models, slacken the locknut at the top of the clevis and rotate the pushrod to make adjustment; tighten the locknut when complete.

> ⚠ **Warning: The master cylinder pushrod must have at least 10 mm of thread engaged in the clevis.**

25 Fill the fluid reservoir with the specified fluid (see Chapter 1) and bleed the system following the procedure in Section 11.

26 On Tiger models, fit the master cylinder cover.

27 Check the operation of the brake carefully before riding the motorcycle. Ensure that the pedal height is a comfortable distance below the top of the footrest, and if necessary readjust as described in Step 24.

7

9.24 On Thunderbird and Tiger, pedal height adjustment is made at clevis

10 Brake hoses and unions - inspection and replacement

Inspection

1 Brake hose condition should be checked regularly and the hoses replaced at the specified interval (see Chapter 1).

2 Twist and flex the rubber hoses while looking for cracks, bulges and seeping fluid. Check extra carefully around the areas where the hoses connect with the banjo fittings, as these are common areas for hose failure.

3 Inspect the metal banjo fittings connected to the brake hoses. If the fittings are rusted, scratched or cracked, replace them.

Replacement

4 The brake hoses have banjo union fittings on each end. Cover the surrounding area with plenty of rags and unscrew the banjo bolt on each end of the hose. Detach the hose from any clips that may be present and remove the hose. Discard the sealing washers.

5 Position the new hose, making sure it isn't twisted or otherwise strained, and abut the tab on the hose union with the lug on the component casting. Install the banjo bolts, using new sealing washers on both sides of the unions, and tighten them to the torque setting specified at the beginning of this Chapter. Make sure they are correctly aligned and routed clear of all moving components.

6 Flush the old brake fluid from the system, refill with the recommended fluid (see Chapter 1) and bleed the air from the system (see Section 11). Check the operation of the brakes carefully before riding the motorcycle.

11 Brake system bleeding

1 Bleeding the brakes is simply the process of removing all the air bubbles from the brake fluid reservoirs, the hoses and the brake calipers. Bleeding is necessary whenever a brake system hydraulic connection is loosened, when a component or hose is replaced, or when the master cylinder or caliper is overhauled. Leaks in the system may also allow air to enter, but leaking brake fluid will reveal their presence and warn you of the need for repair.

2 To bleed the brakes, you will need some new, clean brake fluid of the recommended type (see Chapter 1), a length of clear vinyl or plastic tubing, a small container partially filled with clean brake fluid, some rags and a spanner to fit the brake caliper bleed valves.

3 Cover the fuel tank and other painted components to prevent damage in the event that brake fluid is spilled.

4 If the front brake lever is equipped with a span adjuster, set it to position No. 1.

5 If bleeding the rear brake, remove the right side panel and pull off the air intake duct for access to the fluid reservoir.

6 Remove the reservoir cap/cover and diaphragm and slowly pump the brake lever or pedal a few times, until no air bubbles can be seen floating up from the holes in the bottom of the reservoir. Doing this bleeds the air from the master cylinder end of the line. Loosely refit the reservoir cap/cover.

7 Pull the dust cap off the bleed valve. Attach one end of the clear vinyl or plastic tubing to the bleed valve and submerge the other end in the brake fluid in the container.

8 Remove the reservoir cap/cover and check the fluid level. Do not allow the fluid level to drop below the lower mark during the bleeding process.

9 Carefully pump the brake lever or pedal three or four times and hold it in (front) or down (rear) while opening the caliper bleed valve. When the valve is opened, brake fluid will flow out of the caliper into the clear tubing and the lever will move toward the handlebar or the pedal will move down.

10 Retighten the bleed valve (note the torque setting in the Specifications of this Chapter), then release the brake lever or pedal gradually. Repeat the process until no air bubbles are visible in the brake fluid leaving the caliper and the lever or pedal is firm when applied. Disconnect the bleeding equipment and install the dust cap on the bleed valve.

11 Install the diaphragm and cap/cover assembly, wipe up any spilled brake fluid and check the entire system for leaks.

12 Where applicable, return the front brake lever span adjuster to its original position.

> **HAYNES HiNT** *If it's not possible to produce a firm feel to the lever or pedal the fluid may be aerated. Let the brake fluid in the system stabilise for a few hours and then repeat the procedure when the tiny bubbles in the system have settled out.*

12 Wheels - inspection and repair

1 In order to carry out a proper inspection of the wheels, it is necessary to support the bike upright so that the wheel being inspected is raised off the ground. Position the motorcycle on its centre stand or an auxiliary stand. Clean the wheels thoroughly to remove mud and dirt that may interfere with the inspection procedure or mask defects. Make a general check of the wheels and tyres as described in Chapter 1.

2 Attach a dial indicator to the fork slider or the swingarm and position its stem against the side of the rim **(see illustration)**. Spin the wheel slowly and check the side-to-side (axial) runout of the rim. In order to accurately

check radial runout with the dial indicator, the wheel would have to be removed from the machine. With the axle clamped in a vice, the wheel can be rotated to check the runout.

3 An easier, though slightly less accurate, method is to attach a stiff wire pointer to the fork slider or the swingarm and position the end a fraction of an inch from the wheel (where the wheel and tyre join). If the wheel is true, the distance from the pointer to the rim will be constant as the wheel is rotated. **Note:** *If wheel runout is excessive, check the wheel bearings very carefully before replacing the wheel.*

4 The wheels should also be visually inspected for cracks, flat spots on the rim and other damage. On all cast alloy wheels, look very closely for dents in the area where the tyre bead contacts the rim. Dents in this area may prevent complete sealing of the tyre against the rim, which leads to deflation of the tyre over a period of time. If damage is evident, or if runout in either direction is excessive, the wheel will have to be replaced with a new one. Never attempt to repair a damaged cast alloy wheel.

5 On spoked wheels, check for loose or broken spokes as described in Chapter 1. Spoke tensioning must be carried out by a wheel building specialist.

13 Wheels - alignment check

1 Misalignment of the wheels, which may be due to a cocked rear wheel or a bent frame or fork yokes, can cause strange and possibly

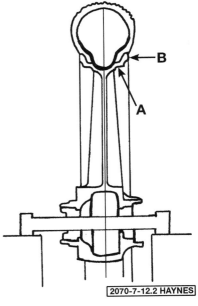

12.2 Use a dial indicator to measure wheel runout

A Radial runout   B Axial runout

serious handling problems. This is clearly dangerous. If the frame or yokes are at fault, repair by a frame specialist or replacement with new parts are the only alternatives. Check first that the rear wheel is correctly aligned in the swingarm (refer to the alignment check under the drive chain adjustment procedure in Chapter 1).

2 To check the alignment you will need an assistant, a length of string or a perfectly straight piece of wood and a ruler. A plumb bob or other suitable weight will also be required.

3 In order to make a proper check of the wheels it is necessary to support the bike in an upright position, either on its centre stand (where equipped) or on an auxiliary stand. Measure the width of both tyres at their widest points. Subtract the smaller measurement from the larger measurement, then divide the difference by two. The result is the amount of offset that should exist between the front and rear tyres on both sides.

4 If a string is used, have your assistant hold one end of it about halfway between the floor and the rear axle, touching the rear sidewall of the tyre.

5 Run the other end of the string forward and pull it tight so that it is roughly parallel to the floor. Slowly bring the string into contact with the front sidewall of the rear tyre, then turn the front wheel until it is parallel with the string. Measure the distance from the front tyre sidewall to the string.

6 Repeat the procedure on the other side of the motorcycle. The distance from the front tyre sidewall to the string should be equal on both sides.

7 As was previously pointed out, a perfectly straight length of wood may be substituted for the string. The checking procedure is the same.

8 If the distance between the string and tyre is greater on one side, or if the rear wheel appears to be cocked, refer to Chapter 6, *"Swingarm bearings - check"*, and make sure the swingarm is tight.

9 If the front-to-back alignment is correct, it's possible that the wheels still may be out of alignment vertically.

10 Using the plumb bob, or other suitable weight, and a length of string, check the rear wheel to make sure that it is vertical. To do this, hold the string against the tyre upper sidewall and allow the weight to settle so that it is just off the floor. When the string touches both the upper and lower tyre sidewalls and is perfectly straight, the wheel is vertical. If it is not, place thin spacers under one leg of the stand.

11 Once the rear wheel is vertical, check the front wheel in the same manner. If both wheels are not perfectly vertical, the frame and/or major suspension components are bent.

14.3 Remove the speedometer cable retaining screw and withdraw the cable

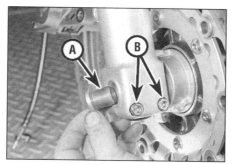

14.4b Unscrew the axle bolt (A), and loosen the axle clamp bolts (B)

14 Front wheel - removal and installation

Removal

1 Where equipped, position the motorcycle on its centre stand and support it under the crankcase so that the front wheel is off the ground; use an auxiliary stand on models not equipped with a centre stand. Always make sure the motorcycle is properly supported.

2 Remove the brake caliper mounting bolts and slide the caliper(s) off the disc(s). Support each caliper with a piece of wire or a bungee cord so that no strain is placed on its hydraulic hose. There is no need to disconnect the brake hose from the caliper(s).

3 Remove the speedometer cable retaining screw on the right side of the wheel hub (left side on Thunderbird and Tiger) and detach the cable from its drive unit **(see illustration)**.

4 On Tiger models, remove the domed nut and washer from the wheel axle **(see illustration)**. On all other models, remove the axle bolt and loosen the four axle clamp bolts **(see illustration)**.

5 Support the wheel, then withdraw the axle and carefully lower the wheel **(see illustration)**.

6 Remove the spacer from the left side of the wheel (right side on Tiger models), and the speedometer drive from the right side (left side on Thunderbird and Tiger). *Caution: Don't lay the wheel down and allow it to rest on one of the discs - the disc could*

14.4a On Tiger the axle is secured by a domed nut

14.5 Support the wheel and withdraw the axle

become warped. Set the wheel on wood blocks so the disc doesn't support the weight of the wheel. Note: Do not operate the front brake lever with the wheel removed.

7 Check the axle for straightness by rolling it on a flat surface such as a piece of plate glass (first wipe off all old grease and remove any corrosion using fine emery cloth). If the axle is bent, replace it.

8 Check the condition of the wheel bearings (see Section 16).

Installation

9 Fit the speedometer drive to the wheel's right side (left on Thunderbird and Tiger), aligning its drive gear slots with the driveplate tabs **(see illustration)**.

10 Apply a smear of grease to the outer surface of the spacer (where it contacts the

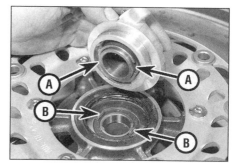

14.9 Align the slots in the speedometer drive gear (A) with the tabs on the driveplate (B)

7

14.10 Fit the spacer into the wheel

14.12 Lug on speedometer drive must abut rear of lug on fork slider (arrowed)

14.15a Tighten the axle bolt to the specified torque setting

14.15b Tighten the axle clamp bolts on both fork sliders to the specified torque

14.17a Pass the speedometer cable through its guide . . .

14.17b . . . and connect it to the speedometer drive

grease seal) and install the spacer in the left side of the wheel (right side on Thunderbird and Tiger) **(see illustration)**.

11 Manoeuvre the wheel into position. Apply a thin coat of grease to the axle.

12 Lift the wheel into position making sure the spacer remains in place. Position the speedometer drive lug against the rear of the lug on the fork slider **(see illustration)**.

13 Slide the axle into position from the right side on Tiger models. On all other models, slide it in from the left side.

14 On Tiger models, install the washer and domed axle nut. Tighten the nut to the specified torque setting.

15 On models except the Tiger, install the axle bolt and tighten it to the specified torque setting **(see illustration)**. Make sure the groove in the axle head aligns with the outside of the fork slider. Tighten all four axle clamp

bolts to the specified torque setting **(see illustration)**.

16 Install the brake calipers making sure the pads sit squarely on either side of the disc. Fit the caliper mounting bolts and tighten them to the torque setting specified at the beginning of this Chapter.

17 Pass the speedometer cable through its guide, then connect the cable to the drive, aligning the inner cable slot with the drive dog, and securely tighten its retaining screw **(see illustrations)**.

18 Apply the front brake a few times to bring the pads back into contact with the disc(s). Move the motorcycle off its stand, apply the front brake and pump the front forks a few times to settle all components in position. Check for correct operation of the front brake before riding the motorcycle.

15 Rear wheel - removal and installation

Removal

1 Position the motorcycle on its centre stand. On models without a centre stand, use an auxiliary stand to hold the motorcycle upright and the rear wheel off the ground. Always make sure the bike is properly supported.

2 Unscrew the bolts securing the chainguard and remove it from the swingarm.

3 Remove the spring clips on each end of the axle **(see illustration)**. Remove the axle bolt from the right side **(see illustration)**.

4 Support the wheel, then slide out the axle and lower the wheel down **(see illustration)**. Depending on the type of brake caliper fitted,

15.3a Remove the spring clip from each end of the axle . . .

15.3b . . . and unscrew the axle bolt from the right side

15.4 Support the wheel and withdraw the axle

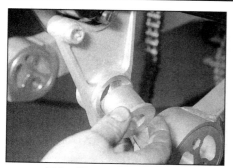

15.8a Fit the spacer into the brake caliper bracket . . .

15.8b . . . and the wheel spacers into each side of the wheel

15.11 Tighten the axle bolt to the specified torque

the caliper/torque arm assembly should be raised or lowered to ease wheel removal.

5 Disengage the chain from the sprocket and remove the wheel from the swingarm. Note which spacer fits on which side of the wheel, and remove them from the wheel. Also note, and take care not to lose, the spacer in the brake caliper bracket. *Caution: Do not lay the wheel down and allow it to rest on the disc or the sprocket - they could become warped. Set the wheel on wood blocks so that neither component supports the weight of the wheel. Do not operate the brake pedal with the wheel removed.*

6 Check the axle for straightness by rolling it on a flat surface such as a piece of plate glass (first wipe off all old grease and remove any corrosion using fine emery cloth). If the axle is bent, replace it.

7 Check the condition of the wheel bearings (see Section 16).

Installation

8 Apply a thin coat of grease to the seal lips, then slide the spacers into their proper positions on both sides of the hub. Fit the spacer in the caliper bracket, making sure it is fitted the right way round **(see illustrations)**.

9 Apply a thin coat of grease to the axle.

10 Engage the drive chain with the sprocket and lift the wheel into position. Make sure both spacers remain in the wheel and that the disc fits correctly in the caliper, with the brake pads sitting squarely on each side of the disc, when the caliper assembly is moved down or up into position (as applicable).

11 Slacken the chain adjuster clamp bolts and rotate the adjusters via the Allen key slots so that the wheel axle hole is positioned further forward in the swingarm - this will relax chain tension and allow easy insertion of the axle. Slide the axle fully into position from the left side, making sure that it passes through the caliper mounting bracket. Synchronise each chain adjuster so that its index mark aligns with the same mark on each side of the swingarm, then tighten the adjuster clamp bolts - this will ensure correct wheel alignment when the axle is later tightened. Fit the axle bolt and tighten it to the specified torque setting **(see illustration)**. Fit new spring clips to both ends of the axle **(see illustration 15.3a)**.

12 Install the chainguard.

13 Apply the rear brake a few times to bring the pads back into contact with the disc. Move the motorcycle off its stand.

14 Adjust drive chain freeplay as described in Chapter 1.

15 Check for correct operation of the rear brake before riding the motorcycle.

16 Wheel bearings - removal, inspection and installation

Front wheel bearings

Note: *Always replace the wheel bearings in pairs. Never replace the bearings individually. Avoid using a high pressure cleaner on the wheel bearing area.*

1 Remove the wheel (see Section 14).

2 Set the wheel on blocks so as not to allow the weight of the wheel to rest on the brake discs.

3 Using a flat-bladed screwdriver, prise out the grease seals from both sides of the wheel **(see illustrations)**.

4 Withdraw the speedometer driveplate from the right side of the wheel (left side on Thunderbird and Tiger), noting how it fits. Remove the circlip from the other side of the wheel **(see illustration)**.

5 Using a metal rod (preferably a brass drift punch) inserted through the centre of the hub

THUNDERBIRD

TIGER

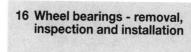

H28652

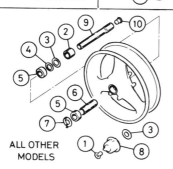

ALL OTHER MODELS

16.3a Front wheel detail

1 Axle bolt	*5 Bearing*	*9 Axle*
2 Spacer	*6 Spacer*	*10 Cap*
3 Grease seal	*7 Speedometer driveplate*	*11 Washer*
4 Circlip	*8 Speedometer drive gear*	*12 Domed nut*

7

16.3b Prise out the grease seal using a flat-bladed screwdriver

16.4 Remove the circlip from the wheel

16.5 Drift the first wheel bearing out using a metal rod passed through from the opposite side of the wheel

bearing, tap evenly around the inner race of the opposite bearing to drive it from the hub **(see illustration)**. The bearing spacer will also come out.

6 Lay the wheel on its other side and remove the other bearing using the same technique.

7 If the bearings are of the unsealed type or are only sealed on one side, clean them with a high flash-point solvent (one which won't leave any residue) and blow them dry with compressed air (don't let the bearings spin as you dry them). Apply a few drops of oil to the bearing. **Note:** *If the bearing is sealed on both sides don't attempt to clean it.*

8 Hold the outer race of the bearing and rotate the inner race - if the bearing doesn't turn smoothly, has rough spots or is noisy, replace it with a new one.

9 If the bearing is good and can be re-used, wash it in solvent once again and dry it, then pack the bearing with high-quality wheel bearing grease.

10 Thoroughly clean the hub area of the wheel. Install a bearing into the recess in the hub, with the marked or sealed side facing outwards. Using a bearing driver or a socket large enough to contact the outer race of the bearing, drive it in until it's completely seated **(see illustrations)**.

11 Turn the wheel over and install the bearing spacer **(see illustration)**. Drive the other bearing into place as described above.

12 Fit the speedometer driveplate to the right side of the wheel (left side on Thunderbird and Tiger); ensure its locating tangs are correctly located in the hub slots **(see illustration)**. Fit

the circlip to the other side of the wheel, making sure it is properly seated in its groove.

13 Install new grease seals, using a seal driver, large socket or a flat piece of wood to drive them into place **(see illustrations)**.

14 Clean off all traces of grease from the brake disc(s) using acetone or brake system cleaner, then install the wheel as described in Section 14.

Sprocket coupling bearing

15 Remove the rear wheel as described in Section 15 and remove the spacer from the left side of the wheel **(see illustration)**.

16 Lift the sprocket coupling away from the wheel leaving the rubber dampers in position in the wheel. Remove the spacer from the inside of the coupling bearing **(see illustration)**.

16.10a Install the bearing with the marked or sealed side facing out . . .

16.10b . . . then drive the bearing squarely into the hub using a drift or socket which bears only on the bearing's outer race

16.11 Install the spacer into the wheel before fitting the other bearing

16.12 Fit speedometer driveplate to the left side of wheel, making sure its tangs are seated in the hub slots (arrowed) . . .

16.13a . . . then press in a new grease seal . . .

16.13b . . . and drift it squarely into position using a suitably sized drift or socket

16.15 Rear wheel detail

1 Spring clip
2 Axle bolt
3 Washer
4 Brake caliper bracket spacer
5 Spacer
6 Grease seal
7 Circlip
8 Bearing
9 Spacer
10 O-ring carrier
11 O-ring
12 Rubber damper
13 Sprocket coupling
14 Spacer
15 Sprocket
16 Spacer
17 Axle

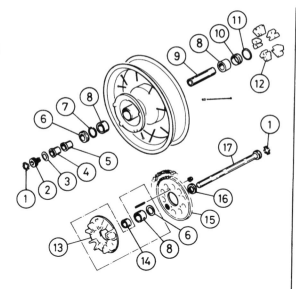

THUNDERBIRD AND TIGER

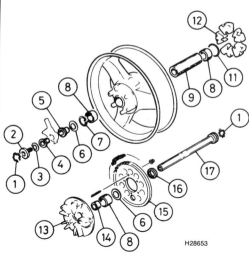

ALL OTHER MODELS

H28653

17 Prise out the grease seal from the outside of the coupling **(see illustration)**.
18 Support the coupling on blocks of wood and drive the bearing out from the inside with a bearing driver or socket **(see illustration)**.
19 Inspect the bearing as described above in Steps 7 through 9.
20 Thoroughly clean the bearing recess then install the bearing into the recess in the coupling, with the marked or sealed side facing out. Using a bearing driver or a socket large enough to contact the outer race of the bearing, drive it in until it's completely seated **(see illustration)**.
21 Install a new grease seal, using a seal driver, large socket or a flat piece of wood to drive it into place. Fit the spacer to the inside of the coupling bearing **(see illustration 16.16)**.
22 Apply a smear of grease to the hub O-ring and fit the sprocket coupling to the wheel **(see illustration)**.
23 Clean off all grease from the brake disc using acetone or brake system cleaner then install the wheel as described in Section 15.

Rear wheel bearings

Note: *Always replace the wheel bearings in pairs. Never replace the bearings individually. Avoid using a high pressure cleaner on the wheel bearing area.*
24 Remove the rear wheel as described in Section 15.
25 Lift the sprocket coupling away from the wheel leaving the rubber dampers in position

in the wheel. Take care not to lose the spacer from inside the sprocket coupling, and note how it fits **(see illustration 16.16)**.
26 Prise out the grease seal from the right side of the wheel and remove the circlip **(see illustrations)**.
27 Set the wheel on blocks so as not to allow the weight of the wheel to rest on the brake disc or sprocket.

16.16 Lift the sprocket coupling out of the wheel and remove the spacer

16.17 Lever out the seal - use a flat-bladed screwdriver if necessary

16.18 Support the coupling and drive the bearing out from the inside using a hammer and bearing driver or socket

16.20 Drive the new coupling bearing into position using a large tubular drift which bears only on the bearing's outer race

16.22 Ensure the hub O-ring (arrowed) is in position on the wheel and apply a smear of grease to it to aid installation

7

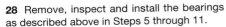

16.26a Lever out the seal - use a flat-bladed screwdriver if necessary . . .

16.26b . . . and remove the circlip

28 Remove, inspect and install the bearings as described above in Steps 5 through 11.

29 Fit the circlip to the right side of the wheel, making sure it is properly seated in its groove, and then install a new grease seal, using a seal driver, large socket or a flat piece of wood to drive it into place.

30 Install a new hub O-ring and smear it with grease **(see illustration 16.22)**. Fit the sprocket coupling to the wheel, making sure both the spacers are in position.

31 Clean off all grease from the brake disc

using acetone or brake system cleaner then install the wheel as described in Section 15.

17 Tyres - general information and fitting

General information

1 Thunderbird and Tiger models have tubed-type tyres, due to their spoked wheel design. All other models use tubeless tyres.

2 Refer to the "*Daily (pre-ride) checks*" listed at the beginning of this manual, and to the scheduled checks in Chapter 1 for tyre and wheel maintenance.

Fitting new tyres

3 When selecting new tyres, refer to the tyre information label on the drive chain guard and the tyre options listed in the owners handbook. Ensure that front and rear tyre types are compatible, the correct size and correct speed rating; if necessary seek advice from a Triumph dealer or tyre fitting specialist **(see illustration)**.

4 It is recommended that tyres are fitted by a motorcycle tyre specialist rather than attempted in the home workshop. This is particularly relevant in the case of tubeless tyres because the force required to break the seal between the wheel rim and tyre bead is substantial, and is usually beyond the capabilities of an individual working with normal tyre levers. Additionally, the specialist will be able to balance the wheels after tyre fitting.

5 Note that although punctured tyres can in some cases be repaired, Triumph do not recommend it.

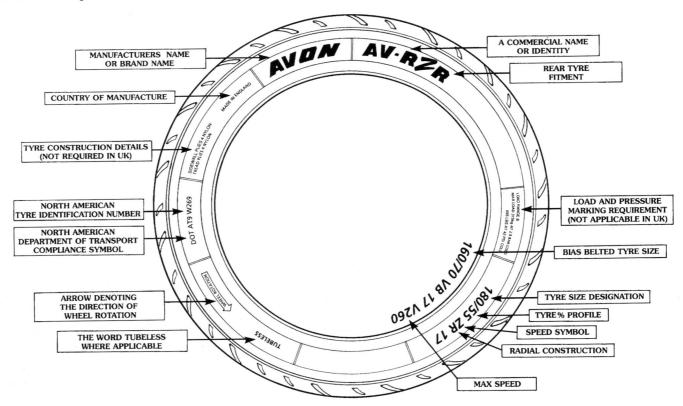

17.3 Common tyre sidewall markings

Chapter 8
Fairing and bodywork

Contents

Degrees of difficulty

Easy, suitable for novice with little experience	Fairly easy, suitable for beginner with some experience	Fairly difficult, suitable for competent DIY mechanic	Difficult, suitable for experienced DIY mechanic	Very difficult, suitable for expert DIY or professional

1 General information

This Chapter covers the procedures necessary to remove and install the fairing and other body parts. Since many service and repair operations on these motorcycles require the removal of the fairing and/or other body parts, the procedures are grouped here and referred to from other Chapters.

In the case of damage to the fairing or other body parts, it is usually necessary to remove the broken component and replace it with a new (or used) one. The material that the fairing and other body parts are composed of doesn't lend itself to conventional repair techniques. There are however some shops that specialise in "plastic welding", so it may be worthwhile seeking the advice of one of these specialists before consigning an expensive component to the bin. The Daytona Super III model has a carbon fibre front mudguard and fairing facia panels.

When attempting to remove any fairing panel, first study it closely, noting any fasteners and associated fittings, to be sure of returning everything to its correct place on installation. In most cases the aid of an assistant will be required when removing panels, to help avoid the risk of damage to paintwork. Once the evident fasteners have been removed, try to withdraw the panel as described but DO NOT FORCE IT - if it will not release, check that all fasteners have been removed and try again. Where a panel engages another by means of tabs, so it is careful not to break the tab or its mating slot or to damage the paintwork. Remember that a few moments of patience at this stage will save you a lot of money in replacing broken fairing panels!

When installing a fairing panel, first study it closely, noting any fasteners and associated

fittings removed with it, to be sure of returning everything to its correct place. Check that all fasteners are in good condition, including all trim nuts or clips and damping/rubber mounts; any of these must be replaced if faulty before the panel is reassembled. Check also that all mounting brackets are straight and repair or replace them if necessary before attempting to install the panel. Where assistance was required to remove a panel, make sure your assistant is on hand to install it.

Carefully settle the panel in place, following the instructions provided, and check that it engages correctly with its partners (where applicable) before tightening any of the fasteners. Where a panel engages another by means of tabs, be careful not to break the tab or its mating slot.

Tighten the fasteners securely, but be careful not to overtighten any of them or the panel may break (not always immediately) due to the uneven stress.

2 Fairing panels - removal and installation

Main fairing

Removal

Trophy and Daytona models

1 Remove the seat (Section 9) and disconnect the battery negative (-ve) terminal. Unscrew the screws securing both left and right side instrument facia panels to the fairing. Carefully raise the right side facia panel and disconnect the clock wiring, then remove the panels from the fairing, noting how they fit to each other, to the fairing, and around the instrument panel **(see illustrations)**.

2 Remove the front turn signal assemblies as described in Chapter 9.

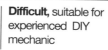

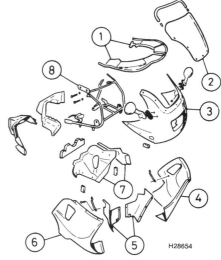

2.1a Fairing panel detail - Trophy and Daytona models

1 Facia panels
2 Windshield
3 Main fairing
4 Lower fairing panel (left)
5 Radiator ducts
6 Lower fairing panel (right)
7 Valve cover cowls
8 Fairing stay

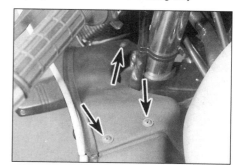

2.1b Instrument facia panels are secured by three screws (arrows) - Daytona shown

8

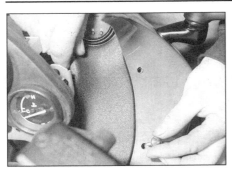

2.6a Unscrew the instrument facia panel retaining screws

2.6b Note how the facia panels join together

Note how the instrument facia fits against the front fairing panel and around the instruments.

12 Remove the screws securing each fairing side panel to the fuel tank and to the radiator bottom bracket, and carefully remove the panel **(see illustration)**.

Installation

13 Installation on all models is the reverse of removal. Make sure that all cables and wires are correctly routed and connected, and secured by any clips or ties. Reconnect the battery negative terminal. On completion, check the headlight aim as described in Chapter 9, and check that the turn signals, headlights and instruments all function correctly.

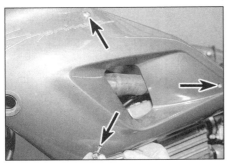

2.9 Unscrew the fairing mounting screws (arrowed)

2.10 Remove the fairing by carefully drawing it forwards from the bike

Lower fairing panels - Trophy and Daytona models

Removal

14 Where fitted, remove the screws securing the instrument facia panel to the lower fairing panel.

15 Unscrew the bolt securing the lower fairing panel bracket to the cylinder head. This bolt is accessed via the aperture in the panel **(see illustration)**..

16 Remove the screws securing the bottom of the lower fairing panel to the sub-frame **(see illustration)**.

17 On early models, unscrew the screws securing the left and right side radiator ducts to the oil cooler and to each other.

18 Remove the screws joining the lower

3 Unscrew the three screws securing each side of the fairing to the lower fairing panels **(see illustration 2.16)**. Where fitted, recover the nuts from these screws.

4 Remove the rear view mirrors as described in Section 4.

5 On Trophy models, move the fairing forward slightly if necessary and disconnect the headlight and sidelight wiring connectors. On all models, release any other wiring clips and cable guides and check that the fairing is free from all restraints. Carefully remove the fairing from the bike.

Sprint model

6 Remove the seat (Section 9) and disconnect the battery negative (-ve) terminal. Unscrew the screws securing both left and right side instrument facia panels to the fairing. Carefully raise the right side facia panel and disconnect the clock wiring, then remove the panels from the fairing, noting how they fit to each other, to the fairing, and around the instrument panel **(see illustrations)**.

7 Remove the front turn signal assemblies as described in Chapter 9.

8 Remove the rear view mirrors as described in Section 4.

9 Unscrew the three fairing mounting screws on each side of the fairing **(see illustration)**.

10 Release any other wiring clips and cable guides and check that the fairing is free from all restraints. Carefully remove the fairing by drawing it forwards from the bike **(see illustration)**.

Tiger model

11 Remove the eleven screws (four on each

side, and three along the bottom) securing the fairing front panel to the fairing side panels, and remove the front panel **(see illustration)**.

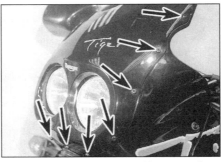

2.11 The fairing front panel is secured to the fairing side panels by a total of eleven screws - see text (arrowed)

2.15 Lower panel bracket-to-cylinder head bolt is accessed through aperture

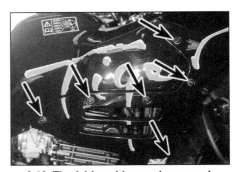

2.12 The fairing side panels are each secured to the tank by five screws, and to the radiator bottom bracket by one screw

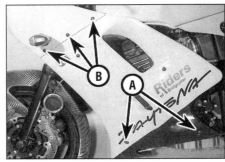

2.16 Lower panel fixings to sub-frame (A) and to main fairing (B)

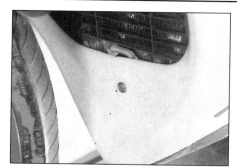

2.18a Lower panels are joined together by a single screw at the front . . .

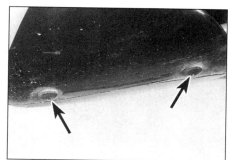

2.18b . . . and by two screws at the bottom

2 On Trident, Speed Triple, Thunderbird and Tiger models, simply unscrew the mirror from its mounting on the handlebar.

Installation

3 Installation is the reverse of removal. Make sure the components are fitted in the correct order.

5 Fairing stay - removal and installation

Removal

1 Remove the main fairing and the lower fairing panels (Trophy and Daytona models) as described in Section 2.
2 Remove the headlight assembly as described in Chapter 9.
3 Remove the instrument cluster as described in Chapter 9.
4 Disconnect and remove the horns as described in Chapter 9.
5 On Tiger models, remove the turn signals as described in Chapter 9.
6 Unscrew the radiator top mounting bolts.
7 Note the routing of all the wiring and cables, and release them from any ties or clips necessary, noting their positions.
8 Unscrew the two bolts securing the fairing stay to the frame headstock and carefully remove the stay, taking care not to snag any wiring (see illustration).

Installation

9 Installation is the reverse of removal. Make sure that the wiring and cables are correctly routed and secured with ties and clips as required.

6 Side panels - removal and installation

Removal

Thunderbird model

1 Remove the seat as described in Section 9.
2 Remove the screw securing the bottom of

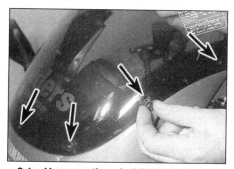

3.1a Unscrew the windshield fasteners (arrowed) - Sprint shown

3.1b Tiger windshield fasteners (arrowed)

fairing panels to each other at the bottom and on the underside of the panels (see illustrations).
19 Support the lower fairing panel, then remove the screws securing the panel to the main fairing and carefully remove the panel (see illustration). Where fitted, recover the nuts from these screws.

Installation

20 Installation is the reverse of removal.

3 Windshield - removal and installation

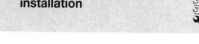

Removal

1 Remove the fasteners securing the windshield to the upper fairing assembly,

noting how they fit, then lift the windshield away from the bike (see illustrations).

Installation

2 Installation is the reverse of removal. Make sure the fasteners are correctly and securely fitted.

4 Rear view mirrors - removal and installation

Removal

1 On Trophy, Daytona and Sprint models, remove the caps from the nuts securing the mirror to the upper fairing assembly. Unscrew the nuts, then carefully remove the mirror along with its mounting pad (see illustrations).

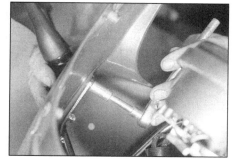

4.1a Unscrew the two nuts from inside of the main fairing . . .

4.1b . . . and remove the mirror

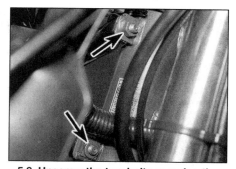

5.8 Unscrew the two bolts securing the fairing stay to the frame (arrowed)

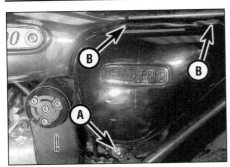

6.2 Thunderbird side panel has a screw (A) and fits over two lugs (B) on top frame rail

6.6a Unscrew the bolts securing the grab rail

6.6b Later Sprint model grab rail fixings (arrows)

6.7a The taillight assembly is secured by two nuts (arrowed)

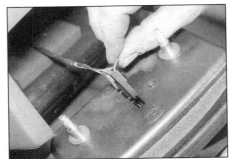

6.7b Disconnect the taillight wiring connectors

---

7 Front mudguard - removal and installation

Removal

Thunderbird model

1 Remove the four bolts securing the mudguard to the inside of the fork sliders (if they can't be withdrawn fully with the wheel in place, remove the front wheel as described in Chapter 7). Carefully remove the mudguard by drawing it forwards through the forks. Note

the side panel to the frame, taking care not to lose the sleeve and noting how it fits, then lift the side panel clear of its two mounting lugs on the frame top rail **(see illustration)**. Check the condition of the two rubber mounting grommets and replace them if necessary.

Tiger model

3 Remove the seat as described in Section 9.
4 Remove the three screws securing the side panel and carefully remove the panel, noting how it fits.

All other models

5 Remove the seat as described in Section 9.
6 Remove the two bolts securing the grab rail and lift it clear (not applicable to Daytona or Speed Triple models when using the seat hump) **(see illustration)**. Note that later Sprint models (from VIN 16922) have two grab rails, each secured by two bolts **(see illustration)**.
7 Unscrew the two nuts securing the taillight assembly, noting the order of the washers, then withdraw the assembly a little way and disconnect the wiring connectors, noting their positions **(see illustrations)**.
8 Unscrew the four screws securing the top cover to the side panels and remove the cover **(see illustrations)**.
9 Remove the screw securing the side panel to the frame **(see illustration)**.
10 The side panel has four lugs which fit into rubber grommets on the frame **(see illustration)**. Gently ease the side panel outwards to release it from the grommets.
11 The above procedure details separate removal of the right and left side panels. However, if care is taken not to overstress the

plastic, both side panels and top cover can be removed as an assembly without disturbing the taillight.

Installation

12 Installation is the reverse of removal.

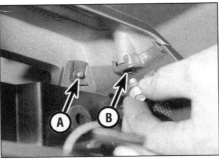

6.8a Remove screw at front (A) and bolt at the rear (B) on each side of top cover . . .

6.9 Remove the screw securing the side panel to the frame

6.8b . . . and lift the top cover away

6.10 Gently ease the lugs (arrowed) out of their mounting grommets

7.3a The mudguard is secured on each side by two bolts at the top . . .

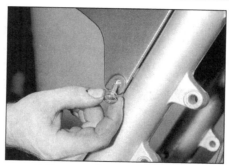

7.3b . . . and one at the bottom

that the rear left mudguard bolt also secures the brake hose guide. On US models, both rear bolts retain the reflector mounting brackets.

Tiger model

2 Unscrew the bolts securing the mudguard side panels to the mudguard and the forks. Remove the side panels, then carefully remove the mudguard by drawing it forwards through the forks.

All other models

3 Remove the speedometer cable retaining screw on the right side of the wheel hub and withdraw the cable, slipping it through the guide on the mudguard **(see illustration 14.3 in Chapter 7)**. Unscrew the bolts securing the mudguard to the forks, noting the positions of the brake hose clamps on the upper mountings and the rubber washers on the lower mountings **(see illustrations)**.

Installation

4 Installation is the reverse of removal. Make sure the speedometer cable and brake hoses are correctly routed and secured by their clamps. On Daytona Super III models, the front mudguard is made of carbon-fibre; take care not to crack or overstress this material.

---

8 Rear mudguard - removal and installation

Frame-mounted mudguard - all models

Removal

Thunderbird

1 Remove the seat as described in Section 9.
2 Unscrew the bolts securing the mudflap at the front of the mudguard to the swingarm **(see Chapter 6, illustration 14.8)**.
3 Disconnect the wiring to the rear turn signals, taillight assembly and licence plate light. Release the wiring from any clips or ties on the mudguard.
4 Unscrew the nuts securing the taillight assembly to the mudguard, noting the positions of the sleeves and grommets, and remove the assembly.

5 Remove the rear turn signals as described in Chapter 9.
6 Unscrew the bolts securing the mudguard to the frame, and carefully remove the mudguard.

All other models

7 Remove the seat as described in Section 9 and the side panels as described in Section 6.
8 Remove the coolant reservoir as described in Chapter 3.
9 Unscrew the two nuts securing the taillight assembly, noting the order of the washers, then withdraw the assembly a little way and disconnect the wiring connectors, noting their positions **(see illustrations 6.7a and 6.7b)**.
10 Disconnect the wiring connectors from the rear turn signal assemblies.
11 Remove the igniter from its mounts and disconnect it at the connector block (not applicable to Tiger models) **(see Chapter 5, illustrations 5.2 and 5.3)**.
12 Disconnect the fusebox wiring connector, then unscrew the fusebox mounting bolts and remove it from the mudguard **(see illustration)**.
13 Disconnect the turn signal relay wiring connectors, then release the relay from its clamp **(see illustration 8.12)**.
14 Release the wire clips from the mudguard **(see illustration)**.
15 Unscrew the bolts securing the mudflap at the front of the mudguard to the swingarm **(see Chapter 6, illustration 14.8)**. Unscrew the six rear mudguard mounting bolts located underneath, noting how the sleeves and grommets fit. Lower the mudguard and carefully draw it back away from the machine, taking care not to snag any wiring.

Installation

16 Installation is the reverse of removal. Make sure that all wires are correctly reconnected and routed, and test the turn signals, rear light and brake light before riding the bike.

Swingarm-mounted mudguard - Speed Triple and later Daytona models

Removal

17 On all Speed Triple models and Daytona models from VIN 9083 (including the Super III), the chainguard is integral with a swingarm-mounted mudguard. Remove the two screws from the chainguard, the single screw from the rear of the mudguard, followed by the two throughbolts and nuts which secure the mudguard to the front of the swingarm. Carefully withdraw the mudguard from the swingarm.

Installation

18 Installation is the reverse of removal. On Daytona Super III models, the mudguard is made of carbon-fibre; take care not to crack or overstress this material.

---

9 Seat - removal and installation

Seat

Removal

1 Insert the ignition key into the seat lock and unlock the seat. On Thunderbird models, the seat lock is located in the left side cover. On Tiger models the lock is located on the left-hand side of the seat end cover, underneath the luggage rack. On all other models the seat lock is located in the left-hand side silencer carrier.
2 Lift the rear of the seat and draw it back and away from the bike. Note how the tab at the front of the seat locates under the tank mounting bracket, and also how the two brackets locate under the frame rail **(see illustrations)**.

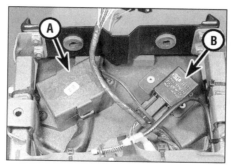

8.12 Fusebox (A) and turn signal relay (B) locations on rear mudguard

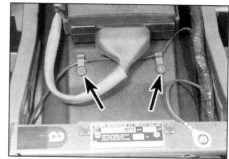

8.14 Release the two wiring clips from the mudguard (arrowed)

8

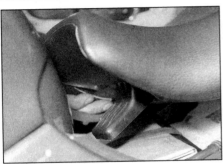

9.2a Locate the tab at the front of the seat under the tank . . .

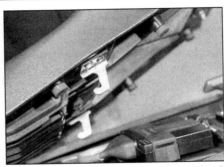

9.2b . . . and the brackets in the middle of the seat under the frame rail

3 The seat locking device is mounted to the frame rail under the seat, and is connected to the lock by a cable. Check that the locking device works smoothly and apply some general purpose grease to the moving parts.

Installation

4 Locate the tab at the front of the seat under the fuel tank mounting bracket. Align the seat at the rear and push down on it to engage it with the lock.

Single seat conversion

Removal

5 The single seat conversion hump is fitted as standard to the Daytona Super III and can be fitted as an option on the Speed Triple and other Daytona models.

6 To remove the hump from the seat, unscrew the two bolts securing the sides of the hump to the seat, then lift the hump up at the front and draw it back from the seat. Note how the hump locates under the rear edge of the seat. When the hump is not fitted, fit the trim to the end cover, then install the grab rail and tighten its mounting bolts securely.

Installation

7 Open the seat and remove the grab rail and trim. Locate the rear edge of the hump under the rear edge of the seat, and drop the front of the hump down so that its mounting holes align correctly. Install the bolts and tighten them securely.

Chapter 9
Electrical system

Contents

Degrees of difficulty

| Easy, suitable for novice with little experience | | Fairly easy, suitable for beginner with some experience | | Fairly difficult, suitable for competent DIY mechanic | | Difficult, suitable for experienced DIY mechanic | | Very difficult, suitable for expert DIY or professional | |

Specifications

Battery
Capacity 12V, 14Ah

Alternator
Rating 12V, 25A
Regulated voltage . . . . 14.5 volts @ 5500 rpm
Stator coil resistance . . . . 1.0 ohm maximum
Brush length
   New . . . . 10.5 mm
   Service limit . . . . 4.5 mm
Slip ring diameter
   New . . . . 14.4 mm
   Service limit . . . . 14.0 mm

Starter motor
Brush length
   New . . . . 12.0 mm
   Service limit . . . . 8.5 mm
Commutator diameter
   New . . . . 28.0 mm
   Service limit . . . . 27.0 mm
Commutator groove depth
   New . . . . 0.7 mm
   Service limit . . . . 0.2 mm

Fusebox fuses
Headlight 10A
Taillight 10A
Main fuse 30A
Radiator fan . . . . 15A (10A up to VIN 4901)
Alarm/clock (where fitted) 10A

In-line fuses

Brake light (All 1995-on models, except Thunderbird)	5A
Starter relay, ignition - Thunderbird only	15A
Evaporative loss system - California only	Not available

Bulbs

Headlight	60/55W H4 halogen
Sidelight	4W
Brake/taillight	21/5W
Turn signal lights	10W
Licence plate light (Thunderbird)	5W
Clock (where fitted)	1.2W
Instrument cluster - Speed Triple and Thunderbird	
Meter illumination	1.2W
Warning lights	2.0W
Instrument cluster - all other models	Refer to existing bulb ratings

Torque settings

Neutral switch	14 Nm
Oil pressure switch	8 Nm
Rear brake light switch	15 Nm
Starter motor retaining bolts	10 Nm

1 General information

All models have a 12-volt electrical system. The components include a three-phase alternator unit with integral regulator and rectifier units.

The regulator maintains the charging system output within the specified range to prevent overcharging, and the rectifier converts the ac (alternating current) output of the alternator to dc (direct current) to power the lights and other components and to charge the battery. The alternator is driven off the alternator driveshaft in the upper crankcase; a shock absorber on the end of the driveshaft cushions the drive to the alternator.

The starter motor is mounted on the crankcase behind the cylinders. The starting system includes the motor, the battery, the relay and the various relevant wires and switches. If the engine stop switch and the ignition (main) switch are both in the "Run" or "On" position, the starter relay allows the starter motor to operate only if the transmission is in neutral (neutral switch on) or, if the transmission is in gear and the clutch lever is pulled into the handlebar (clutch switch on).

The wiring harness includes a take-off point for the Triumph alarm system; refer to a Triumph dealer for details.

Note: *Keep in mind that electrical parts, once purchased, cannot usually be returned (unless an agreement is made when such parts are bought). To avoid unnecessary expense, make absolutely certain that the faulty component has been positively identified before buying a replacement part.*

2 Electrical troubleshooting

Warning: To prevent the risk of short circuits, the ignition (main) switch must always be "OFF" and the battery negative (-ve) terminal should be disconnected before any of the bike's other electrical components are disturbed. Don't forget to reconnect the terminal securely once work is finished or if battery power is needed for circuit testing.

1 A typical electrical circuit consists of an electrical component, the switches, relays, etc. related to that component and the wiring and connectors that hook the component to both the battery and the frame. To aid in locating a problem in any electrical circuit, refer to the wiring diagrams at the end of this Chapter.

2 Before tackling any troublesome electrical circuit, first study the wiring diagram (see end of Chapter) thoroughly to get a complete picture of what makes up that individual circuit. Trouble spots, for instance, can often be narrowed down by noting if other components related to that circuit are operating properly or not. If several components or circuits fail at one time, chances are the fault lies in the fuse or earth connection, as several circuits often are routed through the same fuse and earth connections.

3 Electrical problems often stem from simple causes, such as loose or corroded connections or a blown fuse. Prior to any electrical troubleshooting, always visually check the condition of the fuse, wires and connections in the problem circuit.

Intermittent failures can be especially frustrating, since you can't always duplicate the failure when it's convenient to test. In such situations, a good practice is to clean all connections in the affected circuit, whether or not they appear to be good. All of the connections and wires should also be wiggled to check for looseness which can cause intermittent failure.

4 If testing instruments are going to be utilised, use the wiring diagram to plan where you will make the necessary connections in order to accurately pinpoint the trouble spot.

5 The basic tools needed for electrical troubleshooting include a test light or voltmeter, a continuity tester (which includes a bulb, battery and set of test leads) and a jumper wire, preferably with a circuit breaker incorporated, which can be used to bypass electrical components **(see illustration)**.

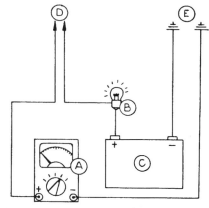

2.5 Simple testing equipment for checking the wiring

A Continuity tester   D Positive probe (+ve)
B Bulb   E Negative probe (-ve)
C Battery

Specific checks described later in this Chapter may also require an ohmmeter. Ideally a multimeter with resistance (ohms), current (amps) and voltage (volts) measuring facilities should be available.

6 Voltage checks should be performed if a circuit is not functioning properly. Connect one lead of a test light or voltmeter to either the negative (-ve) battery terminal or a known good earth. Connect the other lead to a connector in the circuit being tested, preferably nearest to the battery or fuse. If the bulb lights, voltage is reaching that point, which means the part of the circuit between that connector and the battery is problem-free. Continue checking the remainder of the circuit in the same manner. When you reach a point where no voltage is present, the problem almost certainly lies between there and the last good test point. Most of the time the problem is due to a loose connection. Keep in mind that some circuits only receive voltage when the ignition key is in the "ON" position.

7 One method of finding short circuits is to remove the fuse and connect a test light or voltmeter in its place to the fuse terminals. There should be no load in the circuit (it should be switched off). Move the wiring harness from side-to-side while watching the test light. If the bulb lights, there is a short to earth somewhere in that area, probably where insulation has rubbed off a wire. The same test can be performed on other components in the circuit, including the switch.

8 An earth check should be done to see if a component is earthed properly. Disconnect the battery and connect one lead of a self-powered test light (continuity tester) to a known good earth. Connect the other lead to the wire or earth connection being tested. If the bulb lights, the earth connection is good. If the bulb does not light, the earth is not good.

9 A continuity check is performed to see if a circuit, section of circuit, or individual component is capable of passing electricity through it. Disconnect the battery and connect one lead of a self-powered test light (continuity tester) to one end of the circuit being tested and the other lead to the other end of the circuit. If the bulb lights, there is continuity, which means that the circuit is passing electricity through it properly. Note that switches can be checked in the same way.

10 Remember that all electrical circuits are designed to conduct electricity from the battery, through the wires, switches, relays, etc. to the electrical component (light bulb, motor, etc.). From there it is directed to the frame (earth) where it is passed back to the battery. Electrical problems are basically an interruption in the flow of electricity, either from the battery or back to it.

11 Many electrical problems are caused by damp conditions. Spray suspected connectors with a water-dispersant aerosol.

3 Battery - inspection and checks

1 The battery is of the conventional lead/acid type, requiring regular checks of the electrolyte level, as described in Chapter 1, in addition to those detailed below.

2 The battery removal procedure is described in Chapter 1.

3 Check the battery terminals and leads for tightness and corrosion. If corrosion is evident, disconnect the leads from the battery, disconnecting the negative (-ve) terminal first, and clean the terminals and lead ends with a wire brush or knife and emery paper. Reconnect the leads, connecting the negative (-ve) terminal last, and apply a thin coat of petroleum jelly to the connections to slow further corrosion.

4 The battery case should be kept clean to prevent current leakage, which can discharge the battery over a period of time (especially when it sits unused). Wash the outside of the case with a solution of baking soda and water. Rinse the battery thoroughly, then dry it.

5 Look for cracks in the case and replace the battery if any are found. If acid has been spilled on the frame or battery holder, neutralise it with a baking soda and water solution, dry it thoroughly, then touch up any damaged paint. Make sure the battery vent tube is routed correctly and is not kinked or pinched.

6 If the motorcycle sits unused for long periods of time, disconnect the cables from the battery terminals. Refer to Section 4 and charge the battery approximately once every month.

7 The condition of the battery can be assessed by measuring the voltage present at the battery terminals. Connect the voltmeter positive (+ve) probe to the battery positive (+ve) terminal and the negative (-ve) probe to the battery negative (-ve) terminal. When fully charged there should be approximately 13 volts present. If the voltage falls below 12.3 volts the battery must be removed, disconnecting the negative (-ve) terminal first, and recharged as described in Section 4.

4 Battery - charging

Warning: Be extremely careful when handling or working around the battery. The electrolyte is very caustic and an explosive gas (hydrogen) is given off when the battery is charging.

1 To charge the battery it is first necessary to remove it from the motorcycle, as described in Chapter 1.

2 Triumph recommend that the battery is charged at a maximum rate of 1.4 amps. Exceeding this figure can cause the battery to overheat, buckling the plates and rendering it useless. Few owners will have access to an expensive current controlled charger, so if a normal domestic charger is used check that after a possible initial peak, the charge rate falls to a safe level **(see illustration)**. If the battery becomes hot during charging stop. Further charging will cause damage. **Note:** *In emergencies the battery can be charged at a higher rate for a period of 1 hour. However, this is not recommended and the low amp charge is by far the safer method of charging the battery.*

3 If the recharged battery discharges rapidly if left disconnected it is likely that an internal short caused by physical damage or sulphation has occurred. A new battery will be required. A sound item will tend to lose its charge at about 1% per day.

4 Install the battery (refer to Chapter 1).

5 Fuses - check and replacement

1 Most circuits are protected by fuses of different ratings. All fuses are located in the fusebox which on all models except the Thunderbird is situated under the seat. On the Thunderbird it is situated behind the right side panel. The fuses are labelled for easy identification. The in-line brake circuit fuse is located under the seat on the seat left mounting rail.

2 To gain access to the fuses unclip and remove the fusebox lid **(see illustrations)**.

3 The fuses can be removed and checked visually. If you can't pull the fuse out with your fingertips, use a pair of needle-nose pliers. A blown fuse is easily identified by a break in the element. Each fuse is clearly marked with its rating and must only be replaced by a fuse of the correct rating. *Caution: Never put in a fuse of a higher rating or bridge the terminals with any other substitute,*

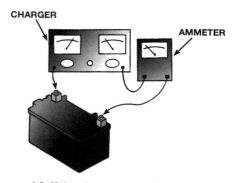

4.2 If the charger doesn't have an ammeter built in, connect one in series as shown; DO NOT connect the ammeter between the battery terminals or it will be ruined

9

5.2a On the Thunderbird, the fusebox is behind the right side panel

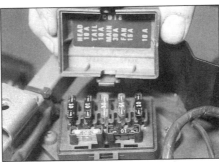

5.2b On all other models the fusebox is located under the seat. Unclip the fusebox lid to reveal the fuses

however temporary it may be. Serious damage may be done to the circuit, or a fire may start. If the spare fuses are used, always replace them so that a spare fuse of each rating is carried on the bike at all times.

4 If a fuse blows, be sure to check the wiring circuit very carefully for evidence of a short-circuit. Look for bare wires and chafed, melted or burned insulation. If a fuse is replaced before the cause is located, the new fuse will blow immediately.

5 Occasionally a fuse will blow or cause an open-circuit for no obvious reason. Corrosion of the fuse ends and fusebox terminals may occur and cause poor fuse contact. If this happens, remove the corrosion with a wire brush or emery paper, then spray the fuse end and terminals with electrical contact cleaner.

6 Lighting system - check

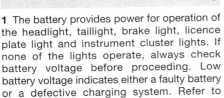

1 The battery provides power for operation of the headlight, taillight, brake light, licence plate light and instrument cluster lights. If none of the lights operate, always check battery voltage before proceeding. Low battery voltage indicates either a faulty battery or a defective charging system. Refer to Section 3 for battery checks and Sections 29 and 30 for charging system tests. Also, check the condition of the fuses and replace any blown fuses with new ones.

Headlight

2 If the headlight fails to work, check the fuse first with the key "ON" (see Section 5), then unplug the electrical connector for the headlight and use jumper wires to connect the bulb directly to the battery terminals. If the light comes on, the problem lies in the wiring or one of the switches in the circuit or the headlight relay (twin headlight models only). Refer to Section 19 for the switch testing procedures, and also the wiring diagrams at the end of this Chapter. On models with twin headlights, if one of the relays is suspected of being faulty, substitute it with the other relay. If the headlight then works, the faulty relay must be replaced.

Taillight and licence plate light

3 If the taillight fails to work, check the bulbs and the bulb terminals first, then the fuses, then check for battery voltage at the taillight electrical connector. If voltage is present, check the earth circuit for an open or poor connection.

4 If no voltage is indicated, check the wiring between the taillight and the ignition switch, then check the switch. Also check the lighting switch.

5 The licence plate light fitted to Thunderbird models only can be checked in the same way as the taillight (see the wiring diagram at the end of this Chapter).

Brake light

6 See Section 13 for the brake light switch checking procedure.

Neutral indicator light

7 If the neutral light fails to operate when the transmission is in neutral, first check the fuses and the bulb (see Sections 5 and 16). If they are in good condition, check for battery voltage at the connector attached to the neutral switch on the left side of the engine. If battery voltage is present, refer to Section 21 for the neutral switch check and replacement procedures.

8 If no voltage is indicated, check the wiring between the switch and the bulb for open-circuits and poor connections.

Oil pressure warning light

9 See Section 17 for the oil pressure switch check.

Sidestand warning light (Trophy and Trident models)

10 If the sidestand light fails to operate when the stand is down (extended), check the fuses and the bulb (see Sections 5 and 16). If they are in good condition, check for battery voltage at the switch wiring connector. If battery voltage is present, refer to Section 22 for the sidestand switch check and replacement procedures.

11 If no voltage is indicated, check the wiring between the switch and the bulb for open-circuits and poor connections.

Low fuel level warning light (all models except Thunderbird)

12 If the low fuel level warning light has not come on by the time the reserve fuel tank is needed, check the fuses and the bulb (see Sections 5 and 16). If the fuses and bulb are in good condition, check for battery voltage at the low fuel level sensor wiring connector. If battery voltage is present, refer to Section 25 for the low fuel level sensor check and replacement procedures.

13 If no voltage is indicated, check the wiring between the switch and the bulb for open-circuits and poor connections.

7 Headlight bulb and sidelight bulb - replacement

Note: *The headlight bulb is of the quartz-halogen type. Do not touch the bulb glass with your fingers, as skin acids will shorten the bulb's service life. If the bulb is accidentally touched, it should be wiped carefully when cold with a rag soaked in methylated spirit and dried before fitting.*

 Warning: Allow the bulb time to cool before removing it if the headlight has just been on.

Headlight

Trophy, Daytona, Sprint and Tiger models

1 Access to the headlight bulb(s) is possible, though restricted, from underneath the fairing. It is better to access the bulb(s) by removing the instrument facia panels and, if necessary, removing the windshield as described in Chapter 8. On Trophy models, if access is still restricted, the fairing must be detached and moved forward (though not entirely removed) as described in Chapter 8.

2 Disconnect the wiring connector from the headlight bulb and remove the rubber dust cover (**see illustrations**).

3 On Daytona, Sprint and Tiger models, release the bulb retaining clip and swing it away, then remove the bulb (**see illustrations**).

4 On Trophy models, turn the bulb retaining ring anti-clockwise, then remove the bulb.

5 Fit the new bulb, bearing in mind the information in the **Note** above, and secure it in position with the retaining clip or ring.

6 Install the dust cover, making sure it is correctly seated and with the "TOP" mark facing up.

7 Reconnect the wiring connector and check the operation of the headlight(s).

8 If removed, fit the fairing, windshield, and facia panels as described in Chapter 8.

Trident, Speed Triple and Thunderbird models

9 Remove the two rim retaining screws and ease the rim out of the headlight shell (**see illustration**).

7.2a Disconnect the wiring connector from the headlight bulb . . .

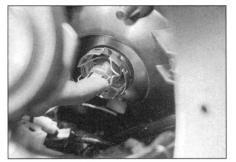

7.2b . . . and pull off the rubber cover

7.3a Unhook the bulb retaining clip ears from the headlight . . .

7.3b . . . then swing the clip away and remove the bulb

7.9 Headlight rim is retained by a screw on each side

7.10 Separate dust cover from headlight to access the bulb

10 Disconnect the wire connector to the headlight bulb, peel off the dust cover, and ease the sidelight bulbholder out of the headlight **(see illustration)**.
11 Release the bulb retaining clip and swing it away, then remove the bulb.

12 Fit the new bulb, bearing in mind the information in the previous **Note**, and secure it in position with the retaining clip.
13 Install the dust cover, making sure it is correctly seated and with the "TOP" mark facing up **(see illustration)**.

14 Reconnect the wiring and operate the light.
15 When installing the headlight, engage the cut-out in the rim with the lip on the shell and secure with the two screws **(see illustration)**.

Sidelight

16 On all models the sidelight bulb is situated just below the headlight bulb. Access to the bulb is as described for the headlight above.
17 Pull the bulbholder out from the base of the headlight **(see illustration)**. Push the bulb inwards and twist it anti-clockwise to release it from the bulbholder. If the socket contacts are dirty or corroded, they should be scraped clean and sprayed with electrical contact cleaner before the new bulb is installed.
18 Install the new bulb in the bulbholder by pressing it in and twisting it clockwise. Press the bulbholder back into the headlight.
19 Check the operation of the sidelight then install the headlight or fit the bodywork as described above, according to model.

7.13 Ensure that the TOP marking faces upwards when fitting dust cover

7.15 Cut-out in headlight rim must engage lip at top of shell

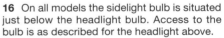
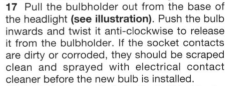

8 Headlight unit - removal and installation

Removal

Daytona, Sprint and Tiger models

1 Remove the main fairing (Chapter 8).
2 Disconnect the headlight wiring connectors from the headlights. Trace the sidelight wiring to the connector block and disconnect it.
3 Disconnect the headlight relay wiring connectors from the relays **(see illustration)**.

7.17 Gently pull the sidelight bulb out of its holder just below the headlight

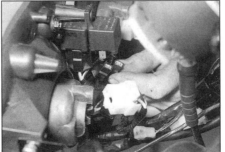

8.3 Disconnect the headlight relay wiring connectors

9

8.4a The headlight assembly is secured to the fairing stay by a bolt on each side . . .

4 Unscrew the three screws securing the headlight assembly to the fairing stay and remove the assembly **(see illustrations)**.

Trophy models

5 Remove the main fairing as described in Chapter 8.
6 Unscrew the four screws securing the headlight to the fairing and remove the headlight.

Trident, Speed Triple and Thunderbird models

7 Remove the two rim retaining screws and ease the rim out of the headlight shell **(see illustration 7.9)**. Disconnect the wire connector to the headlight bulb, peel off the dust cover, and ease the sidelight bulbholder out of the headlight **(see illustration 7.10)**.
8 To remove the headlight shell, remove the bolts securing it to the headlight brackets, then carefully withdraw the shell from the brackets. Free the wiring inside the shell from the clamps and ease it out the back of the shell.

> **HAYNES HiNT** *When disconnecting wiring, label the wire connectors to aid easy reconnection*

Installation

9 Installation is the reverse of removal. Check the operation of the headlight and sidelight. Check the headlight aim (see Section 9).

9.1 Headlight adjusting screws on dual headlights - horizontal (A), vertical (B)

8.4b . . . and one underneath

9 Headlight aim - adjustment

Note: *An improperly adjusted headlight may cause problems for oncoming traffic or provide poor, unsafe illumination of the road ahead. Before adjusting the headlight aim, be sure to consult with local traffic laws and regulations.*

Daytona, Sprint and Tiger models

1 Horizontal (side-to-side) adjustment is made via the adjusters at the top of each headlight. Vertical adjustment of the headlight aim is made via the screws at the bottom of each headlight **(see illustration)**.
2 Adjustment is made using a stubby cross-head screwdriver passed up through the bottom of the upper fairing.
3 On the right side light, turn the horizontal adjuster anti-clockwise to adjust the beam to the right, and clockwise to adjust the beam to the left.
4 On the left side light, turn the horizontal adjuster clockwise to adjust the beam to right, and anti-clockwise to adjust the beam to the left.
5 On both lights, turn the vertical adjuster clockwise to adjust the beam down, and anti-clockwise to adjust the beam up.

Trophy models

6 Adjustment is made either manually or using a suitable spanner passed up through

9.9 Beam horizontal adjustment screw (arrowed) - Thunderbird, Trident and Speed Triple

the bottom of the main fairing. Remove the instrument facia panels (three screws) for access to the back of the headlight.
7 Horizontal (side-to-side) adjustment is made by turning the adjuster screws on either side of the light in opposite directions. To adjust the beam to the right, turn the right side adjuster anti-clockwise and the left side adjuster clockwise. To adjust the beam to the left, turn the right side adjuster clockwise and the left side adjuster anti-clockwise.
8 Vertical adjustment is made by turning both adjusters an equal amount in the same direction. To adjust the beam up, turn the adjusters anti-clockwise. To adjust the beam down, turn the adjusters clockwise.

Trident, Speed Triple and Thunderbird models

9 Horizontal adjustment is made by turning the adjuster screw in the rim on the left side of the headlight **(see illustration)**.
10 Vertical adjustment is made by loosening the headlight shell mounting bolts and manually moving the headlight up or down in the brackets **(see illustration)**. Tighten the bolts after adjustment has been made.

10 Turn signal, taillight and licence plate bulbs - replacement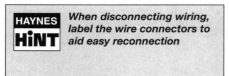

Turn signal bulbs

1 On Thunderbird models, unscrew the turn signal lens retaining screws from the front of the turn signal and withdraw the lens. Note the drain hole on the bottom of the lens - this must face downwards.
2 On all other models, unscrew the turn signal lens retaining screw from the back of the turn signal and withdraw the lens **(see illustrations)**.
3 Push the bulb into the holder and twist it anti-clockwise to remove it **(see illustration)**. Check the socket terminals for corrosion and clean them if necessary. Line up the pins of the new bulb with the slots in the socket, then push the bulb in and turn it clockwise until it locks into place. **Note:** *It is a good idea to use*

9.10 Beam vertical adjustment is made by loosening shell mounting bolts - Thunderbird, Trident and Speed Triple

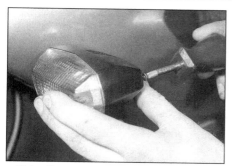

10.2a Unscrew the lens retaining screw from the back of the turn signal . . .

10.2b . . . and remove the lens, noting how it fits

10.3 To release the bulb gently push it in and twist it anti-clockwise

10.5 The taillight lens is secured by two screws

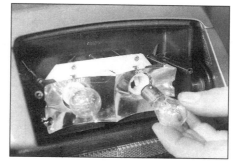

10.6 Twist the bulb anti-clockwise to release it from the taillight unit

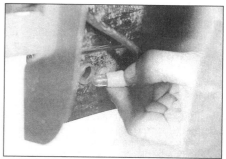

10.8 Pull licence plate light bulbholder out from inside rear mudguard

a paper towel or dry cloth when handling the new bulb to prevent injury if the bulb should break and to increase bulb life.

4 Install the lens back into the turn signal and securely tighten the retaining screw(s). Take care not to overtighten the screw(s) as the lens is easily cracked.

> **HAYNES HINT**
> *If the socket contacts are dirty or corroded, scrape them clean and spray with electrical contact cleaner before a new bulb is fitted.*

Taillight bulbs

5 Unscrew the taillight lens retaining screws and remove the lens **(see illustration)**.
6 Push each bulb into the holder and twist it anti-clockwise to remove it **(see illustration)**. Check the socket terminals for corrosion and clean them if necessary. Line up the pins of

the new bulb with the slots in the socket, then push the bulb in and turn it clockwise until it locks into place. **Note:** *The pins on the bulb are offset so it can only be installed one way. Use a paper towel or dry cloth when handling the new bulb to prevent injury if the bulb should break and to increase bulb life.*

7 Install the lens back onto the taillight and securely tighten the retaining screws. Take care not to overtighten the screws as the lens is easily cracked.

Licence plate bulb - Thunderbird

8 The bulbholder is accessed from inside the rear mudguard. Scrub any dirt from the surrounding area and pull the bulbholder out of the light unit **(see illustration)**.
9 The bulb is of the capless type - simply pull it out of the holder. Take care not to break the new bulb when installing it in the bulbholder. Push the bulbholder back into place.

11 Turn signal assemblies - removal and installation

Front

Removal

Trophy, Daytona, Sprint and Tiger models
1 Trace the turn signal wiring back from the turn signal and disconnect it at the connectors inside the fairing **(see illustration)**.
2 Carefully pull the wiring through to the turn signal mounting, noting its routing for use when refitting. Remove the rubber boot and unscrew the turn signal mounting nut, noting the order of the washers **(see illustrations)**. Slip the nut, spring washer and washer off the wiring and withdraw the turn signal from the fairing.

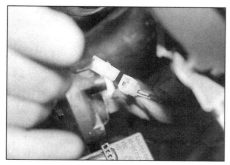

11.1 Disconnect the turn signal wiring

11.2a Remove the rubber boot . . .

11.2b . . . and unscrew the turn signal nut

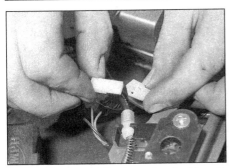

11.10 Disconnect the turn signal wiring at the connectors

11.11 Unscrew the turn signal bracket bolt (arrowed) to release it from the frame

Trident, Speed Triple and Thunderbird models

3 Unscrew the two screws securing the headlight rim to the shell, then carefully withdraw the headlight from the shell, noting how it fits. Trace the wiring back from the turn signal and disconnect it at the connectors inside the headlight shell.

4 Pull the wiring through to the turn signal mounting, noting its routing, then remove the rubber boot and unscrew the turn signal mounting nut, noting the order of the washers (where fitted). Slip the nut, spring washer and washer (where fitted) off the wiring and remove the turn signal from the bracket.

Installation

5 Installation is the reverse of removal.

Rear

Removal

Thunderbird

6 Remove the seat as described in Chapter 8. Trace the turn signal wiring back from the turn signal and disconnect it at the connector.

7 Pull the wiring through to the turn signal mounting, noting its routing, then unscrew the turn signal mounting nut on the inside of the rear mudguard, and remove the turn signal from the mudguard.

Tiger

8 Remove the seat as described in Chapter 8. Release its six retaining screws and remove the top cover for access to the turn signal mounting. Trace the turn signal wiring back from the turn signal and disconnect it at the connector.

9 Slip the rubber boot off the turn signal mounting, and unscrew the mounting nut, noting the order of the washers. Remove the nut, spring washer and washer from the wiring and remove the turn signal from the bracket.

All other models

10 Remove the seat and the side panel as described in Chapter 8. Trace the turn signal wiring back from the turn signal and disconnect it at the connector **(see illustration)**.

11 Release the wiring from its tie and note its routing, then unscrew the bolt securing the turn signal mounting bracket to the frame **(see illustration)**. Remove the bracket and turn signal from the frame. If necessary, remove

the rubber boot and unscrew the turn signal mounting nut, noting the order of the washers. Slip the nut, spring washer and washer off the wiring and remove the turn signal from the bracket.

Installation

12 Installation is the reverse of removal.

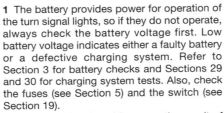

12 Turn signal circuit - check

1 The battery provides power for operation of the turn signal lights, so if they do not operate, always check the battery voltage first. Low battery voltage indicates either a faulty battery or a defective charging system. Refer to Section 3 for battery checks and Sections 29 and 30 for charging system tests. Also, check the fuses (see Section 5) and the switch (see Section 19).

2 Most turn signal problems are the result of a burned out bulb or corroded socket. This is especially true when the turn signals function properly in one direction, but fail to flash in the other direction. Check the bulbs and the sockets (see Section 10).

3 If the bulbs and sockets are good, check for power at the turn signal relay orange/green wire with the ignition "ON". The relay is mounted below the fusebox behind the right side panel on Thunderbird models, and next to the fusebox under the seat on all other models **(see illustrations)**. Turn the ignition OFF when the check is complete.

4 If no power was present at the relay, check the wiring from the relay to the ignition (main) switch for continuity.

5 If power was present at the relay, using the appropriate wiring diagram at the end of this Chapter, check the wiring between the relay, turn signal switch and turn signal lights for continuity. If the wiring and switch are sound, replace the relay with a new one.

6 The turn signal circuit includes a hazard warning switch which, when operated, flashes all four turn signals simultaneously. If the turn signals do not all flash when the switch is operated, yet function normally otherwise, check the hazard switch for continuity.

13 Brake light switches - check and replacement

Circuit check

1 Before checking any electrical circuit, check the bulb (see Section 10) and fuses (see Section 5).

2 Using a test light connected to a good earth, check for voltage at the brake light switch wiring connector. If there's no voltage present, check the wire between the switch and the fusebox (see the wiring diagrams at the end of this Chapter).

3 If voltage is available, touch the probe of the test light to the other terminal of the switch, then pull the brake lever in or depress the brake pedal. If the test light doesn't light up, replace the switch.

4 If the test light does light, check the wiring between the switch and the brake lights (see the wiring diagrams at the end of this Chapter).

Switch replacement

Front brake lever switch

5 Remove the mounting screw and unplug the electrical connectors from the switch **(see illustration)**.

6 Detach the switch from the bottom of the front brake master cylinder.

7 Installation is the reverse of the removal procedure. The switch isn't adjustable.

12.3a The turn signal relay (arrowed) is behind right side panel on Thunderbirds . . .

12.3b . . . and under the seat on all other models (arrowed)

13.5 Remove the single screw to free front brake light switch from the master cylinder

13.8 Prise off the rubber boot to access the rear brake light switch wire connectors

Rear brake pedal switch

Caution: The rear brake switch is of the pressure type and screws into the top of the master cylinder. Take care when the switch is removed to protect the surrounding components from contact with brake fluid spills.

8 Prise up the rubber boot and disconnect the wiring from the switch mounted to the top of the rear brake master cylinder **(see illustration)**.

9 Wrap a rag around the master cylinder to catch any brake fluid that escapes, then unscrew the switch from the top of the cylinder. Discard the sealing washer as a new one must be used. **Note:** *Do not operate the brake pedal with the switch removed.*

10 Fit a new sealing washer to the switch, then install the switch and tighten it to the specified torque setting. Note that on Thunderbird and Tiger models, the brake light switch secures the hydraulic hose to the top of the master cylinder; a new sealing washer should be used between the union and master cylinder and the union positioned at the correct angle.

11 Bleed the hydraulic system as described in Chapter 7. Check that the rear brake works properly before riding the motorcycle and that there is no sign of hydraulic fluid leakage from the disturbed joint.

---

14 Instrument cluster and speedometer cable - removal and installation

Instrument cluster

Removal

1 On Trophy, Daytona and Sprint models remove the instrument facia panels, and on Tiger models remove the fairing front panel (see Chapter 8, Section 2). On Thunderbird, Speed Triple and Trident models, remove the headlight from its shell to access the wiring connectors (see Section 7).

2 Unscrew the speedometer cable retaining ring from the rear of the instrument cluster and detach the cable.

3 Disconnect the instrument cluster wiring at the connectors, and release the wiring from any ties.

4 On Trophy and Trident models, remove the two mounting nuts underneath the instrument cluster and lift the assembly off its mounting bracket. On all other models, unscrew the two main instrument cluster mounting screws from the top of the instruments and carefully lift the instrument cluster off the mounting bracket **(see illustrations)**.

Installation

5 Installation is the reverse of removal. Make sure that the speedometer cable and wiring are correctly routed and secured.

Speedometer cable

Removal

6 On Trophy, Daytona and Sprint models remove the instrument facia panels, and on Tiger models remove the fairing front panel (see Chapter 8, Section 2).

7 Unscrew the speedometer cable retaining ring from the rear of the instrument cluster and detach the cable **(see illustration)**.

8 Unscrew the screw securing the lower end of the cable to the drive unit on the wheel and detach the cable **(refer to Chapter 7, illustration 14.3)**.

9 Slip the cable out of its retaining guide on the brake caliper (Thunderbird), brake hose clamp (Tiger) or front mudguard (all other models) and remove it from the bike, noting its correct routing.

Installation

10 Route the cable correctly and install it in its retaining guide.

11 Align the inner cable slot at the lower end of the cable with the drive gear dog on the front wheel and connect the cable to the drive **(see Chapter 7, illustration 14.17b)**. Install the cable retaining screw and tighten it securely.

12 Connect the cable upper end to the instrument cluster and tighten the retaining ring securely.

13 Check that the cable doesn't restrict steering movement or interfere with any other components.

14 On Trophy, Daytona, Sprint and Tiger models, install the panels as described in Chapter 8.

---

15 Meters and gauges - check and replacement

Coolant temperature gauge (where fitted)

Check

1 The temperature gauge check is described in Chapter 3.

14.4a Instrument cluster mounting screws (arrowed) - Thunderbird and Speed Triple

14.4b Instrument cluster mounting screws (arrowed) - Daytona, Sprint, and Tiger

14.7 Unscrew the cable retaining ring and detach the cable

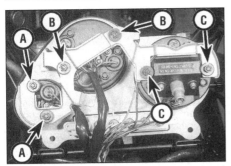

15.3 Rear view of instrument cluster fitted to Daytona, Sprint, and Tiger models - temperature gauge mountings (A), tachometer mountings (B), speedometer mountings (C)

Replacement

2 Remove the instrument cluster from the bike as described in Section 14. On Trophy and Trident models, remove the instrument lower cover; it is retained by two screws.

3 Unscrew the nuts securing the temperature gauge to the casing and withdraw it far enough out of the casing to gain access to the wiring **(see illustration)**.

4 Note the correct fitted position of the temperature gauge wires, then unscrew the wire retaining screws and detach the wires. Carefully pull the bulbholder out from its socket. The temperature gauge can now be fully removed from the casing.

5 Install the temperature gauge by reversing the removal sequence.

Tachometer

Check

6 On Trophy, Daytona and Sprint models remove the instrument facia panels, and on Tiger models remove the fairing front panel (see Chapter 8, Section 2). On Thunderbird, Speed Triple and Trident models, remove the headlight from its casing to access the wiring connectors (see Section 8). Carefully disconnect the instrument cluster wiring connector.

7 Disconnect the igniter wiring connector (see Chapter 5).

8 Using an ohmmeter or continuity tester, check for continuity between the black/blue wire terminal on the instrument cluster connector and the black/blue terminal on the igniter connector. If no continuity is obtained, check the wiring between the two connectors (refer to the wiring diagrams at the end of this Chapter), and repair the wiring if an open circuit is indicated. If continuity is indicated but the tachometer does not work, then it is probably faulty and should be taken to a Triumph dealer for further testing.

Replacement - Speed Triple and Thunderbird models

9 Remove the two domed nuts with washers

from the base of the tachometer; this will free the baseplate and instrument pod **(see illustrations 16.1a and 16.1b)**. Pull the bulbholders from the base of the tachometer and disconnect the wire connector **(see illustration 16.1c)**. Lift the tachometer out of the instrument cluster.

10 Install the tachometer by reversing the removal sequence.

Replacement - all other models

11 Remove the instrument cluster as described in Section 14. On Trophy and Trident models, also remove the two screws to free the bottom cover from the instruments.

12 Unscrew the nuts securing the tachometer to the casing and withdraw it far enough out of the casing to gain access to the wiring **(see illustration 15.3)**. Note the correct fitted position of the tachometer wires, then remove the wire retaining screws and carefully detach the wires. Carefully pull the bulbholders out from their sockets. The tachometer can now be fully removed from the instrument cluster.

13 Install the tachometer by reversing the removal sequence.

Speedometer

Check

14 Special instruments are required to properly check the operation of this meter. Seek the advice of a Triumph dealer for diagnosis.

Replacement - Speed Triple and Thunderbird models

15 Remove the two domed nuts with washers from the base of the speedometer; this will free the baseplate and instrument pod. Pull the bulbholders from the base of the speedometer and lift it out of the instrument cluster.

16 Install the speedometer by reversing the removal sequence.

Replacement - all other models

17 Remove the instrument cluster from the bike as described in Section 14. On Trophy and Trident models, also remove the two screws to free the bottom cover from the instruments.

18 Unplug the bulbholders from the speedometer. Remove the retaining screw from the centre of the odometer trip knob. Unscrew the nuts securing the speedometer to the casing and withdraw it from the instrument cluster **(see illustration 15.3)**.

19 Install the speedometer by reversing the removal sequence.

Clock (where fitted)

Check

20 If the clock does not work, check the fuse (see Section 5). If the fuse is in good condition, remove the instrument facia panel (or fairing side panel on Tiger models) as described in Chapter 8, Section 2 and check

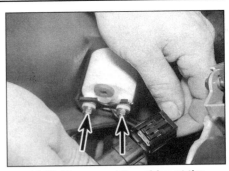

15.22 Disconnect the wiring at the connector, then unscrew the two nuts (arrowed) to release the clock

for battery voltage at the clock red wire connector. If battery voltage is present, the clock is faulty and must be replaced.

21 If no voltage is indicated, check the wiring between the clock and the fusebox for open-circuits and poor connections.

Replacement

22 Remove the instrument facia panel (or fairing side panel on Tiger models) as described in Chapter 8, Section 2. Gently pull the bulbholder from the base of the clock. Disconnect the clock wiring at the connector, then unscrew the two nuts securing the clock to its bracket and remove the clock **(see illustration)**.

23 Install the clock by reversing the removal procedure.

16 Instrument and warning light bulbs - replacement

Speed Triple and Thunderbird models

1 Remove the two domed nuts with washers from the base of the meter; this will free the baseplate and instrument pod **(see illustrations)**. Pull the bulbholders from the base of the meter and gently pull the bulbs out of their holders **(see illustration)**.

2 The warning light bulbs are housed in the display unit between the meters. Remove the retaining screws to free the bottom cover and access the bulbholders. Gently pull the bulbs out of their holders.

All other models

Note: *The instrument and warning light bulb wattages differ; examine the existing bulb and make sure the new bulb is of the same size and wattage.*

3 Remove the instrument cluster as described in Section 14 and on Trophy and Trident models also remove the bottom cover (retained by two screws). **Note:** *Depending on your dexterity, you may be able to access certain bulbholders without removing the instruments.*

4 Pull the relevant bulbholder out of the back

16.1a Remove the two domed nuts and washers to free the baseplate . . .

16.1b . . . then withdraw the instrument pod

16.1c Bulbholders are a push fit in back of meter

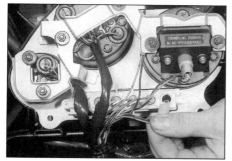

16.4a Pull the relevant bulbholder out of the casing . . .

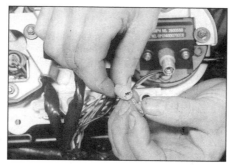

16.4b . . . and gently ease the bulb out of the bulbholder

of the cluster then gently pull the bulb out of its holder **(see illustrations)**.

5 Carefully push the new bulb into position, then push the bulbholder back into the rear of the cluster.

6 Install the bottom cover (Trophy and Trident) and install instrument cluster as described in Section 14.

17 Oil pressure switch - check and replacement

Check

1 The oil pressure warning light should come on when the ignition (main) switch is turned ON and extinguish a few seconds after the engine is started. If the oil pressure light comes on whilst the engine is running, stop the engine immediately and carry out an oil pressure check (see Chapter 2).

2 If the oil pressure warning light does not come on when the ignition is turned on, check the bulb (see Section 16) and fuses (see Section 5).

3 The oil pressure switch is screwed into the back of the sump **(see illustration)**. Slip the protective sleeve back and detach the wiring connector from the switch. With the ignition switched ON, earth the wire on the crankcase and check that the warning light comes on. If the light comes on, the switch is confirmed defective and must be replaced.

4 If the light still does not come on, check for voltage at the wire terminal using a test light. If

there is no voltage present, switch the ignition OFF and using an ohmmeter or continuity tester check the pink wire from the switch to the instrument cluster for continuity (see the wiring diagrams at the end of this Chapter).

5 If the warning light comes on whilst the engine is running, yet the oil pressure is satisfactory, remove the wire from the oil pressure switch. With the wire detached and the ignition switched ON the light should be out. If it is illuminated, the pink wire between the switch and instrument cluster must be earthed at some point. If the wiring is good, the switch must be assumed faulty and replaced.

Replacement

6 Slip the protective sleeve back and detach the wiring connector from the switch.

7 Drain the engine oil (see Chapter 1).

8 Unscrew the switch from the sump and wipe the oil from the hole threads.

17.3 The oil pressure switch is screwed into the back of the sump

9 Apply a few drops of non-permanent thread locking compound to the threads of the new switch and screw it into the sump, tightening it to the specified torque. Reconnect the wire connector and slip the sleeve back into place.

10 Refill the engine oil (see Chapter 1).

11 Check that the oil pressure warning light illuminates when the ignition is turned ON, then extinguishes a few seconds after the engine is started.

18 Ignition (main) switch - check, removal and installation

Check

1 Trace the ignition (main) switch wiring back from the base of the switch and disconnect it at the connector. On Trident, Speed Triple and Thunderbird models the connector is located inside the headlight shell (see Section 7). On Trophy, Daytona and Sprint models remove the instrument facia panels to trace the connector, and on Tiger models remove the fairing front panel (see Chapter 8, Section 2).

2 Using an ohmmeter or a continuity tester, check the continuity of the terminal pairs (see the wiring diagrams at the end of this Chapter). Continuity should exist between the terminals connected by a solid line on the diagram when the switch is in the indicated position.

3 If the switch fails any of the tests, replace it.

Removal and installation

Note: *It is strongly recommended that this task be carried out by a Triumph dealer.*

4 The ignition (main) switch is attached to the top yoke by two shear-head bolts, designed to shear off at the head when they are tightened sufficiently. This is a security measure designed to make it very difficult to remove the ignition switch.

5 If the switch has to be replaced, the top yoke (complete with switch) must be removed (see Chapter 6, Section 8) and the switch retaining bolts drilled out. Apply a few drops of non-permanent thread locking compound to the threads of the new shear-head bolts, then tighten them until their heads shear off.

20.3 Unscrew the two right handlebar switch retaining screws

20.4 When installing the right switch, locate the peg on the switch (A) in the hole in the handlebar (arrowed)

20.7 Unscrew the two left handlebar switch retaining screws

19 Handlebar switches - check

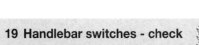

1 Generally speaking, the switches are reliable and trouble-free. Most troubles, when they do occur, are caused by dirty or corroded contacts, but wear and breakage of internal parts is a possibility that should not be overlooked. If breakage does occur, the entire switch and related wiring harness will have to be replaced with a new one, since individual parts are not available.

2 The switches can be checked for continuity using an ohmmeter or a continuity test light. Always disconnect the battery negative (-ve) cable, which will prevent the possibility of a short circuit, before making the checks.

3 Trace the wiring harness of the switch in question back to its connector(s) and disconnect it.

4 Using the ohmmeter or test light, check for continuity between the terminals of the switch harness with the switch in the various positions (see the wiring diagrams at the end of this Chapter).

5 If the continuity check indicates a problem exists, refer to Section 20, remove the switch and spray the switch contacts with electrical contact cleaner. If they are accessible, the contacts can be scraped clean with a knife or polished with crocus cloth. If switch components are damaged or broken, it will be obvious when the switch is disassembled.

20 Handlebar switches - removal and installation

Right handlebar switch

Removal

1 Trace the wiring harness back from the switch to the wiring connector, and then disconnect it.

2 Work back along the harness, freeing it from all the relevant clips and ties, whilst noting its correct routing.

3 Unscrew the two switch screws and remove the switch from the handlebar **(see illustration)**. Disconnect the two wires from the brake light switch and remove the throttle cable and cable elbow from the switch.

Installation

4 Installation is a reversal of the removal procedure, making sure that the locating peg on the back half of the switch is correctly located in the hole in the handlebar **(see illustration)**. If necessary, refer to Chapter 4 for installation of the throttle cable.

Left handlebar switch

Removal

5 Trace the wiring harness back from the switch to the connector and disconnect it.

6 Work back along the harness, freeing it from all the relevant clips and ties, whilst noting its correct routing.

7 Unscrew the two switch retaining screws and remove the switch from the handlebar **(see illustration)**. Disconnect the two wires from the clutch switch, and remove the choke cable, complete with its elbow and lever, from the switch.

Installation

8 Installation is a reversal of the removal procedure, making sure that the locating peg on the back half of the switch is correctly located in the hole in the handlebar. If necessary, refer to Chapter 4 for installation of the choke cable.

21 Neutral switch - check and replacement

Check

1 Before checking the electrical circuit, check the bulb (see Section 16) and fuse (see Section 5).

2 The switch is screwed into the left side of the crankcase, between the water pump and sprocket cover **(see illustration)**. Access can be improved on Trophy and Daytona models by removing the fairing left lower panel (see Chapter 8).

3 Disconnect the wiring connector from the switch. Make sure the transmission is in neutral.

4 With the wire detached and the ignition switched ON, the neutral light should be out. If not, the wire between the switch and instrument cluster must be earthed at some point.

5 Earth the wire on the crankcase and check that the neutral light comes on. If the light comes on, but doesn't when connected to the switch, the switch is confirmed defective.

6 If the light does not come on when the wire is earthed, check for voltage at the wire terminal using a test light. If there's no voltage present, check the wire between the switch, the instrument cluster and fusebox (see the wiring diagrams at the end of this Chapter).

Replacement

7 Disconnect the wiring connector from the switch **(see illustration 21.2)**. Remove the fairing left lower panel if necessary for access on Trophy and Daytona models (refer to Chapter 8).

8 Unscrew the switch from the crankcase. Recover the sealing washer and plug the switch opening to minimise oil loss whilst the switch is removed.

9 Clean the threads of the switch and fit a new sealing washer to it.

10 Remove the plug from the crankcase and install the switch. Tighten the switch to the specified torque setting, then reconnect the wiring connector.

21.2 The neutral switch (arrowed) is located between the water pump and sprocket cover

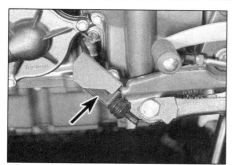

22.2a Sidestand switch location (arrowed)

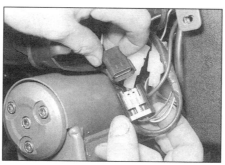

22.2b Disconnect the sidestand switch wiring at the connector behind the left side panel (air chamber removed for access)

22.10 Side stand relay is located under fuel tank's rear mounting on Sprint model

11 Check the operation of the neutral light.
12 Check the oil level as described in Chapter 1 and top-up if necessary.
13 If removed, install the fairing panel on Trophy and Daytona models (see Chapter 8).

22 Sidestand switch - check and replacement

Check

Sidestand warning light - Trophy and Trident models

1 The warning light in the instrument cluster should illuminate with the ignition switched ON and the sidestand down (extended). If it doesn't, first check the bulb (Section 16).
2 Trace the wiring from the sidestand switch up to its connector behind the left side panel and disconnect it **(see illustrations)**. Note that it was found necessary on the machine photographed, to remove the left auxiliary air chamber for access to the wire connector (see Chapter 4 for air chamber removal).
3 Check the operation of the switch using an ohmmeter or continuity test light. Set the meter to the ohms x 1 scale and connect its probes between the blue and green wires on the switch side of the wiring connector. With the sidestand down (extended) there should be continuity between the terminals, and with the stand up there should be no continuity (infinite resistance).
4 If the switch does not perform as expected, it is defective and must be replaced. Check first that the fault is not caused by a sticking switch plunger due to the ingress of road dirt; spray the switch with a water dispersant aerosol.
5 If the switch is good, check the brown/red wire between the wiring connector and the instrument cluster for continuity (refer to the wiring diagrams at the end of this book).

Sidestand switch (ignition cut-out)

6 Depending on the type of circuit fitted, the ignition will be cut out if the sidestand is extended, or if the machine is put into gear

while the sidestand is extended. Make the following checks using the appropriate wiring diagram at the end of this Chapter.
7 Trace the wiring from the switch on the sidestand to its connector behind the left side panel and disconnect it **(see illustration 22.2b)**. Note that it was found necessary on the machine photographed, to remove the left auxiliary air chamber for access to the wire connector (see Chapter 4 for air chamber removal).
8 Check the operation of the switch using an ohmmeter or continuity test light. Connect the meter to the blue and brown wires on the switch side of the connector. With the sidestand up there should be continuity between the terminals; with the stand down there should be no continuity (infinite resistance).
9 If the switch does not perform as expected, it is defective and must be replaced. Check first that the fault is not caused by a sticking switch plunger due to ingress of road dirt; spray the switch with a water dispersant aerosol.
10 If the switch checks out OK, but the circuit fails to function correctly, disconnect the wire connector from the igniter (see Chapter 5). Check the grey/white wire between the sidestand switch connector and the igniter connector for continuity (see the wiring diagrams at the end of this book).
11 On all 1993-on models, except the Thunderbird, if the switch and wiring are good, the sidestand relay may be at fault. The relay is located in the vicinity of the battery **(see illustration)**. No test details are available for checking the relay.

Replacement

12 Disconnect the switch wiring connector as described above in Step 2.
13 Work back along the switch wiring, freeing it from any relevant retaining clips and ties, noting its correct routing. On later models, remove the water pump hose cover for access. On Trophy and Daytona models, access to the wiring can be improved by removing the fairing left lower panel as described in Chapter 8.
14 Unscrew the bolts securing the switch to

the sidestand mounting bracket. **Note:** *It may be found that the wiring will not pass between the water pump and sprocket cover, necessitating the removal of either component (see Chapter 3 for the water pump or Chapter 6 for the sprocket cover).*
15 Fit the new switch to the sidestand bracket and install the retaining bolts, tightening them securely.
16 Make sure the wiring is correctly routed up to the connector and retained by all the necessary clips and ties. If removed, install the water pump or sprocket cover. On later models, install the water pump hose cover.
17 Reconnect the wiring connector and check the operation of the sidestand switch and, where fitted, the warning light.
18 If removed on Trophy and Daytona models, fit the fairing panel as described in Chapter 8.

23 Clutch switch - check and replacement

Check

1 The clutch switch is situated on the base of the clutch master cylinder. The switch is part of the starter safety circuit which prevents the starter motor operating whilst the transmission is in gear unless the clutch lever is pulled in. If the starter circuit is faulty, first check the fuse (see Section 5).
2 To check the switch, disconnect the wiring connector from the switch. Connect the probes of an ohmmeter or a continuity test light between the two switch terminals which connect with the black/red and black wires of the connector. With the clutch lever at rest, continuity should be indicated. No continuity (infinite resistance) should be indicated when the clutch lever is pulled into the handlebar.
3 Now connect the meter probes across the switch terminals which connect with the black/yellow and black wires. With the clutch lever at rest, no continuity (infinite resistance) should be indicated. Continuity (0 ohms) should be indicated when the lever is pulled in to the handlebar.

9

23.5 Unscrew the clutch switch from the clutch master cylinder

24.1a On Trophy, Daytona, Sprint and Tiger models the horns are mounted on the fairing stay

24.1b On Thunderbird models the horn is mounted on the left side of the cylinder head

4 If the switch is satisfactory, check the remaining components in the starter circuit (neutral switch and starter relay) as described in the relevant sections of this Chapter. If all components are good, check the wiring between the various components (refer to the wiring diagrams at the end of this Chapter).

Replacement

5 Disconnect the wiring connector from the clutch switch. Unscrew the screw securing the switch to the base of the master cylinder and remove the switch, noting how it fits **(see illustration)**.
6 Install the new switch and connect the wiring connector.

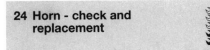

24 Horn - check and replacement

Check

1 On Trophy, Daytona, Sprint and Tiger models, the horns are mounted to the bottom of the fairing stay **(see illustration)**. On Trident and Speed Triple models, the horns are mounted on the bottom yoke. On Thunderbird models, the horn is mounted to the left side of the cylinder head **(see illustration)**.
2 Unplug the wiring connectors from the horn. Using two jumper wires, apply battery voltage directly to the terminals on the horn. If the horn sounds, check the switch (see Section 19) and the wiring between the switch and the horn (see the wiring diagrams at the end of this Chapter).
3 If the horn doesn't sound, check first that the battery is in good condition. If the battery is fully charged, and the horn still does not sound, replace the horn.

Replacement

4 Unplug the wiring connectors from the horn then unscrew the bolt securing the horn to its mounting bracket and remove it from the bike.
5 Connect the wiring connectors to the new horn and securely tighten its retaining bolt.

25 Low fuel level sensor - check and replacement (all models except Thunderbird)

> ⚠ **Warning: Petrol is extremely flammable, so take extra precautions when you work on any part of the fuel system.** Don't smoke or allow open flames or bare light bulbs near the work area, and don't work in a garage where a natural gas-type appliance is present. If you spill any fuel on your skin, rinse it off immediately with soap and water. When you perform any kind of work on the fuel system, wear safety glasses and have a fire extinguisher suitable for a class B type fire (flammable liquids) on hand.

Check

1 If the low fuel level warning light has not come on by the time the reserve fuel is needed (see Chapter 4 Specifications), check the fuses and the bulb (see Sections 5 and 16). If the fuses and bulb are good, check for battery voltage at the low fuel level sensor wiring connector blue/orange wire terminal using a test light.
2 If no voltage is indicated, check the blue/orange wire between the sensor and the warning light bulb for open-circuits and poor connections (see the wiring diagrams at the end of this Chapter).

25.6 The low fuel level sensor is mounted in the bottom of the tank

3 If the light still does not come on, and voltage is present at the connector, the sensor is faulty and must be replaced.
4 If the warning light comes on when the tank is full, disconnect the sensor wiring at the connector (at the sensor on Tiger models). The warning light should be out. If it is illuminated, the blue/orange wire between the sensor and warning light bulb must be earthed at some point. If the light goes out when the wiring is disconnected, the sensor must be assumed faulty and replaced.

Replacement

5 Drain and remove the fuel tank (Chapter 4).
6 Unscrew the sensor from the base of the tank and withdraw it **(see illustration)**. Discard the sealing washer as a new one must be used.
7 Install the sensor by reversing the removal process and use a new sealing washer.

26 Starter relay - check and replacement

Check

1 If the starter circuit is faulty, check the fuses (see Section 5). The starter relay is under the seat, in front of the battery **(see illustration)**.
2 With the ignition switch ON, the engine kill switch in RUN and the transmission in neutral, press the starter switch. The relay should click.
3 If the relay doesn't click, switch off the ignition and remove the relay; test it as follows.

26.1 The starter relay is located in front of the battery, under the seat (arrowed)

27.5 Peel back the rubber cover, then unscrew the nut and disconnect the starter cable from the motor

27.6 Unscrew the starter motor retaining bolts

27.10 Slide the starter motor into position in the crankcase

4 Set a multimeter to the ohms x 1 scale and connect it across the relay's starter motor and battery lead terminals. Using a fully-charged 12 volt battery and two insulated jumper wires, connect the positive (+) terminal of the battery to the black/red terminal of the relay, and the negative (-) terminal to the yellow/green terminal of the relay. At this point the relay should click and the multimeter read 0 ohms (continuity). If this is the case the relay is proved good and the fault lies in the starter switch circuit (check the clutch switch and neutral switch as described elsewhere in this Chapter); if the relay does not click when battery voltage is applied and indicates no continuity (infinite resistance) across its terminals, it is faulty and must be replaced.

Replacement

5 Remove the seat as described in Chapter 8.
6 Disconnect the battery terminals, remembering to disconnect the negative (-ve) terminal first.
7 Disconnect the relay wiring connectors and remove the relay with its rubber sleeve from the mounting lugs.
8 Peel back the rubber boots from the relay terminals, then unscrew the two nuts securing the starter motor and battery leads to the relay and detach the leads.
9 Installation is the reverse of removal ensuring that the terminal screws are securely tightened. Connect the negative (-ve) lead last when reconnecting the battery.

<table>
<tr><td>27</td><td>Starter motor - removal and installation</td></tr>
</table>

Removal

1 Remove the seat and side panels (see Chapter 8). Disconnect the battery negative (-ve) lead.
2 Referring to Chapter 8, remove the fairing lower panels on Trophy and Daytona models, the fairing on Sprint models, and the fairing side panels on Tiger models. On Thunderbird models remove the horn as described in Section 24 of this Chapter.

3 Remove the fuel tank and the carburettors as described in Chapter 4. On Thunderbird models, and later 4 cylinder engines (from VIN 2971), detach the crankcase breather hose from its union on the engine left end cover.
4 Drain the cooling system as described in Chapter 1, then remove the water pump outlet pipe as described in Chapter 3.
5 Peel back the rubber cover and unscrew the nut securing the starter cable to the motor **(see illustration)**.
6 Unscrew the starter motor retaining bolts **(see illustration)**.
7 Slide the starter motor out from the crankcase and remove it from the left side of the machine.
8 Remove the O-ring on the end of the starter motor and replace it; a new one will be needed for installation.

Installation

9 Install a new O-ring on the end of the starter motor and ensure it is seated in its groove; apply a smear of engine oil to the O-ring to aid installation.
10 Manoeuvre the motor into position and slide it into the crankcase **(see illustration)**. Ensure that the starter motor teeth mesh correctly with those of the starter idler gear.
11 Fit the retaining bolts and tighten them to the specified torque setting.
12 Connect the cable and spring washer, and secure with the nut. Make sure the rubber cover is correctly seated over the terminal.
13 Install the remaining components in a reverse of the removal procedure.

28.2a Make alignment marks (arrowed) between the housing . . .

14 Refill the cooling system (see Chapter 1).
15 Connect the battery negative (-ve) lead.

<table>
<tr><td>28</td><td>Starter motor - disassembly, inspection and reassembly</td></tr>
</table>

Disassembly

1 Remove the starter motor (see Section 27).
2 Make alignment marks between the housing and end covers **(see illustrations)**.
3 Unscrew the two long bolts then remove the left end cover from the motor along with its O-ring.
4 Wrap insulating tape around the teeth of the starter motor gear - this will protect the oil seal from damage as the right end cover is withdrawn. Remove the right end cover from the motor along with its O-ring.
5 Withdraw the armature from the housing.
6 Unscrew the nut from the terminal bolt and remove the insulating washer and the O-ring. Withdraw the terminal bolt and brushplate assembly from the housing.
7 Lift the brush springs and slide the brushes out from their holders.

Inspection

Note: *No replacement parts are available from Triumph for the starter motor. If the following checks indicate a worn or faulty internal component, seek the advice of a Triumph dealer or auto electrical specialist before buying a new starter motor.*

28.2b . . . and the end covers before disassembly (arrowed)

9

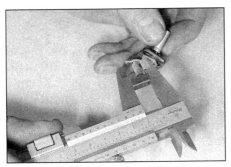

28.8 Measuring brush length

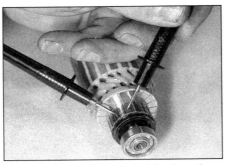

28.10 Inspect the commutator bars for wear and test as described in the text

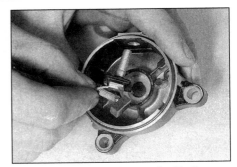

28.14a Install the terminal bolt in the rear cover . . .

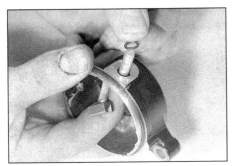

28.14b . . . fit the O-ring . . .

28.14c . . . the insulating washer . . .

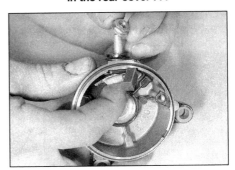

28.14d . . . and the terminal nut

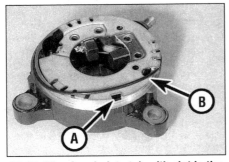

28.15 Align brushplate tab with slot in the rear cover (A) and fit the cover O-ring (B)

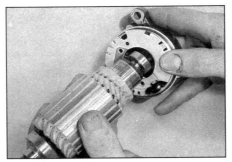

28.16 Fit the armature into the rear cover . . .

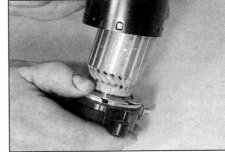

28.17 . . . and fit the main housing over the armature

8 The parts of the starter motor that are most likely to wear are the brushes. Measure the length of the brushes and compare the results to the service limit in this Chapter's Specifications **(see illustration)**. If the brushes are not worn excessively, nor cracked, chipped, or otherwise damaged, they may be re-used.

9 Inspect the commutator for scoring, scratches and discoloration. The commutator can be cleaned and polished with crocus cloth, but do not use sandpaper or emery paper. After cleaning, wipe away any residue with a cloth soaked in electrical system cleaner or denatured alcohol. Measure the diameter of the commutator and compare the reading with the service limit in the Specifications.

10 Using an ohmmeter or a continuity test light, check for continuity between the commutator bars **(see illustration)**. Continuity should exist between each bar and all of the others. Also, check for continuity between the commutator bars and the armature shaft.

There should be no continuity (infinite resistance) between the commutator and the shaft. If the checks indicate otherwise, the armature is defective.

11 Check for continuity between each brush and the brushplate, and between the brush and its terminal bolt. There should be continuity in both cases.

12 Check the starter gear for worn, cracked, chipped and broken teeth. If the gear is damaged or worn, replace the starter motor.

13 Inspect the end covers for signs of cracks or wear. Inspect the magnets in the main housing and the housing itself for cracks.

Reassembly

14 Ensure that the rubber insulating washer is in place on the terminal bolt, then insert the bolt through the rear cover **(see illustration)**. Fit the O-ring and the insulating washer and secure them in place with the nut **(see illustrations)**.

15 Lift the brush springs on the brushplate and slide the brushes back into position in their holders, then install the brushplate assembly in the rear cover making sure its tab is correctly located in the slot in the cover. Make sure the O-ring is fitted to the cover **(see illustration)**.

16 Insert the armature into the rear end cover taking care not to damage the brushes. As it is inserted, locate the brushes on the commutator bars. Check that each brush is securely pressed against the commutator by its spring and is free to move easily in its holder **(see illustration)**.

17 Fit the main housing over the armature, aligning the marks made on removal **(see illustration)**.

18 Fit the O-ring to the front end cover and carefully slide the cover into position, aligning the marks made on removal. Remove any protective tape from the gear teeth.

19 Check the marks made on removal are

28.19 Install the long bolts and tighten them securely

correctly aligned then fit the long bolts and tighten them securely **(see illustration)**.
20 Install the starter motor (see Section 27).

29 Charging system testing - general information and precautions

1 If the performance of the charging system is suspect, the system as a whole should be checked first, followed by testing of the individual components. **Note:** *Before beginning the checks, make sure the battery is fully charged and that all system connections are clean and tight.*
2 Checking the output of the charging system and the performance of the various components within the charging system requires the use of a multimeter (with voltage, current and resistance checking facilities).
3 When making the checks, follow the procedures carefully to prevent incorrect connections or short circuits, as irreparable damage to electrical system components may result if short circuits occur.
4 If a multimeter is not available, the job of checking the charging system should be left to a Triumph dealer.

30 Charging system - output test

1 Remove the seat (see Chapter 8).
2 Remove the three nuts from the alternator end cover and lift off the cover **(see illustration 31.5)**. Make a visual check of the alternator leads and connections; repair or clean as required. If all appears to be in order, proceed as follows.
3 Connect a multimeter set to the dc 0-20 volts scale across the terminals of the battery (positive (+ve) meter lead to battery positive (+ve) terminal, negative (-ve) meter lead to battery negative (-ve) terminal). Start the engine and take note of the voltage reading. If the alternator is in good condition, the measured voltage should be higher than 13.5 volts, although not excessively high. If the voltage is lower than 13.5 volts, stop the engine and repeat the test having first earthed the F terminal

of the regulator (see illustration 31.9 for terminal identification) to the frame using an insulated auxiliary wire; if the voltage reading obtained when the engine is running is now higher than 13.5 volts, the regulator is faulty - confirm this with the check described in Section 31. If the reading is still below 13.5 volts the fault must lie in either the brushes and slip rings, the rectifier, stator coil or rotor coil (see Section 31).
4 Occasionally the condition may arise where the alternator output is excessive. This condition is probably due to a faulty regulator - confirm this with the check in Section 31.
5 If the alternator has become noisy whilst the engine is running it is most likely that its bearings are worn. Check also the condition of the shock absorber dampers in the alternator drive.

> **HAYNES HINT**
> *Clues to a faulty regulator are constantly blowing bulbs, with brightness varying considerably with engine speed, and battery overheating, necessitating frequent topping up of the electrolyte level.*

31 Alternator components - removal, testing and installation

Removal

1 On Thunderbird models, remove the horn as described in Section 24.

31.3 The alternator is secured to the crankcase by three bolts (arrowed)

31.6a Remove the brush holder screws and remove the holder

2 Trace the alternator wiring to its connector behind the left side panel and disconnect it. **Note:** *It was found necessary on the machine photographed, to remove the left auxiliary air chamber for access to the wire connector (see Chapter 4 for air chamber removal).*
3 Unscrew the three alternator mounting bolts, noting that the upper bolt secures the alternator earth lead **(see illustration)**. Withdraw the alternator from the engine, leaving the shock absorber rubbers in the driveshaft housing.

Testing

Note: *No replacement parts are available from Triumph for the alternator. If the following checks indicate a worn or faulty internal component, seek the advice of a Triumph dealer or auto electrical specialist before buying a new alternator.*
4 The following checks can be made without removing the alternator from the engine, although the alternator wiring must first be disconnected as described in Step 2.
5 Unscrew the three nuts securing the alternator end cover and remove the cover **(see illustration)**.

Brushes and slip rings

6 Remove the three screws securing the brush holder and remove the holder **(see illustration)**. Inspect the holder for any signs of damage. Measure the brush lengths (ie the amount of brush extending from the holder) and compare the measurements with the figures given in the Specifications at the beginning of the Chapter **(see illustration)**.

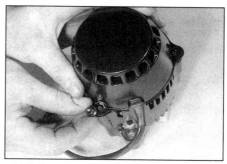

31.5 Unscrew the three nuts and detach the alternator end cover

31.6b Inspect the brush holder for damage and measure the brush lengths

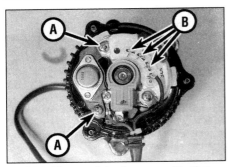

31.8 The regulator is secured to the alternator by two screws (A). Rectifier diode terminals are shown by arrows (B)

7 Whilst the brush holder is removed, clean the slip rings with a rag moistened with solvent. If they are badly marked, tidy them up with very fine emery cloth. Using a vernier caliper, measure the diameter of both slip rings and check that they have not worn down past the service limit (see Specifications).

Regulator

8 Remove the brush holder as described above. Remove the two screws securing the regulator to the alternator and remove the regulator **(see illustration)**.

9 Using a multimeter set to the required ohms range, test the internal resistances of the regulator in accordance with the diagram **(see illustration)**. Further testing of the regulator isn't possible with home workshop equipment - have your findings confirmed by a Triumph dealer before replacing the regulator with a new one.

Rectifier

10 The rectifier connections require unsoldering before it can be fully removed

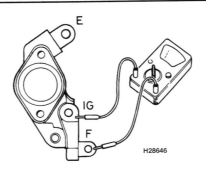

METER RANGE	CONNECTIONS		READING
	METER(+)TO	METER(-)TO	
x100Ω	F	E	170Ω
x1kΩ	E	F	4kΩ
x100Ω	IG	E	800Ω
x1kΩ	E	IG	2kΩ
x1kΩ	F	IG	2kΩ
x100Ω	IG	F	150Ω

31.9 Regulator resistance tests

from the alternator. Since there is a risk of damaging the rectifier diodes if excess heat is applied, it is recommended that the rectifier be tested by a Triumph dealer or auto electrician.

Further checks and overhaul

11 Further testing of the alternator components should be left to a Triumph dealer or auto electrician. This also applies to removal of the rotor and bearing replacement.

Installation

12 If removed, install the rubbers into the shock absorber housing, using a smear of grease to secure them in place if necessary **(see illustration)**.

31.12 Install the rubbers into the shock absorber housing

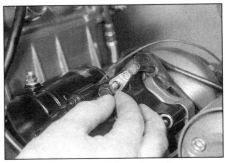

31.14 Install the alternator and fit the earth lead

13 Fit a new O-ring to the alternator and smear it with oil.

14 Install the alternator on the engine and fit the mounting bolts, not forgetting to connect the earth lead **(see illustration)**. Fit the rubber boot over the earth connection.

15 Reconnect the alternator wiring at the connector. On Thunderbird models, fit the horn as described in Section 24.

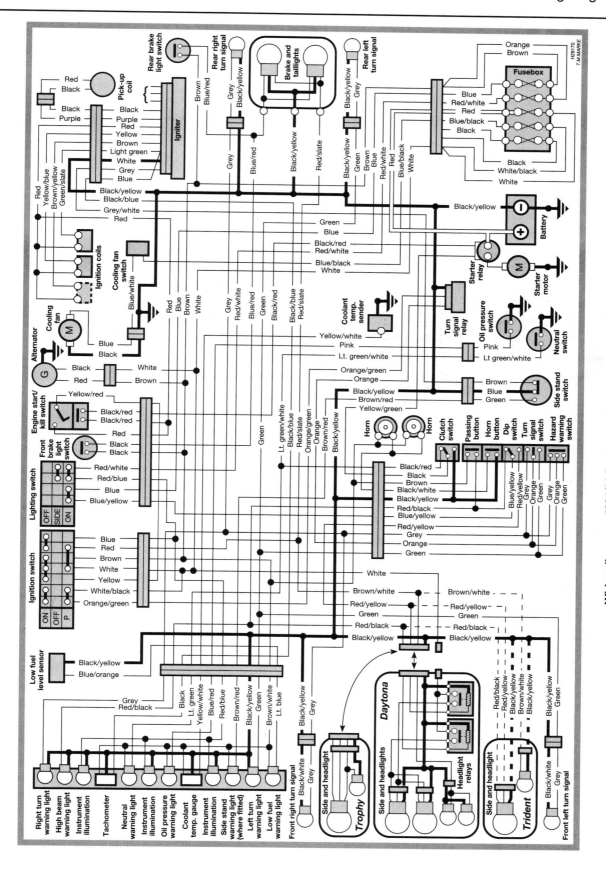

Wiring diagram - 1991/92 Trophy, Trident and Daytona models

9

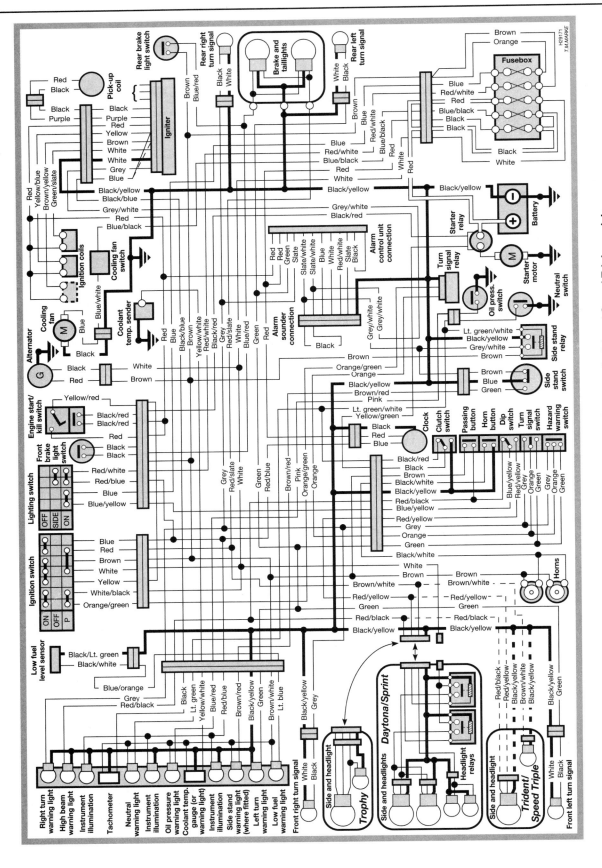

Wiring diagram - 1993/94 Trophy, Trident , Daytona, Sprint and Speed Triple models

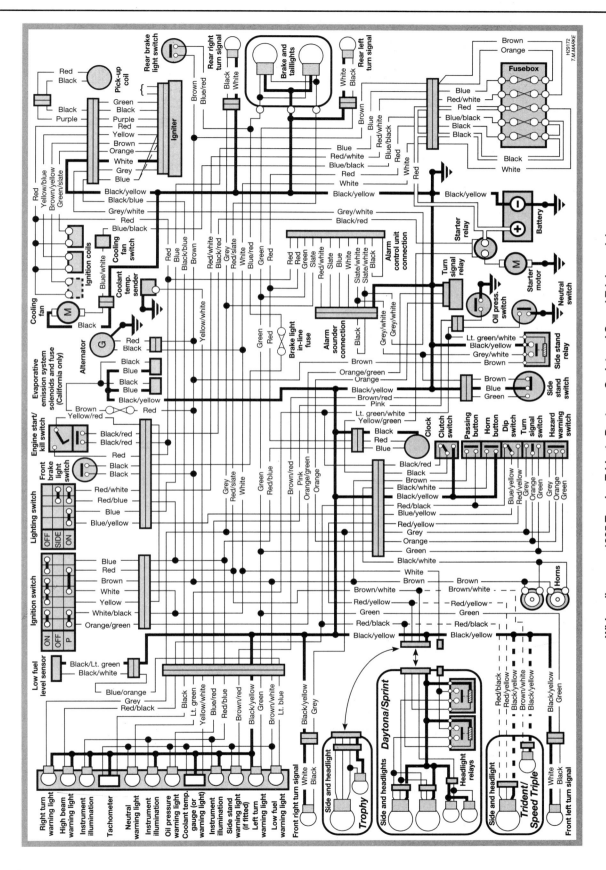

Wiring diagram - 1995 Trophy, Trident, Daytona, Sprint and Speed Triple models

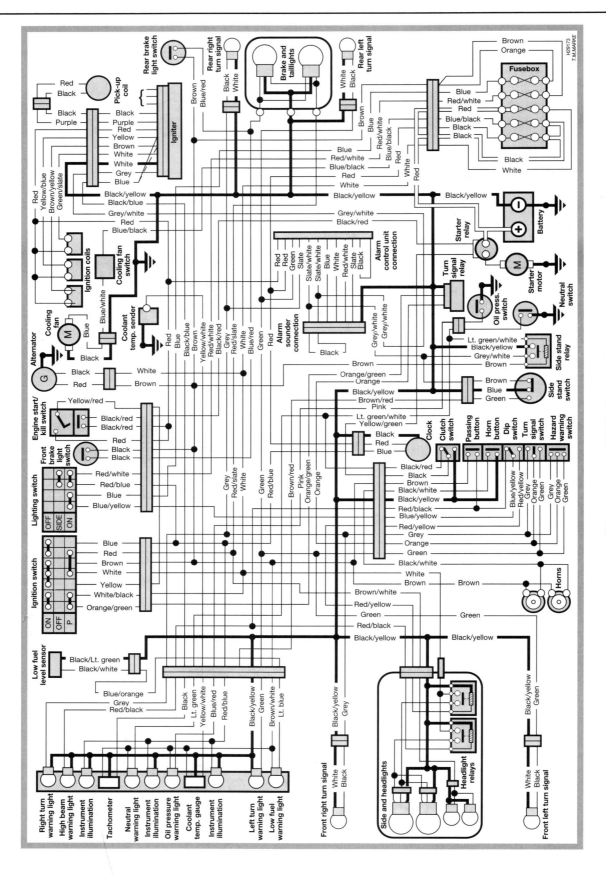

Wiring diagram - 1993/94 Tiger model

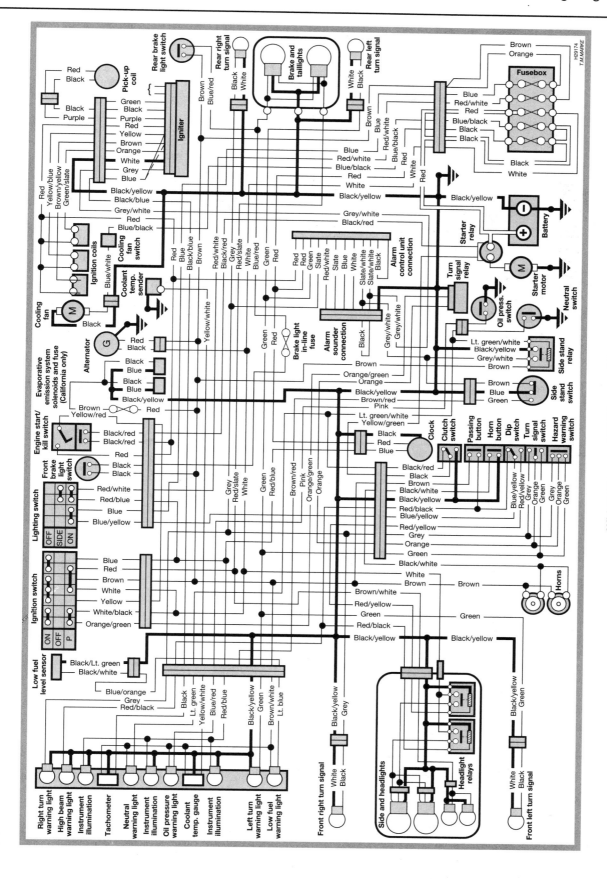

Wiring diagram – 1995 Tiger model

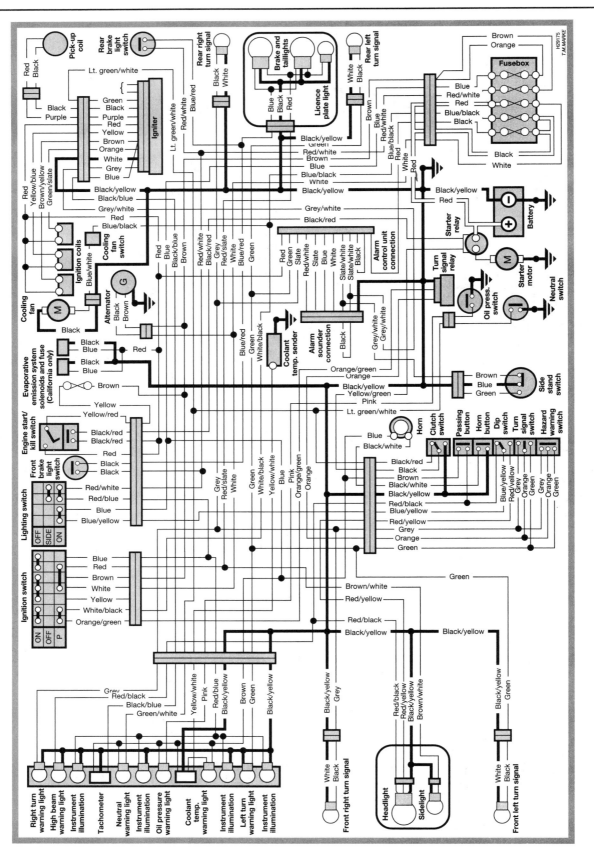

Wiring diagram - Thunderbird model

Dimensions and Weights

Wheelbase
750 and 1000 Daytona, 900 Trident ....1510 mm
Tiger and Thunderbird ....1550 mm
All other models ....1490 mm

Overall length
Trophy, 900 and 1200 Daytona, Speed Triple, Trident, Sprint .2152 mm
750 and 1000 Daytona ....2160 mm
Thunderbird ....2250 mm
Tiger ....2290 mm

Overall width
Trophy, Daytona Super III, Speed Triple, Trident, Sprint .....760 mm
All Daytona models except Super III ....690 mm
Thunderbird ....860 mm
Tiger ....920 mm

Overall height
Trophy, 750 and 1000 Daytona ....1270 mm
900 and 1200 Daytona, Speed Triple ....1185 mm
Trident ....1090 mm
Sprint ....1265 mm
Thunderbird ....1150 mm
Tiger ....1345 mm

Seat height
Trophy ....780 mm
750 and 1000 Daytona ....810 mm
900 and 1200 Daytona, Speed Triple ....790 mm
Trident, Sprint ....775 mm
Thunderbird ....750 mm
Tiger ....850 mm

Weight (dry)
900 Trophy ....217 kg
1200 Trophy ....232 kg
900 Daytona ....213 kg
900 Daytona Super III ....211 kg
750 and 1000 Daytona ....Not available
1200 Daytona ....225 kg
Trident ....212 kg
Sprint ....215 kg
Speed Triple ....209 kg
Thunderbird ....220 kg
Tiger ....209 kg

Conversion Factors

Length (distance)

Inches (in)	25.4	= Millimetres (mm)	x 0.0394	=	Inches (in)
Feet (ft)	0.305	= Metres (m)	x 3.281	=	Feet (ft)
Miles	1.609	= Kilometres (km)	x 0.621	=	Miles

Volume (capacity)

Cubic inches (cu in; in³)	x 16.387	= Cubic centimetres (cc; cm³)	x 0.061	=	Cubic inches (cu in; in³)
Imperial pints (Imp pt)	x 0.568	= Litres (l)	x 1.76	=	Imperial pints (Imp pt)
Imperial quarts (Imp qt)	x 1.137	= Litres (l)	x 0.88	=	Imperial quarts (Imp qt)
Imperial quarts (Imp qt)	x 1.201	= US quarts (US qt)	x 0.833	=	Imperial quarts (Imp qt)
US quarts (US qt)	x 0.946	= Litres (l)	x 1.057	=	US quarts (US qt)
Imperial gallons (Imp gal)	x 4.546	= Litres (l)	x 0.22	=	Imperial gallons (Imp gal)
Imperial gallons (Imp gal)	x 1.201	= US gallons (US gal)	x 0.833	=	Imperial gallons (Imp gal)
US gallons (US gal)	x 3.785	= Litres (l)	x 0.264	=	US gallons (US gal)

Mass (weight)

Ounces (oz)	x 28.35	= Grams (g)	x 0.035	=	Ounces (oz)
Pounds (lb)	x 0.454	= Kilograms (kg)	x 2.205	=	Pounds (lb)

Force

Ounces-force (ozf; oz)	x 0.278	= Newtons (N)	x 3.6	=	Ounces-force (ozf; oz)
Pounds-force (lbf; lb)	x 4.448	= Newtons (N)	x 0.225	=	Pounds-force (lbf; lb)
Newtons (N)	x 0.1	= Kilograms-force (kgf; kg)	x 9.81	=	Newtons (N)

Pressure

Pounds-force per square inch (psi; lbf/in²; lb/in²)	x 0.070	= Kilograms-force per square centimetre (kgf/cm²; kg/cm²)	x 14.223	=	Pounds-force per square inch (psi; lbf/in²; lb/in²)
Pounds-force per square inch (psi; lbf/in²; lb/in²)	x 0.068	= Atmospheres (atm)	x 14.696	=	Pounds-force per square inch (psi; lbf/in²; lb/in²)
Pounds-force per square inch (psi; lbf/in²; lb/in²)	x 0.069	= Bars	x 14.5	=	Pounds-force per square inch (psi; lbf/in²; lb/in²)
Pounds-force per square inch (psi; lbf/in²; lb/in²)	x 6.895	= Kilopascals (kPa)	x 0.145	=	Pounds-force per square inch (psi; lbf/in²; lb/in²)
Kilopascals (kPa)	x 0.01	= Kilograms-force per square centimetre (kgf/cm²; kg/cm²)	x 98.1	=	Kilopascals (kPa)
Millibar (mbar)	x 100	= Pascals (Pa)	x 0.01	=	Millibar (mbar)
Millibar (mbar)	x 0.0145	= Pounds-force per square inch (psi; lbf/in²; lb/in²)	x 68.947	=	Millibar (mbar)
Millibar (mbar)	x 0.75	= Millimetres of mercury (mmHg)	x 1.333	=	Millibar (mbar)
Millibar (mbar)	x 0.401	= Inches of water (inH$_2$O)	x 2.491	=	Millibar (mbar)
Millimetres of mercury (mmHg)	x 0.535	= Inches of water (inH$_2$O)	x 1.868	=	Millimetres of mercury (mmHg)
Inches of water (inH$_2$O)	x 0.036	= Pounds-force per square inch (psi; lbf/in²; lb/in²)	x 27.68	=	Inches of water (inH$_2$O)

Torque (moment of force)

Pounds-force inches (lbf in; lb in)	x 1.152	= Kilograms-force centimetre (kgf cm; kg cm)	x 0.868	=	Pounds-force inches (lbf in; lb in)
Pounds-force inches (lbf in; lb in)	x 0.113	= Newton metres (Nm)	x 8.85	=	Pounds-force inches (lbf in; lb in)
Pounds-force inches (lbf in; lb in)	x 0.083	= Pounds-force feet (lbf ft; lb ft)	x 12	=	Pounds-force inches (lbf in; lb in)
Pounds-force feet (lbf ft; lb ft)	x 0.138	= Kilograms-force metres (kgf m; kg m)	x 7.233	=	Pounds-force feet (lbf ft; lb ft)
Pounds-force feet (lbf ft; lb ft)	x 1.356	= Newton metres (Nm)	x 0.738	=	Pounds-force feet (lbf ft; lb ft)
Newton metres (Nm)	x 0.102	= Kilograms-force metres (kgf m; kg m)	x 9.804	=	Newton metres (Nm)

Power

Horsepower (hp)	x 745.7	= Watts (W)	x 0.0013	=	Horsepower (hp)

Velocity (speed)

Miles per hour (miles/hr; mph)	x 1.609	= Kilometres per hour (km/hr; kph)	x 0.621	=	Miles per hour (miles/hr; mph)

Fuel consumption*

Miles per gallon (mpg)	x 0.354	= Kilometres per litre (km/l)	x 2.825	=	Miles per gallon (mpg)

It is common practice to convert from miles per gallon (mpg) to litres/100 kilometres (l/100km), where mpg x l/100 km = 282

Temperature

Degrees Fahrenheit = (°C x 1.8) + 32

Degrees Celsius (Degrees Centigrade; °C) = (°F - 32) x 0.56

Basic maintenance techniques

There are a number of techniques involved in maintenance and repair that will be referred to throughout this manual. Application of these techniques will enable the amateur mechanic to be more efficient, better organised and capable of performing the various tasks properly, which will ensure that the repair job is thorough and complete.

Fastening systems

Fasteners, basically, are nuts, bolts and screws used to hold two or more parts together, those on the Triumph models are mostly of the Torx head type. There are a few things to keep in mind when working with fasteners. Almost all of them use a locking device of some type (either a lock washer, locknut, locking tab or thread locking compound). All threaded fasteners should be clean, straight, have undamaged threads and undamaged corners on the hex head where the spanner fits. Develop the habit of replacing all damaged nuts and bolts with new ones.

Rusted nuts and bolts should be treated with a penetrating oil to ease removal and prevent breakage. After applying the rust penetrant, let it work for a few minutes before trying to loosen the nut or bolt. Badly rusted fasteners may have to be chiselled off or removed with a special nut breaker, available at tool shops.

If a bolt or stud breaks off in an assembly, it can be drilled out and removed with a special tool called an E-Z out (or screw extractor). Most dealer service departments and motorcycle repair shops can perform this task, as well as others (such as the repair of threaded holes that have been stripped out).

Washers should always be replaced exactly as removed. Replace any damaged washers with new ones. Always use a flat washer between a lock washer and any soft metal surface (such as aluminium), thin sheet metal or plastic. Special locknuts can only be used once or twice before they lose their locking ability and must be replaced.

Tightening sequences and procedures

When threaded fasteners are tightened, they are often tightened to a specific torque value (torque is basically a twisting force). Over-tightening the fastener can weaken it and cause it to break, while under-tightening can cause it to eventually come loose. Each bolt, depending on the material it's made of, the diameter of its shank and the material it is threaded into, has a specific torque value, which is noted in the Specifications. Be sure to follow the torque recommendations closely.

Fasteners laid out in a pattern (ie cylinder head bolts, engine case bolts, etc.) must be loosened or tightened in a sequence to avoid warping the component. Initially, the bolts/nuts should go on finger-tight only. Next, they should be tightened one full turn each, in a criss-cross or diagonal pattern. After each one has been tightened one full turn, return to the first one tightened and tighten them all one half turn, following the same pattern. Finally, tighten each of them one quarter turn at a time until each fastener has been tightened to the proper torque. To loosen and remove the fasteners the procedure would be reversed.

Disassembly sequence

Component disassembly should be done with care and purpose to help ensure that the parts go back together properly during reassembly. Always keep track of the sequence in which parts are removed. Take note of special characteristics or marks on parts that can be installed more than one way (such as convex washers and gear pinions). It's a good idea to lay the disassembled parts out on a clean surface in the order that they were removed. It may also be helpful to make sketches or take instant photos of components before removal.

When removing fasteners from a component, keep track of their locations. Sometimes threading a bolt back in a part, or putting the washers and nut back on a stud, can prevent mix-ups later. If nuts and bolts can't be returned to their original locations, they should be kept in a compartmented box or a series of small boxes or labelled plastic bags. A box of this type is especially helpful when working on assemblies with very small parts (such as the carburettors, tappets, shims etc).

Whenever wiring looms, harnesses or connectors are separated, it's a good idea to identify the two halves with numbered pieces of masking tape so they can be easily reconnected.

Gasket sealing surfaces

Gaskets are used to seal the mating surfaces between components and keep lubricants, fluids, vacuum or pressure contained in an assembly.

Many times these gaskets are coated with a liquid or paste type gasket sealing compound before assembly. Age, heat and pressure can sometimes cause the two parts to stick together so tightly that they are very difficult to separate. In most cases, the part can be loosened by striking it with a soft-faced hammer near the mating surfaces. A normal hammer can be used if a block of wood is placed between the hammer and the part. Do not hammer on cast parts or parts that could be easily damaged. With any particularly stubborn part, always recheck to make sure that every fastener has been removed.

Avoid using a screwdriver or bar to pry apart components, as they can easily mark the gasket sealing surfaces of the parts (which must remain smooth). If prying is absolutely necessary, use a piece of wood, but keep in mind that extra clean-up will be necessary if the wood splinters.

After the parts are separated, the old gasket must be carefully scraped off and the gasket surfaces cleaned. Stubborn gasket material can be soaked with a gasket remover (available in aerosol cans) to soften it so it can be easily scraped off. A scraper can be fashioned from a piece of copper tubing by flattening and sharpening one end. Copper is recommended because it is usually softer than the surfaces to be scraped, which reduces the chance of gouging the part. Some gaskets can be removed with a wire brush, but regardless of the method used, the mating surfaces must be left clean and smooth. If for some reason the gasket surface is gouged, then a gasket sealant thick enough to fill scratches will have to be used during reassembly of the components. For most applications, a non-drying (or semi-drying) gasket sealant is best.

Hose removal tips

Hose removal precautions closely parallel gasket removal precautions. Avoid scratching or gouging the surface that the hose mates against or the connection may leak. Because of various chemical reactions, the rubber in hoses can bond itself to the metal union that the hose fits over. To remove a hose, first loosen the hose clamps that secure it to the union. Then, with slip joint pliers, grab the hose at the clamp and rotate it around the union. Work it back and forth until it is completely free, then pull it off (silicone or other lubricants will ease removal if they can be applied between the hose and the outside of the union). Apply the same lubricant to the inside of the hose and the outside of the union to simplify installation.

If the hose is particularly stubborn, slit the hose with a sharp knife and peel it off the union. The hose will obviously be destroyed using this method.

If a hose clamp is broken or damaged, do not reuse it. Also, do not reuse hoses that are cracked, split or torn.

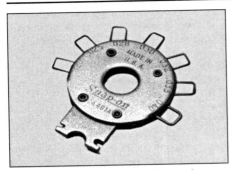

Spark plug gap adjusting tool

Feeler blade set

Allen keys (left), and Allen key sockets (right)

Tools

A selection of good tools is a basic requirement for anyone who plans to maintain and repair a motorcycle. For the owner who has few tools, if any, the initial investment might seem high, but when compared to the spiralling costs of routine maintenance and repair, it is a wise one.

To help the owner decide which tools are needed to perform the tasks detailed in this manual, the following tool lists are offered: Maintenance and minor repair, Repair and overhaul and Special. The newcomer to practical mechanics should start off with the Maintenance and minor repair tool kit, which is adequate for the simpler jobs. Then, as confidence and experience grow, the owner can tackle more difficult tasks, buying additional tools as they are needed. Eventually the basic kit will be built into the Repair and overhaul tool set. Over a period of time, the experienced do-it-yourselfer will assemble a tool set complete enough for most repair and overhaul procedures and will add tools from the Special category when it is felt that the expense is justified by the frequency of use.

Maintenance and minor repair tool kit

The tools in this list should be considered the minimum required for performance of routine maintenance, servicing and minor repair work. We recommend the purchase of combination spanners (ring end and open end combined in one spanner); while more expensive than open-ended ones, they offer the advantages of both types of wrench.

Combination spanner set (6 mm to 22 mm)
Adjustable wrench - 8 in
Spark plug socket (with rubber insert)
Spark plug gap adjusting tool
Feeler blade set
Standard flat-bladed screwdriver set
Phillips screwdriver set
Allen key set (4 mm to 12 mm)
Torx key set (4 mm to 12 mm)
Combination (slip-joint) pliers - 6 in
Slim open-end spanners (for steering head
  bearing adjustment on later models)
Hacksaw and assortment of blades
Tyre pressure gauge
Tyre tread depth gauge
Control cable pressure luber
Grease gun
Oil can
Fine emery cloth
Wire brush
Hand impact screwdriver and bits
Funnel (medium size)
Safety goggles
Drain tray

Repair and overhaul tool set

These tools are essential for anyone who plans to perform major repairs and are intended to supplement those in the Maintenance and minor repair tool kit. Included is a comprehensive set of sockets which, though expensive, are invaluable because of their versatility (especially when various extensions and drives are available). We recommend the 3/8 inch drive over the 1/2 inch drive for general motorcycle maintenance and repair (ideally, the mechanic would have a 3/8 inch drive set and a 1/2 inch drive set).

Socket set(s)
Reversible ratchet
Extension - 6 in
Universal joint
Torque wrench (same size drive as sockets)
Ball pein hammer - 8 oz
Soft-faced hammer (plastic/rubber)
Pliers - needle nose
Pliers - circlip (internal and external)
Cold chisel - 1/2 in
Scriber
Scraper
Centre punch
Pin punches (1/16, 1/8, 3/16 in)
Steel rule/straightedge - 12 in
A selection of files
Wire brush (large)
Degree disc (for angle-tightening)
Clutch centre holder tool
Multimeter

Note: *Another tool which is often useful is an electric drill with a chuck capacity of 3/8 inch (and a set of good quality drill bits).*

Torx bit set

Control cable pressure luber

Hand impact screwdriver and bits

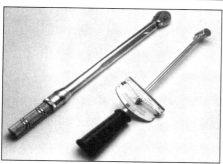

Torque wrenches (left - click; right - beam type)

Circlip pliers (top - external; bottom - internal)

Multimeter (volt/ohm/ammeter)

Special tools

The tools in this list include those which are not used regularly, are expensive to buy, or which need to be used in accordance with their manufacturer's instructions. Unless these tools will be used frequently, it is not very economical to purchase many of them. A consideration would be to split the cost and use between yourself and a friend or friends (ie members of a motorcycle club).

This list primarily contains tools and instruments widely available to the public, as well as some special tools produced by the motorcycle manufacturer for distribution to dealers. As a result, references to the manufacturer's special tools are occasionally included in the text of this manual. Generally, an alternative method of doing the job without the special tool is offered. However, sometimes there is no alternative to their use. Where this is the case, and the tool can't be purchased or borrowed, the work should be entrusted to a dealer.

Valve spring compressor
Piston ring removal and installation tool
Oil pressure gauge adapter and gauge
Telescoping gauges
Micrometer and Vernier calipers
Dial indicator set
Manometer or vacuum gauge set
Replacement crankshaft right end cover - for ignition timing check
Stroboscopic timing light
Small air compressor with blow gun and tyre chuck
Stud extractor set

Buying tools

For the do-it-yourselfer who is just starting to get involved in motorcycle maintenance and repair, there are a number of options available when purchasing tools. If maintenance and minor repair is the extent of the work to be done, the purchase of individual tools is satisfactory. If, on the other hand, extensive work is planned, it would be a good idea to purchase a modest tool set from one of the large retail chain stores. A set can usually be bought at a substantial savings over the individual tool prices (and they often come with a tool box). As additional tools are needed, add-on sets, individual tools and a larger tool box can be purchased to expand the tool selection. Building a tool set gradually allows the cost of the tools to be spread over a longer period of time and gives the mechanic the freedom to choose only those tools that will actually be used.

Tool shops and motorcycle dealers will often be the only source of some of the special tools that are needed, but regardless of where tools are bought, try to avoid cheap ones (especially when buying screwdrivers and sockets) because they won't last very long. There are plenty of tools around at reasonable prices, but always aim to purchase items which meet the relevant national safety standards. The expense involved in replacing cheap tools will eventually be greater than the initial cost of quality tools.

It is obviously not possible to cover the subject of tools fully here. For those who wish to learn more about tools and their use, there is a book entitled *Motorcycle Workshop Practice Manual* (Book no. 1454) available from the publishers of this manual. It also provides an introduction to basic workshop practice which will be of interest to a home mechanic working on any type of motorcycle.

Care and maintenance of tools

Good tools are expensive, so it makes sense to treat them with respect. Keep them clean and in usable condition and store them properly when not in use. Always wipe off any dirt, grease or metal chips before putting them away. Never leave tools lying around in the work area.

Some tools, such as screwdrivers, pliers, spanners and sockets, can be hung on a panel mounted on the garage or workshop wall, while others should be kept in a tool box or tray. Measuring instruments, gauges, meters, etc. must be carefully stored where they can't be damaged by weather or impact from other tools.

When tools are used with care and stored properly, they will last a very long time. Even with the best of care, tools will wear out if used frequently. When a tool is damaged or worn out, replace it; subsequent jobs will be safer and more enjoyable if you do.

Valve spring compressor

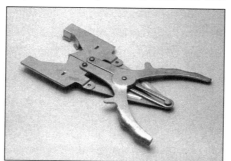

Piston ring removal/installation tool

Telescoping gauges

Micrometer

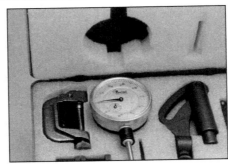

Dial indicator set

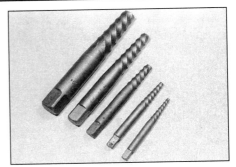

Stud extractor set

Working facilities

Not to be overlooked when discussing tools is the workshop. If anything more than routine maintenance is to be carried out, some sort of suitable work area is essential.

It is understood, and appreciated, that many home mechanics do not have a good workshop or garage available and end up removing an engine or doing major repairs outside (it is recommended, however, that the overhaul or repair be completed under the cover of a roof).

A clean, flat workbench or table of comfortable working height is an absolute necessity. The workbench should be equipped with a vice that has a jaw opening of at least four inches.

As mentioned previously, some clean, dry storage space is also required for tools, as well as the lubricants, fluids, cleaning solvents, etc. which soon become necessary.

Sometimes waste oil and fluids, drained from the engine or cooling system during normal maintenance or repairs, present a disposal problem. Do not pour them on the ground or into the drainage system, simply pour the used fluids into large containers, seal them with caps and take them to an authorised disposal site or garage.

Always keep a supply of old newspapers and clean rags available. Old towels are excellent for mopping up spills. Many mechanics use rolls of paper towels for most work because they are readily available and disposable. To help keep the area under the motorcycle clean, a large cardboard box can be cut open and flattened to protect the garage or workshop floor.

Whenever working over a painted surface (such as the fuel tank) cover it with an old blanket or bedspread to protect the finish.

A number of chemicals and lubricants are available for use in motorcycle maintenance and repair. They include a wide variety of products ranging from cleaning solvents and degreasers to lubricants and protective sprays for rubber, plastic and vinyl.

● **Contact point/spark plug cleaner** is a solvent used to clean oily film and dirt from points, grime from electrical connectors and oil deposits from spark plugs. It is oil free and leaves no residue. It can also be used to remove gum and varnish from carburettor jets and other orifices.

● **Carburettor cleaner** is similar to contact point/spark plug cleaner but it usually has a stronger solvent and may leave a slight oily reside. It is not recommended for cleaning electrical components or connections.

● **Brake system cleaner** is used to remove grease or brake fluid from brake system components (where clean surfaces are absolutely necessary and petroleum-based solvents cannot be used); it also leaves no residue.

● **Silicone-based lubricants** are used to protect rubber parts such as hoses and grommets, and are used as lubricants for hinges and locks.

● **Multi-purpose grease** is an all purpose lubricant used wherever grease is more practical than a liquid lubricant such as oil. Some multi-purpose grease is coloured white and specially formulated to be more resistant to water than ordinary grease.

● **Gear oil** (sometimes called gear lube) is a specially designed oil used in transmissions and final drive units, as well as other areas where high friction, high temperature lubrication is required. It is available in a number of viscosities (weights) for various applications.

● **Motor oil**, of course, is the lubricant specially formulated for use in the engine. It normally contains a wide variety of additives to prevent corrosion and reduce foaming and wear. Motor oil comes in various weights (viscosity ratings) of from 5 to 80. The recommended weight of the oil depends on the seasonal temperature and the demands on the engine. Light oil is used in cold climates and under light load conditions; heavy oil is used in hot climates and where high loads are encountered. Multi-viscosity oils are designed to have characteristics of both light and heavy oils and are available in a number of weights from 5W-20 to 20W-50.

● **Petrol additives** perform several functions, depending on their chemical makeup. They usually contain solvents that help dissolve gum and varnish that build up on carburettor and inlet parts. They also serve to break down carbon deposits that form on the inside surfaces of the combustion chambers. Some additives contain upper cylinder lubricants for valves and piston rings.

● **Brake and clutch fluid** is a specially formulated hydraulic fluid that can withstand the heat and pressure encountered in brake/clutch systems. Care must be taken that this fluid does not come in contact with painted surfaces or plastics. An opened container should always be resealed to prevent contamination by water or dirt.

● **Chain lubricants** are formulated especially for use on motorcycle final drive chains. A good chain lube should adhere well and have good penetrating qualities to be effective as a lubricant inside the chain and on the side plates, pins and rollers. Most chain lubes are either the foaming type or quick drying type and are usually marketed as sprays. Take care to use a lubricant marked as being suitable for O-ring chains.

● **Degreasers** are heavy duty solvents used to remove grease and grime that may accumulate on engine and frame components. They can be sprayed or brushed on and, depending on the type, are rinsed with either water or solvent.

● **Solvents** are used alone or in combination with degreasers to clean parts and assemblies during repair and overhaul. The home mechanic should use only solvents that are non-flammable and that do not produce irritating fumes.

● **Gasket sealing compounds** may be used in conjunction with gaskets, to improve their sealing capabilities, or alone, to seal metal-to-metal joints. Many gasket sealers can withstand extreme heat, some are impervious to petrol and lubricants, while others are capable of filling and sealing large cavities. Depending on the intended use, gasket sealers either dry hard or stay relatively soft and pliable. They are usually applied by hand, with a brush, or are sprayed on the gasket sealing surfaces.

● **Thread locking compound** is an adhesive locking compound that prevents threaded fasteners from loosening because of vibration. It is available in a variety of types for different applications.

● **Moisture dispersants** are usually sprays that can be used to dry out electrical components such as the fuse block and wiring connectors. Some types can also be used as treatment for rubber and as a lubricant for hinges, cables and locks.

● **Waxes and polishes** are used to help protect painted and plated surfaces from the weather. Different types of paint may require the use of different types of wax polish. Some polishes utilise a chemical or abrasive cleaner to help remove the top layer of oxidised (dull) paint on older vehicles. In recent years, many non-wax polishes (that contain a wide variety of chemicals such as polymers and silicones) have been introduced. These non-wax polishes are usually easier to apply and last longer than conventional waxes and polishes.

Fault Finding

The motorcycle owner who does his or her own maintenance according to the recommended service schedules should not have to use this section of the manual very often. Modern component reliability is such that, provided those items subject to wear or deterioration are inspected or renewed at the specified intervals, sudden failure is comparatively rare. Faults do not usually just happen as a result of sudden failure, but develop over a period of time. Major mechanical failures in particular are usually preceded by characteristic symptoms over hundreds or even thousands of miles.

With any fault-finding, the first step is to decide where to begin investigations. Sometimes this is obvious, but on other occasions, a little detective work will be necessary. The owner who makes half a dozen haphazard adjustments or replacements may be successful in curing a fault (or its symptoms), but will be none the wiser if the fault recurs, and ultimately may have spent more time and money than was necessary. A calm and logical approach will be found to be more satisfactory in the long run. Always take into account any warning signs or abnormalities that may have been noticed in the period preceding the fault - power loss, high or low gauge readings, unusual noises or smells, etc - and remember that failure of components such as fuses or spark plugs may only be pointers to some underlying fault.

The pages which follow provide an easy-reference guide to the more common problems which may occur during the operation of the vehicle. These problems and their possible causes are grouped under headings denoting various components or systems, such as Engine, Cooling system, etc. The Chapter and/or Section which deals with the problem is also shown in brackets. Whatever the fault, certain basic principles apply. These are as follows:

Verify the fault. This is simply a matter of being sure that you know what the symptoms are before starting work. This is particularly important if you are investigating a fault for someone else, who may not have described it very accurately.

Don't overlook the obvious. For example, if the vehicle won't start, is there fuel in the tank? (Don't take anyone else's word on this particular point. If an electrical fault is indicated, look for loose or broken wires before digging out the test gear.

Cure the disease, not the symptom. Substituting a flat battery with a fully-charged one will get you under way, but if the underlying cause is not attended to, the new battery will soon become discharged. Similarly, changing oil-fouled spark plugs for a new set will get you moving again, but remember that the reason for the fouling (if it wasn't simply an incorrect grade of plug) will have to be found and corrected.

Don't take anything for granted. Particularly, don't forget that a "new" component may itself be defective, and don't leave components out of a fault diagnosis sequence just because they are new or recently-fitted. When you do finally diagnose a difficult fault, you'll probably realise that all the evidence was there from the start.

1 Engine doesn't start or is difficult to start

- ☐ Starter motor doesn't rotate
- ☐ Starter motor rotates but engine does not turn over
- ☐ Starter works but engine won't turn over (seized)
- ☐ No fuel flow
- ☐ Engine flooded
- ☐ No spark or weak spark
- ☐ Compression low
- ☐ Stalls after starting
- ☐ Rough idle

2 Poor running at low speed

- ☐ Spark weak
- ☐ Fuel/air mixture incorrect
- ☐ Compression low
- ☐ Poor acceleration

3 Poor running or no power at high speed

- ☐ Firing incorrect
- ☐ Fuel/air mixture incorrect
- ☐ Compression low
- ☐ Knocking or pinging
- ☐ Miscellaneous causes

4 Overheating

- ☐ Engine overheats
- ☐ Firing incorrect
- ☐ Fuel/air mixture incorrect
- ☐ Compression too high
- ☐ Engine load excessive
- ☐ Lubrication inadequate
- ☐ Miscellaneous causes

5 Clutch problems

- ☐ Clutch slipping
- ☐ Clutch not disengaging completely

6 Gearshifting problems

- ☐ Doesn't go into gear, or pedal doesn't return
- ☐ Jumps out of gear
- ☐ Overshifts

7 Abnormal engine noise

- ☐ Knocking or pinging
- ☐ Piston slap or rattling
- ☐ Valve noise
- ☐ Other noise

8 Abnormal transmission and final drive noise

- ☐ Clutch noise
- ☐ Transmission noise
- ☐ Final drive noise

9 Abnormal frame and suspension noise

- ☐ Front end noise
- ☐ Shock absorber noise
- ☐ Brake noise

10 Oil pressure indicator light comes on

- ☐ Engine lubrication system
- ☐ Electrical system

11 Excessive exhaust smoke

- ☐ White smoke
- ☐ Black smoke
- ☐ Brown smoke

12 Poor handling or stability

- ☐ Handlebar hard to turn
- ☐ Handlebar shakes or vibrates excessively
- ☐ Handlebar pulls to one side
- ☐ Poor shock absorbing qualities

13 Braking problems

- ☐ Brakes are spongy, don't hold
- ☐ Brake lever or pedal pulsates
- ☐ Brakes drag

14 Electrical problems

- ☐ Battery dead or weak
- ☐ Battery overcharged

1 Engine doesn't start or is difficult to start

Starter motor doesn't rotate

- [ ] Engine kill switch OFF.
- [ ] Fuse blown. Check main fuse (Chapter 9).
- [ ] Battery voltage low. Check and recharge battery (Chapter 9).
- [ ] Starter motor defective. Make sure the wiring to the starter is secure. Make sure the starter relay clicks when the start button is pushed. If the relay clicks, then the fault is in the wiring or motor.
- [ ] Starter relay faulty. Check it according to the procedure in Chapter 9.
- [ ] Starter switch not contacting. The contacts could be wet, corroded or dirty. Disassemble and clean the switch (Chapter 9).
- [ ] Wiring open or shorted. Check all wiring connections and harnesses to make sure that they are dry, tight and not corroded. Also check for broken or frayed wires that can cause a short to ground (earth) (see wiring diagram, Chapter 9).
- [ ] Ignition (main) switch defective. Check the switch according to the procedure in Chapter 9. Replace the switch with a new one if it is defective.
- [ ] Engine kill switch defective. Check for wet, dirty or corroded contacts. Clean or replace the switch as necessary (Chapter 9).
- [ ] Faulty neutral, or clutch switch. Check the wiring to each switch and the switch itself according to the procedures in Chapter 9.

Starter motor rotates but engine does not turn over

- [ ] Starter motor clutch defective. Inspect and repair or replace (Chapter 2).
- [ ] Damaged idler or starter gears. Inspect and replace the damaged parts (Chapter 2).

Starter works but engine won't turn over (seized)

- [ ] Seized engine caused by one or more internally damaged components. Failure due to wear, abuse or lack of lubrication. Damage can include seized valves, tappets, camshafts, pistons, crankshaft, connecting rod bearings. Refer to Chapter 2 for engine disassembly.
- [ ] Fault in starter drive from alternator driveshaft gear, to auxiliary gear, clutch outer drum teeth and primary drive gear on crankshaft.

No fuel flow

- [ ] No fuel in tank.
- [ ] Fuel filter blockage or blocked/pinch fuel hose(s) (see Chapter 1).
- [ ] Fuel tank breather hose obstructed (fault in evaporative loss system on California models).
- [ ] Float needle valve clogged. For all of the valves to be clogged, either a very bad batch of fuel with an unusual additive has been used, or some other foreign material has entered the tank. Many times after a machine has been stored for many months without running, the fuel turns to a varnish-like liquid and forms deposits on the inlet needle valves and jets. The carburettors should be removed and overhauled if draining the float chambers doesn't solve the problem.

Engine flooded

- [ ] Float height too high. Check as described in Chapter 4.
- [ ] Float needle valve worn or stuck open. A piece of dirt, rust or other debris can cause the valve to seat improperly, causing excess fuel to be admitted to the float chamber. In this case, the float chamber should be cleaned and the needle valve and seat inspected. If the needle and seat are worn, then the leaking will persist and the parts should be replaced with new ones (Chapter 4).
- [ ] Starting technique incorrect. Under normal circumstances (ie, if all the carburettor functions are sound) the machine should start with little or no throttle. When the engine is cold, the choke should be operated and the engine started without opening the throttle. When the engine is at operating temperature, only a very slight amount of throttle should be necessary.

No spark or weak spark

- [ ] Ignition switch OFF.
- [ ] Engine kill switch turned to the OFF position.
- [ ] Battery voltage low. Check and recharge the battery as necessary (Chapter 9).
- [ ] Spark plugs dirty, defective or worn out. Locate reason for fouled plugs using spark plug condition chart and follow the plug maintenance procedures (Chapter 1).
- [ ] Spark plug caps or secondary (HT) wiring faulty. Check condition. Replace either or both components if cracks or deterioration are evident (Chapter 5).
- [ ] Spark plug caps not making good contact. Make sure that the plug caps fit snugly over the plug ends.
- [ ] Igniter defective. Check the igniter, referring to Chapter 5 for details.
- [ ] Pick-up coil defective. Check the coil, referring to Chapter 5 for details.
- [ ] Ignition HT coils defective. Check the coils, referring to Chapter 5.
- [ ] Ignition or kill switch shorted. This is usually caused by water, corrosion, damage or excessive wear. The switches can be disassembled and cleaned with electrical contact cleaner. If cleaning does not help, replace the switches (Chapter 9).
- [ ] Wiring shorted or broken between:

  a) Ignition (main) switch and engine kill switch (or blown fuse)
  b) Igniter and engine kill switch
  c) Igniter and ignition HT coils
  d) Ignition HT coils and spark plugs
  e) Igniter and pick-up coil

- [ ] Make sure that all wiring connections are clean, dry and tight. Look for chafed and broken wires (Chapters 5 and 9).

Compression low

☐ Spark plugs loose. Remove the plugs and inspect their threads. Reinstall and tighten to the specified torque (Chapter 1).

☐ Cylinder head not sufficiently tightened down. If the cylinder head is suspected of being loose, then there's a chance that the gasket or head is damaged if the problem has persisted for any length of time. The head bolts should be tightened to the proper torque in the correct sequence (Chapter 2).

☐ Improper valve clearance. This means that the valve is not closing completely and compression pressure is leaking past the valve. Check and adjust the valve clearances (Chapter 1).

☐ Cylinder and/or piston worn. Excessive wear will cause compression pressure to leak past the rings. This is usually accompanied by worn rings as well. A top-end overhaul is necessary (Chapter 2).

☐ Piston rings worn, weak, broken, or sticking. Broken or sticking piston rings usually indicate a lubrication or carburation problem that causes excess carbon deposits or seizures to form on the pistons and rings. Top-end overhaul is necessary (Chapter 2).

☐ Piston ring-to-groove clearance excessive. This is caused by excessive wear of the piston ring lands. Piston replacement is necessary (Chapter 2).

☐ Cylinder head gasket damaged. If the head is allowed to become loose, or if excessive carbon build-up on the piston crown and combustion chamber causes extremely high compression, the head gasket may leak. Retorquing the head is not always sufficient to restore the seal, so gasket replacement is necessary (Chapter 2).

☐ Valve spring broken or weak. Caused by component failure or wear; the springs must be replaced (Chapter 2).

☐ Valve not seating properly. This is caused by a bent valve (from over-revving or improper valve adjustment), burned valve or seat (improper carburation) or an accumulation of carbon deposits on the seat (from carburation or lubrication problems). The valves must be cleaned and/or replaced and the seats serviced if possible (Chapter 2).

Stalls after starting

☐ Improper choke action. Make sure the choke linkage shaft is getting a full stroke and staying in the out position (Chapter 4).

☐ Ignition malfunction. See Chapter 5.

☐ Carburettor malfunction. See Chapter 4.

☐ Fuel contaminated. The fuel can be contaminated with either dirt or water, or can change chemically if the machine is allowed to sit for several months or more. Drain the tank and float chambers (Chapter 4).

☐ Inlet air leak. Check for loose carburettor-to-inlet manifold connections, missing vacuum take-off caps or hoses, or loose carburettor tops (Chapter 4).

☐ Engine idle speed incorrect. Turn idle adjusting screw until the engine idles at the specified rpm (Chapter 1).

Rough idle

☐ Ignition malfunction. See Chapter 5.

☐ Idle speed incorrect. See Chapter 1.

☐ Carburettors not synchronised. Adjust carburettors with vacuum gauge or manometer set as described in Chapter 1.

☐ Carburettor malfunction. See Chapter 4.

☐ Fuel contaminated. The fuel can be contaminated with either dirt or water, or can change chemically if the machine is allowed to sit for several months or more. Drain the tank and float chambers (Chapter 4).

☐ Inlet air leak. Check for loose carburettor-to-inlet manifold connections, missing vacuum take-off caps, or damaged evaporative loss system hoses on California models (Chapter 4).

☐ Airbox requires draining (Chapter 1). In extreme cases, the element or air inlets may be blocked (Chapter 4).

2 Poor running at low speed

Spark weak

☐ Battery voltage low. Check and recharge battery (Chapter 9).

☐ Spark plugs fouled, defective or worn out. Refer to Chapter 1 for spark plug maintenance.

☐ Spark plug cap or HT wiring defective. Refer to Chapters 1 and 5 for details on the ignition system.

☐ Spark plug caps not making contact.

☐ Incorrect spark plugs. Wrong type, heat range or cap configuration. Check and install correct plugs listed in Chapter 1.

☐ Igniter defective. See Chapter 5.

☐ Pick-up coil defective. See Chapter 5.

☐ Ignition HT coils defective. See Chapter 5.

Fuel/air mixture incorrect

☐ Pilot screws out of adjustment (Chapter 4).

☐ Pilot jet or air passage clogged. Remove and overhaul the carburettors (Chapter 4).

☐ Air bleed holes clogged. Remove carburettor and blow out all passages (Chapter 4).

☐ Airbox poorly sealed. Look for cracks, holes or loose clamps and replace or repair defective parts.

☐ Fuel level too high or too low. Check the float height (Chapter 4).

☐ Fuel tank breather hose obstructed (not California models).

☐ Carburettor inlet manifolds loose. Check for cracks, breaks, tears or loose clamps. Replace the rubber inlet manifold joints if split or perished.

Compression low

- ☐ Spark plugs loose. Remove the plugs and inspect their threads. Reinstall and tighten to the specified torque (Chapter 1).
- ☐ Cylinder head not sufficiently tightened down. If the cylinder head is suspected of being loose, then there's a chance that the gasket and head are damaged if the problem has persisted for any length of time. The head bolts should be tightened to the proper torque in the correct sequence (Chapter 2).
- ☐ Improper valve clearance. This means that the valve is not closing completely and compression pressure is leaking past the valve. Check and adjust the valve clearances (Chapter 1).
- ☐ Cylinder and/or piston worn. Excessive wear will cause compression pressure to leak past the rings. This is usually accompanied by worn rings as well. A top-end overhaul is necessary (Chapter 2).
- ☐ Piston rings worn, weak, broken, or sticking. Broken or sticking piston rings usually indicate a lubrication or carburation problem that causes excess carbon deposits or seizures to form on the pistons and rings. Top-end overhaul is necessary (Chapter 2).
- ☐ Piston ring-to-groove clearance excessive. This is caused by excessive wear of the piston ring lands. Piston replacement is necessary (Chapter 2).
- ☐ Cylinder head gasket damaged. If the head is allowed to become loose, or if excessive carbon build-up on the piston crown and combustion chamber causes extremely high compression, the head gasket may leak. Retorquing the head is not always sufficient to restore the seal, so gasket replacement is necessary (Chapter 2).
- ☐ Valve spring broken or weak. Caused by component failure or wear; the springs must be replaced (Chapter 2).
- ☐ Valve not seating properly. This is caused by a bent valve (from over-revving or improper valve adjustment), burned valve or seat (improper carburation) or an accumulation of carbon deposits on the seat (from carburation, lubrication problems). The valves must be cleaned and/or replaced and the seats serviced if possible (Chapter 2).

Poor acceleration

- ☐ Carburettors leaking or dirty. Overhaul the carburettors (Chapter 4).
- ☐ Timing not advancing. The pick-up coil or the igniter may be defective. If so, they must be replaced with new ones, as they can't be repaired. Timing check can be performed to confirm (Chapter 5).
- ☐ Carburettors not synchronised. Adjust them with a vacuum gauge set or manometer (Chapter 1).
- ☐ Engine oil viscosity too high. Using a heavier oil than that recommended in Chapter 1 can damage the oil pump or lubrication system and cause drag on the engine.
- ☐ Brakes dragging. Usually caused by debris which has entered the brake piston seals, or from a warped disc or bent axle. Repair as necessary (Chapter 7).

3 Poor running or no power at high speed

Firing incorrect

- ☐ Airbox element restricted or air inlets blocked. Drain the airbox (Chapter 1) and if necessary replace it (Chapter 4).
- ☐ Spark plugs fouled, defective or worn out. See Chapter 1 for spark plug maintenance.
- ☐ Spark plug caps or HT wiring defective. See Chapters 1 and 5 for details of the ignition system.
- ☐ Spark plug caps not in good contact. See Chapter 5.
- ☐ Incorrect spark plugs. Wrong type, heat range or cap configuration. Check and install correct plugs listed in Chapter 1.
- ☐ Igniter defective. See Chapter 5.
- ☐ Ignition HT coils defective. See Chapter 5.

Fuel/air mixture incorrect

- ☐ Main jet clogged. Dirt, water or other contaminants can clog the main jets. Clean the fuel filter(s), the float chamber area, and the jets and carburettor orifices (Chapter 4).
- ☐ Main jet wrong size. The standard jetting is for sea level atmospheric pressure and oxygen content.
- ☐ Air bleed holes clogged. Remove and overhaul carburettors (Chapter 4).
- ☐ Airbox requires draining (Chapter 1). Airbox element clogged (Chapter 4).
- ☐ Airbox housing poorly sealed. Look for cracks, holes or loose clamps, and replace or repair defective parts.
- ☐ Fuel level too high or too low. Check the float height (Chapter 4).
- ☐ Fuel tank breather hose obstructed (not California models).
- ☐ Carburettor inlet manifolds loose. Check for cracks, breaks, tears or loose clamps. Replace the rubber inlet manifolds if they are split or perished (Chapter 4).

Compression low

- ☐ Spark plugs loose. Remove the plugs and inspect their threads. Reinstall and tighten to the specified torque (Chapter 1).
- ☐ Cylinder head not sufficiently tightened down. If the cylinder head is suspected of being loose, then there's a chance that the gasket and head are damaged if the problem has persisted for any length of time. The head bolts should be tightened to the proper torque in the correct sequence (Chapter 2).

☐ Improper valve clearance. This means that the valve is not closing completely and compression pressure is leaking past the valve. Check and adjust the valve clearances (Chapter 1).

☐ Cylinder and/or piston worn. Excessive wear will cause compression pressure to leak past the rings. This is usually accompanied by worn rings as well. A top-end overhaul is necessary (Chapter 2).

☐ Piston rings worn, weak, broken, or sticking. Broken or sticking piston rings usually indicate a lubrication or carburation problem that causes excess carbon deposits or seizures to form on the pistons and rings. Top-end overhaul is necessary (Chapter 2).

☐ Piston ring-to-groove clearance excessive. This is caused by excessive wear of the piston ring lands. Piston replacement is necessary (Chapter 2).

☐ Cylinder head gasket damaged. If the head is allowed to become loose, or if excessive carbon build-up on the piston crown and combustion chamber causes extremely high compression, the head gasket may leak. Retorquing the head is not always sufficient to restore the seal, so gasket replacement is necessary (Chapter 2).

☐ Valve spring broken or weak. Caused by component failure or wear; the springs must be replaced (Chapter 2).

☐ Valve not seating properly. This is caused by a bent valve (from over-revving or improper valve adjustment), burned valve or seat (improper carburation) or an accumulation of carbon deposits on the seat (from carburation or lubrication problems). The valves must be cleaned and/or replaced and the seats serviced if possible (Chapter 2).

Knocking or pinging

☐ Carbon build-up in combustion chamber. Use of a fuel additive that will dissolve the adhesive bonding the carbon particles to the crown and chamber is the easiest way to remove the build-up. Otherwise, the cylinder head will have to be removed and decarbonised (Chapter 2).

☐ Incorrect or poor quality fuel. Old or improper grades of fuel can cause detonation. This causes the piston to rattle, thus the knocking or pinging sound. Drain old fuel and always use the recommended fuel grade.

☐ Spark plug heat range incorrect. Uncontrolled detonation indicates the plug heat range is too hot. The plug in effect becomes a glow plug. Install the proper heat range plug (Chapter 1).

☐ Improper air/fuel mixture. This will cause the cylinder to run hot, which leads to detonation. Clogged jets or an air leak can cause this imbalance. See Chapter 4.

Miscellaneous causes

☐ Throttle valve doesn't open fully. Adjust the throttle grip freeplay (Chapter 1).

☐ Clutch slipping. May be caused by loose or worn clutch components. Refer to Chapter 2 for clutch overhaul procedures.

☐ Timing not advancing. Check as described in Chapter 5.

☐ Engine oil viscosity too high. Using a heavier oil than the one recommended in Chapter 1 can damage the oil pump or lubrication system and cause drag on the engine.

☐ Brakes dragging. Usually caused by debris which has entered the brake piston seals, or from a warped disc or bent axle. Repair as necessary.

4 Overheating

Engine overheats

☐ Coolant level low. Check and add coolant (Chapter 1).

☐ Leak in cooling system. Check cooling system hoses and radiator for leaks and other damage. Repair or replace parts as necessary (Chapter 3).

☐ Thermostat sticking open or closed. Check and replace as described in Chapter 3.

☐ Faulty radiator cap. Remove the cap and have it pressure tested.

☐ Coolant passages clogged. Have the entire system drained and flushed, then refill with fresh coolant.

☐ Water pump defective. Remove the pump and check the components (Chapter 3).

☐ Clogged radiator fins. Clean them by blowing compressed air through the fins from the rear of the radiator.

☐ Cooling fan or fan switch fault (Chapter 3).

Firing incorrect

☐ Spark plugs fouled, defective or worn out. See Chapter 1 for spark plug maintenance.

☐ Incorrect spark plugs.

☐ Faulty ignition HT coils (Chapter 5).

Fuel/air mixture incorrect

☐ Main jet clogged. Dirt, water and other contaminants can clog the main jets. Clean the fuel filter(s), the float chamber area and the jets and carburettor orifices (Chapter 4).

☐ Main jet wrong size. The standard jetting is for sea level atmospheric pressure and oxygen content.

☐ Airbox requires draining (Chapter 1).

- [ ] Airbox element or air inlets clogged (Chapter 4).
- [ ] Airbox poorly sealed. Look for cracks, holes or loose clamps and replace or repair.
- [ ] Fuel level too low. Check float height (Chapter 4).
- [ ] Fuel tank breather hose obstructed (not California models).
- [ ] Carburettor inlet manifolds loose. Check for cracks, breaks, tears or loose clamps. Replace the rubber inlet manifold joints if split or perished.

Compression too high

- [ ] Carbon build-up in combustion chamber. Use of a fuel additive that will dissolve the adhesive bonding the carbon particles to the piston crown and chamber is the easiest way to remove the build-up. Otherwise, the cylinder head will have to be removed and decarbonised (Chapter 2).

Engine load excessive

- [ ] Clutch slipping. Can be caused by damaged, loose or worn clutch components. Refer to Chapter 2 for overhaul procedures.
- [ ] Engine oil level too high. The addition of too much oil will cause pressurisation of the crankcase and inefficient engine operation. Check Specifications and drain to proper level (Chapter 1).

- [ ] Engine oil viscosity too high. Using a heavier oil than the one recommended in Chapter 1 can damage the oil pump or lubrication system as well as cause drag on the engine.
- [ ] Brakes dragging. Usually caused by debris which has entered the brake piston seals, or from a warped disc or bent axle. Repair as necessary.

Lubrication inadequate

- [ ] Engine oil level too low. Friction caused by intermittent lack of lubrication or from oil that is overworked can cause overheating. The oil provides a definite cooling function in the engine. Check the oil level (Chapter 1).
- [ ] Poor quality engine oil or incorrect viscosity or type. Oil is rated not only according to viscosity but also according to type. Some oils are not rated high enough for use in this engine. Check the Specifications section and change to the correct oil (Chapter 1).

Miscellaneous causes

- [ ] Modification to exhaust system. Most aftermarket exhaust systems cause the engine to run leaner, which make them run hotter. When installing an accessory exhaust system, always rejet the carburettors.

5 Clutch problems

Clutch slipping

- [ ] Clutch master cylinder reservoir fluid level too high (Chapter 1).
- [ ] Friction plates worn or warped. Overhaul the clutch assembly (Chapter 2).
- [ ] Plain plates warped (Chapter 2).
- [ ] Clutch springs broken or weak. Old or heat-damaged (from slipping clutch) springs should be replaced with new ones (Chapter 2).
- [ ] Clutch centre or outer drum unevenly worn. This causes improper engagement of the plates. Replace the damaged or worn parts (Chapter 2).

Clutch not disengaging completely

- [ ] Clutch master cylinder fluid level too low (Chapter 1).
- [ ] Clutch plates warped or damaged. This will cause clutch drag, which in turn will cause the machine to creep. Overhaul the clutch assembly (Chapter 2).
- [ ] Clutch spring tension uneven. Usually caused by a sagged or

broken spring. Check and replace the springs as a set (Chapter 2).

- [ ] Engine oil deteriorated. Old, thin, worn out oil will not provide proper lubrication for the plates, causing the clutch to drag. Replace the oil and filter (Chapter 1).
- [ ] Engine oil viscosity too high. Using a heavier oil than recommended in Chapter 1 can cause the plates to stick together, putting a drag on the engine. Change to the correct weight oil (Chapter 1).
- [ ] Clutch outer drum guide seized on mainshaft. Lack of lubrication, severe wear or damage can cause the bush to seize on the shaft. Overhaul of the clutch, and perhaps transmission, may be necessary to repair the damage (Chapter 2).
- [ ] Clutch pushrod bent. Check and if necessary, replace (Chapter 2).
- [ ] Loose clutch centre nut. Causes drum and centre misalignment putting a drag on the engine. Engagement adjustment continually varies. Overhaul the clutch assembly (Chapter 2).

6 Gearshifting problems

Doesn't go into gear or pedal doesn't return

- [ ] Clutch not disengaging. See Section 27.
- [ ] Gearshift fork(s) bent or seized. Overhaul the transmission (Chapter 2).
- [ ] Gear(s) stuck on shaft. Most often caused by a lack of lubrication or excessive wear in transmission bearings and bushes. Overhaul the transmission (Chapter 2).
- [ ] Gearshift drum binding. Caused by lubrication failure or excessive wear. Replace the drum and bearing (Chapter 2).
- [ ] Gearshift shaft quadrant teeth or carrier pawls faulty. Overhaul gearshift mechanism (Chapter 2).
- [ ] Gearshift shaft return spring weak or broken (Chapter 2).
- [ ] Gearshift shaft splines stripped out of lever/pedal or shaft, caused by allowing the lever to get loose or from dropping the machine. Replace necessary parts (Chapter 2).
- [ ] Gearshift detent arm broken or worn. Full engagement and rotary movement of shift drum results. Replace the arm (Chapter 2).

Jumps out of gear

- [ ] Gearshift fork(s) worn. Overhaul the gearshift mechanism (Chapter 2).
- [ ] Gear groove(s) worn. Overhaul the gearshift mechanism (Chapter 2).
- [ ] Gear dogs or dog slots worn or damaged. The gears should be inspected and replaced. No attempt should be made to service the worn parts. Disassembly the gearshafts and replace the damaged gears (Chapter 2).

Overshifts

- [ ] Gear detent arm spring weak or broken (Chapter 2).
- [ ] Gearshift shaft quadrant teeth or carrier pawls faulty. Overhaul gearshift mechanism (Chapter 2).

7 Abnormal engine noise

Knocking or pinging

- [ ] Carbon build-up in combustion chamber. Use of a fuel additive that will dissolve the adhesive bonding the carbon particles to the piston crown and chamber is the easiest way to remove the build-up. Otherwise, the cylinder head will have to be removed and decarbonised (Chapter 2).
- [ ] Incorrect or poor quality fuel. Old or improper fuel can cause detonation. This causes the pistons to rattle, thus the knocking or pinging sound. Drain the old fuel and always use the recommended grade fuel (Chapter 4).
- [ ] Spark plug heat range incorrect. Uncontrolled detonation indicates that the plug heat range is too hot. The plug in effect becomes a glow plug, raising cylinder temperatures. Install the proper heat range plug (Chapter 1).
- [ ] Improper air/fuel mixture. This will cause the cylinders to run hot and lead to detonation. Clogged jets or an air leak can cause this imbalance. See Chapter 4.

Piston slap or rattling

- [ ] Cylinder-to-piston clearance excessive. Inspect and overhaul top-end parts (Chapter 2).
- [ ] Connecting rod bent. Caused by over-revving, trying to start a badly flooded engine or from ingesting a foreign object into the combustion chamber. Replace the damaged parts (Chapter 2).

- [ ] Piston pin or piston pin bore worn or seized from wear or lack of lubrication. Inspect and damaged parts (Chapter 2).
- [ ] Piston ring(s) worn, broken or sticking. Overhaul the top-end (Chapter 2).
- [ ] Piston seizure damage. Usually from lack of lubrication or overheating. Replace the pistons and liners, as necessary (Chapter 2).
- [ ] Connecting rod upper or lower end clearance excessive. Caused by excessive wear or lack of lubrication. Replace worn parts.

Valve noise

- [ ] Incorrect valve clearances. Adjust the clearances by referring to Chapter 1.
- [ ] Valve spring broken or weak. Check and replace weak valve springs (Chapter 2).
- [ ] Camshaft or cylinder head worn or damaged. Lack of lubrication at high rpm is usually the cause of damage. Insufficient oil or failure to change the oil at the recommended intervals are the chief causes. Since there are no replaceable bearings in the head, the head itself will have to be replaced if there is excessive wear or damage (Chapter 2).

Other noise

- ☐ Cylinder head gasket leaking.
- ☐ Exhaust pipe leaking at cylinder head connection. Caused by improper fit of pipe(s) or loose exhaust flange. All exhaust fasteners should be tightened evenly and carefully. Failure to do this will lead to a leak.
- ☐ Crankshaft runout excessive. Caused by a bent crankshaft (from over-revving) or damage from an upper cylinder component failure. Can also be attributed to dropping the machine on either of the crankshaft ends.
- ☐ Engine mounting bolts loose. Tighten all engine mount bolts (Chapter 2).
- ☐ Crankshaft bearings worn (Chapter 2).
- ☐ Cam chain tensioner defective. Replace according to the procedure in Chapter 2.
- ☐ Cam chain, sprockets or blades worn (Chapter 2).
- ☐ Whine or rattling from balancers on 4 cylinder engine. Adjust (Chapter 2).

8 Abnormal transmission and final drive noise

Clutch noise

- ☐ Clutch outer drum/friction plate clearance excessive (Chapter 2).
- ☐ Loose or damaged clutch pressure plate and/or bolts (Chapter 2).

Transmission noise

- ☐ Bearings worn. Also includes the possibility that the shafts are worn. Overhaul the transmission (Chapter 2).
- ☐ Gears worn or chipped (Chapter 2).
- ☐ Metal chips jammed in gear teeth. Probably pieces from a broken clutch, gear or gearshift mechanism that were picked up by the gears. This will cause early bearing failure (Chapter 2).
- ☐ Engine oil level too low. Causes a howl from transmission. Also affects engine power and clutch operation (Chapter 1).

Final drive noise

- ☐ Chain not adjusted properly (Chapter 1).
- ☐ Engine sprocket or rear sprocket loose. Tighten fasteners (Chapter 6).
- ☐ Sprocket(s) worn. Replace sprocket(s) (Chapter 6).
- ☐ Rear sprocket warped. Replace (Chapter 6).
- ☐ Wheel coupling damper worn. Replace damper (Chapter 6).

9 Abnormal frame and suspension noise

Front end noise

- ☐ Low fluid level or improper viscosity oil in forks. This can sound like spurting and is usually accompanied by irregular fork action (Chapter 6).
- ☐ Spring weak or broken. Makes a clicking or scraping sound. Fork oil, when drained, will have a lot of metal particles in it (Chapter 6).
- ☐ Steering head bearings loose or damaged. Clicks when braking. Check and adjust or replace as necessary (Chapters 1 and 6).
- ☐ Fork yoke clamps loose. Make sure all clamp pinch bolts are tight (Chapter 6).
- ☐ Fork tube bent. Good possibility if machine has been dropped. Replace tube with a new one (Chapter 6).
- ☐ Front axle or axle clamp bolt loose. Tighten them to the specified torque (Chapter 6).

Shock absorber noise

- ☐ Fluid level incorrect. Indicates a leak caused by defective seal. Shock will be covered with oil. Replace shock (Chapter 6).
- ☐ Defective shock absorber with internal damage. This is in the body of the shock and can't be remedied. The shock must be replaced with a new one (Chapter 6).
- ☐ Bent or damaged shock body. Replace the shock with a new one (Chapter 6).

Brake noise

- ☐ Squeal caused by dust on brake pads. Usually found in combination with glazed pads. Clean using brake cleaning solvent (Chapter 7).
- ☐ Contamination of brake pads. Oil, brake fluid or dirt causing brake to chatter or squeal. Clean or replace pads (Chapter 7).

□ Pads glazed. Caused by excessive heat from prolonged use or from contamination. Do not use sandpaper, emery cloth, carborundum cloth or any other abrasive to roughen the pad surfaces as abrasives will stay in the pad material and damage the disc. A very fine flat file can be used, but pad replacement is suggested as a cure (Chapter 7).

□ Disc warped. Can cause a chattering, clicking or intermittent squeal. Usually accompanied by a pulsating lever and uneven braking. Replace the disc (Chapter 7).

□ Loose or worn wheel bearings. Check and replace as needed (Chapter 7).

10 Oil pressure indicator light comes on

Engine lubrication system

□ Engine oil pump defective, blocked oil strainer gauze, blocked oil filter or failed relief valve. Carry out oil pressure check (Chapter 2).

□ Engine oil level low. Inspect for leak or other problem causing low oil level and add recommended oil (Chapter 1).

□ Engine oil viscosity too low. Very old, thin oil or an improper weight of oil used in the engine. Change to correct oil (Chapter 1).

□ Camshaft or journals worn. Excessive wear causing drop in oil pressure. Replace cam and/or cylinder head. Abnormal wear could be caused by oil starvation at high rpm from low oil level or improper weight or type of oil (Chapter 1).

□ Crankshaft and/or bearings worn. Same problems as 'Camshaft or journals worn' above. Check and replace crankshaft and/or bearings (Chapter 2).

Electrical system

□ Oil pressure switch defective. Check the switch according to the procedure in Chapter 9. Replace it if it is defective.

□ Oil pressure indicator light circuit defective. Check for pinched, shorted, disconnected or damaged wiring (Chapter 9).

11 Excessive exhaust smoke

White smoke

□ Piston oil ring worn. The ring may be broken or damaged, causing oil from the crankcase to be pulled past the piston into the combustion chamber. Replace the rings with new ones (Chapter 2).

□ Cylinder liners worn, cracked, or scored. Caused by overheating or oil starvation. Install new liners (Chapter 2).

□ Valve oil seal damaged or worn. Replace oil seals with new ones (Chapter 2).

□ Valve guide worn. Measure the valve guide inside diameter (Chapter 2).

□ Engine oil level too high, which causes the oil to be forced past the rings. Drain oil to the proper level (Chapter 1).

□ Abnormal crankcase pressurisation, which forces oil past the rings. Clogged breather hose is usually the cause.

Black smoke

□ Airbox element or air inlets clogged (Chapter 4).

□ Main jet too large or loose. Compare the jet size to the Specifications (Chapter 4).

□ Choke cable or linkage shaft stuck, causing fuel to be pulled through choke circuit (Chapter 4).

□ No choke cable freeplay (Chapter 1).

□ Fuel level too high. Check and adjust the float height(s) as necessary (Chapter 4).

□ Float needle valve held off needle seat. Clean the float chambers and replace the needles and seats if necessary (Chapter 4).

Brown smoke

□ Main jet too small or clogged. Lean condition caused by wrong size main jet or by a restricted orifice. Clean float chambers and jets and compare jet size to Specifications (Chapter 4).

□ Fuel flow insufficient. Float needle valve stuck closed. Float height incorrect. Restricted fuel hose(s) or filter(s). Clean hose/filter and float chamber and adjust float heights if necessary.

□ Carburettor inlet manifold clamps loose (Chapter 4).

□ Airbox poorly sealed (Chapter 1).

12 Poor handling or stability

Handlebar hard to turn

☐ Steering head bearing freeplay incorrect. Check adjustment as described in Chapter 1.

☐ Bearings damaged. Roughness can be felt as the bars are turned from side-to-side. Replace bearings and races (Chapter 6).

☐ Races dented or worn. Denting results from wear in only one position (eg, straightahead), from a collision, hitting a pothole or dropping the machine. Replace races and bearings (Chapter 6).

☐ Steering stem lubrication inadequate. Causes are grease getting hard from age or being washed out by high pressure jet washes. Disassemble steering head and repack bearings (Chapter 6).

☐ Steering stem bent. Caused by a collision, hitting a pothole or by dropping the machine. Replace damaged part. Don't try to straighten the steering stem (Chapter 6).

☐ Front tyre air pressure too low (Chapter 1).

Handlebar shakes or vibrates excessively

☐ Tyres worn or out of balance (Chapter 7).

☐ Swingarm bearings worn. Replace worn bearings by referring to Chapter 6.

☐ Rim(s) warped or damaged. Inspect wheels for runout (Chapter 7).

☐ Wheel bearings worn. Worn front or rear wheel bearings can cause poor tracking. Worn front bearings will cause wobble (Chapter 7).

☐ Handlebar clamp bolts loose (Chapter 6).

☐ Fork yoke clamp bolts loose. Tighten them to the specified torque (Chapter 6).

☐ Engine mounting bolts loose. Will cause excessive vibration with increased engine rpm (Chapter 2).

Handlebar pulls to one side

☐ Frame bent. Definitely suspect this if the machine has been dropped. May or may not be accompanied by cracking near the bend. Replace the frame (Chapter 6).

☐ Wheels out of alignment. May be caused by incorrect alignment of rear wheel in swingarm, or more seriously, from bent steering stem or frame (Chapter 6).

☐ Swingarm bent or twisted. Replace the arm (Chapter 6).

☐ Steering stem bent. Caused by impact damage or by dropping the motorcycle. Replace the steering stem (Chapter 6).

☐ Fork tube bent. Disassemble the forks and replace the damaged parts (Chapter 6).

☐ Fork oil level uneven. Check and add or drain as necessary (Chapter 6).

Poor shock absorbing qualities

☐ Too hard:

a) Fork oil level excessive (Chapter 6).
b) Fork oil viscosity too high. Use a lighter oil (see the Specifications in Chapter 6).
c) Fork tube bent. Causes a harsh, sticking feeling (Chapter 6).
d) Fork internal damage (Chapter 6).
e) Shock shaft or body bent or damaged (Chapter 6).
f) Shock internal damage.
g) Tyre pressure too high (Chapter 1).
h) Incorrect suspension adjustment (Chapter 6).

☐ Too soft:

a) Fork or shock oil insufficient and/or leaking (Chapter 6).
b) Fork oil level too low (Chapter 6).
c) Fork oil viscosity too light (Chapter 6).
d) Fork springs weak or broken (Chapter 6).
e) Shock internal damage or leakage (Chapter 6).
f) Incorrect suspension adjustment (Chapter 6).

13 Braking problems

Brakes are spongy, don't hold

☐ Air in brake line. Caused by inattention to master cylinder fluid level or by leakage. Locate problem and bleed brakes (Chapter 7).

☐ Pad or disc worn (Chapters 1 and 7).

☐ Brake fluid leak. Inspect system carefully and rectify leak.

☐ Contaminated pads. Caused by contamination with oil, grease, brake fluid, etc. Clean or replace pads. Clean disc thoroughly with brake cleaner (Chapter 7).

☐ Brake fluid deteriorated. Fluid is old or contaminated. Drain system, replenish with new fluid and bleed the system (Chapter 7).

☐ Master cylinder internal parts worn or damaged causing fluid to bypass (Chapter 7).

☐ Master cylinder bore scratched by foreign material or broken spring. Repair or replace master cylinder (Chapter 7).

☐ Disc warped. Replace disc (Chapter 7).

Brake lever or pedal pulsates

☐ Disc warped. Replace disc (Chapter 7).

☐ Axle bent. Replace axle (Chapter 7).

☐ Brake caliper bolts loose (Chapter 7).

☐ Brake caliper slider bracket pins (sliding caliper), causing caliper to bind. Lubricate the pins or replace them if they are corroded or bent (Chapter 7).

☐ Wheel bearings damaged or worn (Chapter 7).

Brakes drag

☐ Master cylinder piston seized. Caused by wear or damage to piston or cylinder bore (Chapter 7).

☐ Lever balky or stuck. Check pivot and lubricate (Chapter 7).

☐ Brake caliper binds. Caused by inadequate lubrication or damage to caliper slider bracket pins (sliding caliper) (Chapter 7).

☐ Brake caliper piston seized in bore. Caused by wear or ingestion of dirt past deteriorated seal (Chapter 7).

☐ Brake pad damaged. Pad material separated from backing plate. Usually caused by faulty manufacturing process or from contact with chemicals. Replace pads (Chapter 7).

☐ Pads improperly installed (Chapter 7).

14 Electrical problems

Battery dead or weak

☐ Battery faulty. Caused by sulphated plates which are shorted through sedimentation. Also, broken battery terminal making only occasional contact (Chapter 9).

☐ Battery cables making poor contact (Chapter 9).

☐ Load excessive. Caused by addition of high wattage lights or other electrical accessories.

☐ Ignition (main) switch defective. Switch either earths internally or fails to shut off system. Replace the switch (Chapter 9).

☐ Rectifier defective (Chapter 9).

☐ Alternator stator coil open or shorted (Chapter 9).

☐ Wiring faulty. Wiring earthed or connections loose (Chapter 9).

Battery overcharged

☐ Regulator defective. Overcharging is noticed when battery gets excessively warm (Chapter 9).

☐ Battery defective. Replace battery with a new one (Chapter 9).

☐ Battery amperage too low, wrong type or size. Install manufacturer's specified amp-hour battery to handle charging load (Chapter 9)

Note: *References throughout this index are in the form - "Chapter number" • "page number"*

R

Radiator
pressure cap - 3•2
removal and installation - 3•6
Rear brake
caliper - 7•8
disc - 7•9
master cylinder - 7•10
pads - 1•9, 7•7
Rear mudguard - 8•5
Rear shock absorber - 6•12
Rear suspension linkage
bearing lubrication - 1•19
removal, inspection and installation - 6•14
Rear view mirrors - 8•3
Rear wheel
bearings - 7•17
coupling/rubber damper - 6•22
removal and installation - 7•14
Rectifier - 9•18
Regulator - 9•18
Rings, piston - 2•19
Routine maintenance - 1•1

S

Safety checks - 0•8, 0•13
Seat - 8•5
Servicing - 1•1
Side panels - 8•3
Sidestand switch - 9•13
Spark plug
gap check - 1•17
replacement - 1•18
Specifications
brakes - 7•1
clutch - 2•2
cooling system - 3•1
electrical system - 9•1
engine - 2•1
front forks - 6•1

fuel system - 4•1
ignition system - 5•1
routine maintenance and servicing - 1•1
transmission - 2•3
wheels and tyres - 7•1, 7•2
Speedometer *see* **Instruments**
Speedometer cable - 9•9
Sprocket coupling
bearing - 7•16
check and replacement - 6•22
Sprockets, final drive - 6•21
Stands
lubrication - 6•4
pivot lubrication - 1•18
Starter clutch - 2•49
Starter motor
removal and overhaul - 9•15
specifications - 9•1
Starter relay - 9•14
Steering head bearings
freeplay check and adjustment - 1•7
greasing - 1•18
inspection and replacement - 6•12
Steering stem - 6•11
Sump - 2•27
Suspension
adjustments - 6•16
checks - 0•13, 1•9
Swingarm - 6•18
Swingarm bearings
check - 6•18
inspection and replacement - 6•20
lubrication - 1•19

T

Tachometer *see* **Instruments**
Taillight - 9•6
Tank and tap, fuel - 4•2, 4•4
Tappets - 2•10
Temperature gauge/warning light and sender unit - 3•4
Tensioner, cam chain - 2•9, 2•12
Thermostat - 3•5

Throttle cable
check - 1•14
removal and installation - 4•10
Timing, ignition - 5•4
Tools and working facilities - REF•4
Torque settings - 1•2, 2•3, 3•1, 4•1, 5•1, 6•1, 7•1, 9•2
Transmission
shafts - 2•37, 2•38
specifications - 2•3
Troubleshooting *see* **Fault Finding**
Turn signal
assemblies - 9•7
bulb replacement - 9•6
circuit check and relay - 9•8
Tyre
checks - 1•9
general information and fitting - 7•18
pressures - 0•12
specifications - 7•2
tread depth - 0•13

V

Valve cover - 2•8
Valve clearance check - 1•12
Valves/seats/guides - 2•15, 2•16
VIN (Vehicle Identification Number) - 0•9

W

Water pump - 3•7
Weights, model - REF•1
Wheel
alignment - 1•7, 7•12
bearings - 7•15
checks - 1•9, 7•12
coupling/rubber damper - 6•22
removal and installation - 7•13, 7•14
specifications - 7•1
Windshield - 8•3
Wiring diagrams - 9•19

Haynes Motorcycle Manuals – The Complete List

Title	Book No.
BMW	
BMW 2-valve Twins (70 - 93)	0249
BMW K100 & 75 2-valve Models (83 - 93)	1373
BSA	
BSA Bantam (48 - 71)	0117
BSA Unit Singles (58 - 72)	0127
BSA Pre-unit Singles (54 - 61)	0326
BSA A7 & A10 Twins (47 - 62)	0121
BSA A50 & A65 Twins (62 - 73)	0155
BULTACO	
Bultaco Competition Bikes (72 - 75)	0219
CZ	
CZ 125 & 175 Singles (69 - 90)	◊ 0185
DUCATI	
Ducati 600, 750 & 900 2-valve V-Twins (91 - 96)	3290
HARLEY-DAVIDSON	
Harley-Davidson Sportsters (70 - 93)	0702
Harley-Davidson Big Twins (70 - 93)	0703
HONDA	
Honda PA50 Camino (76 - 91)	0644
Honda SH50 City Express (84 - 89)	◊ 1597
Honda NB, ND, NP & NS50 Melody (81 - 85)	◊ 0622
Honda NE/NB50 Vision & SA50 Vision Met-in (85 - 93)	◊ 1278
Honda MB, MBX, MT & MTX50 (80 - 93)	0731
Honda C50, C70 & C90 (67 - 95)	0324
Honda ATC70, 90, 110, 185 & 200 (71 - 85)	0565
Honda XR80R & XR100R (85 - 96)	2218
Honda XL/XR 80, 100, 125, 185 & 200 2-valve Models (78 - 87)	0566
Honda CB/CL100 & 125 Singles (70 - 76)	0188
Honda CB100N & CB125N (78 - 86)	◊ 0569
Honda H100 & H100S Singles (80 - 92)	◊ 0734
Honda CB/CD125T & CM125C Twins (77 - 88)	◊ 0571
Honda CG125 (76 - 94)	◊ 0433
Honda NS125 (86 - 93)	◊ 3056
Honda CB125, 160, 175, 200 & CD175 Twins (64 - 78)	0067
Honda MBX/MTX125 & MTX200 (83 - 93)	◊ 1132
Honda CD/CM185 200T & CM250C 2-valve Twins (77 - 85)	0572
Honda XL/XR 250 & 500 (78 - 84)	0567
Honda CB250RS Singles (80 - 84)	◊ 0732
Honda CB250 & CB400N Super Dreams (78 - 84)	◊ 0540
Honda Elsinore 250 (73 - 75)	0217
Honda TRX300 Shaft Drive ATVs (88 - 95)	2125
Honda CB400 & CB550 Fours (73 - 77)	0262
Honda CX/GL500 & 650 V-Twins (78 - 86)	0442
Honda CBX550 Four (82 - 86)	◊ 0940
Honda XL600R & XR600R (83 - 96)	2183
Honda CBR600F1 & 1000F Fours (87 - 96)	1730
Honda CBR600F2 Fours (91 - 94)	2070
Honda CB650 sohc Fours (78 - 84)	0665
Honda NTV600 & 650 V-Twins (88 - 96)	3243
Honda CB750 sohc Four (69 - 79)	0131
Honda V45/65 Sabre & Magna (82 - 88)	0820
Honda VFR750 & 700 V-Fours (86 - 94)	2101
Honda CB750 & CB900 dohc Fours (78 - 84)	0535
Honda CBR900RR FireBlade (92 - 95)	2161
Honda GL1000 Gold Wing (75 - 79)	0309
Honda GL1100 Gold Wing (79 - 81)	0669

Title	Book No.
KAWASAKI	
Kawasaki AE/AR 50 & 80 (81 - 95)	1007
Kawasaki KC, KE & KH100 (75 - 93)	1371
Kawasaki AR125 (82 - 94)	◊ 1006
Kawasaki KMX125 & 200 (86 - 96)	◊ 3046
Kawasaki 250, 350 & 400 Triples (72 - 79)	0134
Kawasaki 400 & 440 Twins (74 - 81)	0281
Kawasaki 400, 500 & 550 Fours (79 - 91)	0910
Kawasaki EN450 & 500 Twins (Ltd/Vulcan) (85 - 93)	2053
Kawasaki EX500 (GPZ500S) Twins (87 - 93)	2052
Kawasaki ZX600 (Ninja ZX-6, ZZ-R600) Fours (90 - 95)	2146

Title	Book No.
Kawasaki ZX600 & 750 Liquid-cooled Fours (85 - 97)	1780
Kawasaki 650 Four (76 - 78)	0373
Kawasaki 750 Air-cooled Fours (80 - 91)	0574
Kawasaki ZX750 (Ninja ZX-7 & ZXR750) Fours (89 - 95)	2054
Kawasaki 900 & 1000 Fours (73 - 77)	0222
Kawasaki ZX900, 1000 & 1100 Liquid-cooled Fours (83 - 97)	1681
MOTO GUZZI	
Moto Guzzi 750, 850 & 1000 V-Twins (74 - 78)	0339
MZ	
MZ TS125 (76 - 86)	◊ 1270
MZ ES, ETS, TS150 & 250 (69 - 86)	◊ 0253
MZ ETZ Models (81 - 95)	◊ 1680
NORTON	
Norton 500, 600, 650 & 750 Twins (57 - 70)	0187
Norton Commando (68 - 77)	0125
SUZUKI	
Suzuki FR50, 70 & 80 (74 - 87)	◊ 0801
Suzuki GT, ZR & TS50 (77 - 90)	◊ 0799
Suzuki TS50X (84 - 95)	◊ 1599
Suzuki 100, 125, 185 & 250 Air-cooled Trail bikes (79 - 89)	0797
Suzuki GP100 & 125 Singles (78 - 93)	◊ 0576
Suzuki GS & DR125 Singles (82 - 94)	◊ 0888
Suzuki 250 & 350 Twins (68 - 78)	0120
Suzuki GT250X7, GT200X5 & SB200 Twins (78 - 83)	◊ 0469
Suzuki GS/GSX250, 400 & 450 Twins (79 - 85)	0736
Suzuki GS500E Twin (89 - 97)	3238
Suzuki GS550 (77 - 82) & GS750 Fours (76 - 79)	0363
Suzuki GS/GSX550 4-valve Fours (83 - 88)	1133
Suzuki GSF600 & 1200 Bandit Fours (95 - 97)	3367
Suzuki GS850 Fours (78 - 88)	0536
Suzuki GS1000 Four (77 - 79)	0484
Suzuki GSX-R750, GSX-R1100, GSX600F, GSX750F, GSX1100F (Katana) Fours (85 - 96)	2055
Suzuki GS/GSX1000, 1100 & 1150 4-valve Fours (79 - 88)	0737

Title	Book No.
TOMOS	
Tomos A3K, A3M, A3MS & A3ML Mopeds (82 - 91)	◊ 1062
TRIUMPH	
Triumph Tiger Cub & Terrier (52 - 68)	0414
Triumph 350 & 500 Unit Twins (58 - 73)	0137
Triumph Pre-Unit Twins (47 - 62)	0251
Triumph 650 & 750 2-valve Unit Twins (63 - 83)	0122
Triumph Trident & BSA Rocket 3 (69 - 75)	0136
Triumph Triples & Fours (91 - 95)	2162
VESPA	
Vespa P/PX125, 150 & 200 Scooters (78 - 95)	0707
Vespa Scooters (59 - 78)	0126
YAMAHA	
Yamaha FS1E, FS1 & FS1M (72 - 90)	◊ 0166
Yamaha RD50 & 80 (78 - 89)	◊ 1255
Yamaha DT50 & 80 Trail Bikes (78 - 95)	◊ 0800
Yamaha T50 & 80 Townmate (83 - 95)	◊ 1247
Yamaha YT, YFM, YTM & YTZ ATVs (80 - 85)	1154
Yamaha YB100 Singles (73 - 91)	◊ 0474
Yamaha 100, 125 & 175 Trail bikes (71 - 85)	0210
Yamaha RS/RXS100 & 125 Singles (74 - 95)	0331
Yamaha RD & DT125LC (82 - 87)	◊ 0887
Yamaha TZR125 (87 - 93) & DT125R (88 - 95)	◊ 1655
Yamaha TY50, 80, 125 & 175 (74 - 84)	◊ 0464
Yamaha XT & SR125 (82 - 96)	1021
Yamaha 250 & 350 Twins (70 - 79)	0040
Yamaha XS250, 360 & 400 sohc Twins (75 - 84)	0378
Yamaha YBF250 Timberwolf ATV (92 - 96)	2217
Yamaha YFM350 Big Bear and ER ATVs (87 - 95)	2126
Yamaha RD250 & 350LC Twins (80 - 82)	0803
Yamaha RD350 YPVS Twins (83 - 95)	1158
Yamaha RD400 Twin (75 - 79)	0333
Yamaha XT, TT & SR500 Singles (75 - 83)	0342
Yamaha XZ550 Vision V-Twins (82 - 85)	0821
Yamaha FJ, FZ, XJ & YX600 Radian (84 - 92)	2100
Yamaha XJ600S (Seca II, Diversion) & XJ600N Fours (92 - 95 UK) (92 - 96 USA)	2145
Yamaha 650 Twins (70 - 83)	0341
Yamaha XJ650 & 750 Fours (80 - 84)	0738
Yamaha XS750 & 850 Triples (76 - 85)	0340
Yamaha FZR600, 750 & 1000 Fours (87 - 93)	2056
Yamaha XV V-Twins (81 - 96)	0802
Yamaha XJ900F Fours (83 - 94)	3239
Yamaha FJ1100 & 1200 Fours (84 - 96)	2057
PRACTICAL MANUALS	
ATV Basics	10450
Motorcycle Basics Manual	1083
Motorcycle Carburettor Manual	0603
Motorcycle Electrical Manual (2nd Edition)	0446
Motorcycle Workshop Practice Manual	1454

◊ *denotes manual not available in the USA.*

The manuals featured on this page are available through good motorcycle dealers and accessory shops. In case of difficulty, contact:
Haynes Publishing (UK) on 01963 440635
Haynes Publications (USA) on 805 4986703
Haynes Publishing Nordiska AB (Sweden) on +46 18 124016
Editions Haynes S.A. (France) on +33 1 47 03 61 80

C6685.CL04.04/97

Preserving Our Motoring Heritage

< The Model J Duesenberg Derham Tourster. Only eight of these magnificent cars were ever built – this is the only example to be found outside the United States of America

Almost every car you've ever loved, loathed or desired is gathered under one roof at the Haynes Motor Museum. Over 300 immaculately presented cars and motorbikes represent every aspect of our motoring heritage, from elegant reminders of bygone days, such as the superb Model J Duesenberg to curiosities like the bug-eyed BMW Isetta. There are also many old friends and flames. Perhaps you remember the 1959 Ford Popular that you did your courting in? The magnificent 'Red Collection' is a spectacle of classic sports cars including AC, Alfa Romeo, Austin Healey, Ferrari, Lamborghini, Maserati, MG, Riley, Porsche and Triumph.

A Perfect Day Out

Each and every vehicle at the Haynes Motor Museum has played its part in the history and culture of Motoring. Today, they make a wonderful spectacle and a great day out for all the family. Bring the kids, bring Mum and Dad, but above all bring your camera to capture those golden memories for ever. You will also find an impressive array of motoring memorabilia, a comfortable 70 seat video cinema and one of the most extensive transport book shops in Britain. The Pit Stop Cafe serves everything from a cup of tea to wholesome, home-made meals or, if you prefer, you can enjoy the large picnic area nestled in the beautiful rural surroundings of Somerset.

> John Haynes O.B.E., Founder and Chairman of the museum at the wheel of a Haynes Light 12.

< The 1936 490cc sohc-engined International Norton – well known for its racing success

The Museum is situated on the A359 Yeovil to Frome road at Sparkford, just off the A303 in Somerset. It is about 40 miles south of Bristol, and 25 minutes drive from the M5 intersection at Taunton.
Open 9.30am - 5.30pm (10.00am - 4.00pm Winter) 7 days a week, *except Christmas Day, Boxing Day and New Years Day*
Special rates available for schools, coach parties and outings Charitable Trust No. 292048